PEARSON CUSTOM LIBRARY

MATH 10060
Statistics for Business Volume 1
McKeil School of Business
Mohawk College

PEARSON

Attention bookstores: For permission to return any unsold stock, contact us at *pe-uscustomreturns@pearson.com*.

Pearson Learning Solutions, 501 Boylston Street, Suite 900, Boston, MA 02116
A Pearson Education Company
www.pearsoned.com

Printed in the United States of America
V0TX

ISBN 10: 1-256-61887-X
ISBN 13: 978-1-256-61887-4

Table of Contents

Statistics and Variation

Ocean/Corbis

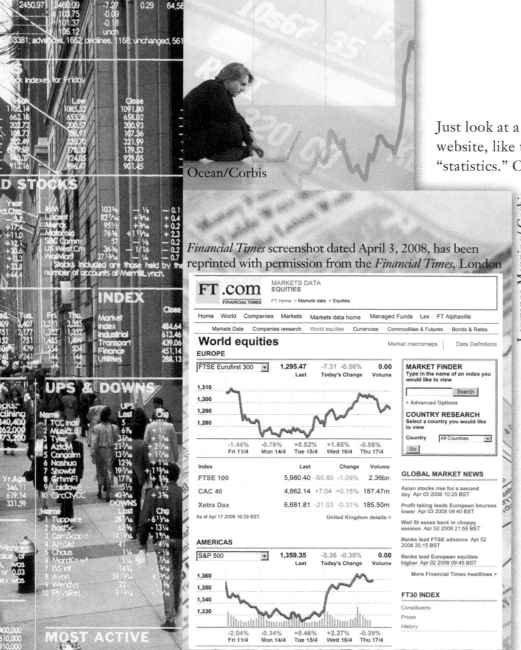

Ocean/Corbis

Financial Times screenshot dated April 3, 2008, has been reprinted with permission from the *Financial Times*, London

Lawrence Manning/Corbis

Just look at a page from the *Financial Times* website, like the one shown here. It's full of "statistics." Obviously, the writers of the *Financial Times* think all this information is important, but is this what Statistics is all about? Well, yes and no. This page may contain a lot of facts, but as we'll see, the subject is much more interesting and rich than just spreadsheets and tables.

"Why should I learn Statistics?" you might ask. "After all, I don't plan to do this kind of work. In fact, I'm going to hire people to do all of this for me." That's fine. But the decisions you make based on data are too important to delegate. You'll want to be able to interpret the data that surrounds you and to come to your own conclusions. And you'll find that studying Statistics is much more important and enjoyable than you thought.

From Chapter 1 of *Business Statistics*, Second Edition, Norean R. Sharpe, Richard D. De Veaux, Paul F. Velleman.

1 So, What Is Statistics?

> **Q:** What is Statistics?
> **A:** Statistics is a way of reasoning, along with a collection of tools and methods, designed to help us understand the world.
> **Q:** What are statistics?
> **A:** Statistics (plural) are quantities calculated from data.
> **Q:** So what is data?
> **A:** You mean, "what *are* data?" Data is the plural form. The singular is datum.
> **Q:** So, what are data?
> **A:** Data are values along with their context.

It seems every time we turn around, someone is collecting data on us, from every purchase we make in the grocery store to every click of our mouse as we surf the Web. The United Parcel Service (UPS) tracks every package it ships from one place to another around the world and stores these records in a giant database. You can access part of it if you send or receive a UPS package. The database is about 17 terabytes—about the same size as a database that contained every book in the Library of Congress would be. (But, we suspect, not quite as interesting.) What can anyone hope to do with all these data?

Statistics plays a role in making sense of our complex world. Statisticians assess the risk of genetically engineered foods or of a new drug being considered by the Food and Drug Administration (FDA). Statisticians predict the number of new cases of AIDS by regions of the country or the number of customers likely to respond to a sale at the supermarket. And statisticians help scientists, social scientists, and business leaders understand how unemployment is related to environmental controls, whether enriched early education affects the later performance of school children, and whether vitamin C really prevents illness. Whenever you have data and a need to understand the world, you need Statistics.

If we want to analyze student perceptions of business ethics, should we administer a survey to every single university student in the United States—or, for that matter, in the world? Well, that wouldn't be very practical or cost effective. What should we do instead? Give up and abandon the survey? Maybe we should try to obtain survey responses from a smaller, representative group of students. Statistics can help us make the leap from the data we have at hand to an understanding of the world at large. We hope this text will empower *you* to draw conclusions from data and make valid business decisions in response to such questions as:

- Do university students from different parts of the world perceive business ethics differently?
- What is the effect of advertising on sales?
- Do aggressive, "high-growth" mutual funds really have higher returns than more conservative funds?
- Is there a seasonal cycle in your firm's revenues and profits?
- What is the relationship between shelf location and cereal sales?
- How reliable are the quarterly forecasts for your firm?
- Are there common characteristics about your customers and why they choose your products?—and, more importantly, are those characteristics the same among those who aren't your customers?

Our ability to answer questions such as these and draw conclusions from data depends largely on our ability to understand *variation*. That may not be the term you expected to find at the end of that sentence, but it is the essence of Statistics. The key to learning from data is understanding the variation that is all around us.

Data vary. People are different. So are economic conditions from month to month. We can't see everything, let alone measure it all. And even what we do measure, we measure imperfectly. So the data we wind up looking at and basing our decisions on provide, at best, an imperfect picture of the world. Variation lies at the heart of what Statistics is all about. How to make sense of it is the central challenge of Statistics.

2 How Will This Text Help?

A fair question. Most likely, this text will not turn out to be what you expect. It emphasizes graphics and understanding rather than computation and formulas. Instead of learning how to plug numbers in formulas you'll learn the process of model development and come to understand the limitations both of the data you analyze and the methods you use. We use real data and real business scenarios so you can see how to use data to make decisions.

Graphs

Close your eyes and open your statistics text at random. Is there a graph or table on the page? Do it again, say, ten times. You probably saw data displayed in many ways, even near the back of the text and in the exercises. Graphs and tables help you understand what the data are saying. So, each story and data set and every new statistical technique from this text will come with graphics to help you understand both the methods and the data.

Process

To help you use Statistics to make business decisions, we'll lead you through the entire process of thinking about a problem, finding and showing results, and telling others what you have discovered. The three simple steps to doing Statistics for business right are: **Plan**, **Do**, and **Report**.

PLAN

Plan first. Know where you're headed and why. Clearly defining and understanding your objective will save you a lot of work.

DO

Do is what most students think Statistics is about. The mechanics of calculating statistics and making graphical displays are important, but the computations are usually the least important part of the process. In fact, we usually turn the computations over to technology and get on with understanding what the results tell us.

REPORT

Report what you've learned. Until you've explained your results in a context that someone else can understand, the job is not done.

"Get your facts first, and then you can distort them as much as you please. (Facts are stubborn, but statistics are more pliable.)"

—MARK TWAIN

For Example

In this text, we present a short example to help you put what you've learned to immediate use. After reading the example, try the corresponding end-of-section exercises at the end of the chapter. These will help prepare you for the other exercises that tend to use all the skills of the chapter.

Guided Example

New concepts are taught in worked examples called **Guided Examples**. These examples model how you should approach and solve problems using the Plan, Do, Report framework. They illustrate how to plan an analysis, the appropriate techniques to use, and how to report what it all means. These step-by-step examples show you how to produce the kind of solutions and case study reports that instructors and managers or, better yet, clients expect to see. You will find a model solution in the right-hand column and background notes and discussion in the left-hand column.

Just Checking

Sometimes, in the middle of the chapter, you'll find sections called **Just Checking**, which pose a few short questions you can answer without much calculation. Use them to check that you've understood the basic ideas in the chapter. You'll find the answers at the end-of-chapter exercises.

Ethics in Action

Statistics often requires judgment, and the decisions based on statistical analyses may influence people's health and even their lives. Decisions in government can affect policy decisions about how people are treated. In science and industry, interpretations of data can influence consumer safety and the environment. And in business, misunderstanding what the data say can lead to disastrous decisions. The central guiding principle of statistical judgment is the ethical search for a true understanding of the real world. In all spheres of society it is vitally important that a statistical analysis of data be done in an ethical and unbiased way. Allowing preconceived notions, unfair data gathering, or deliberate slanting to affect statistical conclusions is harmful to business and to society.

At various points throughout the text, you will encounter a scenario under the title **Ethics in Action** in which you'll read about an ethical issue. Think about the issue and how you might deal with it. Then read the summary of the issue and one solution to the problem, which follow the scenario. We've related the ethical issues to guidelines that the American Statistical Association has developed.[1] These scenarios can be good topics for discussion. We've presented one solution, but we invite you to think of others.

What Can Go Wrong?

One of the interesting challenges of Statistics is that, unlike some math and science courses, there can be more than one right answer. This is why two statisticians can testify honestly on opposite sides of a court case. And it's why some people think that you can prove anything with statistics. But that's not true. People make mistakes using statistics, and sometimes people misuse statistics to mislead others. Most of the mistakes are avoidable. We're not talking about arithmetic. Mistakes usually involve using a method in the wrong situation or misinterpreting results. So this text has a section called **What Can Go Wrong?** to help you avoid some of the most common mistakes that we've seen in our years of consulting and teaching experience.

Brief CASE

In this text you may encounter a problem or two that use real data sets and ask you to investigate a question or make a decision. These "brief cases" are a good way to test your ability to attack an open-ended (and thus more realistic) problem. You'll be asked to define the objective, plan your process, complete the analysis, and report your conclusion. These are good opportunities to apply the template provided by the **Guided Examples**. And they provide an opportunity to practice reporting your conclusions in written form to refine your communication skills where statistical results are involved.

"Far too many scientists have only a shaky grasp of the statistical techniques they are using. They employ them as an amateur chef employs a cookbook, believing the recipes will work without understanding why. A more cordon bleu attitude . . . might lead to fewer statistical soufflés failing to rise."

—THE ECONOMIST, JUNE 3, 2004, "SLOPPY STATS SHAME SCIENCE."

---

[1]http://www.amstat.org/about/ethicalguidelines.cfm

C A S E
Study

In this text, you may encounter a larger project that will help you integrate your knowledge from the entire section you've been studying. These more open-ended projects will help you acquire the skills you'll need to put your knowledge to work in the world of business.

Technology Help: Using the Computer

Although we show you all the formulas you need to understand the calculations, you will most often use a calculator or computer to perform the mechanics of a statistics problem. And the easiest way to calculate statistics with a computer is with a statistics package. Several different statistics packages are used widely. Although they differ in the details of how to use them, they all work from the same basic information and find the same results. Rather than adopt one package for this text, we present generic output and point out common features that you should look for. We also give a table of instructions to get you started on four packages: Excel, Minitab, SPSS, and JMP.

> From time to time we'll take time out to discuss an interesting or important side issue. We indicate these by setting them apart like this.[2]

You'll find all sorts of stuff in margin notes, such as stories and quotations. For example:

"Computers are useless. They can only give you answers."

— PABLO PICASSO

While Picasso underestimated the value of good statistics software, he did know that creating a solution requires more than just *Doing*—it means you have to *Plan* and *Report*, too!

What Have We Learned?

In this text, you'll see a brief summary of the chapter's learning objectives in a section called **What Have We Learned?** That section also includes a list of the **Terms** you've encountered in the chapter. You won't be able to learn the material from these summaries, but you can use them to check your knowledge of the important ideas in the chapter. If you have the skills, know the terms, and understand the concepts, you should be well prepared—and ready to use Statistics!

Exercises

Beware: No one can learn Statistics just by reading or listening. The only way to learn it is to do it. So, you'll find **Exercises** designed to help you learn to use the Statistics you've just read about. Some exercises are marked with a red ⓣ. You'll find the data for these exercises on this text's website, www.aw-bc.com/sharpe, so you can use technology as you work the exercises.

We've structured the exercises so that the end-of-section exercises are found first. These can be answered after reading each section. After that you'll find end-of-chapter exercises, designed to help you integrate the topics you've learned in the chapter. We've also paired up and grouped the exercises, so if you're having trouble doing an exercise, you'll find a similar exercise either just before or just after it. You'll find answers to the odd-numbered exercises at the end of the chapter from this text. But these are only "answers" and not complete solutions. What's the difference? The answers are sketches of the complete solutions. For most problems, your solution

---

[2]Or in a footnote.

should follow the model of the **Guided Examples**. If your calculations match the numerical parts of the answer and your argument contains the elements shown in the answer, you're on the right track. Your complete solution should explain the context, show your reasoning and calculations, and state your conclusions. Don't worry too much if your numbers don't match the printed answers to every decimal place. Statistics is more than computation—it's about getting the reasoning correct—so pay more attention to how you interpret a result than to what the digit in the third decimal place is.

Getting Started

It's only fair to warn you: You can't get there by just picking out the highlighted sentences and the summaries. This text is different. It's not about memorizing definitions and learning equations. It's deeper than that. And much more interesting. But . . .
   You have to read the text!

Data

iStockphoto

Amazon.com

Amazon.com opened for business in July 1995, billing itself even then as "Earth's Biggest Bookstore," with an unusual business plan: They didn't plan to turn a profit for four to five years. Although some shareholders complained when the dotcom bubble burst, Amazon continued its slow, steady growth, becoming profitable for the first time in 2002. Since then, Amazon has remained profitable and has continued to grow. By 2004, they had more than 41 million active customers in over 200 countries and were ranked the 74th most valuable brand by *Business Week*. Their selection of merchandise has expanded to include almost anything you can imagine, from $400,000 necklaces, to yak cheese from Tibet, to the largest book in the world. In 2008, Amazon.com sold nearly $20 billion worth of products online throughout the world.

Amazon R&D is constantly monitoring and evolving their website to best serve their customers and maximize their sales performance. To make changes to the site, they experiment by collecting data and analyzing what works best. As Ronny Kohavi, former director of Data Mining and Personalization, said, "Data trumps intuition. Instead of using our intuition, we experiment on the live site and let our customers tell us what works for them."

Gregory Bajor/iStockphoto

Feng Yu/iStockphoto

Justin Sullivan/ Getty Images News

From Chapter 2 of *Business Statistics*, Second Edition, Norean R. Sharpe, Richard D. De Veaux, Paul F. Velleman.

Amazon.com has recently stated "many of the important decisions we make at Amazon.com can be made with data. There is a right answer or a wrong answer, a better answer or a worse answer, and math tells us which is which. These are our favorite kinds of decisions."[1] While we might prefer that Amazon refer to these methods as Statistics instead of math, it's clear that data analysis, forecasting, and statistical inference are the core of the decision-making tools of Amazon.com.

"Data is king at Amazon. Clickstream and purchase data are the crown jewels at Amazon. They help us build features to personalize the website experience."

—RONNY KOHAVI,
FORMER DIRECTOR OF DATA
MINING AND
PERSONALIZATION,
AMAZON.COM

Many years ago, stores in small towns knew their customers personally. If you walked into the hobby shop, the owner might tell you about a new bridge that had come in for your Lionel train set. The tailor knew your dad's size, and the hairdresser knew how your mom liked her hair. There are still some stores like that around today, but we're increasingly likely to shop at large stores, by phone, or on the Internet. Even so, when you phone an 800 number to buy new running shoes, customer service representatives may call you by your first name or ask about the socks you bought six weeks ago. Or the company may send an e-mail in October offering new head warmers for winter running. This company has millions of customers, and you called without identifying yourself. How did the sales rep know who you are, where you live, and what you had bought?

The answer to all these questions is data. Collecting data on their customers, transactions, and sales lets companies track inventory and know what their customers prefer. These data can help them predict what their customers may buy in the future so they know how much of each item to stock. The store can use the data and what they learn from the data to improve customer service, mimicking the kind of personal attention a shopper had 50 years ago.

1   What *Are* Data?

Businesses have always relied on data for planning and to improve efficiency and quality. Now, more than ever before, businesses rely on the information in data to compete in the global marketplace. Most modern businesses collect information on virtually every transaction performed by the organization, including every item bought or sold. These data are recorded and stored electronically, in vast digital repositories called **data warehouses**.

In the past few decades these data warehouses have grown enormously in size, but with the use of powerful computers, the information contained in them is accessible and used to help make decisions, sometimes almost instantaneously. When you pay with your credit card, for example, the information about the transaction is transmitted to a central computer where it is processed and analyzed. A decision whether to approve or deny your purchase is made and transmitted back to the point of sale, all within a few seconds.

---

[1]Amazon.com 2008 Annual Report

Companies use data to make decisions about other aspects of their business as well. By studying the past behavior of customers and predicting their responses, they hope to better serve their customers and to compete more effectively. This process of using data, especially of **transactional** data (data collected for recording the companies' transactions) to make other decisions and predictions, is sometimes called **data mining** or *predictive analytics*. The more general term **business analytics** (or sometimes simply analytics) describes *any* use of statistical analysis to drive business decisions from data whether the purpose is predictive or simply descriptive.

Leading companies are embracing business analytics. Richard Fairbank, the CEO and founder of Capital One, revolutionized the credit card industry by realizing that credit card transactions hold the key to understanding customer behavior. Reed Hastings, a former computer science major, is the founder and CEO of Netflix. Netflix uses analytics on customer information both to recommend new movies and to adapt the website that customers see to individual tastes. Netflix offered a $1 million prize to anyone who could improve on the accuracy of their recommendations by more than 10%. That prize was won in 2009 by a team of statisticians and computer scientists using predictive analytics and data-mining techniques. The Oakland Athletics use analytics to judge players instead of the traditional methods used by scouts and baseball experts for over a hundred years. The book *Moneyball* documents how business analytics enabled them to put together a team that could compete against the richer teams in spite of the severely limited resources available to the front office.

To understand better what data are, let's look at some hypothetical company records that Amazon might collect:

105-2686834-3759466	B0000010AA	10.99	Chris G.	902	Boston	15.98	Kansas	Illinois
Samuel P.	Orange County	105-9318443-4200264	105-1872500-0198646	N	B000068ZV Q	Bad Blood	Nashville	Katherine H.
Canada	Garbage	16.99	Ohio	N	Chicago	N	11.99	Massachusetts
B000002BK9	312	Monique D.	Y	413	B00000I5Y6	440	103-2628345-9238664	Let Go

Table 1   An example of data with no context. It's impossible to say anything about what these values might mean without knowing their context.

THE W'S:
WHO
WHAT
WHEN
WHERE
WHY

Try to guess what these data represent. Why is that hard? Because these data have no *context*. Whether the data are numerical (consisting only of numbers), alphabetic (consisting only of letters), or alphanumerical (mixed numbers and letters), they are useless unless we know what they represent. Newspaper journalists know that the lead paragraph of a good story should establish the "Five W's": *who, what, when, where,* and (if possible) *why.* Often, we add *how* to the list as well. Answering these questions can provide a **context** for data values and make them meaningful. The answers to the first two questions are essential. If you can't answer *who* and *what,* you don't have data, and you don't have any useful information.

We can make the meaning clear if we add the context of *who* the data are about and *what* was measured and organize the values into a **data table** such as this one.

Order Number	Name	State/Country	Price	Area Code	Previous Album Download	Gift?	ASIN	Artist
105-2686834-3759466	Katherine H.	Ohio	10.99	440	Nashville	N	B00000I5Y6	Kansas
105-9318443-4200264	Samuel P.	Illinois	16.99	312	Orange County	Y	B000002BK9	Boston
105-1872500-0198646	Chris G.	Massachusetts	15.98	413	Bad Blood	N	B000068ZVQ	Chicago
103-2628345-9238664	Monique D.	Canada	11.99	902	Let Go	N	B0000010AA	Garbage
002-1663369-6638649	Katherine H.	Ohio	10.99	440	Best of Kansas	N	B002MXA7Q0	Kansas

Table 2   Example of a data table. The variable names are in the top row. Typically, the *Who* of the table are found in the leftmost column.

Look at the rows of Table 2. Now we can see that these are five purchase records, relating to album downloads from Amazon. In general, the rows of a data table correspond to individual **cases** about which we've recorded some characteristics called **variables**.

Cases go by different names, depending on the situation. Individuals who answer a survey are referred to as **respondents**. People on whom we experiment are **subjects** or (in an attempt to acknowledge the importance of their role in the experiment) **participants**, but animals, plants, websites, and other inanimate subjects are often called **experimental units**. Often we call cases just what they are: for example, *customers*, *economic quarters*, or *companies*. In a database, rows are called **records**—in this example, purchase records. Perhaps the most generic term is **cases**. In Table 2, the cases are the individual orders.

The column titles (variable names) tell *what* has been recorded. What does a row of Table 2 represent? Be careful. Even if people are involved, the cases may not correspond to people. For example, in Table 2, each row is a different order and not the customer who made the purchases (notice that the same person made two different orders). A common place to find the *who* of the table is the leftmost column. It's often an identifying variable for the cases, in this example, the order number.

If you collect the data yourself, you'll know what the cases are and how the variables are defined. But, often, you'll be looking at data that someone else collected. The information about the data, called the metadata, might have to come from the company's database administrator or from the *information technology* department of a company. **Metadata** typically contains information about *how*, *when*, and *where* (and possibly *why*) the data were collected; *who* each case represents; and the definitions of all the variables.

A general term for a data table like the one shown in Table 2 is a **spreadsheet**, a name that comes from bookkeeping ledgers of financial information. The data were typically spread across facing pages of a bound ledger, the book used by an accountant for keeping records of expenditures and sources of income. For the accountant, the columns were the types of expenses and income, and the cases were transactions, typically invoices or receipts. These days, it is common to keep modest-size datasets in a spreadsheet even if no accounting is involved. It is usually easy to move a data table from a spreadsheet program to a program designed for statistical graphics and analysis, either directly or by copying the data table and pasting it into the statistics program.

Although data tables and spreadsheets are great for relatively small data sets, they are cumbersome for the complex data sets that companies must maintain on a day-to-day basis. Try to imagine a spreadsheet from Amazon with customers in the rows and products in the columns. Amazon has tens of millions of customers and hundreds of thousands of products. But very few customers have purchased more than a few dozen items, so almost all the entries would be blank—not a very efficient way to store information. For that reason, various other database architectures are used to store data. The most common is a relational database.

In a **relational database**, two or more separate data tables are linked together so that information can be merged across them. Each data table is a *relation* because it is about a specific set of cases with information about each of these cases for all (or at least most) of the variables ("fields" in database terminology). For example, a table of customers, along with demographic information on each, is such a relation. A data table with information about a different collection of cases is a different relation. For example, a data table of all the items sold by the company, including information on price, inventory, and past history, is a relation as well (for example, as in Table 3). Finally, the day-to-day transactions may be held in a third database where each purchase of an item by a customer is listed as a case. In a relational database, these three relations can be linked together. For example, you can look up a customer to see what he or she purchased or look up an item to see which customers purchased it.

In statistics, all analyses are performed on a single data table. But often the data must be retrieved from a relational database. Retrieving data from these databases often requires specific expertise with that software. In the rest of the text, we'll assume that all data have been downloaded to a data table or spreadsheet with variables listed as columns and cases as the rows.

Customers

Customer Number	Name	City	State	Zip Code	Customer since	Gold Member?
473859	R. De Veaux	Williamstown	MA	01267	2007	No
127389	N. Sharpe	Washington	DC	20052	2000	Yes
335682	P. Velleman	Ithaca	NY	14580	2003	No
...						

Items

Product ID	Name	Price	Currently in Stock?
SC5662	Silver Cane	43.50	Yes
TH2839	Top Hat	29.99	No
RS3883	Red Sequined Shoes	35.00	Yes
...			

Transactions

Transaction Number	Date	Customer Number	Product ID	Quantity	Shipping Method	Free Ship?
T23478923	9/15/08	473859	SC5662	1	UPS 2nd Day	N
T23478924	9/15/08	473859	TH2839	1	UPS 2nd Day	N
T63928934	10/20/08	335682	TH2839	3	UPS Ground	N
T72348299	12/22/08	127389	RS3883	1	Fed Ex Ovnt	Y

Table 3 A relational database shows all the relevant information for three separate relations linked together by customer and product numbers.

For Example   Identifying variables and the W's

Carly, a marketing manager at a credit card bank, wants to know if an offer mailed 3 months ago has affected customers' use of their cards. To answer that, she asks the information technology department to assemble the following information for each customer: total spending on the card during the 3 months before the offer (*Pre Spending*); spending for 3 months after the offer (*Post Spending*); the customer's *Age* (by category); what kind of expenditure they made (*Segment*); if customers are enrolled in the website (*Enroll?*); what offer they were sent (*Offer*); and the amount each customer has spent on the card in their segment (*Segment Spend*). She gets a spreadsheet whose first six rows look like this:

Account ID	Pre Spending	Post Spending	Age	Segment	Enroll?	Offer	Segment Spend
393371	$2,698.12	$6,261.40	25–34	Travel/Ent	NO	None	$887.36
462715	$2,707.92	$3,397.22	45–54	Retail	NO	Gift Card	$5,062.55
433469	$800.51	$4,196.77	65+	Retail	NO	None	$673.80
462716	$3,459.52	$3,335.00	25–34	Services	YES	Double Miles	$800.75
420605	$2,106.48	$5,576.83	35–44	Leisure	YES	Double Miles	$3,064.81
473703	$2,603.92	$7,397.50	<25	Travel/Ent	YES	Double Miles	$491.29

Question: Identify the cases and the variables. Describe as many of the W's as you can for this data set.

Answer: The cases are individual customers of the credit card bank. The data are from the internal records of the credit card bank from the past 6 months (3 months before and 3 months after an offer was sent to the customers). The variables include the account ID of the customer (*Account ID*) and the amount charged on the card before (*Pre Spending*) and after (*Post Spending*) the offer was sent out. Also included are the customer's *Age*, marketing *Segment*, whether they enrolled on the website (*Enroll?*), what offer they were sent (*Offer*), and how much they charged on the card in their marketing segment (*Segment Spend*).

2   Variable Types

Categorical, or Quantitative?
It is wise to be careful. The *what* and *why* of area codes are not as simple as they may first seem.

When area codes were first introduced all phones had dials. To reduce wear and tear on the dials and to speed the most number of calls, the lowest-digit codes (the easiest to dial) were assigned to the largest cities. So, New York City was given 212, Chicago 312, LA 213 and Philadelphia 215, but rural upstate New York was 607, Joliet was 815, and San Diego 619. Back then, the numerical value of an area code could be used to guess something about the population of its region. But after dials gave way to push buttons, new area codes were assigned without regard to population and area codes are now just categories.

Variables play different roles, and knowing the variable's *type* is crucial to knowing what to do with it and what it can tell us. When a variable names categories and answers questions about how cases fall into those categories, we call it a **categorical**, or **qualitative, variable**. When a variable has measured numerical values with *units* and the variable tells us about the quantity of what is measured, we call it a **quantitative variable**. Classifying a variable into categorical or quantitative can help us decide what to do with a variable, but doing so is often more about what we hope to learn from a variable than about the variable itself. It's the questions we ask of a variable (the *why* of our analysis) that shape how we think about it and how we treat it.

Descriptive responses to questions are often categories. For example, the responses to the questions "What type of mutual fund do you invest in?" or "What kind of advertising does your firm use?" yield categorical values. An important special case of categorical variables is one that has only two possible responses (usually "yes" or "no"), which arise naturally from questions like "Do you invest in the stock market?" or "Do you make online purchases from this website?"

If the variable has values that are not numbers, it's clearly categorical (or needs to be recoded). However, if the values are numbers, you need to be careful. It may be considered quantitative if the values actually measure a quantity of something. Otherwise, it's categorical. For example, area codes are numbers, but the numerical values of area codes don't have numerical meaning (see the side bar). The numbers assigned by the area codes are codes that *categorize* the phone number into a geographical area. So, we treat area code as a categorical variable.

For quantitative variables, the **units** tell how each value has been measured. Even more important, units such as yen, cubits, carats, angstroms, nanoseconds, miles per hour, or degrees Celsius tell us the *scale* of measurement, so we know how far apart two values are. Without units, the values of a measured variable have no meaning. It does little good to be promised a raise of 5000 a year if you don't know whether it will be paid in euros, dollars, yen, or Estonian krooni. An essential part of a quantitative variable is its units.

Sometimes the type of the variable is clear. But some variables can answer both kinds of questions and how they are classified depends on their use. For example, the variable *Age* would be considered quantitative if the responses were numerical and they had units. A doctor would certainly need *Age* to be quantitative. The units could be years, but for infants, the doctor would want even more precise units, like months, or even days. On the other hand, if Amazon asked your *Age*, it might lump together the values into categories like "Child (12 years or less)," "Teen (13 to 19)," "Adult (20 to 64)," or "Senior (65 or over)." For many purposes, like knowing which CD ad to send you, that might be all the information Amazon might need. In this case, Amazon has made *Age* a categorical variable.

Question	Categories or Responses
Do you invest in the stock market?	__ Yes __ No
What kind of advertising do you use?	__ Newspapers __ Internet __ Direct mailings
What is your class at school?	__ Freshman __ Sophomore __ Junior __ Senior
I would recommend this course to another student.	__ Strongly Disagree __ Slightly Disagree __ Slightly Agree __ Strongly Agree
How satisfied are you with this product?	__ Very Unsatisfied __ Unsatisfied __ Satisfied __ Very Satisfied

Table 4   Some examples of categorical variables.

When Amazon considers a special offer of free shipping to customers, they might first analyze how purchases have been shipped in the recent past. They might start by counting the number of purchases shipped in each category: ground transportation, second-day air, and overnight air. Counting is a natural way to summarize a categorical variable like *Shipping Method*.

Shipping Method	Number of Purchases
Ground	20,345
Second-day	7890
Overnight	5432

Table 5   A summary of the categorical variable *Shipping Method* that shows the counts, or number of cases for each category.

Identifiers

What's your student ID number? It may be numerical, but is it a quantitative variable? No, it doesn't have units. Is it categorical? Yes, but a special kind. Look at how many categories there are and at how many individuals there are in each category. There are exactly as many categories as individuals and only one individual in each category. While it's easy to count the totals for each category, it's not very interesting. This is an **identifier variable**. Amazon wants to know who you are when you sign in again and doesn't want to confuse you with some other customer. So they assign you a unique identifier.

Identifier variables themselves don't tell us anything useful about the categories because we know there is exactly one individual in each. However, they are crucial in this era of large data sets because by uniquely identifying the cases, they make it possible to combine data from different sources, protect confidentiality, and provide unique labels. Most company databases are, in fact, relational databases. The identifier is crucial to linking one data table to another in a relational database. The identifiers in Table 3 are the *Customer Number*, *Product ID*, and *Transaction Number*. Variables like *UPS Tracking Number*, *Social Security Number*, and Amazon's *ASIN* are other examples of identifiers.

You'll want to recognize when a variable is playing the role of an identifier so you won't be tempted to analyze it. Knowing that Amazon's average ASIN number increased 10% from 2007 to 2008 doesn't really tell you anything—any more than analyzing any categorical variable as if it were quantitative would.

Be careful not to be inflexible in your typing of variables. Variables can play different roles, depending on the question we ask of them, and classifying variables rigidly into types can be misleading. For example, in their annual reports, Amazon refers to its database and looks at the variables *Sales* and *Year*. When analysts ask how many books Amazon sold in 2005, what role does *Year* play? There's only one row for 2005, and *Year* identifies it, so it plays the role of an identifier variable. In its role as an identifier, you might match other data from Amazon, or the economy in general, for the same year. But analysts also track sales growth over time. In this role, *Year* measures time. Now it's being treated as a quantitative variable with units of years.

Other Data Types

A survey might ask:
"How satisfied were you with the service you received?"
1) Not satisfied; 2) Somewhat satisfied; 3) Moderately satisfied; or 4) Extremely satisfied.
Is this variable categorical or quantitative? There is certainly an *order* of perceived worth; higher numbers indicate higher perceived worth. An employee whose customer responses average around 4 seems to be doing a better job than one whose averages are around 2, but are they *twice* as good? Because the values are not strictly numbers, we can't really say and so we should be careful about treating *Customer Satisfaction* as purely quantitative. When, as in this example, the values of a categorical value have an intrinsic order, we can say that the categorical variable is **ordinal**. By contrast, a categorical variable that names categories that don't have order is sometimes called **nominal**. Values can be individually ordered (e.g., the ranks of employees based on the number of days they've worked for the company) or ordered in classes (e.g., Freshman, Sophomore, Junior, Senior). Ordering is not absolute; how the values are ordered depends on the purpose of the ordering. For example, are the categories Infant, Youth, Teen, Adult, and Senior ordinal? Well, if we are ordering on age, they surely are and how to order the categories is clear. But if we are ordering (as Amazon might) on purchase volume, it is likely that either Teen or Adult will be the top group.[2]

Cross-Sectional and Time Series Data

The quantitative variable *Total Revenue* in Table 6 is an example of a time series. A **time series** is a single variable measured at regular intervals over time. Time series are common in business. Typical measuring points are months, quarters, or

---

[2]Some people differentiate quantitative variables according to whether their measured values have a defined value for zero. This is a technical distinction and usually not one we'll need to make. (For example, it isn't correct to say that a temperature of 80°F is twice as hot as 40°F because 0° is an arbitrary value. On the Celsius scale those temperatures are 26.67°C and 4.44°C—a ratio of 6.) The term *interval scale* is sometimes applied to data such as these, and the term *ratio scale* is applied to measurements for which such ratios are appropriate.

Year	Total Revenue (in $M)
2002	3288.9
2003	4075.5
2004	5294.2
2005	6369.3
2006	7786.9
2007	9441.5
2008	10,383.0
2009	9774.6

Table 6   Starbucks's total revenue (in $M) for the years 2002 to 2009.

years, but virtually any consistently-spaced time interval is possible. Variables collected over time hold special challenges for statistical analysis.

By contrast, most of the methods in this text are better suited for **cross-sectional data**, where several variables are measured at the same time point. On the other hand, if we collect data on sales revenue, number of customers, and expenses for last month at *each* Starbucks (more than 16,000 locations as of 2010) at one point in time, this would be cross-sectional data. Cross-sectional data may contain some time information (such as dates), but it isn't a time series because it isn't measured at regular intervals. Because different methods are used to analyze these different types of data, it is important to be able to identify both time series and cross-sectional data sets.

For Example   Identifying the types of variables

Question: Before she can continue with her analysis, Carly (from the example earlier in this chapter) must classify each variable as being quantitative or categorical (or possibly both), and whether the data are a time series or cross-sectional. For quantitative variables, what are the units? For categorical variables, are they nominal or ordinal?

Answer:

Account ID – categorical (nominal, identifier)

Pre Spending – quantitative (units $)

Post Spending – quantitative (units $)

Age – categorical (ordinal). Could be quantitative if we had more precise information

Segment – categorical (nominal)

Enroll? – categorical (nominal)

Offer – categorical (nominal)

Segment Spend – quantitative (units $)

The data are cross-sectional. We do not have successive values of a single variable over time.

3   Data Sources: Where, How, and When

We must know *who*, *what*, and *why* to analyze data. Without knowing these three, we don't have enough to start. Of course, we'd always like to know more because the more we know, the more we'll understand. If possible, we'd like to know the *where*, *how*, and *when* of data as well. Values recorded in 1947 may mean something different than similar values recorded last year. Values measured in Abu Dhabi may differ in meaning from similar measurements made in Mexico.

How the data are collected can make the difference between insight and nonsense. As we'll see later, data that come from a voluntary survey on the Internet are almost always worthless. In a recent Internet poll, 84% of respondents said "no" to the question of whether subprime borrowers should be bailed out. While it may be true that 84% of those 23,418 respondents did say that, it's dangerous to assume that that group is representative of any larger group. To make inferences from the data you have at hand to the world at large, you need to ensure that the data you have are representative of the larger group.

Another way to collect valid data is by performing an experiment in which you actively manipulate variables (called factors) to see what happens. Most of the "junk mail" credit card offers that you receive are actually experiments done by marketing groups in those companies. They may make different versions of an offer to selected groups of customers to see which one works best before rolling out the winning idea to the entire customer base.

Sometimes, the answer to the question you have may be found in data that someone, or more typically, some organization has already collected. Internally, companies may analyze data from their own data bases or data warehouse. They may also supplement or rely entirely on data collected by others. Many companies, nonprofit organizations, and government agencies collect vast amounts of data via the Internet. Some organizations may charge a fee for accessing or downloading their data. The U.S. government collects information on nearly every aspect of life in the United States, both social and economic (see for example www.census.gov, or more generally, www.usa.gov), as the European Union does for Europe (see ec.europa.eu/eurostat). International organizations such as the World Health Organization (www.who.org) and polling agencies such as Gallup (www.gallup.com) offer information on a variety of topics as well. Data like these typically do not come from a designed survey or experiment. They are most often collected for different purposes than the analysis you may want to perform. Although they are plentiful, you should be careful when generalizing from data like these. Information about how, when, where, and why the data were collected may not be available. Unless the data were collected in a way that ensures that they are representative of the population in which you are interested, you may be misled if you try to draw conclusions from them. Data mining attempts to use large amounts of "found" data to make hypotheses and draw insights. While it can be tempting, interesting, and even useful to analyze such happenstance data, remember that the only way to be sure that a generalization is valid is if the data come from a properly designed survey or experiment.

There's a world of data on the Internet

These days, one of the richest sources of data is the Internet. With a bit of practice, you can learn to find data on almost any subject. We found many of the data sets used in this text by searching on the Internet. The Internet has both advantages and disadvantages as a source of data. Among the advantages are the fact that often you'll be able to find even more current data than we present. One disadvantage is that references to Internet addresses can "break" as sites evolve, move, and die. Another disadvantage is that important metadata—information about the collection, quality, and intent of the data—may be missing.

Our solution to these challenges is to offer the best advice we can to help you search for the data, wherever they may be residing. We usually point you to a website. We'll sometimes suggest search terms and offer other guidance.

Some words of caution, though: Data found on Internet sites may not be formatted in the best way for use in statistics software. Although you may see a data table in standard form, an attempt to copy the data may leave you with a single column of values. You may have to work in your favorite statistics or spreadsheet program to reformat the data into variables. You will also probably want to remove commas from large numbers and such extra symbols as money indicators ($, ¥, £, €); few statistics packages can handle these.

Data

In this text, whenever we introduce data, we will provide a margin note listing some of the W's of the data and, where possible, offer a reference for the source of the data. It's a habit we recommend. The first step of any data analysis is to know why you are examining the data (what you want to know), whom each row of your data table refers to, and what the variables (the columns of the table) record. These are the *Why*, the *Who*, and the *What*. Identifying them is a key part of the *Plan* step of any analysis. Make sure you know all three before you spend time analyzing the data.

For Example Identifying data sources

On the basis of her initial analysis, Carly asks her colleague Ying Mei to e-mail a sample of customers from the Travel and Entertainment segment and ask about their card use and household demographics. Carly asks another colleague, Gregg, to design a study about their double miles offer. In this study, a random sample of customers receives one of three offers: the standard double miles offer; a double miles offer good on any airline; or no offer.

Question: For each of the three data sets—Carly's original data set and Ying Mei's and Gregg's sets—state whether they come from a designed survey or a designed experiment or are collected in another way.

Answer: Carly's data set was derived from transactional data, not part of a survey or experiment. Ying Mei's data come from a designed survey, and Gregg's data come from a designed experiment.

Just Checking

An insurance company that specializes in commercial property insurance has a separate database for their policies that involve churches and schools. Here is a small portion of that database.

Policy Number	Years Claim Fre	Net Property Premium ($)	Net Liability Premium ($)	Total Property Value ($1,000)	Median Age in Zip Code	School?	Territory	Coverage
4000174699	1	3107	503	1036	40	FALSE	AL580	BLANKET
8000571997	2	1036	261	748	42	FALSE	PA192	SPECIFIC
8000623296	1	438	353	344	30	FALSE	ID60	BLANKET
3000495296	1	582	339	270	35	TRUE	NC340	BLANKET
5000291199	4	993	357	218	43	FALSE	OK590	BLANKET
8000470297	2	433	622	108	31	FALSE	NV140	BLANKET
1000042399	4	2461	1016	1544	41	TRUE	NJ20	BLANKET
4000554596	0	7340	1782	5121	44	FALSE	FL530	BLANKET
3000260397	0	1458	261	1037	42	FALSE	NC560	BLANKET
8000333297	2	392	351	177	40	FALSE	OR190	BLANKET
4000174699	1	3107	503	1036	40	FALSE	AL580	BLANKET

1 List as many of the W's as you can for this data set.
2 Classify each variable as to whether you think it should be treated as categorical or quantitative (or both); if quantitative, identify the units.

What Can Go Wrong?

- **Don't label a variable as categorical or quantitative without thinking about the data and what they represent.** The same variable can sometimes take on different roles.

- **Don't assume that a variable is quantitative just because its values are numbers.** Categories are often given numerical labels. Don't let that fool you into thinking they have quantitative meaning. Look at the context.

- **Always be skeptical.** One reason to analyze data is to discover the truth. Even when you are told a context for the data, it may turn out that the truth is a bit (or even a lot) different. The context colors our interpretation of the data, so those who want to influence what you think may slant the context. A survey that seems to be about all students may in fact report just the opinions of those who visited a fan website. The question that respondents answered may be posed in a way that influences responses.

Ethics in Action

Sarah Potterman, a doctoral student in educational psychology, is researching the effectiveness of various interventions recommended to help children with learning disabilities improve their reading skills. Among the approaches examined is an interactive software system that uses analogy-based phonics. Sarah contacted the company that developed this software, RSPT Inc., in order to obtain the system free of charge for use in her research. RSPT Inc. expressed interest in having her compare their product with other intervention strategies and was quite confident that their approach would be the most effective. Not only did the company provide Sarah with free software, but RSPT Inc. also generously offered to fund her research with a grant to cover her data collection and analysis costs.

ETHICAL ISSUE *Both the researcher and company should be careful about the funding source having a vested interest in the research result (related to Item H, ASA Ethical Guidelines).*

ETHICAL SOLUTION *RSPT Inc. should not pressure Sarah Potterman to obtain a particular result. Both parties should agree on paper before the research is begun that the research results can be published even if they show that RSPT's interactive software system is not the most effective.*

Jim Hopler is operations manager for a local office of a top-ranked full-service brokerage firm. With increasing competition from both discount and online brokers, Jim's firm has redirected attention to attaining exceptional customer service through its client-facing staff, namely brokers. In particular, they wish to emphasize the excellent advisory services provided by their brokers. Results from surveying clients about the advice received from brokers at the local office revealed that 20% rated it *poor*, 5% rated it *below average*, 15% rated it *average*, 10% rated it *above average,* and 50% rated it *outstanding.* With corporate approval, Jim and his management team instituted several changes in an effort to provide the best possible advisory services at the local office. Their goal was to increase the percentage of clients who viewed their advisory services as *outstanding.* Surveys conducted after the changes were implemented showed the following results: 5% *poor*, 5% *below average*, 20% *average*, 40% *above average,* and 30% *outstanding*. In discussing these results, the management team expressed concern that the percentage of clients who considered their advisory services *outstanding* fell from 50% to 30%. One member of the team suggested an alternative way of summarizing the data. By coding the categories on a scale from 1 = poor to 5 = outstanding and computing the average, they found that the average rating increased from 3.65 to 3.85 as a result of the changes implemented. Jim was delighted to see that their changes were successful in improving the level of advisory services offered at the local office. In his report to corporate, he only included average ratings for the client surveys.

ETHICAL ISSUE *By taking an average, Jim is able to show improved customer satisfaction. However, their goal was to increase the percentage of outstanding ratings. Jim redefined his study after the fact to support a position (related to Item A, ASA Ethical Guidelines).*

ETHICAL SOLUTION *Jim should report the percentages for each rating category. He can also report the average. He may wish to include in his report a discussion of what those different ways of looking at the data say and why they appear to differ. He may also want to explore with the survey participants the perceived differences between "above average" and "outstanding."*

What Have We Learned?

Learning Objectives

■ Understand that data are values, whether numerical or labels, together with their context.

- *who, what, why, where, when* (and *how*)—the W's—help nail down the context of the data.
- We must know *who, what,* and *why* to be able to say anything useful based on the data. The *who* are the cases. The *what* are the variables. A variable gives information about each of the cases. The *why* helps us decide which way to treat the variables.
- Stop and identify the W's whenever you have data, and be sure you can identify the cases and the variables.

■ Identify whether a variable is being used as categorical or quantitative.

- Categorical variables identify a category for each case. Usually we think about the counts of cases that fall in each category. (An exception is an identifier variable that just names each case.)
- Quantitative variables record measurements or amounts of something; they must have units.
- Sometimes we may treat the same variable as categorical or quantitative depending on what we want to learn from it, which means some variables can't be pigeonholed as one type or the other.

■ Consider the source of your data and the reasons the data were collected. That can help you understand what you might be able to learn from the data.

Terms

Business analytics	The process of using statistical analysis and modeling to drive business decisions.
Case	A case is an individual about whom or which we have data.
Categorical (or qualitative) variable	A variable that names categories (whether with words or numerals) is called categorical or qualitative.
Context	The context ideally tells *who* was measured, *what* was measured, *how* the data were collected, *where* the data were collected, and *when* and *why* the study was performed.
Cross-sectional data	Data taken from situations that vary over time but measured at a single time instant is said to be a cross-section of the time series.
Data	Recorded values whether numbers or labels, together with their context.
Data mining	The process of using a variety of statistical tools to analyze large data bases or data warehouses.
Data table	An arrangement of data in which each row represents a case and each column represents a variable.
Data warehouse	A large data base of information collected by a company or other organization usually to record transactions that the organization makes, but also used for analysis via data mining.
Experimental unit	An individual in a study for which or for whom data values are recorded. Human experimental units are usually called subjects or participants.
Identifier variable	A categorical variable that records a unique value for each case, used to name or identify it.
Metadata	Auxiliary information about variables in a database, typically including *how, when,* and *where* (and possibly *why*) the data were collected; *who* each case represents; and the definitions of all the variables.
Nominal variable	The term "nominal" can be applied to a variable whose values are used only to name categories.
Ordinal variable	The term "ordinal" can be applied to a variable whose categorical values possess some kind of order.

Participant	A human experimental unit. Also called a subject.
Quantitative variable	A variable in which the numbers are values of measured quantities with units.
Record	Information about an individual in a database.
Relational database	A relational database stores and retrieves information. Within the database, information is kept in data tables that can be "related" to each other.
Respondent	Someone who answers, or responds to, a survey.
Spreadsheet	A spreadsheet is layout designed for accounting that is often used to store and manage data tables. Excel is a common example of a spreadsheet program.
Subject	A human experimental unit. Also called a participant.
Time series	Data measured over time. Usually the time intervals are equally spaced or regularly spaced (e.g., every week, every quarter, or every year).
Transactional Data	Data collected to record the individual transactions of a company or organization.
Units	A quantity or amount adopted as a standard of measurement, such as dollars, hours, or grams.
Variable	A variable holds information about the same characteristic for many cases.

Technology Help: Data on the Computer

Most often we find statistics on a computer using a program, or *package,* designed for that purpose. There are many different statistics packages, but they all do essentially the same things. If you understand what the computer needs to know to do what you want and what it needs to show you in return, you can figure out the specific details of most packages pretty easily.

For example, to get your data into a computer statistics package, you need to tell the computer:

- Where to find the data. This usually means directing the computer to a file stored on your computer's disk or to data on a database. Or it might just mean that you have copied the data from a spreadsheet program or Internet site and it is currently on your computer's clipboard. Usually, the data should be in the form of a data table. Most computer statistics packages prefer the *delimiter* that marks the division between elements of a data table to be a *tab* character and the delimiter that marks the end of a case to be a *return* character.

- Where to put the data. (Usually this is handled automatically.)

- What to call the variables. Some data tables have variable names as the first row of the data, and often statistics packages can take the variable names from the first row automatically.

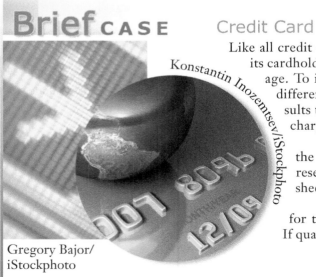

Brief**CASE**

Credit Card Bank

Like all credit and charge card companies, this company makes money on each of its cardholders' transactions. Thus, its profitability is directly linked to card usage. To increase customer spending on its cards, the company sends many different offers to its cardholders, and market researchers analyze the results to see which offers yield the largest increases in the average amount charged.

On the website for this text, www.pearsonhighered.com/sharpe, (in the file **Credit_Card_Bank**) is part of a database like the one used by the researchers. For each customer, it contains several variables in a spreadsheet.

Examine the data in the data file. List as many of the W's as you can for these data and classify each variable as categorical or quantitative. If quantitative, identify the units.

Konstantin Inozemtsev/iStockphoto

Gregory Bajor/
iStockphoto

Exercises

SECTION 1

1. A real estate major collected information on some recent local home sales. The first 6 lines of the database appear below. The columns correspond to the house identification number, the community name, the zip code, the number of acres of the property, the year the house was built, the market value, and the size of the living area (in square feet).

a) What does a row correspond to in this data table? How would you best describe its role: as a participant, subject, case, respondent, or experimental unit?
b) How many variables are measured on each row?

HOUSE_ID	NEIGHBORHOOD	MAIL_ZIP	ACRES	YR_BUILT	FULL_MARKET_VALUE	SFLA
413400536	Greenfield Manor	12859	1.00	1967	100400	960
4128001474	Fort Amherst	12801	0.09	1961	132500	906
412800344	Dublin	12309	1.65	1993	140000	1620
4128001552	Granite Springs	10598	0.33	1969	67100	900
412800352	Arcady	10562	2.29	1955	190000	1224
413400322	Ormsbee	12859	9.13	1997	126900	1056

2. A local bookstore is keeping a database of its customers to find out more about their spending habits and so that the store can start to make personal recommendations based on past purchases. Here are the first five rows of their database:

a) What does a row correspond to in this data table? How would you best describe its role: as a participant, subject, case, respondent, or experimental unit?
b) How many variables are measured on each row?

Transaction ID	Customer ID	Date	ISBN Number of Purchase	Price	Coupon?	Gift?	Quantity
29784320912	4J438	11/12/2009	345-23-2355	$29.95	N	N	1
26483589001	3K729	9/30/2009	983-83-2739	$16.99	N	N	1
26483589002	3K729	9/30/2009	102-65-2332	$9.95	Y	N	1
36429489305	3U034	12/5/2009	295-39-5884	$35.00	N	Y	1
36429489306	3U034	12/5/2009	183-38-2957	$79.95	N	Y	1

SECTION 2

3. Referring to the real estate data table of Exercise 1,

a) For each variable, would you describe it as primarily categorical, or quantitative? If quantitative, what are the units? If categorical, is it ordinal or simply nominal?
b) Are these data a time series, or are these cross-sectional? Explain briefly.

4. Referring to the bookstore data table of Exercise 2,

a) For each variable, would you describe it as primarily categorical, or quantitative? If quantitative, what are the units? If categorical, is it ordinal or simply nominal?
b) Are these data a time series, or are these cross-sectional? Explain briefly.

SECTION 3

5. For the real estate data of Exercise 1, do the data appear to have come from a designed survey or experiment? What concerns might you have about drawing conclusions from this data set?

6. A student finds data on an Internet site that contains financial information about selected companies. He plans to analyze the data and use the results to develop a stock investment strategy. What kind of data source is he using? What concerns might you have about drawing conclusions from this data set?

CHAPTER EXERCISES

For each description of data in Exercises 7 to 26, identify the W's, name the variables, specify for each variable whether its use indicates it should be treated as categorical or quantitative, and for any quantitative variable identify the units in which it was measured (or note that they were not provided). Specify whether the data come from a designed survey or experiment. Are the variables time series or cross-sectional? Report any concerns you have as well.

7. The news. Find a newspaper or magazine article in which some data are reported (e.g., see *The Wall Street Journal*, *Financial Times*, *Business Week*, or *Fortune*). For the data discussed in the article, answer the questions above. Include a copy of the article with your report.

8. The Internet. Find an Internet site on which some data are reported. For the data found on the site, answer as many of the questions above as you can. Include a copy of the URL with your report.

9. Sales. A major U.S. company is interested in seeing how various promotional activities are related to domestic sales. Analysts decide to measure the money spent on different forms of advertising ($ thousand) and sales ($ million) on a monthly basis for three years (2004–2006).

10. Food store. A food retailer that specializes in selling organic food has decided to open a new store. To help determine the best location in the United States for the new store, researchers decide to examine data from existing stores, including weekly sales ($), town population (thousands), median age of town, median income of town ($), and whether or not the store sells wine and beer.

11. Sales II. The company in Exercise 2 is also interested in the impact of national indicators on their sales. It decides to obtain measurements for unemployment rate (%) and inflation rate (%) on a quarterly basis to compare to their quarterly sales ($ million) over the same time period (2004–2006).

12. Arby's menu. A listing posted by the Arby's restaurant chain gives, for each of the sandwiches it sells, the type of meat in the sandwich, number of calories, and serving size in ounces. The data might be used to assess the nutritional value of the different sandwiches.

13. MBA admissions. A school in the northeastern United States is concerned with the recent drop in female students in its MBA program. It decides to collect data from the admissions office on each applicant, including: sex of each applicant, age of each applicant, whether or not they were accepted, whether or not they attended, and the reason for not attending (if they did not attend). The school hopes to find commonalities among the female accepted students who have decided not to attend the business program.

14. MBA admissions II. An internationally recognized MBA program in London intends to also track the GPA of the MBA students and compares MBA performance to standardized test scores over a 5-year period (2000–2005).

15. Pharmaceutical firm. Scientists at a major pharmaceutical firm conducted an experiment to study the effectiveness of an herbal compound to treat the common cold. They exposed volunteers to a cold virus, then gave them either the herbal compound or a sugar solution known to have no effect on colds. Several days later they assessed each patient's condition using a cold severity scale ranging from 0–5. They found no evidence of the benefits of the compound.

16. Start-up company. A start-up company is building a database of customers and sales information. For each customer, it records name, ID number, region of the country (1 = East, 2 = South, 3 = Midwest, 4 = West), date of last purchase, amount of purchase, and item purchased.

17. Vineyards. Business analysts hoping to provide information helpful to grape growers sent out a questionnaire to a sample of growers requesting these data about vineyards: size (acres), number of years in existence, state, varieties of grapes grown, average case price, gross sales, and percent profit.

18. Gallup Poll. The Gallup Poll conducted a representative telephone survey of 1180 American voters. Among the reported results were the voter's region (Northeast, South, etc.), age, political party affiliation, whether the respondent owned any shares of stock, and their attitude (on a scale of 1 to 5) toward unions.

19. EPA. The Environmental Protection Agency (EPA) tracks fuel economy of automobiles. Among the data EPA analysts collect from the manufacturer are the manufacturer (Ford, Toyota, etc.), vehicle type (car, SUV, etc.), weight, horsepower, and gas mileage (mpg) for city and highway driving.

20. Consumer Reports. In 2002, Consumer Reports published an article evaluating refrigerators. It listed 41 models, giving the brand, cost, size (cu ft), type (such as top-freezer), estimated annual energy cost, overall rating (good, excellent, etc.), and repair history for that brand (percentage requiring repairs over the past 5 years).

21. Lotto. A study of state-sponsored Lotto games in the United States (*Chance*, Winter 1998) listed the names of the states and whether or not the state had Lotto. For states that did, the study indicated the number of numbers in the lottery, the number of matches required to win, and the probability of holding a winning ticket.

22. L.L. Bean. L.L. Bean is a large U.S. retailer that depends heavily on its catalog sales. It collects data internally and tracks the number of catalogs mailed out, the number of square inches in each catalog, and the sales ($ thousands) in the 4 weeks following each mailing. The company is interested in learning more about the relationship (if any) among the timing and space of their catalogs and their sales.

23. Stock market. An online survey of students in a large MBA Statistics class at a business school in the northeastern

United States asked them to report their total personal investment in the stock market ($), total number of different stocks currently held, total invested in mutual funds ($), and the name of each mutual fund in which they have invested. The data were used in the aggregate for classroom illustrations.

24. Theme park sites. A study on the potential for developing theme parks in various locations throughout Europe in 2008 collects the following information: the country where the proposed site is located, estimated cost to acquire site (in euros), size of population within a one-hour drive of the site, size of the site (in hectares), mass transportation within 5 minutes of the site. The data will be used to present to prospective developers.

25. Indy 2009. The 2.5-mile Indianapolis Motor Speedway has been the home to a race on Memorial Day nearly every year since 1911. Even during the first race there were controversies. Ralph Mulford was given the checkered flag first but took three extra laps just to make sure he'd completed 500 miles. When he finished, another driver, Ray Harroun, was being presented with the winner's trophy, and Mulford's protests were ignored.

Harroun averaged 74.6 mph for the 500 miles. Here are the data for the first few and three recent Indianapolis 500 races.

Year	Winner	Car	Time (hrs)	Speed (mph)	Car #
1911	Ray Harroun	Marmon Model 32	6.7022	74.602	32
1912	Joe Dawson	National	6.3517	78.719	8
1913	Jules Goux	Peugeot	6.5848	75.933	16
...					
...					
2005	Dan Wheldon	Dallara/Honda	3.1725	157.603	26
2006	Sam Hornish, Jr.	Dallara/Honda	3.1830	157.085	6
2007	Dario Franchitti	Dallara/Honda	2.7343	151.774	27
2008	Scott Dixon	Dallara	3.4826	143.567	9
2009	Hélio Castroneves	Dallara	3.3262	150.318	3

26. Kentucky Derby. The Kentucky Derby is a horse race that has been run every year since 1875 at Churchill Downs, Louisville, Kentucky. The race started as a 1.5-mile race, but in 1896 it was shortened to 1.25 miles because experts felt that 3-year-old horses shouldn't run such a long race that early in the season. (It has been run in May every year but one—1901—when it took place on April 29.) The table at the bottom of the page shows the data for the first few and a few recent races.

Date	Winner	Margin (lengths)	Jockey	Winner's Payoff ($)	Duration (min:sec)	Track Condition
May 17, 1875	Aristides	2	O. Lewis	2850	2:37.75	Fast
May 15, 1876	Vagrant	2	B. Swim	2950	2:38.25	Fast
May 22, 1877	Baden-Baden	2	W. Walker	3300	2:38.00	Fast
May 21, 1878	Day Star	1	J. Carter	4050	2:37.25	Dusty
May 20, 1879	Lord Murphy	1	C. Shauer	3550	2:37.00	Fast
...						
May 5, 2001	Monarchos	4 3/4	J. Chavez	812,000	1:59.97	Fast
May 4, 2002	War Emblem	4	V. Espinoza	1,875,000	2:01.13	Fast
May 3, 2003	Funny Cide	1 3/4	J. Santos	800,200	2:01.19	Fast
May 1, 2004	Smarty Jones	2 3/4	S. Elliott	854,800	2:04.06	Sloppy

When you organize data in a spreadsheet, it is important to lay it out as a data table. For each of these examples in Exercises 27 to 30, show how you would lay out these data. Indicate the headings of columns and what would be found in each row.

27. Mortgages. For a study of mortgage loan performance: amount of the loan, the name of the borrower.

28. Employee performance. Data collected to determine performance-based bonuses: employee ID, average contract closed (in $), supervisor's rating (1–10), years with the company.

29. Company performance. Data collected for financial planning: weekly sales, week (week number of the year), sales predicted by last year's plan, difference between predicted sales and realized sales.

30. Command performance. Data collected on investments in Broadway shows: number of investors, total invested, name of the show, profit/loss after one year.

For the following examples in Exercises 31 to 34, indicate whether the data are a time series or a cross section.

31. Car sales. Number of cars sold by each salesperson in a dealership in September.

32. Motorcycle sales. Number of motorcycles sold by a dealership in each month of 2008.

33. Cross sections. Average diameter of trees brought to a sawmill in each week of a year.

34. Series. Attendance at the third World Series game recording the age of each fan.

Just Checking Answers

1 Who—policies on churches and schools
   What—policy number, years claim free, net property premium ($), net liability premium ($), total property value ($000), median age in zip code, school?, territory, coverage
   How—company records
   When—not given

2 Policy number: identifier (categorical)
   Years claim free: quantitative
   Net property premium: quantitative ($)
   Net liability premium: quantitative ($)
   Total property value: quantitative ($)
   Median age in zip code: quantitative
   School?: categorical (true/false)
   Territory: categorical
   Coverage: categorical

Answers

SECTION EXERCISE ANSWERS

1. a) Each row represents a different house. It is a case.
    b) There are 7 variables including the house identifier.

3. a) House _ID is an identifier (categorical, not ordinal). Neighborhood is categorical (nominal). Mail_ZIP is categorical (nominal – ordinal in a sense, but only on a national level). YR_BUILT is quantitative (units – year). FULL_MARKET_VALUE is quantitative (units – dollars). SFLA is quantitative (units – square feet).
    b) These data are cross-sectional. All variables were measured at about the same time.

5. It is not clear if the data were obtained from a survey. They are certainly not from an experiment. Most likely they are just a collection of recent sales. We don't know if those sales are representative of all sales, so we should be cautious in drawing conclusions from these data about the housing market in general.

CHAPTER EXERCISE ANSWERS

7. Answers will vary.

9. *Who*—months; *What*—money spent on advertising ($ thousand) and sales ($ million); *When*—monthly from 2004–2006; *Where*—United States; *Why*—To compare money spent on advertising to sales; *How*—not specified; *Variables*—There are two quantitative variables. The data form a time series.

11. *Who*—quarters; *What*—sales ($ million), unemployment rate (%), and inflation rate (%); *When*—quarterly from 2004–2006; *Where*—United States; *Why*—to relate sales to unemployment and inflation rates; *How*—not specified; *Variables*—There are 3 quantitative variables: sales ($ million), unemployment rate (%), and inflation rate (%). The data form a time series.

13. *Who*—MBA applicants; *What*—sex, age, whether or not they accepted, whether or not they attended, and the reasons; *When*—not specified; *Where*—United States; *Why*—The researchers wanted to investigate any patterns in female acceptance and attendance; *How*—Data obtained internally from admissions office; *Variables*—There are 5 variables. Sex, whether or not they accepted, whether or not they attended, and the reasons are all categorical variables; only age (years) of applicant is quantitative. The data are a cross section.

15. *Who*—experiment volunteers; *What*—herbal cold remedy or sugar solution, and cold severity; *When*—not specified; *Where*—major pharmaceutical firm; *Why*—Scientists were testing the efficacy of a herbal compound on the severity of the common cold; *How*—The scientists set up an experiment; *Variables*—There are 2 variables. Type of treatment (herbal or sugar solution) is categorical, and severity rating is quantitative; *Concerns*—The severity of a cold seems subjective and difficult to quantify. Also, the scientists may feel pressure to report negative findings about the herbal product. The data are cross sectional and from a designed experiment.

17. *Who*—vineyards; *What*—size of vineyard (in acres), number of years in existence, state, varieties of grapes grown, average case price (in dollars), gross sales (probably in dollars), and percent profit; *When*—not specified; *Where*—not specified; *Why*—Business analysts hoped to provide information that would be helpful to producers of U.S. wines; *How*—not specified; *Variables*—There are 5 quantitative variables and 2 categorical variables. Size of vineyard, number of years in existence, average case price, gross sales, and percent profit are quantitative variables. State and variety of grapes grown are categorical variables. The data are a cross section collected in a designed survey.

19. *Who*—every model of automobile in the United States; *What*—vehicle manufacturer, vehicle type, weight (probably in pounds), horsepower (in horsepower), and gas mileage (in miles per gallon) for city and highway driving; *When*—This information is collected currently; *Where*—United States; *Why*—The Environmental Protection Agency uses the information to track fuel economy of vehicles; *How*—The data is collected from the manufacturer of each model; *Variables*—There are 6 variables. City mileage, highway mileage, weight, and horsepower are quantitative variables. Manufacturer and type of car are categorical variables. The data are a cross section.

21. *Who*—states in the United States; *What*—state name, whether or not the state sponsors a lottery, the number of numbers in the lottery, the number of matches required to win, and the probability of holding a winning ticket; *When*—1998; *Where*—United States; *Why*—It is likely that this study was performed in order to compare the chances of winning the lottery in each state; *How*—Although not specified, the researchers probably simply gathered data from a number of different sources, such as state lottery website and publications; *Variables*—There are 5 variables. State name and whether or not the state sponsors a lottery are categorical variables, and number, matches, and probability of winning are quantitative variables. The data are a cross section.

23. *Who*—students in an MBA statistics class; *What*—total personal investment in stock market ($), number of different stocks held, total invested in mutual funds ($), and name of each mutual fund; *When*—not specified; *Where*—United States; *Why*—The information was collected for use in classroom illustrations; *How*—An online survey was conducted. Presumably, participation was required for all members of the class; *Variables*—There are 4 variables. Name of mutual fund is a categorical variable. Number of stocks held, total amount invested in market ($), and in mutual funds ($) are quantitative variables. The data are a cross section.

25. *Who*—Indy 500 races; *What*—year, winner, car, time (hours), speed (mph) and car #. *When*—1911–2009; *Where*—Indianapolis, Indiana; *Why*—It is interesting to examine the trends in Indy 500 races; *How*—Official statistics are kept for the race every year; *Variables*—There are 6 variables. Winner, car, and car # are categorical variables. Year, time, and speed are quantitative variables. The quantitative variables can be viewed as time series.

27. Each row should be a single mortgage loan. Columns hold the borrower name (which identifies the rows) and amount.

29. Each row is a week. Columns hold week number (to identify the row), sales prediction, sales, and difference.

31. Cross-sectional.

33. Time series.

Surveys and Sampling

Stockbyte   Digital Vision

Roper Polls

Public opinion polls are a relatively new phenomenon. In 1948, as a result of telephone surveys of likely voters, all of the major organizations—Gallup, Roper, and Crossley—consistently predicted, throughout the summer and into the fall, that Thomas Dewey would defeat Harry Truman in the November presidential election. By October the results seemed so clear that *Fortune* magazine declared, "Due to the overwhelming evidence, *Fortune* and Mr. Roper plan no further detailed reports on change of opinion in the forthcoming presidential campaign. . . ."

New York World and Telegraph/Library of Congress Prints and Photographs Division [LC-USZ62-115068]

Of course, Harry Truman went on to win the 1948 election, and the picture of Truman in the early morning after the election holding up the *Chicago Tribune* (printed the night before), with its headline declaring Dewey the winner, has become legend.

The public's faith in opinion polls plummeted after the election, but Elmo Roper vigorously defended the pollsters. Roper was a principal and founder of one of the first market research firms, Cherington, Wood, and Roper, and director of the *Fortune Survey*, which was the first national poll to use scientific sampling

From Chapter 3 of *Business Statistics*, Second Edition, Norean R. Sharpe, Richard D. De Veaux, Paul F. Velleman.

techniques. He argued that rather than abandoning polling, business leaders should learn what had gone wrong in the 1948 polls so that market research could be improved. His frank admission of the mistakes made in those polls helped to restore confidence in polling as a business tool.

For the rest of his career, Roper split his efforts between two projects, commercial polling and public opinion. He established the Roper Center for Public Opinion Research at Williams College as a place to house public opinion archives, convincing fellow polling leaders Gallup and Crossley to participate as well. Now located at the University of Connecticut, the Roper Center is one of the world's leading archives of social science data. Roper's market research efforts started as Roper Research Associates and later became the Roper Organization, which was acquired in 2005 by GfK. Founded in Germany in 1934 as the Gesellschaft für Konsumforschung (literally, "Society for Consumption Research"), GfK now stands for "growth from knowledge." It is the fourth largest international market research organization, with over 130 companies in 70 countries and more than 7700 employees worldwide.

GfK Roper Consulting conducts a yearly, global study to examine cultural, economic, and social information that may be crucial to companies doing business worldwide. These companies use the information provided by GfK Roper to help make marketing and advertising decisions in different markets around the world.

How do the researchers at GfK Roper know that the responses they get reflect the real attitudes of consumers? After all, they don't ask everyone, but they don't want to limit their conclusions to just the people they surveyed. Generalizing from the data at hand to the world at large is something that market researchers, investors, and pollsters do every day. To do it wisely, they need three fundamental ideas.

1   Three Ideas of Sampling

Idea 1: Sample—Examine a Part of the Whole

We'd like to know about an entire collection of individuals, called a **population**, but examining all of them is usually impractical, if not impossible. So we settle for examining a smaller group of individuals—a **sample**—selected from the population. For the Roper researchers the population of interest is the entire world, but it's not practical, cost-effective, or feasible to survey everyone. So they examine a sample selected from the population.

The W's and Sampling

The population we are interested in is usually determined by the *why* of our study. The participants or cases in the sample we draw will be the *who*. *when* and *how* we draw the sample may depend on what is practical.

You take samples every day. For example, if you want to know how the vegetable soup you're cooking for dinner tonight is going to taste, you blow on a spoonful and try it. You certainly don't consume the whole pot. You trust that the taste will *represent* the flavor of the population—the entire pot. The idea of tasting is that a small sample, if selected properly, can represent the larger population.

The GfK Roper Reports® Worldwide poll is an example of a **sample survey**, designed to ask questions of a small group of people in the hope of learning something about the entire population. Most likely, you've never been selected to be part of a national opinion poll. That's true of most people. So how can the pollsters claim that a sample represents the entire population? Selecting a sample to represent the population fairly is easy in theory, but in practice, it's more difficult than it sounds. Polls or surveys most often fail because the sample fails to represent part of the population. For example, a telephone survey may get no responses from people with caller ID and may favor other groups, such as the retired or the homebound, who would be more likely to be near their phones when the interviewer calls. Samples that over- or underemphasize some characteristics of the population are said to be biased. When a sample is **biased**, the summary characteristics of a sample differ from the corresponding characteristics of the population it is trying to represent, so they can produce misleading information. Conclusions based on biased samples are inherently flawed. There is usually no way to fix bias after the sample is drawn and no way to salvage useful information from it.

To make the sample as representative as possible, you might be tempted to handpick the individuals included in the sample. But the best strategy is to do something quite different: We should select individuals for the sample *at random*.

Idea 2: Randomize

Think back to our soup example. Suppose you add some salt to the pot (the population). If you sample it from the top before stirring, you'll get the misleading idea that the whole pot is salty. If you sample from the bottom, you'll get the equally misleading idea that the whole pot is bland. But by stirring the soup, you **randomize** the amount of salt throughout the pot, making each taste more typical of the saltiness of the whole pot. Deliberate randomization is one of the great tools of Statistics.

Randomization can protect against factors that you aren't aware of, as well as those you know are in the data. Suppose, while you aren't looking, a friend adds a handful of peas to the soup. The peas sink to the bottom of the pot, mixing with the other vegetables. If you don't randomize the soup by stirring, your test spoonful from the top won't have any peas. By stirring in the salt, you *also* randomize the peas throughout the pot, making your sample taste more typical of the overall pot *even though you didn't know the peas were there*. So randomizing protects us by giving us a representative sample even for effects we were unaware of.

For a survey, we "stir" the population by selecting the participants at random. Randomizing protects us from the influences of *all* the features of our population by making sure that *on average* the sample looks like the rest of the population.

The essential feature of randomness that we need is that the selection is "fair." What makes the sample fair is that each participant has an equal chance to be selected.

- **Why not match the sample to the population?** Rather than randomizing, we could try to design our sample to include every possible, relevant characteristic: income level, age, political affiliation, marital status, number of children, place of residence, etc. Clearly we can't possibly think of all the things that might be important. Even if we could, we wouldn't be able to match our sample to the population for all these characteristics.

Michael LaMotte/Cole Group/
PhotoDisc/Getty Images

How well can a sample represent the population from which it was selected? Here's an example using the database of the Paralyzed Veterans of America, a philanthropic organization with a donor list of about 3.5 million people. We've taken two samples, each of 8000 individuals at random from the population. Table 1 shows how the means and proportions match up on seven variables.

	A	Age (yr)	White (%)	Female (%)	# of children	Income Bracket (1-7)	Wealth Bracket (1-9)	Homeowner? (% Yes)
1								
2	Sample 1	61.4	85.12	56.2	1.54	3.91	5.29	71.36
3	Sample 2	61.2	84.44	56.4	1.51	3.88	5.33	72.3

Table 1   Means and proportions for seven variables from two samples of size 8000 from the Paralyzed Veterans of America data (created in **Excel**). The fact that the summaries of the variables from these two samples are so similar gives us confidence that either one would be representative of the entire population.

The two samples match closely in every category. You can see how well randomizing has stirred the population. We didn't preselect the samples for these variables, but randomizing has matched the results closely. The two samples don't vary much from each other, so we can assume that they don't differ much from the rest of the population either.

Even if a survey is given to multiple random samples, the samples will differ from each other and so, therefore, will the responses. These sample-to-sample differences are referred to as **sampling error** even though no error has occurred.

Idea 3: The Sample Size Is What Matters

You probably weren't surprised by the idea that a sample can represent the whole. And the idea of sampling randomly to make the sample fair makes sense too. But the third important idea of sampling often surprises people. The third idea is that the *size of the sample* determines what we can conclude from the data *regardless of the size of the population*. Many people think that to provide a good representation of the population, the sample must be a large percentage, or *fraction*, of the population, but in fact all that matters is the size of the sample. The size of the *population* doesn't matter at all.[1] A random sample of 100 students in a college represents the student body just about as well as a random sample of 100 voters represents the entire electorate of the United States. This is perhaps the most surprising idea in designing surveys.

Think about the pot of soup again. If you're cooking for a banquet rather than just for a few people, your pot will be bigger, but you don't need a bigger spoon to decide how the soup tastes. You'll get the same information from an ordinary spoonful that you got before, no matter how large the pot—as long as the pot is sufficiently stirred. That's what randomness does for us. What *fraction* of the population you sample doesn't matter. It's the **sample size** itself that's important. This idea is of key importance to the design of any sample survey, because it determines the balance between how well the survey can measure the population and how much the survey costs.

How big a sample do you need? That depends on what you're estimating, but too small a sample won't be representative of the population. To get an idea of what's really in the soup, you need a large enough taste to be a *representative* sample

---

[1]Well, that's not exactly true. If sample is more than about 10% of the whole population, it *can* matter. It doesn't matter whenever, as usual, our sample is a very small fraction of the population.

from the pot, including, say, a selection of the vegetables. For a survey that tries to find the proportion of the population falling into a category, you'll usually need at least several hundred respondents.

- **What do the professionals do?** How do professional polling and market research companies do their work? The most common polling method today is to contact respondents by telephone. Computers generate random telephone numbers for telephone exchanges known to include residential customers; so pollsters can contact people with unlisted phone numbers. The person who answers the phone will be invited to respond to the survey—if that person qualifies. (For example, only adults are usually surveyed, and the respondent usually must live at the residence phoned.) If the person answering doesn't qualify, the caller will ask for an appropriate alternative. When they conduct the interview, the pollsters often list possible responses (such as product names) in randomized orders to avoid biases that might favor the first name on the list.

Do these methods work? The Pew Research Center for the People and the Press, reporting on one survey, says that

> *Across five days of interviewing, surveys today are able to make some kind of contact with the vast majority of households (76%), and there is no decline in this contact rate over the past seven years. But because of busy schedules, skepticism and outright refusals, interviews were completed in just 38% of households that were reached using standard polling procedures.*

Nevertheless, studies indicate that those actually sampled can give a good snapshot of larger populations from which the surveyed households were drawn.

A Census—Does It Make Sense?

Why bother determining the right sample size? If you plan to open a store in a new community, why draw a sample of residents to understand their interests and needs? Wouldn't it be better to just include everyone and make the "sample" be the entire population? Such a special sample is called a **census**. Although a census would appear to provide the best possible information about the population, there are a number of reasons why it might not.

First, it can be difficult to complete a census. There always seem to be some individuals who are hard to locate or hard to measure. Do you really need to contact the folks away on vacation when you collect your data? How about those with no telephone or mail address? The cost of locating the last few cases may far exceed the budget. It can also be just plain impractical to take a census. The quality control manager for Hostess® Twinkies® doesn't want to taste *all* the Twinkies on the production line to determine their quality. Aside from the fact that nobody could eat that many Twinkies, it would defeat their purpose: There would be none left to sell.

Second, the population you're studying may change. For example, in any human population, babies are born, people travel, and folks die during the time it takes to complete the census. News events and advertising campaigns can cause sudden shifts in opinions and preferences. A sample, surveyed in a shorter time frame, may actually generate more accurate information.

Finally, taking a census can be cumbersome. A census usually requires a team of pollsters and the cooperation of the population. Even with both, it's almost impossible to avoid errors. Because it tries to count everyone, the U.S. Census records too many college students. Many are included both by their families and in a report filed by their schools. Errors of this sort, of both under- and overcounting can be found throughout the U.S. Census.

Identifying sampling terms

A nonprofit organization has taken over the historic State Theater and hopes to preserve it with a combination of attractive shows and fundraising. The organization has asked a team of students to help them design a survey to better understand the customer base likely to purchase tickets. Fortunately, the theater's computerized ticket system records contact and some demographic information for ticket purchasers, and that database of 7345 customers is available.

Questions: What is the population of interest?

What would a census be in this case? Would it be practical?

What is the sampling frame?

Answers: The population is all potential ticket purchasers.

A census would have to reach all potential purchasers. We don't know who they are or have any way to contact them.

The sampling frame is the list of previous ticket purchasers.

2 Populations and Parameters

GfK Roper Reports Worldwide reports that 60.5% of people over 50 worry about food safety, but only 43.7% of teens do. What does this claim mean? We can be sure the Roper researchers didn't take a census. So they can't possibly know *exactly* what percentage of teenagers worry about food safety. So what does "43.7%" mean?

To generalize from a sample to the world at large, we need a model of reality. Such a model doesn't need to be complete or perfect. Just as a model of an airplane in a wind tunnel can tell engineers what they need to know about aerodynamics even though it doesn't include every rivet of the actual plane, models of data can give us summaries that we can learn from and use even though they don't fit each data value exactly. It's important to remember that they're only models of reality and not reality itself. But without models, what we can learn about the world at large is limited to only what we can say about the data we have at hand.

Models use mathematics to represent reality. We call the key numbers in those models **parameters**. Sometimes a parameter used in a model for a population is called (redundantly) a **population parameter**.

But let's not forget about the data. We use the data to try to estimate values for the population parameters. Any summary found from the data is a **statistic**. Those statistics that estimate population parameters are particularly interesting. Sometimes—and especially when we match statistics with the parameters they estimate—we use the term **sample statistic**.

We draw samples because we can't work with the entire population. We hope that the statistics we compute from the sample will estimate the corresponding parameters accurately. A sample that does this is said to be **representative**.

> **Statistic**
>
> Any quantity that we calculate from data could be called a "statistic." But in practice, we usually obtain a statistic from a sample and use it to estimate a population parameter.

> **Parameter**
>
> Population model parameters are not just unknown—usually they are *unknowable*. We take a sample and use the sample statistics to estimate them.

1   Various claims are often made for surveys. Why is each of the following claims not correct?

   a) It is always better to take a census than to draw a sample.

   b) Stopping customers as they are leaving a restaurant is a good way to sample opinions about the quality of the food.

   c) We drew a sample of 100 from the 3000 students in a school. To get the same level of precision for a town of 30,000 residents, we'll need a sample of 1000.

   d) A poll taken at a popular website (www.statsisfun.org) garnered 12,357 responses. The majority of respondents said they enjoy doing Statistics. With a sample size that large, we can be sure that most Americans feel this way.

   e) The true percentage of all Americans who enjoy Statistics is called a "population statistic."

3   Common Sampling Designs

We've said that every individual in the population should have an equal chance of being selected in a sample. That makes the sample fair, but it's not quite enough to ensure that the sample is representative. Consider, for example, a market analyst who samples customers by drawing at random from product registration forms, half of which arrived by mail and half by online registration. She flips a coin. If it comes up heads, she'll draw 100 mail returns; tails, she'll draw 100 electronic returns. Each customer has an equal chance of being selected, but if tech-savvy customers are different, then the samples are hardly representative.

Simple Random Sample (SRS)

To make the sample representative, we must ensure that our sampling method gives each *combination* of individuals an equal chance as well. A sample drawn in this way is called a **simple random sample**, usually abbreviated **SRS**. An SRS is the sampling method on which the theory of working with sampled data is based and thus the standard against which we measure other sampling methods.

We'd like to select from the population, but often we don't have a list of all the individuals in the population. The list we actually draw from is called a **sampling frame**. A store may want to survey all its regular customers. But it can't draw a sample from the population of all regular customers, because it doesn't have such a list. The store may have a list of customers who have registered as "frequent shoppers." That list can be the sampling frame from which the store can draw its sample.

Of course, whenever the sampling frame and the population differ (as they almost always will), we must deal with the differences. Are the opinions of those who registered as frequent shoppers different from the rest of the regular shoppers? What about customers who used to be regulars but haven't shopped there recently? The answers to questions like these about the sampling frame may depend on the purpose of the survey and may impact the conclusions that one can draw.

Once we have a sampling frame, we need to *randomize* it so we can choose an SRS. Fortunately, random numbers are readily available these days in spreadsheets, statistics programs, and even on the Internet. Before this technology existed, people used to literally draw numbers out of a hat to randomize. But now, the easiest way to randomize your sampling frame is to match it with a parallel list of random numbers and then sort the random numbers, carrying along the cases so that they get "shuffled" into random order. Then you can just pick cases off the top of the randomized list until you have enough for your sample.

Samples drawn at random generally differ one from another. If we were to repeat the sampling process, a new draw of random numbers would select different people for our sample. These differences would lead to different values for the variables we measure. We call these sample-to-sample differences **sampling variability**. Surprisingly, sampling variability isn't a problem; it's an opportunity. If different samples from a population vary little from each other, then most likely the underlying population harbors little variation. If the samples show much sampling variability, the underlying population probably varies a lot. We'll spend much time and attention working with sampling variability to better understand what we are trying to measure.

f_x	=RAND()
C	**D**
0.750306	

A Different Answer Every Time?
The RAND() function in Excel can take you by surprise. Every time the spreadsheet reopens, you get a new column of random numbers. But don't worry. Once you've shuffled the rows, you can ignore the new numbers. The order you got by shuffling won't keep changing.

For Example   Choosing a random sample

Continuing the example on the previous page, the student consultants select 200 ticket buyers at random from the database. First, the State Theater database is placed in a spreadsheet. Next, to draw random numbers, the students use the Excel command RAND(). (They type =RAND() in the top cell of a column next to the data and then use *Fill Down* to populate the column down to the bottom.) They then sort the spreadsheet to put the random column in order and select ticket buyers from the top of the randomized

(continued)

spreadsheet until they complete 200 interviews. This makes it easy to select more respondents when (as always happens) some of the people they select can't be reached by telephone or decline to participate.

Questions: What is the sampling frame?

If the customer database held 30,000 records instead of 7345, how much larger a sample would we need to get the same information?

If we then draw a different sample of 200 customers and obtain different answers to the questions on the survey, how do we refer to these differences?

Answers: The sampling frame is the customer database.

The size of the sample is all that matters, not the size of the population. We would need a sample of 200.

The differences in the responses are called sampling error, or sampling variability.

Sampling Errors vs. Bias

We referred to sample-to-sample variability earlier in this chapter as *sampling error*, making it sound like it's some kind of mistake. It's not. We understand that samples will vary, so "sampling errors" are to be expected. It's *bias* we must strive to avoid. Bias means our sampling method distorts our view of the population. Of course, bias leads to mistakes. Even more insidious, bias introduces errors that we cannot correct with subsequent analysis.

Simple random sampling is not the only fair way to sample. More complicated designs may save time or money or avert sampling problems. All statistical sampling designs have in common the idea that chance, rather than human choice, is used to select the sample.

Stratified Sampling

Designs that are used to sample from large populations—especially populations residing across large areas—are often more complicated than simple random samples. Sometimes we slice the population into homogeneous groups, called **strata,** and then use simple random sampling within each stratum, combining the results at the end. This is called **stratified random sampling.**

Why would we want to stratify? Suppose we want to survey how shoppers feel about a potential new anchor store at a large suburban mall. The shopper population is 60% women and 40% men, and we suspect that men and women have different views on their choice of anchor stores. If we use simple random sampling to select 100 people for the survey, we could end up with 70 men and 30 women or 35 men and 65 women. Our resulting estimates of the attractiveness of a new anchor store could vary widely. To help reduce this sampling variability, we can force a representative balance, selecting 40 men at random and 60 women at random. This would guarantee that the proportions of men and women within our sample match the proportions in the population, and that should make such samples more accurate in representing population opinion.

You can imagine that stratifying by race, income, age, and other characteristics can be helpful, depending on the purpose of the survey. When we use a sampling method that restricts by strata, additional samples are more like one another, so statistics calculated for the sampled values will vary less from one sample to another. This reduced sampling variability is the most important benefit of stratifying, but the analysis of data sampled with these designs is beyond the scope of our text.

Cluster and Multistage Sampling

Sometimes dividing the sample into homogeneous strata isn't practical, and even simple random sampling may be difficult. For example, suppose we wanted to assess the reading level of a product instruction manual based on the length of the sentences. Simple random sampling could be awkward; we'd have to number each sentence and then find, for example, the 576th sentence or the 2482nd sentence, and so on. Doesn't sound like much fun, does it?

We could make our task much easier by picking a few pages at random and then counting the lengths of the sentences on those pages. That's easier than picking

Strata or Clusters?

We create strata by dividing the population into groups of similar individuals so that each stratum is different from the others. (For example, we often stratify by age, race, or sex.) By contrast, we create clusters that all look pretty much alike, each representing the wide variety of individuals seen in the population.

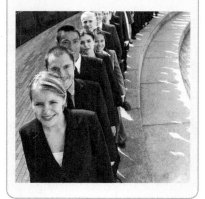

Digital Vision

individual sentences and works if we believe that the pages are all reasonably similar to one another in terms of reading level. Splitting the population in this way into parts or **clusters** that each represent the population can make sampling more practical. We select one or a few clusters at random and perform a census within each of them. This sampling design is called **cluster sampling.** If each cluster fairly represents the population, cluster sampling will generate an unbiased sample.

What's the difference between cluster sampling and stratified sampling? We stratify to ensure that our sample represents different groups in the population, and sample randomly within each stratum. This reduces the sample-to-sample variability. Strata are homogeneous, but differ from one another. By contrast, clusters are more or less alike, each heterogeneous and resembling the overall population. We cluster to save money or even to make the study practical.

Sometimes we use a variety of sampling methods together. In trying to assess the reading level of our instruction manual, we might worry that the "quick start" instructions are easy to read, but the "troubleshooting" chapter is more difficult. If so, we'd want to avoid samples that selected heavily from any one chapter. To guarantee a fair mix of sections, we could randomly choose one section from this chapter of the manual. Then we would randomly select a few pages from each of those sections. If altogether that made too many sentences, we might select a few sentences at random from each of the chosen pages. So, what is our sampling strategy? First we stratify by the chapter of the manual and randomly choose a section to represent each stratum. Within each selected section, we choose pages as clusters. Finally, we consider an SRS of sentences within each cluster. Sampling schemes that combine several methods are called **multistage samples**. Most surveys conducted by professional polling organizations and market research firms use some combination of stratified and cluster sampling as well as simple random samples.

For Example   Identifying more complex designs

The theater board wants to encourage people to come from out of town to attend theater events. They know that, in general, about 40% of ticket buyers are from out of town. These customers often purchase dinner at a local restaurant or stay overnight in a local inn, generating business for the town. The board hopes this information will encourage local businesses to advertise in the theater program, so they want to be sure out-of-town customers are represented in the samples. The database includes zip codes. The student consultants decide to sample 80 ticket buyers from zip codes outside the town and 120 from the town's zip code.

Questions: What kind of sampling scheme are they using to replace the simple random sample?

What are the advantages of selecting 80 out of town and 120 local customers?

Answers: A stratified sample, consisting of a sample of 80 out-of-town customers and a sample of 120 local customers.

By stratifying, they can guarantee that 40% of the sample is from out of town, reflecting the overall proportions among ticket buyers. If out-of-town customers differ in important ways from local ticket buyers, a stratified sample will reduce the variation in the estimates for each group so that the combined estimates can be more precise.

Systematic Samples

Sometimes we draw a sample by selecting individuals systematically. For example, a **systematic sample** might select every tenth person on an alphabetical list of employees. To make sure our sample is random, we still must start the systematic selection with a randomly selected individual—not necessarily the first person on the list. When there is no reason to believe that the order of the list could be associated in any way with the responses measured, systematic sampling can give a

Just Checking

2 We need to survey a random sample of the 300 passengers on a flight from San Francisco to Tokyo. Name each sampling method described below.

a) Pick every tenth passenger as people board the plane.

b) From the boarding list, randomly choose five people flying first class and 25 of the other passengers.

c) Randomly generate 30 seat numbers and survey the passengers who sit there.

d) Randomly select a seat position (right window, right center, right aisle, etc.) And survey all the passengers sitting in those seats.

representative sample. Systematic sampling can be much less expensive than true random sampling. When you use a systematic sample, you should justify the assumption that the systematic method is not associated with any of the measured variables.

Think about the reading level sampling example again. Suppose we have chosen a section of the manual at random, then three pages at random from that section, and now we want to select a sample of 10 sentences from the 73 sentences found on those pages. Instead of numbering each sentence so we can pick a simple random sample, it would be easier to sample systematically. A quick calculation shows $73/10 = 7.3$, so we can get our sample by picking every seventh sentence on the page. But where should you start? At random, of course. We've accounted for $10 \times 7 = 70$ of the sentences, so we'll throw the extra three into the starting group and choose a sentence at random from the first 10. Then we pick every seventh sentence after that and record its length.

Guided Example **Market Demand Survey**

Shutterstock

In a course at a business school in the United States, the students form business teams, propose a new product, and use seed money to launch a business to sell the product on campus.

Before committing funds for the business, each team must complete the following assignment: "Conduct a survey to determine the potential market demand on campus for the product you are proposing to sell." Suppose your team's product is a 500-piece jigsaw puzzle of the map of your college campus. Design a marketing survey and discuss the important issues to consider.

PLAN

Setup State the goals and objectives of the survey.

Our team designed a study to find out how likely students at our school are to buy our proposed product—a 500-piece jigsaw puzzle of the map of our college campus.

Population and Parameters Identify the population to be studied and the associated sampling frame. What are the parameters of interest?

The population studied will be students at our school. We have obtained a list of all students currently enrolled to use as the sampling frame. The parameter of interest is the proportion of students likely to buy this product. We'll also collect some demographic information about the respondents.

Sampling Plan Specify the sampling method and the sample size, *n*. Specify how the sample was actually drawn. What is the sampling frame?

The description should, if possible, be complete enough to allow someone to replicate the procedure, drawing another sample from the same population in the same manner. A good description of the procedure is essential, even if it could never practically be repeated. The question you ask is important, so state the wording of the question clearly. Be sure that the question is useful in helping you with the overall goal of the survey.

We will select a simple random sample of students. We decided against stratifying by sex or class because we thought that students were all more or less alike in their likely interest in our product.

We will ask the students we contact:

Do you solve jigsaw puzzles for fun?

Then we will show them a prototype puzzle and ask:

If this puzzle sold for $10, would you purchase one?

We will also record the respondent's sex and class.

DO

Sampling Practice Specify *when, where,* and *how* the sampling will be performed. Specify any other details of your survey, such as how respondents were contacted, any incentives that were offered to encourage them to respond, how nonrespondents were treated, and so on.

The survey will be administered in the middle of the fall semester during October. We have a master list of registered students, which we will randomize by matching it with random numbers from www.random.org and sorting on the random numbers, carrying the names. We will contact selected students by phone or e-mail and arrange to meet with them. If a student is unwilling to participate, the next name from the randomized list will be substituted until a sample of 200 participants is found.

We will meet with students in an office set aside for this purpose so that each will see the puzzle under similar conditions.

REPORT

Summary and Conclusion This report should include a discussion of all the elements needed to design the study. It's good practice to discuss any special circumstances or other issues that may need attention.

MEMO

Re: Survey Plans

Our team's plans for the puzzle market survey call for a simple random sample of students. Because subjects need to be shown the prototype puzzle, we must arrange to meet with selected participants. We have arranged an office for that purpose.

We will also collect demographic information so we can determine whether there is in fact a difference in interest level among classes or between men and women.

The Real Sample

We have been discussing sampling in a somewhat idealized setting. In the real word, things can be a bit messier. Here are some things to consider.

The population may not be as well-defined as it seems. For example, if a company wants the opinions of a typical mall "shopper," who should they sample? Should they only ask shoppers carrying a purchase? Should they include people eating at the food court? How about teenagers just hanging out by the mall's video store? Even when the population is clear, it may not be possible to establish an appropriate sampling frame.

Usually, the practical sampling frame is not the group you *really* want to know about. For example, election polls want to sample from those who will actually vote in the next election—a group that is particularly tricky to identify before election day. The sampling frame limits what your survey can find out.

Then there's your target sample. These are the individuals selected according to your sample design for whom you *intend* to measure responses. You're not likely to get responses from all of them. ("I know it's dinner time, but I'm sure you wouldn't mind answering a few questions. It'll only take 20 minutes or so. Oh, you're busy?") Nonresponse is a problem in many surveys.

Sample designs are usually about the target sample. But in the real world, you won't get responses from everyone your design selects. So in reality, your sample consists of the actual respondents. These are the individuals about whom you *do* get data and can draw conclusions. Unfortunately, they might not be representative of either the sampling frame or the population.

At each step, the group we can study may be constrained further. The *who* of our study keeps changing, and each constraint can introduce biases. A careful study should address the question of how well each group matches the population of interest. The *who* in an SRS is the population of interest from which we've drawn a representative sample. That's not always true for other kinds of samples.

When people (or committees!) decide on a survey, they often fail to think through the important questions about who are the *who* of the study and whether they are the individuals about whom the answers would be interesting or have meaningful business consequences. This is a key step in performing a survey and should not be overlooked.

4 The Valid Survey

It isn't sufficient to draw a sample and start asking questions. You want to feel confident your survey can yield the information you need about the population you are interested in. We want a *valid survey*.

To help ensure a valid survey, you need to ask four questions:

- What do I want to know?
- Who are the right respondents?
- What are the right questions?
- What will be done with the results?

These questions may seem obvious, but there are a number of specific pitfalls to avoid:

Know what you want to know. Far too often, decisionmakers decide to perform a survey without any clear idea of what they hope to learn. Before considering a survey, you must be clear about what you hope to learn and what population you want to learn about. If you don't know that, you can't even judge whether you have a valid survey. The survey *instrument*—the questionnaire itself—can be a source of errors. Perhaps the most common error is to ask unnecessary questions. The longer the survey, the fewer people will complete it, leading to greater nonresponse bias. For each question on your survey, you should ask yourself whether you really want to know this and what you would do with the responses if you had them. If you don't have a good use for the answer to a question, don't ask it.

Use the right sampling frame. A valid survey obtains responses from appropriate respondents. Be sure you have a suitable sampling frame. Have you identified the population of interest and sampled from it appropriately? A company looking to expand its base might survey customers who returned warrantee registration cards—after all, that's a readily available sampling frame—but if the company wants to know how to make its product more attractive, it needs to survey customers who rejected its product in favor of a competitor's product. This is the population that can tell the company what about its product needs to change to capture a larger market share. The errors in the presidential election polls of 1948 were likely due to the use of telephone samples in an era when telephones were not affordable by the less affluent—who were the folks most likely to vote for Truman.

It is equally important to be sure that your respondents actually know the information you hope to discover. Your customers may not know much about the competing products, so asking them to compare your product with others may not yield useful information.

Ask specific rather than general questions. It is better to be specific. "Do you usually recall TV commercials?" won't be as useful as "How many TV commercials can you recall from last night?" or better, yet, "Please describe for me all the TV commercials you can recall from your viewing last night."

Watch for biases. Even with the right sampling frame, you must beware of bias in your sample. If customers who purchase more expensive items are less likely to respond to your survey, this can lead to **nonresponse bias**. Although you can't expect all mailed surveys to be returned, if those individuals who don't respond have common characteristics, your sample will no longer represent the population you hope to learn about. Surveys in which respondents volunteer to participate, such as online surveys, suffer from **voluntary response bias**. Individuals with the strongest feelings on either side of an issue are more likely to respond; those who don't care may not bother.

Be careful with question phrasing. Questions must be carefully worded. A respondent may not understand the question—or may not understand the question the way the researcher intended it. For example, "Does anyone in your family own a Ford truck?" leaves the term "family" unclear. Does it include only spouses and children or parents and siblings, or do in-laws and second cousins count too? A question like "Was your Twinkie fresh?" might be interpreted quite differently by different people.

Be careful with answer phrasing. Respondents and survey-takers may also provide inaccurate responses, especially when questions are politically or sociologically sensitive. This also applies when the question does not take into account all possible answers, such as a true-false or multiple-choice question to which there may be other answers. Or the respondent may not know the correct answer to the question on the survey. In 1948, there were four major candidates for President,[2] but some

---

[2] Harry Truman, Thomas Dewey, Strom Thurmond, and Henry Wallace.

survey respondents might not have been able to name them all. A survey question that just asked "Who do you plan to vote for?" might have underrepresented the less prominent candidates. And one that just asked "What do you think of Wallace?" might yield inaccurate results from voters who simply didn't know who he was. We refer to inaccurate responses (intentional or unintentional) as **measurement errors**. One way to cut down on measurement errors is to provide a range of possible responses. But be sure to phrase them in neutral terms.

The best way to protect a survey from measurement errors is to perform a pilot test. In a **pilot test,** a small sample is drawn from the sampling frame, and a draft form of the survey instrument is administered. A pilot test can point out flaws in the instrument. For example, during a staff cutback at one of our schools, a researcher surveyed faculty members to ask how they felt about the reduction in staff support. The scale ran from "It's a good idea" to "I'm very unhappy." Fortunately, a pilot study showed that everyone was very unhappy or worse. The scale was retuned to run from "unhappy" to "ready to quit."

For Example | **Survey design**

A nonprofit organization has enlisted some student consultants to help design a fundraising survey. The student consultants suggest to the board of directors that they may want to rethink their survey plans. They point out that there are differences between the population, the sampling frame, the target sample contacted by telephone, and the actual sample.

Question: How do the population, sampling frame, target sample, and sample differ?

Answer: The population is all potential ticket buyers.

The sampling frame is only those who have previously purchased tickets. Anyone who wasn't attracted to previous productions wouldn't be surveyed. That could keep the board from learning of ways to make the theater's offering more attractive to those who hadn't purchased tickets before.

The target sample is those selected from the database who can be contacted by telephone. Those with unlisted numbers or who had declined to give their phone number can't be contacted. It may be more difficult to contact those with caller ID.

The actual sample will be those previous customers selected at random from the database who can be reached by telephone and who agree to complete the survey.

---

5 How to Sample Badly

Bad sample designs yield worthless data. Many of the most convenient forms of sampling can be seriously biased. And there is no way to correct for the bias from a bad sample. So it's wise to pay attention to sample design—and to beware of reports based on poor samples.

Voluntary Response Sample

One of the most common dangerous sampling methods is the voluntary response sample. In a **voluntary response sample,** a large group of individuals is invited to respond, and all who do respond are counted. This method is used by call-in shows, 900 numbers, Internet polls, and letters written to members of Congress. Voluntary response samples are almost always biased, and so conclusions drawn from them are almost always wrong.

It's often hard to define the sampling frame of a voluntary response study. Practically, the frames are groups such as Internet users who frequent a particular website or viewers of a particular TV show. But those sampling frames don't correspond to the population you are likely to be interested in.

Even if the sampling frame is of interest, voluntary response samples are often biased toward those with strong opinions or those who are strongly motivated—and especially from those with strong negative opinions. A request that travelers who have used the local airport visit a survey site to report on their experiences is much more likely to hear from those who had long waits, cancelled flights, and lost luggage than from those whose flights were on time and carefree. The resulting voluntary response bias invalidates the survey.

Convenience Sampling

Another sampling method that doesn't work is convenience sampling. As the name suggests, in **convenience sampling** we simply include the individuals who are convenient. Unfortunately, this group may not be representative of the population. A survey of 437 potential home buyers in Orange County, California, found, among other things, that

> *all but 2 percent of the buyers have at least one computer at home, and 62 percent have two or more. Of those with a computer, 99 percent are connected to the Internet (Jennifer Hieger, "Portrait of Homebuyer Household: 2 Kids and a PC," Orange County Register, July 27, 2001).*

Later in the article, we learn that the survey was conducted via the Internet. That was a convenient way to collect data and surely easier than drawing a simple random sample, but perhaps home builders shouldn't conclude from this study that *every* family has a computer and an Internet connection.

Many surveys conducted at shopping malls suffer from the same problem. People in shopping malls are not necessarily representative of the population of interest. Mall shoppers tend to be more affluent and include a larger percentage of teenagers and retirees than the population at large. To make matters worse, survey interviewers tend to select individuals who look "safe," or easy to interview.

Convenience sampling is not just a problem for beginners. In fact, convenience sampling is a widespread problem in the business world. When a company wants to find out what people think about its products or services, it may turn to the easiest people to sample: its own customers. But the company will never learn how those who *don't* buy its product feel about it.

Bad Sampling Frame?

An SRS from an incomplete sampling frame introduces bias because the individuals included may differ from the ones not in the frame. It may be easier to sample workers from a single site, but if a company has many sites and they differ in worker satisfaction, training, or job descriptions, the resulting sample can be biased. There is serious concern among professional pollsters that the increasing numbers of people who can be reached only by cell phone may bias telephone-based market research and polling.

Undercoverage

Many survey designs suffer from **undercoverage,** in which some portion of the population is not sampled at all or has a smaller representation in the sample than it has in the population. Undercoverage can arise for a number of reasons, but it's always a potential source of bias. Are people who use answering machines to screen callers (and are thus less available to blind calls from market researchers) different from other customers in their purchasing preferences?

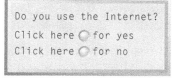

Internet Surveys

Internet convenience surveys are often worthless. As voluntary response surveys, they have no well-defined sampling frame (all those who use the Internet and visit their site?) and thus report no useful information. Do not use them.

For Example | Common mistakes in survey design

A board member proposes that rather than telephoning past customers, they simply post someone at the door to ask theater goers their opinions. Another suggests that it would be even easier to post a questionnaire on the theater website and invite responses there. A third suggests that rather than working with random numbers, they simply phone every 200th person on the list of past customers.

Question: Identify the three methods proposed and explain what strengths and weaknesses they have.

Answer: Questioning customers at the door would be a convenience sample. It would be cheap and fast but is likely to be biased by the nature and quality of the particular performance where the survey takes place.

Inviting responses on the website would be a voluntary response sample. Only customers who frequented the website and decided to respond would be surveyed. This might, for example, underrepresent older customers or those without home Internet access.

Sampling every 200th name from the customer list would be a systematic sample. It is slightly easier than randomizing. If the order of names on the list is unrelated to any questions asked, then this might be an acceptable method. But if, for example, the list is kept in the order of first purchases (when a customer's name and information were added to the database), then there might be a relationship between opinions and location on the list.

What Can Go Wrong?

- **Nonrespondents.** No survey succeeds in getting responses from everyone. The problem is that those who don't respond may differ from those who do. And if they differ on just the variables we care about, the lack of response will bias the results. Rather than sending out a large number of surveys for which the response rate will be low, it is often better to design a smaller, randomized survey for which you have the resources to ensure a high response rate.

- **Long, dull surveys.** Surveys that are too long are more likely to be refused, reducing the response rate and biasing all the results. Keep it short.

- **Response bias.** Response bias includes the tendency of respondents to tailor their responses to please the interviewer and the consequences of slanted question wording.

- **Push polls.** Push polls, which masquerade as surveys, present one side of an issue before asking a question. For example, a question like

    Would the fact that the new store that just opened by the mall sells mostly goods made overseas by workers in sweatshop conditions influence your decision to shop there rather than in the downtown store that features American-made products?

    is designed not to gather information, but to spread ill-will toward the new store.

THE WIZARD OF ID   **parker and hart**

By permission of Johnny Hart FLP and Creators Syndicate, Inc.

How to Think about Biases

- **Look for biases in any survey.** If you design a survey of your own, ask someone else to help look for biases that may not be obvious to you. Do this *before* you collect your data. There's no way to recover from a biased sample or a survey that asks biased questions.

    A bigger sample size for a biased study just gives you a bigger useless study. A really big sample gives you a really big useless study.

- **Spend your time and resources reducing biases.** No other use of resources is as worthwhile as reducing the biases.

- **If you possibly can, pretest or pilot your survey.** Administer the survey in the exact form that you intend to use it to a small sample drawn from the population you intend to sample. Look for misunderstandings, misinterpretation, confusion, or other possible biases. Then redesign your survey instrument.

- **Always report your sampling methods in detail.** Others may be able to detect biases where you did not expect to find them.

Ethics in Action

The Lackawax River Group is interested in applying for state funds in order to continue their restoration and conservation of the Lackawax River, a river that has been polluted from years of industry and agricultural discharge. While they have managed to gain significant support for their cause through education and community involvement, the executive committee is now interested in presenting the state with more compelling evidence. They decided to survey local residents regarding their attitudes toward the proposed expansion of the river restoration and conservation project. With limited time and money (the deadline for the grant application was fast approaching), the executive committee was delighted that one of its members, Harry Greentree, volunteered to undertake the project. Harry owned a local organic food store and agreed to have a sample of his shoppers interviewed during the next one-week period. The only concern that the committee had was that the shoppers be selected in a systematic fashion, for instance, by interviewing every fifth person who entered the store. Harry had no problem with this request and was eager to help the Lackawax River Group.

ETHICAL ISSUE *Introducing bias into the results (even if not intentional). One might expect consumers of organic food to be more concerned about the environment than the general population (related to Item C, ASA Ethical Guidelines).*

ETHICAL SOLUTION *Harry is using a convenience sample from which results cannot be generalized. If the Lackawax River Group cannot improve their sampling scheme and survey design (for example, for lack of expertise or time), they should openly discuss the weaknesses of their sampling method when they disclose details of their study. When reporting the results, they should note that their findings are from a convenience sample and include an appropriate disclaimer.*

What Have We Learned?

Learning Objectives

■ Know the three ideas of sampling.
- Examine a part of the whole: A sample can give information about the population.
- Randomize to make the sample representative.
- The sample size is what matters. It's the size of the sample—and not its fraction of the larger population—that determines the precision of the statistics it yields.

■ Be able to draw a Simple Random Sample (SRS) using a table of random digits or a list of random numbers from technology or an Internet site.
- In a **simple random sample** (SRS), every possible group of n individuals has an equal chance of being our sample.

■ Know the definitions of other sampling methods:
- **Stratified samples** can reduce sampling variability by identifying homogeneous subgroups and then randomly sampling within each.
- **Cluster samples** randomly select among heterogeneous subgroups that each resemble the population at large, making our sampling tasks more manageable.
- **Systematic samples** can work in some situations and are often the least expensive method of sampling. But we still want to start them randomly.
- **Multistage samples** combine several random sampling methods.

■ Identify and avoid causes of bias.
- **Nonresponse bias** can arise when sampled individuals will not or cannot respond.
- **Response bias** arises when respondents' answers might be affected by external influences, such as question wording or interviewer behavior.
- **Voluntary response samples** are almost always biased and should be avoided and distrusted.
- **Convenience samples** are likely to be flawed for similar reasons.
- **Undercoverage** occurs when individuals from a subgroup of the population are selected less often than they should be.

Terms

Bias	Any systematic failure of a sampling method to represent its population.
Census	An attempt to collect data on the entire population of interest.
Cluster	A representative subset of a population chosen for reasons of convenience, cost, or practicality.
Cluster sampling	A sampling design in which groups, or clusters, representative of the population are chosen at random and a census is then taken of each.
Convenience sampling	A sample that consists of individuals who are conveniently available.
Measurement error	Any inaccuracy in a response, from any source, whether intentional or unintentional.
Multistage sample	A sampling scheme that combines several sampling methods.
Nonresponse bias	Bias introduced to a sample when a large fraction of those sampled fails to respond.
Parameter	A numerically valued attribute of a model for a population. We rarely expect to know the value of a parameter, but we do hope to estimate it from sampled data.
Pilot test	A small trial run of a study to check that the methods of the study are sound.
Population	The entire group of individuals or instances about whom we hope to learn.

Population parameter	A numerically valued attribute of a model for a population.
Randomization	A defense against bias in the sample selection process, in which each individual is given a fair, random chance of selection.
Representative sample	A sample from which the statistics computed accurately reflect the corresponding population parameters.
Response bias	Anything in a survey design that influences responses.
Sample	A subset of a population, examined in hope of learning about the population.
Sample size	The number of individuals in a sample.
Sample survey	A study that asks questions of a sample drawn from some population in the hope of learning something about the entire population.
Sampling frame	A list of individuals from which the sample is drawn. Individuals in the population of interest but who are not in the sampling frame cannot be included in any sample.
Sampling variability (or sampling error)	The natural tendency of randomly drawn samples to differ, one from another.
Simple random sample (SRS)	A sample in which each set of n elements in the population has an equal chance of selection.
Statistic, sample statistic	A value calculated for sampled data, particularly one that corresponds to, and thus estimates, a population parameter. The term "sample statistic" is sometimes used, usually to parallel the corresponding term "population parameter."
Strata	Subsets of a population that are internally homogeneous but may differ one from another.
Stratified random sample	A sampling design in which the population is divided into several homogeneous subpopulations, or strata, and random samples are then drawn from each stratum.
Systematic sample	A sample drawn by selecting individuals systematically from a sampling frame.
Voluntary response bias	Bias introduced to a sample when individuals can choose on their own whether to participate in the sample.
Voluntary response sample	A sample in which a large group of individuals are invited to respond and decide individually whether or not to participate. Voluntary response samples are generally worthless.
Undercoverage	A sampling scheme that biases the sample in a way that gives a part of the population less representation than it has in the population.

Technology Help: Random Sampling XLSTAT

Computer-generated pseudorandom numbers are usually quite good enough for drawing random samples. But there is little reason not to use the truly random values available on the Internet. Here's a convenient way to draw an SRS of a specified size using a computer-based sampling frame. The sampling frame can be a list of names or of identification numbers arrayed, for example, as a column in a spreadsheet, statistics program, or database:

1. Generate random numbers of enough digits so that each exceeds the size of the sampling frame list by several digits. This makes duplication unlikely. (For example, in Excel, use the RAND function to fill a column with random numbers between 0 and 1. With many digits they will almost surely be unique.)

2. Assign the random numbers arbitrarily to individuals in the sampling frame list. For example, put them in an adjacent column.

3. Sort the list of random numbers, *carrying* along the sampling frame list.

4. Now the first *n* values in the sorted sampling frame column are an SRS of *n* values from the entire sampling frame.

Brief CASE

iStockphoto

Digital Vision

Market Survey Research

You are part of a marketing team that needs to research the potential of a new product. Your team decides to e-mail an interactive survey to a random sample of consumers. Write a short questionnaire that will generate the information you need about the new product. Select a sample of 200 using an SRS from your sampling frame. Discuss how you will collect the data and how the responses will help your market research.

The GfK Roper Reports Worldwide Survey

GfK Roper Consulting conducts market research for multinational companies who want to understand attitudes in different countries so they can market and advertise more effectively to different cultures. Every year they conduct a poll worldwide, which asks hundreds of questions of people in approximately 30 different countries. Respondents are asked a variety of questions about food. Some of the questions are simply yes/no (agree/disagree) questions: Please tell me whether you agree or disagree with each of these statements about your appearance: (Agree = 1; Disagree = 2; Don't know = 9).

The way you look affects the way you feel.

I am very interested in new skin care breakthroughs.

People who don't care about their appearance don't care about themselves.

Other questions are asked on a 5-point scale (Please tell me the extent to which you disagree or agree with it using the following scale: Disagree completely = 1; Disagree somewhat = 2; Neither disagree nor agree = 3; Agree somewhat = 4; Agree completely = 5; Don't know = 9).

Examples of such questions include:

I read labels carefully to find out about ingredients, fat content, and/or calories.

I try to avoid eating fast food.

When it comes to food I'm always on the lookout for something new.

Think about designing a survey on such a global scale:

- What is the population of interest?
- Why might it be difficult to select an SRS from this sampling frame?
- What are some potential sources of bias?
- Why might it be difficult to ensure a representative number of men and women and all age groups in some countries?
- What might be a reasonable sampling frame?

Exercises

SECTION 1

1. Indicate whether each statement below is true or false. If false, explain why.

a) We can eliminate sampling error by selecting an unbiased sample.

b) Randomization helps to ensure that our sample is representative.

c) Sampling error refers to sample-to-sample differences and is also known as sampling variability.

d) It is better to try to match the characteristics of the sample to the population rather than relying on randomization.

2. Indicate whether each statement below is true or false. If false, explain why.

a) To get a representative sample, you must sample a large fraction of the population.

b) Using modern methods, it is best to select a representative subset of a population systematically.

c) A census is the only true representative sample.

d) A random sample of 100 students from a school with 2000 students has the same precision as a random sample of 100 from a school with 20,000 students.

SECTION 2

3. A consumer advocacy group is interested in gauging perceptions about food safety among professionals in the food industry. Specifically, they wish to determine the percentage of professional food preparers in the United States that believe food safety has improved. They use an alphabetized list of members of the organization *Chef's Collaborative* and use Excel to generate a randomly shuffled list of the members. They then select members to contact from this list until they have succeeded in contacting 150 members.

a) What is the population?

b) What is the sampling frame?

c) What is the population parameter of interest?

d) What sampling method is used?

4. An airline company is interested in the opinions of their frequent flyer customers about their proposed new routes. Specifically they want to know what proportion of them plan to use one of their new hubs in the next 6 months. They take a random sample of 10,000 from the database of all frequent flyers and send them an e-mail message with a request to fill out a survey in exchange for 1500 miles.

a) What is the population?

b) What is the sampling frame?

c) What is the population parameter of interest?

d) What sampling method is used?

SECTION 3

5. As discussed in the chapter, GfK Roper Consulting conducts a global consumer survey to help multinational companies understand different consumer attitudes throughout the world. In India, the researchers interviewed 1000 people aged 13–65 (www.gfkamerica.com). Their sample is designed so that they get 500 males and 500 females.

a) Are they using a simple random sample? How do you know?

b) What kind of design do you think they are using?

6. For their class project, a group of Business students decide to survey the student body to assess opinions about a proposed new student coffee shop to judge how successful it might be. Their sample of 200 contained 50 first-year students, 50 sophomores, 50 juniors, and 50 seniors.

a) Do you think the group was using an SRS? Why?

b) What kind of sampling design do you think they used?

7. The consumer advocacy group from Exercise 3 that was interested in gauging perceptions about food safety among professionals in the food industry has decided to use a different method to sample. Instead of randomly selecting members from a shuffled list, they listed the members in alphabetical order and took every tenth member until they succeeded in contacting 150 members. What kind of sampling method have they used?

8. The airline company from Exercise 4, interested in the opinions of their frequent flyer customers about their proposed new routes, has decided that different types of customers might have different opinions. Of their customers, 50% are silver-level, 30% are blue, and 20% are red. They first compile separate lists of silver, blue, and red members and then randomly select 5000 silver members, 3000 blue members, and 2000 red members to e-mail. What kind of sampling method have they used?

For Exercises 9 and 10, identify the following if possible. (If not, say why.)

a) The population

b) The population parameter of interest

c) The sampling frame

d) The sample

e) The sampling method, including whether or not randomization was employed

f) Any potential sources of bias you can detect and any problems you see in generalizing to the population of interest

9. A business magazine mailed a questionnaire to the human resources directors of all Fortune 500 companies, and received responses from 23% of them. Those responding reported that they did not find that such surveys intruded significantly on their workday.

10. A question posted on the Lycos website asked visitors to the site to say whether they thought that businesses should be required to pay for their employees' health insurance.

SECTION 4

11. An intern for the consumer advocacy group in Exercise 3 has decided to make the survey process simpler by calling 150 of the members who attended the recent symposium on "Food Safety in the 21st century" that was recently held in Las Vegas. He has all the phone numbers, so it will be easy to contact them. He will start calling members from the top of the list, which was generated as the members enrolled for the symposium. He has written a script to read to them that follows,

"As we learned in Las Vegas, food safety is of utmost importance in the restaurant business today. Given the enormous effort of the Food Safety Institute in developing proper guidelines and education for food professionals, do you agree that food safety has improved in the U.S.?"

a) What is the population of interest?
b) What is the sampling frame?
c) Point out any problems you see either with the sampling procedure and/or the survey itself. What are the potential impacts of these problems?

12. The airline company in Exercise 4 has realized that some of its customers don't have e-mail or don't read it regularly. They decide to restrict the mailing only to customers who have recently registered for a "Win a trip to Miami" contest, figuring that those with Internet access are more likely to read and to respond to their e-mail. They send an e-mail with the following message:

"Did you know that National Airlines has just spent over $3 million refurbishing our brand new hub in Miami? By answering the following question, you may be eligible to win $1000 worth of coupons that can be spent in any of the fabulous restaurants or shops in the Miami airport. Might you possibly think of traveling to Miami in the next six months on your way to one of your destinations?"

a) What is the population?
b) What is the sampling frame?
c) Point out any problems you see either with the sampling procedure and/or the survey itself. What are the potential impacts of these problems?

13. An intern is working for Pacific TV (PTV), a small cable and Internet provider, and has proposed some questions that might be used in the survey to assess whether customers are willing to pay $50 for a new service.

Question 1: If PTV offered state-of-the-art high-speed Internet service for $50 per month, would you subscribe to that service?

Question 2: Would you find $50 per month—less than the cost of a daily cappuccino—an appropriate price for high-speed Internet service?

a) Do you think these are appropriately worded questions? Why or why not?
b) Suggest a question with better wording.

14. Here are more proposed survey questions for the survey in Exercise 13:

Question 3: Do you find that the slow speed of dial-up Internet access reduces your enjoyment of web services?

Question 4: Given the growing importance of high-speed Internet access for your children's education, would you subscribe to such a service if it were offered?

a) Do you think these are appropriately worded questions? Why or why not?
b) Which one has more neutral wording? Explain.

SECTION 5

15. Indicate whether each statement below is true or false. If false, explain why.

a) A local television news program that asks viewers to call in and give their opinion on an issue typically results in a biased voluntary response sample.
b) Convenience samples are generally not representative of the population.
c) Measurement error is the same as sampling error.
d) A pilot test can be useful for identifying poorly worded questions on a survey.

16. Indicate whether each statement below is true or false. If false, explain why.

a) Asking viewers to call into a 900 number (for which there is a toll charge) is a good way to produce a representative sample.
b) When writing a survey, it's a good idea to include as many questions as possible to ensure efficiency and to lower costs.
c) A recent poll on a website was valid because the sample size was over 1,000,000 respondents.
d) Malls are not necessarily good places to conduct surveys because people who frequent malls may not be representative of the population at large.

17. For your marketing class, you'd like to take a survey from a sample of all the Catholic Church members in your city to assess the market for a DVD about the pope's visit to the United States. A list of churches shows 17 Catholic churches within the city limits. Rather than try to obtain a list of all members of all these churches, you decide to pick 3 churches at random. For those churches, you'll ask to get a list of all current members and contact 100 members at random.

a) What kind of design have you used?
b) What could go wrong with the design that you have proposed?

18. The U.S. Fish and Wildlife Service plans to study the fishing industry around Saginaw Bay. To do that, they decide to randomly select 5 fishing boats at the end of a randomly chosen fishing day and to count the numbers and types of all the fish on those boats.

a) What kind of design have they used?

b) What could go wrong with the design that they have proposed?

CHAPTER EXERCISES

19. Software licenses. The website www.gamefaqs.com asked, as their question of the day to which visitors to the site were invited to respond, *"Do you ever read the end-user license agreements when installing software or games?"* Of the 98,574 respondents, 63.47% said they never read those agreements—a fact that software manufacturers might find important.

a) What kind of sample was this?

b) How much confidence would you place in using 63.47% as an estimate of the fraction of people who don't read software licenses?

20. Drugs in baseball. Major League Baseball, responding to concerns about their "brand," tests players to see whether they are using performance-enhancing drugs. Officials select a team at random, and a drug-testing crew shows up unannounced to test all 40 players on the team. Each testing day can be considered a study of drug use in Major League Baseball.

a) What kind of sample is this?

b) Is that choice appropriate?

21. Gallup. At its website (www.galluppoll.com) the Gallup Poll publishes results of a new survey each day. Scroll down to the end, and you'll find a statement that includes an explanation such as this:

Results are based on telephone interviews with 1,008 national adults, aged 18 and older, conducted April 2–5, 2007. . . . In addition to sampling error, question wording and practical difficulties in conducting surveys can introduce error or bias into the findings of public opinion polls.

a) For this survey, identify the population of interest.

b) Gallup performs its surveys by phoning numbers generated at random by a computer program. What is the sampling frame?

c) What problems, if any, would you be concerned about in matching the sampling frame with the population?

22. Defining the survey. At its website (www.gallupworldpoll .com) the Gallup World Poll reports results of surveys conducted in various places around the world. At the end of one of these reports, they describe their methods, including explanations such as the following:

Results are based on face-to-face interviews with randomly selected national samples of approximately 1000 adults, aged 15 and older, who live permanently in each of the 21 sub-Saharan African nations surveyed. Those countries include Angola (areas where land mines might be expected were excluded), Benin, Botswana, Burkina Faso, Cameroon, Ethiopia, Ghana, Kenya, Madagascar (areas where interviewers had to walk more than 20 kilometers from a road were excluded), Mali, Mozambique, Niger, Nigeria, Senegal, Sierra Leone, South Africa, Tanzania, Togo, Uganda (the area of activity of the Lord's Resistance Army was excluded from the survey), Zambia, and Zimbabwe. . . . In all countries except Angola, Madagascar, and Uganda, the sample is representative of the entire population.

a) Gallup is interested in sub-Saharan Africa. What kind of survey design are they using?

b) Some of the countries surveyed have large populations. (Nigeria is estimated to have about 130 million people.) Some are quite small. (Togo's population is estimated at 5.4 million.) Nonetheless, Gallup sampled 1000 adults in each country. How does this affect the precision of its estimates for these countries?

23–30. Survey details. *For the following reports about statistical studies, identify the following items (if possible). If you can't tell, then say so—this often happens when we read about a survey.*

a) The population

b) The population parameter of interest

c) The sampling frame

d) The sample

e) The sampling method, including whether or not randomization was employed

f) Any potential sources of bias you can detect and any problems you see in generalizing to the population of interest

23. Alternative medicine. Consumers Union asked all subscribers whether they had used alternative medical treatments and, if so, whether they had benefited from them. For almost all of the treatments, approximately 20% of those responding reported cures or substantial improvement in their condition.

24. Global warming. The Gallup Poll interviewed 1012 randomly selected U.S. adults aged 18 and older, March 6–9, 2008. Gallup reports that when asked when (if ever) the effects of global warming will begin to happen, 61% of respondents said the effects had already begun. Only 11% thought that they would never happen.

25. At the bar. Researchers waited outside a bar they had randomly selected from a list of such establishments. They stopped every 10th person who came out of the bar and asked whether he or she thought drinking and driving was a serious problem.

26. Election poll. Hoping to learn what issues may resonate with voters in the coming election, the campaign director for a mayoral candidate selects one block from each of the city's election districts. Staff members go there and interview all the residents they can find.

27. Toxic waste. The Environmental Protection Agency took soil samples at 16 locations near a former industrial waste dump and checked each for evidence of toxic chemicals. They found no elevated levels of any harmful substances.

28. Housing discrimination. Inspectors send trained "renters" of various races and ethnic backgrounds, and of both sexes to inquire about renting randomly assigned advertised apartments. They look for evidence that landlords deny access illegally based on race, sex, or ethnic background.

29. Quality control. A company packaging snack foods maintains quality control by randomly selecting 10 cases from each day's production and weighing the bags. Then they open one bag from each case and inspect the contents.

30. Contaminated milk. Dairy inspectors visit farms unannounced and take samples of the milk to test for contamination. If the milk is found to contain dirt, antibiotics, or other foreign matter, the milk will be destroyed and the farm is considered to be contaminated pending further testing.

31. Instant poll. A local TV station conducted an "Instant Poll" to predict the winner in the upcoming mayoral election. Evening news viewers were invited to phone in their votes, with the results to be announced on the late-night news. Based on the phone calls, the station predicted that Amabo would win the election with 52% of the vote. They were wrong: Amabo lost, getting only 46% of the vote. Do you think the station's faulty prediction is more likely to be a result of bias or sampling error? Explain.

32. Paper poll. Prior to the mayoral election discussed in Exercise 31, the newspaper also conducted a poll. The paper surveyed a random sample of registered voters stratified by political party, age, sex, and area of residence. This poll predicted that Amabo would win the election with 52% of the vote. The newspaper was wrong: Amabo lost, getting only 46% of the vote. Do you think the newspaper's faulty prediction is more likely to be a result of bias or sampling error? Explain.

33. Cable company market research. A local cable TV company, Pacific TV, with customers in 15 towns is considering offering high-speed Internet service on its cable lines. Before launching the new service they want to find out whether customers would pay the $50 per month that they plan to charge. An intern has prepared several alternative plans for assessing customer demand. For each, indicate what kind of sampling strategy is involved and what (if any) biases might result.

a) Put a big ad in the newspaper asking people to log their opinions on the PTV website.
b) Randomly select one of the towns and contact every cable subscriber by phone.

c) Send a survey to each customer and ask them to fill it out and return it.
d) Randomly select 20 customers from each town. Send them a survey, and follow up with a phone call if they do not return the survey within a week.

34. Cable company market research, part 2. Four new sampling strategies have been proposed to help PTV determine whether enough cable subscribers are likely to purchase high-speed Internet service. For each, indicate what kind of sampling strategy is involved and what (if any) biases might result.

a) Run a poll on the local TV news, asking people to dial one of two phone numbers to indicate whether they would be interested.
b) Hold a meeting in each of the 15 towns, and tally the opinions expressed by those who attend the meetings.
c) Randomly select one street in each town and contact each of the households on that street.
d) Go through the company's customer records, selecting every 40th subscriber. Send employees to those homes to interview the people chosen.

35. Amusement park riders. An amusement park has opened a new roller coaster. It is so popular that people are waiting for up to three hours for a two-minute ride. Concerned about how patrons (who paid a large amount to enter the park and ride on the rides) feel about this, they survey every 10th person on the line for the roller coaster, starting from a randomly selected individual.

a) What kind of sample is this?
b) Is it likely to be representative?
c) What is the sampling frame?

36. Playground. Some people have been complaining that the children's playground at a municipal park is too small and is in need of repair. Managers of the park decide to survey city residents to see if they believe the playground should be rebuilt. They hand out questionnaires to parents who bring children to the park. Describe possible biases in this sample.

37. Another ride. The survey of patrons waiting in line for the roller coaster in Exercise 35 asks whether they think it is worthwhile to wait a long time for the ride and whether they'd like the amusement park to install still more roller coasters. What biases might cause a problem for this survey?

38. Playground bias. The survey described in Exercise 36 asked,

Many people believe this playground is too small and in need of repair. Do you think the playground should be repaired and expanded even if that means raising the entrance fee to the park?

Describe two ways this question may lead to response bias.

39. (Possibly) Biased questions. Examine each of the following questions for possible bias. If you think the question is biased, indicate how and propose a better question.

a) *Should companies that pollute the environment be compelled to pay the costs of cleanup?*

b) *Should a company enforce a strict dress code?*

40. More possibly biased questions. Examine each of the following questions for possible bias. If you think the question is biased, indicate how and propose a better question.

a) *Do you think that price or quality is more important in selecting an MP3 player?*

b) *Given humanity's great tradition of exploration, do you favor continued funding for space flights?*

41. Phone surveys. Anytime we conduct a survey, we must take care to avoid undercoverage. Suppose we plan to select 500 names from the city phone book, call their homes between noon and 4 p.m., and interview whoever answers, anticipating contacts with at least 200 people.

a) Why is it difficult to use a simple random sample here?

b) Describe a more convenient, but still random, sampling strategy.

c) What kinds of households are likely to be included in the eventual sample of opinion? Who will be excluded?

d) Suppose, instead, that we continue calling each number, perhaps in the morning or evening, until an adult is contacted and interviewed. How does this improve the sampling design?

e) Random-digit dialing machines can generate the phone calls for us. How would this improve our design? Is anyone still excluded?

42. Cell phone survey. What about drawing a random sample only from cell phone exchanges? Discuss the advantages and disadvantages of such a sampling method compared with surveying randomly generated telephone numbers from non–cell phone exchanges. Do you think these advantages and disadvantages have changed over time? How do you expect they'll change in the future?

43. Change. How much change do you have on you right now? Go ahead, count it.

a) How much change do you have?

b) Suppose you check on your change every day for a week as you head for lunch and average the results. What parameter would this average estimate?

c) Suppose you ask 10 friends to average *their* change every day for a week, and you average those 10 measurements. What is the population now? What parameter would this average estimate?

d) Do you think these 10 average change amounts are likely to be representative of the population of change amounts in your class? In your college? In the country? Why or why not?

44. Fuel economy. Occasionally, when I fill my car with gas, I figure out how many miles per gallon my car got. I wrote down those results after six fill-ups in the past few months. Overall, it appears my car gets 28.8 miles per gallon.

a) What statistic have I calculated?

b) What is the parameter I'm trying to estimate?

c) How might my results be biased?

d) When the Environmental Protection Agency (EPA) checks a car like mine to predict its fuel economy, what parameter is it trying to estimate?

45. Accounting. Between quarterly audits, a company likes to check on its accounting procedures to address any problems before they become serious. The accounting staff processes payments on about 120 orders each day. The next day, the supervisor rechecks 10 of the transactions to be sure they were processed properly.

a) Propose a sampling strategy for the supervisor.

b) How would you modify that strategy if the company makes both wholesale and retail sales, requiring different bookkeeping procedures?

46. Happy workers? A manufacturing company employs 14 project managers, 48 foremen, and 377 laborers. In an effort to keep informed about any possible sources of employee discontent, management wants to conduct job satisfaction interviews with a simple random sample of employees every month.

a) Do you see any danger of bias in the company's plan? Explain.

b) How might you select a simple random sample?

c) Why do you think a simple random sample might not provide the best estimate of the parameters the company wants to estimate?

d) Propose a better sampling strategy.

e) Listed below are the last names of the project managers. Use random numbers to select two people to be interviewed. Be sure to explain your method carefully.

Barrett	Bowman	Chen
DeLara	DeRoos	Grigorov
Maceli	Mulvaney	Pagliarulo
Rosica	Smithson	Tadros
Williams	Yamamoto	

47. Quality control. Sammy's Salsa, a small local company, produces 20 cases of salsa a day. Each case contains 12 jars and is imprinted with a code indicating the date and batch number. To help maintain consistency, at the end of each day, Sammy selects three bottles of salsa, weighs the contents, and tastes the product. Help Sammy select the sample jars. Today's cases are coded 07N61 through 07N80.

a) Carefully explain your sampling strategy.

b) Show how to use random numbers to pick the three jars for testing.

c) Did you use a simple random sample? Explain.

48. Fish quality. Concerned about reports of discolored scales on fish caught downstream from a newly sited chemical plant, scientists set up a field station in a shoreline public park. For one week they asked fishermen there to bring any fish they caught to the field station for a brief inspection. At the end of the week, the scientists said that 18% of the 234 fish that were submitted for inspection displayed the discoloration. From this information, can the researchers estimate what proportion of fish in the river have discolored scales? Explain.

49. Sampling methods. Consider each of these situations. Do you think the proposed sampling method is appropriate? Explain.

a) We want to know what percentage of local doctors accept Medicaid patients. We call the offices of 50 doctors randomly selected from local Yellow Page listings.
b) We want to know what percentage of local businesses anticipate hiring additional employees in the upcoming month. We randomly select a page in the Yellow Pages and call every business listed there.

50. More sampling methods. Consider each of these situations. Do you think the proposed sampling method is appropriate? Explain.

a) We want to know if business leaders in the community support the development of an "incubator" site at a vacant lot on the edge of town. We spend a day phoning local businesses in the phone book to ask whether they'd sign a petition.
b) We want to know if travelers at the local airport are satisfied with the food available there. We go to the airport on a busy day and interview every 10th person in line in the food court.

Just Checking Answers

1. a) It can be hard to reach all members of a population, and it can take so long that circumstances change, affecting the responses. A well-designed sample is often a better choice.
   b) This sample is probably biased—people who didn't like the food at the restaurant might not choose to eat there.
   c) No, only the sample size matters, not the fraction of the overall population.
   d) Students who frequent this website might be more enthusiastic about Statistics than the overall population of Statistics students. A large sample cannot compensate for bias.
   e) It's the population "parameter." "Statistics" describe samples.
2. a) systematic
   b) stratified
   c) simple
   d) cluster

Answers

SECTION EXERCISE ANSWERS

1. a) False. Sampling error cannot be avoided, even with unbiased samples.
   b) True.
   c) True.
   d) False. Randomization will match the characteristics in a way that is unbiased. We can't possibly think of all the characteristics that might be important or match our sample to the population on all of them.

3. a) Professional food preparers in the United States.
   b) *Chef's Collaborative* membership listing.
   c) Proportion who believe that food safety has improved.
   d) Simple random sample.

5. a) No. It would be nearly impossible to get exactly 500 males and 500 females by random chance.
   b) A stratified sample, stratified by whether the respondent is male or female.

7. A systematic sample.

9. a) Population—Human resources directors of Fortune 500 companies.
   b) Parameter—Proportion who don't feel surveys intruded on their work day.
   c) Sampling Frame—List of HR directors at Fortune 500 companies.
   d) Sample—23% who responded.

   e) Method—Questionnaire mailed to all (nonrandom).
   f) Bias—Hard to generalize because who responds is related to the question itself.

11. a) Professional food preparers in the United States.
    b) The members who attended the recent symposium.
    c) The sampling frame is not necessarily representative of the entire group of food preparers. Those who attended the symposium may have different opinions from those who didn't. His sample isn't random and may be biased toward those most interested in the topic. Finally, the script is biased and may lead to an estimate of a higher proportion who think food safety has improved than is true within the population.

13. a) Answers will vary. Question 1 seems appropriate. Question 2 predisposes the participant to agree that $50 is a reasonable price, and does not seem appropriate.
    b) Question 1 is the more neutrally worded. Question 2 is biased in its wording.

15. a) True.
    b) True.
    c) False. Measurement error refers to inaccurate responses. Sampling error refers to sample-to-sample variability.
    d) True.

17. a) This is a multistage design, with a cluster sample at the first stage and a simple random sample for each cluster.
    b) If any of the three churches you pick at random is not representative of all churches then you'll introduce sampling error by the choice of that church.

CHAPTER EXERCISE ANSWERS

19. a) Voluntary response.
b) We have no confidence at all in estimates from such studies.

21. a) The population of interest is all adults in the United States aged 18 and older.
b) The sampling frame is U.S. adults with landline telephones.
c) Some members of the population (e.g., many college students) don't have landline phones, which could create a bias.

23. a) Population—Consumers Union subscribers.
b) Parameter—Proportion who have used and benefited from alternative medicine.
c) Sampling Frame—All Consumers Union subscribers.
d) Sample—Those who responded.
e) Method—Census of subscribers (nonrandom).
f) Bias—Voluntary response: Those who respond may have strong feelings one way or another.

25. a) Population—Adults.
b) Parameter—Proportion who think drinking and driving is a serious problem.
c) Sampling Frame—Bar patrons.
d) Sample—Every 10th person leaving the bar.
e) Method—Systematic sampling.
f) Bias—Those interviewed had just left a bar. They probably think drinking and driving is less of a problem than do adults in general.

27. a) Population—Soil around a former waste dump.
b) Parameter—Concentrations of toxic chemicals.
c) Sampling Frame—Accessible soil around the dump.
d) Sample—16 soil samples.
e) Method—Not clear.
f) Bias—Don't know if soil samples were randomly chosen. If not, may be biased toward more or less polluted soil.

29. a) Population—Snack food bags.
b) Parameter—Weight of bags, proportion passing inspection.
c) Sampling Frame—All bags produced each day.
d) Sample—10 randomly selected cases, 1 bag from each case for inspection.
e) Method—Multistage sampling.
f) Bias—Should be unbiased.

31. Bias. Only people watching the news will respond, and their preference may differ from that of other voters. The sampling method may systematically produce samples that don't represent the population of interest.

33. a) Voluntary response. Only those who both see the ad *and* feel strongly enough will respond.
b) Cluster sampling. One town may not be typical of all.
c) Attempted census. Will have nonresponse bias.
d) Stratified sampling with follow-up. Should be unbiased.

35. a) This is a systematic sample.
b) It is likely to be representative of those waiting for the roller coaster. Indeed, it may do quite well if those at the front of

the line respond differently (after their long wait) than those at the back of the line.
c) The sampling frame is patrons willing to wait for the roller coaster on that day at that time. It should be representative of the people in line, but not of all people at the amusement park.

37. Only those who think it worth the wait are likely to be in line. Those who don't like roller coasters are unlikely to be in the sampling frame, so the poll won't get a fair picture of whether park patrons overall would favor still more roller coasters.

39. a) Biased toward yes because of "pollute." "Should companies be responsible for any costs of environmental cleanup?"
b) Biased toward no because of "enforce" and "strict." "Should companies have dress codes?"

41. a) Not everyone has an equal chance. People with unlisted numbers, people without phones, and those at work cannot be reached.
b) Generate random numbers and call at random times.
c) Under the original plan, those families in which one person stays home are more likely to be included. Under the second plan, many more are included. People without phones are still excluded.
d) It improves the chance of selected households being included.
e) This takes care of phone numbers. Time of day may be an issue. People without phones are still excluded.

43. a) Answers will vary.
b) The amount of change you typically carry. Parameter is the true mean amount of change. Population is the amount on each day around noon.
c) Population is now the amount of change carried by your friends. The average estimates the mean of these amounts.
d) Possibly for your class. Probably not for larger groups. Your friends are likely to have similar needs for change during the day.

45. a) Assign numbers 001 to 120 to each order. Use random numbers to select 10 transactions to examine.
b) Sample proportionately within each type. (Do a stratified random sample.)

47. a) Select three cases at random; then select one jar randomly from each case.
b) Use random numbers to choose three cases from numbers 61 through 80; then use random numbers between 1 and 12 to select the jar from each case.
c) No. Multistage sampling.

49. a) Depends on the Yellow Page listings used. If from regular (line) listings, this is fair if all doctors are listed. If from ads, probably not, as those doctors may not be typical.
b) Not appropriate. This cluster sample will probably contain listings for only one or two business types.

Displaying and Describing Categorical Data

Ben Moon/Keen, Inc.

image100/Corbis

Mike Watson Images/Corbis

Keen, Inc.

Keen, Inc.

KEEN, Inc. was started to create a sandal designed for a variety of water activities. The sandals quickly became popular due to their unique patented toe protection—a black bumper to protect the toes when adventuring out on rivers and trails. Today the KEEN brand offers over 300 different outdoor performance and outdoor inspired casual footwear styles as well as bags and socks.

Few companies experience the kind of growth that KEEN did in less than seven years. Amazingly, they've done this with relatively little advertising and by selling primarily to specialty footwear and outdoor stores, in addition to online outlets.

After the 2004 Tsunami disaster, KEEN cut its advertising budget almost completely and donated over $1 million to help the victims and establish the KEEN Foundation to support environmental and social causes. Philanthropy and community projects continue to play an integral part of the KEEN brand values. In fact, KEEN has established a giving program with a philanthropic effort devoted to helping the environment, conservation, and social movements involving the outdoors.

From Chapter 4 of *Business Statistics*, Second Edition, Norean R. Sharpe, Richard D. De Veaux, Paul F. Velleman.

WHO	Visits to the KEEN, Inc. website
WHAT	Search Engine that led to KEEN's website
WHEN	September 2006
WHERE	Worldwide
HOW	Data compiled via *Google® Analytics* from KEEN website
WHY	To understand customer use of the website and how they got there

K EEN, Inc., like most companies, collects data on visits to its website. Each visit to the site and each subsequent action the visitor takes (changing the page, entering data, etc.) is recorded in a file called a usage, or access weblog. These logs contain a lot of potentially worthwhile information, but they are not easy to use. Here's one line from a log:

```
245.240.221.71 -- [03/Jan/2007:15:20:06-0800]" GET
http://www.keenfootwear.com/pdp_page.cfm?productID=148"
200 8788 "http://www.google.com/" "Mozilla/3.0WebTV/1.2
(compatible; MSIE 2.0)"
```

Unless the company has the analytic resources to deal with these files, it must rely on a third party to summarize the data. KEEN, like many other small and midsized companies, uses *Google Analytics* to collect and summarize its log data.

Imagine a whole table of data like the one above—with a line corresponding to every visit. In September 2006 there were 93,173 visits to the KEEN site, which would be a table with 93,173 rows. The problem with a file like this—and in fact even with data tables—is that we can't see what's going on. And seeing is exactly what we want to do. We need ways to show the data so that we can see patterns, relationships, trends, and exceptions.

1 Summarizing a Categorical Variable

The Three Rules of Data Analysis

There are three things you should always do with data:

1. **Make a picture.** A display of your data will reveal things you are not likely to see in a table of numbers and will help you to *plan* your approach to the analysis and think clearly about the patterns and relationships that may be hiding in your data.

2. **Make a picture.** A well-designed display will *do* much of the work of analyzing your data. It can show the important features and patterns. A picture will also reveal things you did not expect to see: extraordinary (possibly wrong) data values or unexpected patterns.

3. **Make a picture.** The best way to *report* to others what you find in your data is with a well-chosen picture.

These are the three rules of data analysis. These days, technology makes drawing pictures of data easy, so there is no reason not to follow the three rules. Here are some displays showing various aspects of traffic on one of the authors' websites.

Some displays communicate information better than others. We'll discuss some general principles for displaying information honestly in this chapter.

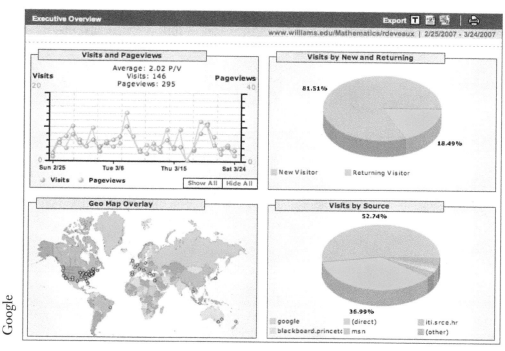

Figure 1   Part of the output from *Google Analytics* (www.google.com/analytics) for the period Feb. 25 to March 24, 2007 displaying website traffic.

Search Engine	Visits
Google	50,629
Direct	22,173
Yahoo	7272
MSN	3166
SnapLink	946
All Others	8987
Total	**93,167**

Table 1   A frequency table of the Search Engine used by visitors to the KEEN, Inc. website.

Search Engine	Visits by %
Google	54.34%
Direct	23.80%
Yahoo	7.80%
MSN	3.40%
SnapLink	1.02%
All Others	9.65%
Total	**100.00%**

Table 2   A relative frequency table for the same data.

Frequency Tables

KEEN might be interested to know how people find their website. They might use the information to allocate their advertising revenue to various search engines, putting ads where they'll be seen by the most potential customers. The variable *Search Engine* records, for each visit to KEEN's website, where the visit came from. The categories are all the search engines used, plus the label "Direct," which indicates that the customer typed in KEEN's web address (or URL) directly into the browser. In order to make sense of the 93,167 visits for which they have data, they'd like to summarize the variable and display the information in a way that can easily communicate the results to others.

In order to make a picture of any variable, we first need to organize its values. For a categorical variable, like *Search Engine*, this is easy—we just count the number of cases corresponding to each category. A **frequency table** (Table 1) records the counts for each of the categories of the variable and lists the counts under the category name. By ordering the categories by number of counts, we can easily see, for example, that the most popular source was Google.

The names of the categories label each row in the frequency table. For *Search Engine* these are "Google," "Direct," "Yahoo," and so on. Even with thousands of cases, a variable that doesn't have too many categories produces a frequency table that is easy to read. A frequency table with dozens or hundreds of categories would be much harder to read. Notice the label of the last line of the table—"All Others." When the number of categories gets too large, we often lump together values of the variable into "Other." When to do that is a judgment call, but it's a good idea to have fewer than about a dozen categories.

Counts are useful, but sometimes we want to know the fraction or **proportion** of the data in each category, so we divide the counts by the total number of cases. Usually we multiply by 100 to express these proportions as **percentages**. A **relative frequency table** (Table 2) displays the *percentages*, rather than the counts, of the values in each category. Both types of table show how the cases are distributed across the categories. In this way, they describe the **distribution** of a categorical variable because they name the possible categories and tell how frequently each occurs.

For Example | Making frequency and relative frequency tables

The Super Bowl, the championship game of the National Football League of the United States, is an important annual social event for Americans, with tens of millions of viewers. The ads that air during the game are expensive: a 30-second ad during the 2010 Super Bowl cost about $3M. The high price of these commercials makes them high-profile and much anticipated, and so the advertisers feel pressure to be innovative, entertaining, and often humorous. Some people, in fact, watch the Super Bowl mainly for the commercials. Before the 2007 Super Bowl, the Gallup Poll asked 1008 U.S. adults whether they were more interested in watching the game or the commercials. Here are 40 of those responses (NA/Don't Know = No Answer or Don't Know):

Won't Watch	Game	Commercials	Won't Watch	Game
Game	Won't Watch	Commercials	Game	Game
Commercials	Commercials	Game	Won't Watch	Commercials
Game	NA/Don't Know	Commercials	Game	Game
Won't Watch	Game	Game	Won't Watch	Game
Game	Won't Watch	Won't Watch	Game	Won't Watch
Won't Watch	Commercials	Commercials	Game	Won't Watch
NA/Don't Know	Won't Watch	Game	Game	Game

Question: Make a frequency table for this variable. Include the percentages to display both a frequency and relative frequency table at the same time.

Answer: There were four different responses to the question about watching the Super Bowl. Counting the number of participants who responded to each of these gives the following table:

Response	Counts	Percentage
Commercials	8	20.0%
Game	18	45.0%
Won't Watch	12	30.0%
No Answer/Don't Know	2	5.0%
Total	**40**	**100.0%**

---

2 Displaying a Categorical Variable

The Area Principle

Now that we have a frequency table, we're ready to follow the three rules of data analysis. But we can't make just any display; a bad picture can distort our understanding rather than help it. For example, Figure 2 is a graph of the frequencies of Table 1. What impression do you get of the relative frequencies of visits from each source?

While it's true that the majority of people came to KEEN's website from Google, in Figure 2 it looks like nearly all did. That doesn't seem right. What's wrong? The lengths of the sandals *do* match the totals in the table. But our eyes tend to be more impressed by the *area* (or perhaps even the *volume*) than by other aspects of each sandal image, and it's that aspect of the image that we notice. Since there were about twice as many people who came from Google as those who typed

> **100.01%?**
>
> If you are careful to add the percentages in Table 2, you will notice the total is 100.01%. Of course the real total has to be 100.00%. The discrepancy is due to individual percentages being rounded. You'll often see this in tables of percents, sometimes with explanatory footnotes.

Figure 2 Although the length of each sandal corresponds to the correct number, the impression we get is all wrong because we perceive the entire area of the sandal. In fact, only a little more than 50% of all visitors used Google to get to the website.

the URL in directly, the sandal depicting the number of Google visitors is about two times longer than the sandal below it, but it occupies about four times the area. As you can see from the frequency table, that just isn't a correct impression.

The best data displays observe a fundamental principle of graphing data called the **area principle**, which says that the area occupied by a part of the graph should correspond to the magnitude of the value it represents.

Bar Charts

Figure 3 gives us a chart that obeys the area principle. It's not as visually entertaining as the sandals, but it does give a more *accurate* visual impression of the distribution. The height of each bar shows the count for its category. The bars are the

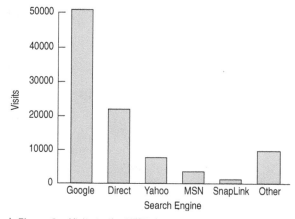

Figure 3 Visits to the KEEN, Inc. website by *Search Engine* choice. With the area principle satisfied, the true distribution is clear.

same width, so their heights determine their areas, and the areas are proportional to the counts in each class. Now it's easy to see that nearly half the site hits came from places other than Google—not the impression that the sandals in Figure 2 conveyed. We can also see that there were a little more than twice as many visits that originated with a Google search as there were visits that came directly. Bar charts make these kinds of comparisons easy and natural.

A **bar chart** displays the distribution of a categorical variable, showing the counts for each category next to each other for easy comparison. Bar charts should have small spaces between the bars to indicate that these are freestanding bars that could be rearranged into any order. The bars are lined up along a common base with labels for each category. The variable name is often used as a subtitle for the x-axis.

Bar charts are usually drawn vertically in columns, 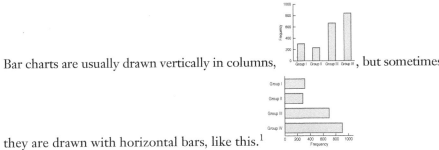, but sometimes

they are drawn with horizontal bars, like this.[1]

If we want to draw attention to the relative *proportion* of visits from each *Search Engine*, we could replace the counts with percentages and use a **relative frequency bar chart**, like the one shown in Figure 4.

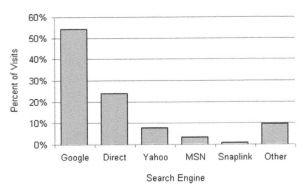

Figure 4   The relative frequency bar chart, created in **Excel**, looks the same as the bar chart (Figure 3) but shows the proportion of visits in each category rather than the counts.

Pie Charts

Another common display that shows how a whole group breaks into several categories is a pie chart. **Pie charts** show the whole group of cases as a circle. They slice the circle into pieces whose size is proportional to the fraction of the whole in each category.

---

[1]Excel refers to this display as a column chart when the bars are vertical and a bar chart when they are horizontal.

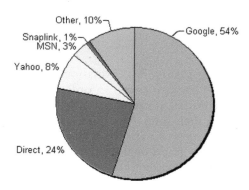

Figure 5 A pie chart shows the proportion of visits by Search Engine. Pie chart created in **Excel**.

Pie charts give a quick impression of how a whole group is partitioned into smaller groups. Because we're used to cutting up pies into 2, 4, or 8 pieces, pie charts are good for seeing relative frequencies near 1/2, 1/4, or 1/8. For example, in Figure 5, you can easily see that the slice representing Google is just slightly more than half the total. Unfortunately, other comparisons are harder to make with pie charts. Were there more visits from Yahoo, or from All Others? It's hard to tell since the two slices look about the same. Comparisons such as these are usually easier in a bar chart. (Compare to Figure 4.)

- **Think before you draw.** Our first rule of data analysis is *Make a picture*. But what kind of picture? We don't have a lot of options—yet. There's more to Statistics than pie charts and bar charts, and knowing when to use every type of display we'll discuss is a critical first step in data analysis. That decision depends in part on what type of data you have and on what you hope to communicate.

We always have to check that the data are appropriate for whatever method of analysis we choose. Before you make a bar chart or a pie chart, always check the **Categorical Data Condition:** that the data are counts or percentages of individuals in categories.

If you want to make a pie chart or relative frequency bar chart, you'll need to also make sure that the categories don't overlap, so that no individual is counted in two categories. If the categories do overlap, it's misleading to make a pie chart, since the percentages won't add up to 100%. For the *Search Engine* data, either kind of display is appropriate because the categories don't overlap—each visit comes from a unique source.

Throughout this course, you'll see that doing Statistics right means selecting the proper methods. That means you have to think about the situation at hand. An important first step is to check that the type of analysis you plan is appropriate. The Categorical Data Condition is just the first of many such checks.

For Example   Making a bar chart

Question: Make a bar chart for the 40 Super Bowl responses of the example earlier in this chapter.

Answer: Use the frequencies in the table in the example to produce the heights of the bars:

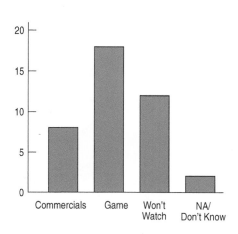

3 Exploring Two Categorical Variables: Contingency Tables

WHO	Respondents in the GfK Roper Reports Worldwide Survey
WHAT	Responses to questions relating to perceptions of food and health
WHEN	Fall 2005; published in 2006
WHERE	Worldwide
HOW	Data collected by GfK Roper Consulting using a multistage design
WHY	To understand cultural differences in the perception of the food and beauty products we buy and how they affect our health

You may recall seeing how GfK Roper Consulting gathered information on consumers attitudes about health, food, and health care products. In order to effectively market food products across different cultures, it's essential to know how strongly people in different cultures feel about their food. One question in the Roper survey asked respondents whether they agreed with the following statement: "I have a strong preference for regional or traditional products and dishes from where I come from." Here is a frequency table (Table 3) of the responses.

Response to *Regional Food Preference Question*	Counts	Relative Frequency
Agree Completely	2346	30.51%
Agree Somewhat	2217	28.83%
Neither Disagree Nor Agree	1738	22.60%
Disagree Somewhat	811	10.55%
Disagree Completely	498	6.48%
Don't Know	80	1.04%
Total	**7690**	**100.00%**

Table 3 A combined frequency and relative frequency table for the responses (from all 5 countries represented: China, France, India, the U.K., and the U.S.) to the statement "I have a strong preference for regional or traditional products and dishes from where I come from."

The pie chart (Figure 6) shows clearly that more than half of all the respondents agreed with the statement.

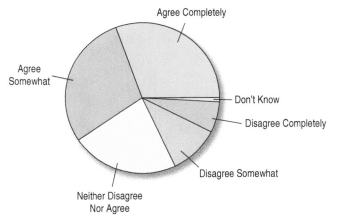

Regional Food Preference

Figure 6 It's clear from the pie chart that the majority of respondents identify with their local foods.

But if we want to target our marketing differently in different countries, wouldn't it be more interesting to know how opinions vary from country to country?

To find out, we need to look at the two categorical variables *Regional Preference* and *Country* together, which we do by arranging the data in a two-way table. Table 4 is a two-way table of *Regional Preference* by *Country*. Because the table shows how the individuals are distributed along each variable, depending on, or *contingent on*, the value of the other variable, such a table is called a **contingency table**.

		Regional Preference						
		Agree Completely	Agree Somewhat	Neither Disagree Nor Agree	Disagree Somewhat	Disagree Completely	Don't Know	Total
Country	China	518	576	251	117	33	7	**1502**
	France	347	475	400	208	94	15	**1539**
	India	960	282	129	65	95	4	**1535**
	U.K.	214	407	504	229	175	28	**1557**
	U.S.	307	477	454	192	101	26	**1557**
	Total	**2346**	**2217**	**1738**	**811**	**498**	**80**	**7690**

Table 4   Contingency table of *Regional Preference* and *Country*. The bottom line "Totals" are the values that were in Table 3.

The margins of a contingency table give totals. In the case of Table 4, these are shown in both the right-hand column (in bold) and the bottom row (also in bold). The totals in the bottom row of the table show the frequency distribution of the variable *Regional Preference*. The totals in the right-hand column of the table show the frequency distribution of the variable *Country*. When presented like this, at the margins of a contingency table, the frequency distribution of either one of the variables is called its **marginal distribution**. The marginal distribution for a variable in a contingency table is the same frequency distribution we found by considering each variable separately.

Each **cell** of a contingency table (any intersection of a row and column of the table) gives the count for a combination of values of the two variables. For example, in Table 4 you can see that 504 people in the United Kingdom neither agreed nor disagreed. Looking down the Agree Completely column, you can see that the largest number of responses in that column (960) are from India. Are Britons less likely to agree with the statement than Indians or Chinese? Questions like this are more naturally addressed using percentages.

We know that 960 people from India agreed completely with the statement. We could display this number as a percentage, but as a percentage of what? The total number of people in the survey? (960 is 12.5% of the total.) The number of Indians in the survey? (960 is 62.5% of the row total.) The number of people who agree completely? (960 is 40.9% of the column total.) All of these are possibilities, and all are potentially useful or interesting. You'll probably wind up calculating (or letting your technology calculate) lots of percentages. Most statistics programs offer a choice of **total percent, row percent**, or **column percent** for contingency tables. Unfortunately, they often put them all together with several numbers in each cell of the table. The resulting table (Table 5) holds lots of information but is hard to understand.

Regional Preference

Country		Agree Completely	Agree Somewhat	Neither Disagree Nor Agree	Disagree Somewhat	Disagree Completely	Don't Know	Total
China		518	576	251	117	33	7	**1502**
	% of Row	*34.49*	*38.35*	*16.71*	*7.79*	*2.20*	*0.47*	**100.00%**
	% of Column	*22.08*	*25.98*	*14.44*	*14.43*	*6.63*	*8.75*	**19.53%**
	% of Total	*6.74*	*7.49*	*3.26*	*1.52*	*0.43*	*0.09*	**19.53%**
France		347	475	400	208	94	15	**1539**
	% of Row	*22.55*	*30.86*	*25.99*	*13.52*	*6.11*	*0.97*	**100.00%**
	% of Column	*14.79*	*21.43*	*23.01*	*25.65*	*18.88*	*18.75*	**20.01%**
	% of Total	*4.51*	*6.18*	*5.20*	*2.70*	*1.22*	*0.20*	**20.01%**
India		960	282	129	65	95	4	**1535**
	% of Row	*62.54*	*18.37*	*8.40*	*4.23*	*6.19*	*0.26*	**100.00%**
	% of Column	*40.92*	*12.72*	*7.42*	*8.01*	*19.08*	*5.00*	**19.96%**
	% of Total	*12.48*	*3.67*	*1.68*	*0.85*	*1.24*	*0.05*	**19.96%**
U.K.		214	407	504	229	175	28	**1557**
	% of Row	*13.74*	*26.14*	*32.37*	*14.71*	*11.24*	*1.80*	**100.00%**
	% of Column	*9.12*	*18.36*	*29.00*	*28.24*	*35.14*	*35.00*	**20.24%**
	% of Total	*2.78*	*5.29*	*6.55*	*2.98*	*2.28*	*0.36*	**20.24%**
U.S.		307	477	454	192	101	26	**1557**
	% of Row	*19.72*	*30.64*	*29.16*	*12.33*	*6.49*	*1.67*	**100.00%**
	% of Column	*13.09*	*21.52*	*26.12*	*23.67*	*20.28*	*32.50*	**20.24%**
	% of Total	*3.99*	*6.20*	*5.90*	*2.50*	*1.31*	*0.34*	**20.24%**
Total		**2346**	**2217**	**1738**	**811**	**498**	**80**	**7690**
	% of Row	**30.51%**	**28.83%**	**22.60%**	**10.55%**	**6.48%**	**1.04%**	**100.00%**
	% of Column	**100.00%**	**100.00%**	**100.00%**	**100.00%**	**100.00%**	**100.00%**	**100.00%**
	% of Total	**30.51%**	**28.83%**	**22.60%**	**10.55%**	**6.48%**	**1.04%**	**100.00%**

Table 5   Another contingency table of *Regional Preference* and *Country*. This time we see not only the counts for each combination of the two variables, but also the percentages these counts represent. For each count, there are three choices for the percentage: by row, by column, and by table total. There's probably too much information here for this table to be useful.

To simplify the table, let's pull out the values corresponding to the percentages of the total.

Regional Preference

Country	Agree Completely	Agree Somewhat	Neither Disagree Nor Agree	Disagree Somewhat	Disagree Completely	Don't Know	Total
China	*6.74*	*7.49*	*3.26*	*1.52*	*0.43*	*0.09*	**19.53**
France	*4.51*	*6.18*	*5.20*	*2.70*	*1.22*	*0.20*	**20.01**
India	*12.48*	*3.67*	*1.68*	*0.85*	*1.24*	*0.05*	**19.96**
U.K.	*2.78*	*5.29*	*6.55*	*2.98*	*2.28*	*0.36*	**20.25**
U.S.	*3.99*	*6.20*	*5.90*	*2.50*	*1.31*	*0.34*	**20.25**
Total	**30.51**	**28.83**	**22.60**	**10.55**	**6.48**	**1.04**	**100.00**

Table 6   A contingency table of *Regional Preference* and *Country* showing only the total percentages.

These percentages tell us what percent of *all* respondents belong to each combination of column and row category. For example, we see that 3.99% of the respondents were Americans who agreed completely with the question, which is slightly more than the percentage of Indians who agreed somewhat. Is this fact useful? Is that really what we want to know?

> Always be sure to ask "percent of what?" That will help define the *who* and will help you decide whether you want *row, column,* or *table* percentages.

Percent of what?

The English language can be tricky when we talk about percentages. If asked, "What percent of those answering 'I Don't Know' were from India?" it's pretty clear that you should focus only on the *Don't Know* column. The question itself seems to restrict the *who* in the question to that column, so you should look at the number of those in each country among the 80 people who replied "I don't know." You'd find that in the column percentages, and the answer would be 4 out of 80 or 5.00%.

But if you're asked, "What percent were Indians who replied 'I don't know?' you'd have a different question. Be careful. The question really means "what percent of the entire sample were both from India and replied 'I don't know'?" So the *who* is all respondents. The denominator should be 7690, and the answer is the table percent 4/7690 = 0.05%.

Finally, if you're asked, "What percent of the Indians replied 'I don't know'?" you'd have a third question. Now the *who* is Indians. So the denominator is the 1535 Indians, and the answer is the row percent, 4/1535 = 0.26%.

Conditional Distributions

The more interesting questions are contingent on something. We'd like to know, for example, what percentage *of Indians* agreed completely with the statement and how that compares to the percentage *of Britons* who also agreed. Equivalently, we might ask whether the chance of agreeing with the statement depended on the *Country* of the respondent. We can look at this question in two ways. First, we could ask how the distribution of *Regional Preference* changes across *Country*. To do that we look at the row percentages.

		Regional Preference						
Country		Agree Completely	Agree Somewhat	Neither Disagree Nor Agree	Disagree Somewhat	Disagree Completely	Don't Know	Total
	India	960	282	129	65	95	4	1535
		62.54	18.37	8.40	4.23	6.19	0.26	100%
	U.K.	214	407	504	229	175	28	1557
		13.74	26.14	32.37	14.71	11.24	1.80	100%

Table 7   The conditional distribution of *Regional Preference* conditioned on two values of *Country:* India and the United Kingdom. This table shows the row percentages.

By focusing on each row separately, we see the distribution of *Regional Preference* under the condition of being in the selected *Country*. The sum of the percentages in each row is 100%, and we divide that up by the responses to the question. In effect, we can temporarily restrict the *who* first to Indians and look at how their responses are distributed. A distribution like this is called a **conditional distribution** because it shows the distribution of one variable for just those cases that satisfy a condition on another. We can compare the two conditional distributions with pie

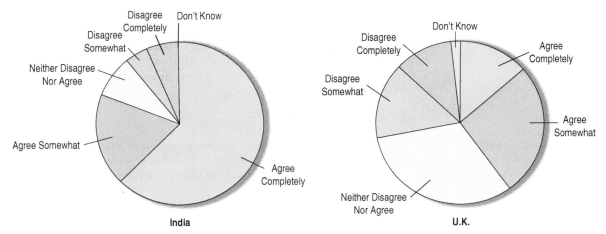

Figure 7   Pie charts of the conditional distributions of *Regional Food Preference* importance for India and the United Kingdom. The percentage of people who agree is much higher in India than in the United Kingdom.

charts (Figure 7). Of course, we could also turn the question around. We could look at the distribution of *Country* for each category of *Regional Preference*. To do this, we would look at the column percentages.

Looking at how the percentages change across each row, it sure looks like the distribution of responses to the question is different in each *Country*. To make the differences more vivid, we could also display the conditional distributions. Figure 8 shows an example of a side-by-side bar chart, displaying the responses to the questions for India and the United Kingdom.

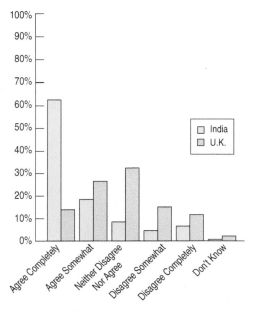

Figure 8   Side-by-side bar charts showing the conditional distribution of *Regional Food Preference* for both India and the United Kingdom. It's easier to compare percentages within each country with side-by-side bar charts than pie charts.

From Figure 8, it is clear that Indians have a stronger preference for their own cuisine than Britons have for theirs. For food companies, including GfK Roper's clients, that means Indians are less likely to accept a food product they perceive as foreign, and people in Great Britain are more accepting of "foreign" foods. This could be invaluable information for marketing products.

Variables can be associated in many ways and to different degrees. The best way to tell whether two variables are associated is to ask whether they are *not*.[2] In a contingency table, when the distribution of one variable is the same for all categories of another variable, we say that the two variables are **independent**. That tells us there's no association between these variables. We'll see a way to check for independence formally later in the text. For now, we'll just compare the distributions.

For Example   Contingency tables and side-by-side bar charts

Here is a contingency table of the responses to the question Gallup asked about the Super Bowl by sex:

	Female	Male	**Total**
	\multicolumn{2}{c}{**Sex**}	
Game	198	277	**475**
Commercials	154	79	**233**
NA/Don't Know	4	4	**8**
Won't Watch	160	132	**292**
Total	**516**	**492**	**1008**

Question: Does it seem that there is an association between what viewers are interested in watching and their sex?

Answer: First, find the conditional distributions of the four responses for each sex:

For Men:

Game = 277/492 = 56.3%

Commercials = 79/492 = 16.1%

Won't Watch = 132/492 = 26.8%

NA/Don't Know = 4/492 = 0.8%

For Women:

Game = 198/516 = 38.4%

Commercials = 154/516 = 29.8%

Won't Watch = 160/516 = 31.0%

NA/Don't Know = 4/516 = 0.8%

Now display the two distributions with side-by-side bar charts:

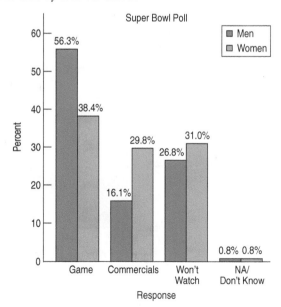

(continued)

---

[2] This kind of "backwards" reasoning shows up surprisingly often in science—and in statistics.

Based on this poll it appears that women were only slightly less interested than men in watching the Super Bowl telecast: 31% of the women said they didn't plan to watch, compared to just under 27% of men. Among those who planned to watch, however, there appears to be an association between the viewer's sex and what the viewer is most looking forward to. While more women are interested in the game (38%) than the commercials (30%), the margin among men is much wider: 56% of men said they were looking forward to seeing the game, compared to only 16% who cited the commercials.

Just Checking

So that they can balance their inventory, an optometry shop collects the following data for customers in the shop.

		Eye Condition			
		Nearsighted	**Farsighted**	**Need Bifocals**	**Total**
Sex	**Males**	6	20	6	**32**
	Females	4	16	12	**32**
	Total	**10**	**36**	**18**	**64**

1 What percent of females are farsighted?
2 What percent of nearsighted customers are female?
3 What percent of all customers are farsighted females?
4 What's the distribution of *Eye Condition*?
5 What's the conditional distribution of *Eye Condition* for males?
6 Compare the percent who are female among nearsighted customers to the percent of all customers who are female.
7 Does it seem that *Eye Condition* and *Sex* might be dependent? Explain.

Segmented Bar Charts

We could display the Roper survey information by dividing up bars rather than circles as we did when making pie charts. The resulting **segmented bar chart** treats each bar as the "whole" and divides it proportionally into segments corresponding to the percentage in each group. We can see that the distributions of responses to the question are very different in the two countries, indicating again that *Regional Preference* is not independent of *Country*.

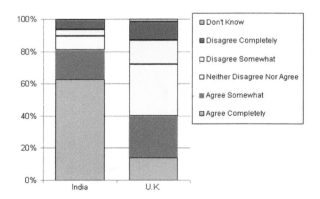

Figure 9   Although the totals for India and the United Kingdom are different, the bars are the same height because we have converted the numbers to percentages. Compare this display (created in **Excel**) with the side-by-side pie charts of the same data in Figure 7.

Guided Example   Food Safety

Food storage and food safety are major issues for multinational food companies. A client wants to know if people of all age groups have the same degree of concern so GfK Roper Consulting asked 1500 people in five countries whether they agree with the following statement: "I worry about how safe the food I buy is." We might want to report to a client who was interested in how concerns about food safety were related to age.

Joao Virissimo/Shutterstock

PLAN

Setup

- State the objectives and goals of the study.
- Identify and define the variables.
- Provide the time frame of the data collection process.

Determine the appropriate analysis for data type.

The client wants to examine the distribution of responses to the food safety question and see whether they are related to the age of the respondent. GfK Roper Consulting collected data on this question in the fall of 2005 for their 2006 Worldwide report. We will use the data from that study.

The variable is *Food Safety*. The responses are in nonoverlapping categories of agreement, from Agree Completely to Disagree Completely (and Don't Know). There were originally 12 Age groups, which we can combine into five:

Teen	13–19
Young Adult	20–29
Adult	30–39
Middle Aged	40–49
Mature	50 and older

Both variables, *Food Safety* and *Age*, are ordered categorical variables. To examine any differences in responses across age groups, it is appropriate to create a contingency table and a side-by-side bar chart. Here is a contingency table of "Food Safety" by "Age."

DO

Mechanics For a large data set like this, we rely on technology to make table and displays.

| | | Food Safety | | | | | | |
		Agree Completely	Agree Somewhat	Neither Disagree Nor Agree	Disagree Somewhat	Disagree Completely	Don't Know	Total
Age	Teen	16.19	27.50	24.32	19.30	10.58	2.12	100%
	Young Adult	20.55	32.68	23.81	14.94	6.98	1.04	100%
	Adult	22.23	34.89	23.28	12.26	6.75	0.59	100%
	Middle Aged	24.79	35.31	22.02	12.43	5.06	0.39	100%
	Mature	26.60	33.85	21.21	11.89	5.82	0.63	100%

(continued)

A side-by-side bar chart is particularly helpful when comparing multiple groups.

A side-by-side bar chart shows the percent of each response to the question by Age group.

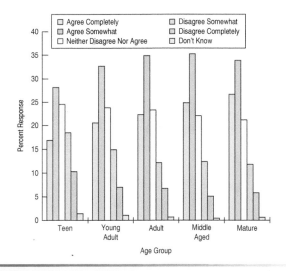

REPORT

Summary and Conclusions Summarize the charts and analysis in context. Make recommendations if possible and discuss further analysis that is needed.

MEMO

Re: Food safety concerns by age

Our analysis of the GfK Roper Reports™ Worldwide survey data for 2006 shows a pattern of concern about food safety that generally increases from youngest to oldest.

Our analysis thus far has not considered whether this trend is consistent across countries. If it were of interest to your group, we could perform a similar analysis for each of the countries.

The enclosed tables and plots provide support for these conclusions.

What Can Go Wrong?

- **Don't violate the area principle.** This is probably the most common mistake in a graphical display. Violations of the area principle are often made for the sake of artistic presentation. Here, for example, are two versions of the same pie chart for the *Regional Preference* data.

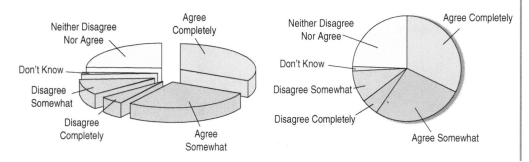

The one on the left looks interesting, doesn't it? But showing the pie three dimensionally on a slant violates the area principle and makes it much more difficult to compare fractions of the whole made up of each category of the response—the principal feature that a pie chart ought to show.

- **Keep it honest.** Here's a pie chart that displays data on the percentage of high school students who engage in specified dangerous behaviors as reported by the Centers for Disease Control. What's wrong with this plot?

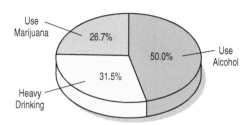

Try adding up the percentages. Or look at the 50% slice. Does it look right? Then think: What are these percentages of? Is there a "whole" that has been sliced up? In a pie chart, the proportions shown by each slice of the pie must add up to 100%, and each individual must fall into only one category. Of course, showing the pie on a slant makes it even harder to detect the error.

Here's another example. This bar chart shows the number of airline passengers searched by security screening.

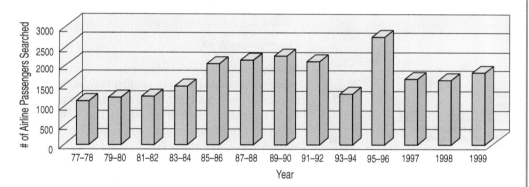

Looks like things didn't change much in the final years of the 20th century— until you read the bar labels and see that the last three bars represent single years, while all the others are for *pairs* of years. The false depth makes it even harder to see the problem.

- **Don't confuse percentages.** Many percentages based on a conditional and joint distributions sound similar, but are different (see Table 5):
  - The percentage of French who answered "Agree Completely": This is 347/1539 or 22.55%.
  - The percentage of those who answered "Don't Know" who were French: This is 15/80 or 18.75%.
  - The percentage of those who were French *and* answered "Agree Completely": This is 347/7690 or 4.51%.

(continued)

In each instance, pay attention to the wording that makes a restriction to a smaller group (those who are French, those who answered "Don't Know," and all respondents, respectively) before a percentage is found. This restricts the *who* of the problem and the associated denominator for the percentage. Your discussion of results must make these differences clear.

- **Don't forget to look at the variables separately, too.** When you make a contingency table or display a conditional distribution, be sure to also examine the marginal distributions. It's important to know how many cases are in each category.

- **Be sure to use enough individuals.** When you consider percentages, take care that they are based on a large enough number of individuals (or cases). Take care not to make a report such as this one:

  We found that 66.67% of the companies surveyed improved their performance by hiring outside consultants. The other company went bankrupt.

- **Don't overstate your case.** Independence is an important concept, but it is rare for two variables to be *entirely* independent. We can't conclude that one variable has no effect whatsoever on another. Usually, all we know is that little effect was observed in our study. Other studies of other groups under other circumstances could find different results.

- **Don't use unfair or inappropriate percentages.** Sometimes percentages can be misleading. Sometimes they don't make sense at all. Be careful when finding percentages across different categories not to combine percentages inappropriately. The next section gives an example.

Simpson's Paradox

Here's an example showing that combining percentages across very different values or groups can give absurd results. Suppose there are two sales representatives, Peter and Katrina. Peter argues that he's the better salesperson, since he managed to close 83% of his last 120 prospects compared with Katrina's 78%. But let's look at the data a little more closely. Here (Table 8) are the results for each of their last 120 sales calls, broken down by the product they were selling.

	Product		
Sales Rep	Printer Paper	USB Flash Drive	Overall
Peter	90 out of 100 90%	10 out of 20 50%	100 out of 120 83%
Katrina	19 out of 20 95%	75 out of 100 75%	94 out of 120 78%

Table 8   Look at the percentages within each Product category. Who has a better success rate closing sales of paper? Who has the better success rate closing sales of Flash Drives? Who has the better performance overall?

Look at the sales of the two products separately. For printer paper sales, Katrina had a 95% success rate, and Peter only had a 90% rate. When selling flash drives, Katrina closed her sales 75% of the time, but Peter only 50%. So Peter has better "overall" performance, but Katrina is better selling each product. How can this be?

This problem is known as **Simpson's Paradox**, named for the statistician who described it in the 1960s. Although it is rare, there have been a few well-publicized cases of it. As we can see from the example, the problem results from inappropriately combining percentages of different groups. Katrina concentrates on selling flash drives, which is more difficult, so her *overall* percentage is heavily influenced by her flash drive average. Peter sells more printer paper, which appears to be easier to sell. With their different patterns of selling, taking an overall percentage is misleading. Their manager should be careful not to conclude rashly that Peter is the better salesperson.

The lesson of Simpson's Paradox is to be sure to combine comparable measurements for comparable individuals. Be especially careful when combining across different levels of a second variable. It's usually better to compare percentages *within* each level, rather than across levels.

Discrimination?

One famous example of Simpson's Paradox arose during an investigation of admission rates for men and women at the University of California at Berkeley's graduate schools. As reported in an article in *Science*, about 45% of male applicants were admitted, but only about 30% of female applicants got in. It looked like a clear case of discrimination. However, when the data were broken down by school (Engineering, Law, Medicine, etc.), it turned out that within each school, the women were admitted at nearly the same or, in some cases, much *higher* rates than the men. How could this be? Women applied in large numbers to schools with very low admission rates. (Law and Medicine, for example, admitted fewer than 10%.) Men tended to apply to Engineering and Science. Those schools have admission rates above 50%. When the total applicant pool was combined and the percentages were computed, the women had a much lower *overall* rate, but the combined percentage didn't really make sense.

Ethics in Action

Lyle Erhart has been working in sales for a leading vendor of Customer Relationship Management (CRM) software for the past three years. He was recently made aware of a published research study that examined factors related to the successful implementation of CRM projects among firms in the financial services industry. Lyle read the research report with interest and was excited to see that his company's CRM software product was included. Among the results were tables reporting the number of projects that were successful based on type of CRM implementation (Operational versus Analytical) for each of the top leading CRM products of 2006. Lyle quickly found the results for his company's product and their major competitor. He summarized the results into one table as follows:

	His Company	Major Competitor
Operational	16 successes out of 20	68 successes out of 80
Analytical	90 successes out of 100	19 successes out of 20

At first he was a bit disappointed, especially since most of their potential clients were interested in Operational CRM. He had hoped to be able to disseminate the findings of this report among the sales force so they could refer to it when visiting potential clients. After some thought, he realized that he could combine the results. His company's overall success rate was 106 out of 120 (over 88%) and was higher than that of its major competitor. Lyle was now happy that he found and read the report.

ETHICAL ISSUE *Lyle, intentionally or not, has benefited from Simpson's Paradox. By combining percentages, he can present the findings in a manner favorable to his company (related to item A, ASA Ethical Guidelines).*

ETHICAL SOLUTION *Lyle should not combine the percentages as the results are misleading. If he decides to disseminate the information to his sales force, he must do so without combining.*

What Have We Learned?

Learning Objectives

- Make and interpret a frequency table for a categorical variable.
  - We can summarize categorical data by counting the number of cases in each category, sometimes expressing the resulting distribution as percentages.

- Make and interpret a bar chart or pie chart.
  - We display categorical data using the area principle in either a **bar chart** or a **pie chart**.

- Make and interpret a contingency table.
  - When we want to see how two categorical variables are related, we put the counts (and/or percentages) in a two-way table called a **contingency table**.

- Make and interpret bar charts and pie charts of marginal distributions.
  - We look at the **marginal distribution** of each variable (found in the margins of the table). We also look at the **conditional distribution** of a variable within each category of the other variable.
  - Comparing conditional distributions of one variable across categories of another tells us about the association between variables. If the conditional distributions of one variable are (roughly) the same for every category of the other, the variables are **independent**.

Terms

Area principle	In a statistical display, each data value is represented by the same amount of area.
Bar chart (relative frequency bar chart)	A chart that represents the count (or percentage) of each category in a categorical variable as a bar, allowing easy visual comparisons across categories.
Cell	Each location in a contingency table, representing the values of two categorical variables, is called a cell.
Segmented bar chart	A segmented bar chart displays the conditional distribution of a categorical variable within each category of another variable.
Column percent	The proportion of each column contained in the cell of a frequency table.
Conditional distribution	The distribution of a variable restricting the *who* to consider only a smaller group of individuals.
Contingency table	A table displaying the frequencies (sometimes percentages) for each combination of two or more variables.
Distribution	The distribution of a variable is a list of:
	• all the possible values of the variable
	• the relative frequency of each value
Frequency table (relative frequency table)	A table that lists the categories in a categorical variable and gives the number (the percentage) of observations for each category. The row percent is the proportion of each row contained in the cell of a frequency table, while the column percent is the proportion of each column contained in the cell of a frequency table.
Independent variables	Variables for which the conditional distribution of one variable is the same for each category of the other.
Marginal distribution	In a contingency table, the distribution of either variable alone. The counts or percentages are the totals found in the margins (usually the right-most column or bottom row) of the table.
Pie chart	Pie charts show how a "whole" divides into categories by showing a wedge of a circle whose area corresponds to the proportion in each category.

Row percent	The proportion of each row contained in the cell of a frequency table.
Simpson's paradox	A phenomenon that arises when averages, or percentages, are taken across different groups, and these group averages appear to contradict the overall averages.
Total percent	The proportion of the total contained in the cell of a frequency table.

Technology Help: Displaying Categorical Data on the Computer

Although every package makes a slightly different bar chart, they all have similar features:

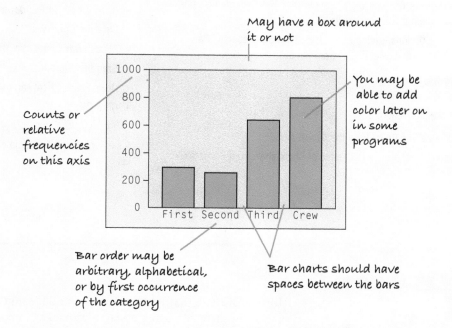

May have a box around it or not

You may be able to add color later on in some programs

Counts or relative frequencies on this axis

Bar order may be arbitrary, alphabetical, or by first occurrence of the category

Bar charts should have spaces between the bars

Sometimes the count or a percentage is printed above or on top of each bar to give some additional information. You may find that your statistics package sorts category names in annoying orders by default. For example, many packages sort categories alphabetically or by the order the categories are seen in the data set. Often, neither of these is the best choice.

EXCEL 2007 XLSTAT⁷

To make a bar chart:

- Select the variable in Excel you want to work with.
- Choose the **Column** command from the Insert tab in the Ribbon.
- Select the appropriate chart from the drop down dialog.

To change the bar chart into a pie chart:

- Right-click the chart and select **Change Chart Type**. . . from the menu. The Chart type dialog opens.
- Select a pie chart type.
- Click the **OK** button. Excel changes your bar chart into a pie chart.

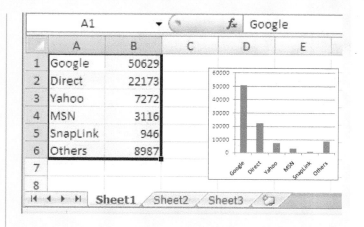

(continued)

JMP

JMP makes a bar chart and frequency table together.

- From the **Analyze** menu, choose **Distribution.**
- In the Distribution dialog, drag the name of the variable into the empty variable window beside the label "Y, Columns"; click **OK.**
- To make a pie chart, choose **Chart** from the **Graph** menu.
- In the Chart dialog, select the variable name from the Columns list, click on the button labeled "Statistics," and select "N" from the drop-down menu.
- Click the "**Categories, X, Levels**" button to assign the same variable name to the X-axis.
- Under Options, click on the **second** button—labeled "**Bar Chart**"—and select "Pie" from the drop-down menu.

MINITAB

To make a bar chart,

- Choose **Bar Chart** from the **Graph** menu.
- Then select a Simple, Cluster, or Stack chart from the options and click **OK**.

- To make a **Simple** bar chart, enter the name of the variable to graph in the dialog box.
- To make a relative frequency chart, click **Chart Options**, and choose **Show Y as Percent**.
- In the Chart dialog, enter the name of the variable that you wish to display in the box labeled "Categorical variables."
- Click **OK.**

SPSS

To make a bar chart,

- Open the **Chart Builder** from the **Graphs** menu.
- Click the **Gallery** tab.
- Choose **Bar Chart** from the list of chart types.
- Drag the appropriate bar chart onto the canvas.
- Drag a categorical variable onto the x-axis drop zone.
- Click **OK**.

Comments

A similar path makes a pie chart by choosing **Pie chart** from the list of chart types.

Brief CASE

KEEN

More of the data that KEEN, Inc. obtained from *Google Analytics* are in the file **KEEN**. Open the data file using a statistics package and find data on *Country of Origin*, *Top Keywords*, *Online Retailers*, *User Statistics*, and *Page Visits*. Create frequency tables, bar charts, and pie charts using your software. What might KEEN want to know about their Web traffic? Which of these tables and charts is most useful to address the question of where they should advertise and how they should position their products? Write a brief case report summarizing your analysis and results.

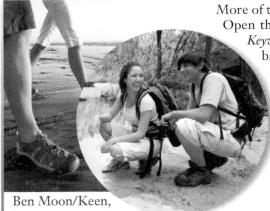

Ben Moon/Keen, Inc.

Tetra Images/Corbis

Exercises

SECTION 1

1. As part of the human resource group of your company you are asked to summarize the educational levels of the 512 employees in your division. From company records, you find that 164 have no college degree (None), 42 have an associate's degree (AA), 225 have a bachelor's degree (BA), 52 have a master's degree (MA), and 29 have PhDs. For the educational level of your division:

a) Make a frequency table.
b) Make a relative frequency table.

2. As part of the marketing group at Pixar, you are asked to find out the age distribution of the audience of Pixar's latest film. With the help of 10 of your colleagues, you conduct exit interviews by randomly selecting people to question at 20 different movie theatres. You ask them to tell you if they are younger than 6 years old, 6 to 9 years old, 10 to 14 years old, 15 to 21 years old, or older than 21. From 470 responses, you find out that 45 are younger than 6, 83 are 6 to 9 years old, 154 are 10 to 14, 18 are 15 to 21, and 170 are older than 21. For the age distribution:

a) Make a frequency table.
b) Make a relative frequency table.

SECTION 2

3. From the educational level data described in Exercise 1:

a) Make a bar chart using counts on the *y*-axis.
b) Make a relative frequency bar chart using percentages on the *y*-axis.
c) Make a pie chart.

4. From the age distribution data described in Exercise 2:

a) Make a bar chart using counts on the *y*-axis.
b) Make a relative frequency bar chart using percentages on the *y*-axis.
c) Make a pie chart.

5. For the educational levels described in Exercise 1:

a) Write two to four sentences summarizing the distribution.
b) What conclusions, if any, could you make about the educational level at other companies?

6. For the ages described in Exercise 2:

a) Write two to four sentences summarizing the distribution.
b) What possible problems do you see in concluding that the age distribution from these surveys accurately represents the ages of the national audience for this film?

SECTION 3

7. From Exercise 1, we also have data on how long each person has been with the company (tenure) categorized into three levels: less than 1 year, between 1 and 5 years, and more than 5 years. A table of the two variables together looks like:

	None	AA	BA	MA	PhD
<1 year	10	3	50	20	12
1–5 years	42	9	112	27	15
more than 5 years	112	30	63	5	2

a) Find the marginal distribution of the tenure. (*Hint*: find the row totals.)
b) Verify that the marginal distribution of the education level is the same as that given in Exercise 1.

8. In addition to their age levels, the movie audiences in Exercise 2 were also asked if they had seen the movie before (Never, Once, More than Once). Here is a table showing the responses by age group:

	Under 6	6 to 9	10 to 14	15 to 21	Over 21
Never	39	60	84	16	151
Once	3	20	38	2	15
More than Once	3	3	32	0	4

a) Find the marginal distribution of their previous viewing of the movie. (Hint: find the row totals.)
b) Verify that the marginal distribution of the ages is the same as that given in Exercise 2.

9. For the table in Exercise 7,

a) Find the column percentages.
b) Looking at the column percentages in part a, does the *tenure* distribution (how long the employee has been with the company) for each educational level look the same? Comment briefly.
c) Make a stacked bar chart showing the *tenure* distribution for each educational level.
d) Is it easier to see the differences in the distributions using the column percentages or the stacked bar chart?

10. For the table in Exercise 8,

a) Find the column percentages.
b) Looking at the column percentages in part a, does the distribution of how many times someone has seen the movie look the same for each age group? Comment briefly.
c) Make a stacked bar chart, showing the distribution of viewings for each age level.

d) Is it easier to see the differences in the distributions using the column percentages or the stacked bar chart?

CHAPTER EXERCISES

11. Graphs in the news. Find a bar graph of categorical data from a business publication (e.g., *Business Week, Fortune, The Wall Street Journal*, etc.).

a) Is the graph clearly labeled?
b) Does it violate the area principle?
c) Does the accompanying article tell the W's of the variable?
d) Do you think the article correctly interprets the data? Explain.

12. Graphs in the news, part 2. Find a pie chart of categorical data from a business publication (e.g., *Business Week, Fortune, The Wall Street Journal*, etc.).

a) Is the graph clearly labeled?
b) Does it violate the area principle?
c) Does the accompanying article tell the W's of the variable?
d) Do you think the article correctly interprets the data? Explain.

13. Tables in the news. Find a frequency table of categorical data from a business publication (e.g., *Business Week, Fortune, The Wall Street Journal*, etc.).

a) Is it clearly labeled?
b) Does it display percentages or counts?
c) Does the accompanying article tell the W's of the variable?
d) Do you think the article correctly interprets the data? Explain.

14. Tables in the news, part 2. Find a contingency table of categorical data from a business publication (e.g., *Business Week, Fortune, The Wall Street Journal*, etc.).

a) Is it clearly labeled?
b) Does it display percentages or counts?
c) Does the accompanying article tell the W's of the variable?
d) Do you think the article correctly interprets the data? Explain.

15. U.S. market share. An article in the *The Wall Street Journal* (March 16, 2007) reported the 2006 U.S. market share of leading sellers of carbonated drinks, summarized in the following pie chart:

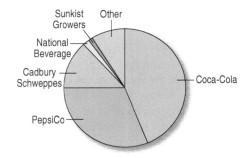

a) Is this an appropriate display for these data? Explain.
b) Which company had the largest share of the market?

16. World market share. *The Wall Street Journal* article described in Exercise 15 also indicated the 2005 world market share for leading distributors of total confectionery products. The following bar chart displays the values:

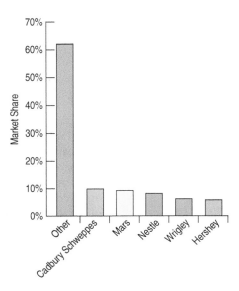

a) Is this an appropriate display for these data? Explain.
b) Which company had the largest share of the candy market?

17. Market share again. Here's a bar chart of the data in Exercise 15.

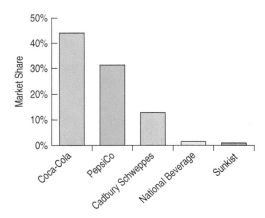

a) Compared to the pie chart in Exercise 15, which is better for displaying the relative portions of market share? Explain.
b) What is missing from this display that might make it misleading?

18. World market share again. Here's a pie chart of the data in Exercise 16.

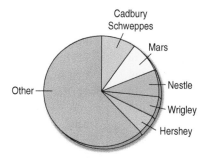

a) Which display of these data is best for comparing the market shares of these companies? Explain.
b) Does Cadbury Schweppes or Mars have a bigger market share?

19. Insurance company. An insurance company is updating its payouts and cost structure for their insurance policies. Of particular interest to them is the risk analysis for customers currently on heart or blood pressure medication. The Centers for Disease Control lists causes of death in the United States during one year as follows.

Cause of Death	Percent
Heart disease	30.3
Cancer	23.0
Circulatory diseases and stroke	8.4
Respiratory diseases	7.9
Accidents	4.1

a) Is it reasonable to conclude that heart or respiratory diseases were the cause of approximately 38% of U.S. deaths during this year?
b) What percent of deaths were from causes not listed here?
c) Create an appropriate display for these data.

20. Revenue growth. A 2005 study by Babson College and The Commonwealth Institute surveyed the top women-led businesses in the state of Massachusetts in 2003 and 2004. The study reported the following results for continuing participants with a 9% response rate. (Does not add up to 100% due to rounding.)

2003–2004 Revenue Growth	
Decline	7%
Modest Decline	9%
Steady State	10%
Modest Growth	18%
Growth	54%

a) Describe the distribution of companies with respect to revenue growth.
b) Is it reasonable to conclude that 72% of all women-led businesses in the U.S. reported some level of revenue growth? Explain.

21. Web conferencing. Cisco Systems Inc. announced plans in March 2007 to buy WebEx Communications, Inc. for $3.2 billion, demonstrating their faith in the future of Web conferencing. The leaders in market share for the vendors in the area of Web conferencing in 2006 are as follows: WebEx 58.4% and Microsoft 26.3%. Create an appropriate graphical display of this information and write a sentence or two that might appear in a newspaper article about the market share.

22. Mattel. In their 2006 annual report, Mattel Inc. reported that their domestic market sales were broken down as follows: 44.1% Mattel Girls and Boys brand, 43.0% Fisher-Price brand and the rest of the nearly $3.5 billion revenues were due to their American Girl brand. Create an appropriate graphical display of this information and write a sentence or two that might appear in a newspaper article about their revenue breakdown.

23. Small business productivity. The Wells Fargo/Gallup Small Business Index asked 592 small business owners in March 2004 what steps they had taken in the past year to increase productivity. They found that 60% of small business owners had updated their computers, 52% had made other (noncomputer) capital investments, 37% hired part-time instead of full-time workers, 24% had not replaced workers who left voluntarily, 15% had laid off workers, and 10% had lowered employee salaries.

a) What do you notice about the percentages listed? How could this be?
b) Make a bar chart to display the results and label it clearly.
c) Would a pie chart be an effective way of communicating this information? Why or why not?
d) Write a couple of sentences on the steps taken by small businesses to increase productivity.

24. Small business hiring. In 2004, the Wells Fargo/Gallup Small Business Index found that 86% of the 592 small business owners they surveyed said their productivity for the previous year had stayed the same or increased and most had substituted productivity gains for labor. (See Exercise 23.) As a follow-up question, the survey gave them a list of possible economic outcomes and asked if that would make them hire more employees. Here are the percentages of owners saying that they would "definitely or probably hire more employees" for each scenario: a substantial increase in sales—79%, a major backlog of sales orders—71%, a general improvement in the economy—57%, a gain in productivity—50%, a reduction in overhead costs—43%, and more qualified employees available—39%.

a) What do you notice about the percentages listed?

b) Make a bar chart to display the results and label it clearly.

c) Would a pie chart be an effective way of communicating this information? Why or why not?

d) Write a couple of sentences on the responses to small business owners about hiring given the scenarios listed.

25. Environmental hazard. Data from the International Tanker Owners Pollution Federation Limited (www.itopf .com) give the cause of spillage for 312 large oil tanker accidents from 1974–2006. Here are the displays. Write a brief report interpreting what the displays show. Is a pie chart an appropriate display for these data? Why or why not?

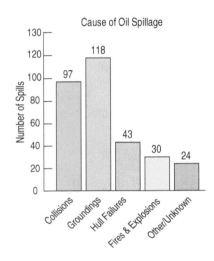

Cause of Oil Spillage

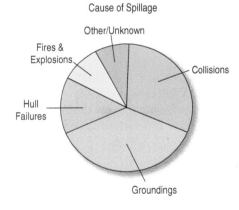

Cause of Spillage

26. Winter Olympics. Twenty-six countries won medals in the 2010 Winter Olympics. The following table lists them, along with the total number of medals each won.

a) Try to make a display of these data. What problems do you encounter?

b) Can you find a way to organize the data so that the graph is more successful?

Country	Medals	Country	Medals
United States	37	Poland	6
Germany	30	Italy	5
Canada	26	Japan	5
Norway	23	Finland	5
Austria	16	Australia	3
Russia	15	Belarus	3
South Korea	14	Slovakia	3
China	11	Croatia	3
Sweden	11	Slovenia	3
France	11	Latvia	2
Switzerland	9	Great Britain	1
Netherlands	8	Estonia	1
Czech Republic	6	Kazakhstan	1

27. Importance of wealth. GfK Roper Reports Worldwide surveyed people in 2004, asking them "How important is acquiring wealth to you?" The percent who responded that it was of more than average importance were: 71.9% China, 59.6% France, 76.1% India, 45.5% UK, and 45.3% USA. There were about 1500 respondents per country. A report showed the following bar chart of these percentages.

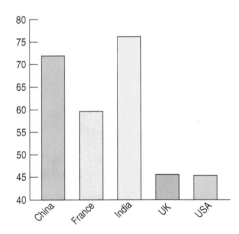

a) How much larger is the proportion of those who said acquiring wealth was important in India than in the United States?

b) Is that the impression given by the display? Explain.

c) How would you improve this display?

d) Make an appropriate display for the percentages.

e) Write a few sentences describing what you have learned about attitudes toward acquiring wealth.

28. Importance of power. In the same survey as that discussed in Exercise 27, GfK Roper Consulting also asked

"How important is having control over people and resources to you?" The percent who responded that it was of more than average importance are given in the following table:

China	49.1%
France	44.1%
India	74.2%
UK	27.8%
USA	36.0%

Here's a pie chart of the data:

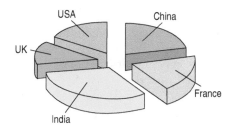

a) List the errors you see in this display.
b) Make an appropriate display for the percentages.
c) Write a few sentences describing what you have learned about attitudes toward acquiring power.

29. Google financials. Google Inc. derives revenue from three major sources: advertising revenue from their websites, advertising revenue from the thousands of third-party websites that comprise the Google Network, and licensing and miscellaneous revenue. The following table shows the percentage of all revenue derived from these sources for the period 2002 to 2006.

		Year				
		2002	2003	2004	2005	2006
Revenue Source	Google websites	70%	54%	50%	55%	60%
	Google network websites	24%	43%	49%	44%	39%
	Licensing & other revenue	6%	3%	1%	1%	1%

a) Are these row or column percentages?
b) Make an appropriate display of these data.
c) Write a brief summary of this information.

30. Real estate pricing. A study of a sample of 1057 houses in upstate New York reports the following percentages of houses falling into different Price and Size categories.

		Price			
		Low	Med Low	Med High	High
Size	Small	61.5%	35.2%	5.2%	2.4%
	Med Small	30.4%	45.3%	26.4%	4.7%
	Med Large	5.4%	17.6%	47.6%	21.7%
	Large	2.7%	1.9%	20.8%	71.2%

a) Are these column, row, or total percentages? How do you know?
b) What percent of the highest priced houses were small?
c) From this table, can you determine what percent of all houses were in the low price category?
d) Among the lowest prices houses, what percent were small or medium small?
e) Write a few sentences describing the association between *Price* and *Size*.

31. Stock performance. The following table displays information for 40 widely held U.S. stocks, on how their one-day change on March 15, 2007 compared with their previous 52-week change.

		Over prior 52 weeks	
		Positive Change	Negative Change
MARCH 15, 2007	Positive Change	14	9
	Negative Change	11	6

a) What percent of the companies reported a positive change in their stock price over the prior 52 weeks?
b) What percent of the companies reported a positive change in their stock price over both time periods?
c) What percent of the companies reported a negative change in their stock price over both time periods?
d) What percent of the companies reported a positive change in their stock price over one period and then a negative change in the other period?
e) Among those companies reporting a positive change in their stock price over the prior day what percentage also reported a positive change over the prior year?
f) Among those companies reporting a negative change in their stock price over the prior day what percentage also reported a positive change over the prior year?
g) What relationship, if any, do you see between the performance of a stock on a single day and its 52-week performance?

32. New product. A company started and managed by business students is selling campus calendars. The students have conducted a market survey with the various campus constituents to determine sales potential and identify which market segments should be targeted. (Should they advertise in the Alumni Magazine and/or the local newspaper?) The following table shows the results of the market survey.

		Buying Likelihood		
	Unlikely	**Moderately Likely**	**Very Likely**	**Total**
Students	197	388	320	**905**
Faculty/Staff	103	137	98	**338**
Alumni	20	18	18	**56**
Town Residents	13	58	45	**116**
Total	**333**	**601**	**481**	**1415**

Campus Group (row label)

a) What percent of all these respondents are alumni?
b) What percent of these respondents are very likely to buy the calendar?
c) What percent of the respondents who are very likely to buy the calendar are alumni?
d) Of the alumni, what percent are very likely to buy the calendar?
e) What is the marginal distribution of the campus constituents?
f) What is the conditional distribution of the campus constituents among those very likely to buy the calendar?
g) Does this study present any evidence that this company should focus on selling to certain campus constituents?

33. Real estate. *The Wall Street Journal* reported in March 2007 that the real estate market in Nashville, Tennessee, slowed slightly from 2006 to 2007. The supporting data are summarized in the following table.

		Type of Sale			
	Condos	**Farms/ Land**	**Residential**	**Multi-family**	**Total**
2006	266	177	2119	48	**2610**
2007	341	190	2006	38	**2575**
Total	**607**	**367**	**4125**	**86**	**5185**

Year (row label)

a) What percent of all sales in February 2006 were condominiums (condos)? In February 2007?
b) What percent of the sales in February 2006 were multifamily? In February 2007?
c) What was the change in the percent of residential real estate sales in Nashville, Tennessee, from February 2006 to February 2007?

34. Google financials, part 2. Google Inc. divides their total costs and expenses into five categories: cost of revenues, research and development, sales and marketing, general administrative, and miscellaneous. See the table at the bottom of the page.

a) What percent of all costs and expenses were cost of revenues in 2005? In 2006?
b) What percent of all costs and expenses were due to research and development in 2005? In 2006?
c) Have general administrative costs grown as a percentage of all costs and expenses over this time period?

35. Movie ratings. The movie ratings system is a voluntary system operated jointly by the Motion Picture Association of America (MPAA) and the National Association of Theatre Owners (NATO). The ratings themselves are given by a board of parents who are members of the Classification and Ratings Administration (CARA). The board was created in response to outcries from parents in the 1960s for some kind of regulation of film content, and the first ratings were introduced in 1968. Here is information on

Cost and Expenses	2002	2003	2004	2005	2006
Cost of revenues	$132,575	$634,411	$1,468,967	$2,577,088	$4,225,027
Research and development	$40,494	$229,605	$385,164	$599,510	$1,228,589
Sales and marketing	$48,783	$164,935	$295,749	$468,152	$849,518
General administrative	$31,190	$94,519	$188,151	$386,532	$751,787
Miscellaneous	$0	$0	$201,000	$90,000	$0
Total Costs and Expenses	**$253,042**	**$1,123,470**	**$2,539,031**	**$4,121,282**	**$7,054,921**

Table for Exercise 34

the ratings of 120 movies that came out in 2005, also classified by their genre.

		G	PG	PG-13	R	Total
				Rating		
Genre	Action/Adventure	4	5	17	9	35
	Comedy	2	12	20	4	38
	Drama	0	3	8	17	28
	Thriller/Horror	0	0	11	8	19
	Total	**6**	**20**	**56**	**38**	**120**

a) Find the conditional distribution (in percentages) of movie ratings for action/adventure films.
b) Find the conditional distribution (in percentages) of movie ratings for thriller/horror films.
c) Create a graph comparing the ratings for the four genres.
d) Are *Genre* and *Rating* independent? Write a brief summary of what these data show about movie ratings and the relationship to the genre of the film.

36. Wireless access. The Pew Internet and American Life Project has monitored access to the Internet since the 1990s. Here is an income breakdown of 798 Internet users surveyed in December 2006, asking whether they have logged on to the Internet using a wireless device or not.

		Wireless Users	Other Internet Users	Total
Income	Under $30K	34	128	162
	$30K–50K	31	133	164
	$50K–$75K	44	72	116
	Over $75K	83	111	194
	Don't know/ refused	51	111	162
	Total	**243**	**555**	**798**

a) Find the conditional distribution (in percentages) of income distribution for the wireless users.
b) Find the conditional distribution (in percentages) of income distribution for other Internet users.
c) Create a graph comparing the income distributions of the two groups.
d) Do you see any differences between the conditional distributions? Write a brief summary of what these data show about wireless use and its relationship to income.

37. MBAs. A survey of the entering MBA students at a university in the United States classified the country of origin of the students, as seen in the table.

		Two-Year MBA	Evening MBA	Total
			MBA Program	
Origin	Asia/Pacific Rim	31	33	64
	Europe	5	0	5
	Latin America	20	1	21
	Middle East/Africa	5	5	10
	North America	103	65	168
	Total	**164**	**104**	**268**

a) What percent of all MBA students were from North America?
b) What percent of the Two-Year MBAs were from North America?
c) What percent of the Evening MBAs were from North America?
d) What is the marginal distribution of origin?
e) Obtain the column percentages and show the conditional distributions of origin by MBA Program.
f) Do you think that origin of the MBA student is independent of the MBA program? Explain.

38. MBAs, part 2. The same university as in Exercise 37 reported the following data on the gender of their students in their two MBA programs.

		Two-Year	Evening	Total
			Type	
Sex	Men	116	66	182
	Women	48	38	86
	Total	**164**	**104**	**268**

a) What percent of all MBA students are women?
b) What percent of Two-Year MBAs are women?
c) What percent of Evening MBAs are women?
d) Do you see evidence of an association between the *Type* of MBA program and the percentage of women students? If so, why do you believe this might be true?

39. Top producing movies. The following table shows the Motion Picture Association of America (MPA) (www.mpaa .org) ratings for the top 20 grossing films in the United States for each of the 10 years from 1999 to 2008. (Data are number of films.)

a) What percent of all these top 20 films are G rated?
b) What percent of all top 20 films in 2005 were G rated?
c) What percent of all top 20 films were PG-13 and came out in 1999?
d) What percent of all top 20 films produced in 2006 or later were PG-13?

		Rating				
		G	PG	PG-13	R	Total
Year	2008	2	4	10	4	**20**
	2007	1	5	11	3	**20**
	2006	1	4	13	2	**20**
	2005	1	4	13	2	**20**
	2004	1	6	10	3	**20**
	2003	1	3	11	5	**20**
	2002	1	6	13	0	**20**
	2001	2	4	10	4	**20**
	2000	0	3	12	5	**20**
	1999	2	3	7	8	**20**
	Total	**12**	**42**	**110**	**36**	**200**

e) What percent of all top 20 films produced from 1999 to 2002 were rated PG-13 or R?

f) Compare the conditional distributions of the ratings for films produced in 2004 or later to those produced from 1999 to 2003. Write a couple of sentences summarizing what you see.

T **40.** Movie admissions. The following table shows attendance data collected by the Motion Picture Association of America during the period 2002 to 2006. Figures are in millions of movie admissions.

		Patron Age						
		12 to 24	25 to 29	30 to 39	40 to 49	50 to 59	60 and over	Total
Year	2006	485	136	246	219	124	124	**1334**
	2005	489	135	194	216	125	122	**1281**
	2004	567	132	265	236	145	132	**1477**
	2003	567	124	269	193	152	118	**1423**
	2002	551	158	237	211	119	130	**1406**
	Total	**2659**	**685**	**1211**	**1075**	**665**	**626**	**6921**

a) What percent of all admissions during this period were bought by people between the ages of 12 and 24?

b) What percent of admissions in 2003 were bought by people between the ages of 12 and 24?

c) What percent of the admission were bought by people between the ages of 12 and 24 in 2006?

d) What percent of admissions in 2006 were bought by people 60 years old and older?

e) What percent of the admissions bought by people 60 and over were in 2002?

f) Compare the conditional distributions of the age groups across years. Write a couple of sentences summarizing what you see.

41. Tattoos. A study by the University of Texas Southwestern Medical Center examined 626 people to see if there was an increased risk of contracting hepatitis C associated with having a tattoo. If the subject had a tattoo, researchers asked whether it had been done in a commercial tattoo parlor or elsewhere. Write a brief description of the association between tattooing and hepatitis C, including an appropriate graphical display.

	Tatto done in commercial parlor	Tattoo done elsewhere	No tattoo
Has hepatitis C	17	8	18
No hepatitis C	35	53	495

42. Working parents. In July 1991 and again in April 2001, the Gallup Poll asked random samples of 1015 adults about their opinions on working parents. The following table summarizes responses to this question: "*Considering the needs of both parents and children, which of the following do you see as the ideal family in today's society?*" Based upon these results, do you think there was a change in people's attitudes during the 10 years between these polls? Explain.

		Year	
		1991	2001
Response	Both work full-time	142	131
	One works full-time, other part-time	274	244
	One works, other works at home	152	173
	One works, other stays home for kids	396	416
	No opinion	51	51

43. Revenue growth, last one. The study completed in 2005 and described in Exercise 20 also reported on education levels of the women chief executives. The column percentages for CEO education for each level of revenue are summarized in the following table. (Revenue is in $ million.)

	Graduate Education and Firm Revenue Size		
	< $10 M revenue	$10–$49.999 M revenue	≥ $50 M revenue
% with High School Education only	8%	4%	8%
% with College Education, but no Graduate Education	48%	42%	33%
% with Graduate Education	44%	54%	59%
Total	**100%**	**100%**	**100%**

a) What percent of these CEOs in the highest revenue category had only a high school education?

b) From this table, can you determine what percent of all these CEOs had graduate education? Explain.

c) Among the CEOs in the lowest revenue category, what percent had more than a high school education?

d) Write a few sentences describing the association between *Revenue* and *Education*.

44. Minimum wage workers. The U.S. Department of Labor (www.bls.gov) collects data on the number of U.S. workers who are employed at or below the minimum wage. Here is a table showing the number of hourly workers by *Age* and *Sex* and the number who were paid at or below the prevailing minimum wage:

Age	Hourly Workers (in thousands)		At or Below Minimum Wage (in thousands)	
	Men	Women	Men	Women
16–24	7978	7701	384	738
25–34	9029	7864	150	332
35–44	7696	7783	71	170
45–54	7365	8260	68	134
55–64	4092	4895	35	72
65+	1174	1469	22	50

a) What percent of the women were ages 16 to 24?

b) Using side-by-side bar graphs, compare the proportions of the men and women who worked at or below minimum wage at each *Age* group. Write a couple of sentences summarizing what you see.

45. Moviegoers and ethnicity. The Motion Picture Association of America studies the ethnicity of moviegoers to understand changes in the demographics of moviegoers over time. Here are the numbers of moviegoers (in millions) classified as to whether they were Hispanic, African-American, or Caucasian for the years 2002 to 2006.

		Year					Total
		2002	2003	2004	2005	2006	
Ethnicity	Hispanic	21	23	25	25	26	120
	African-American	21	20	22	21	20	104
	Caucasian	118	127	127	113	120	605
	Total	160	170	174	159	166	829

a) Find the marginal distribution *Ethnicity* of moviegoers.

b) Find the conditional distribution of *Ethnicity* for the year 2006.

c) Compare the conditional distribution of *Ethnicity* for all 5 years with a segmented bar graph.

d) Write a brief description of the association between *Year* and *Ethnicity* among these respondents.

46. Department store. A department store is planning its next advertising campaign. Since different publications are read by different market segments, they would like to know if they should be targeting specific age segments. The results of a marketing survey are summarized in the following table by *Age* and *Shopping Frequency* at their store.

		Age			
	Shopping	Under 30	30–49	50 and Over	Total
Frequency	Low	27	37	31	95
	Moderate	48	91	93	232
	High	23	51	73	147
	Total	98	179	197	474

a) Find the marginal distribution of *Shopping Frequency*.

b) Find the conditional distribution of *Shopping Frequency* within each age group.

c) Compare these distributions with a segmented bar graph.

d) Write a brief description of the association between *Age* and *Shopping Frequency* among these respondents.

e) Does this prove that customers ages 50 and over are more likely to shop at this department store? Explain.

47. Women's business centers. A study conducted in 2002 by Babson College and the Association of Women's Centers surveyed women's business centers in the United States. The data showing the location of established centers (at least 5 years old) and less established centers are summarized in the following table.

	Location	
	Urban	Nonurban
Less Established	74%	26%
Established	80%	20%

a) Are these percentages column percentages, row percentages, or table percentages?

b) Use graphical displays to compare these percentages of women's business centers by location.

48. Advertising. A company that distributes a variety of pet foods is planning their next advertising campaign. Since different publications are read by different market segments, they would like to know how pet ownership is distributed across different income segments. The U.S. Census Bureau reports the number of households owning various types of pets. Specifically, they keep track of dogs, cats, birds, and horses.

INCOME DISTRIBUTION OF HOUSEHOLDS OWING PETS (PERCENT)

		Pet			
		Dog	Cat	Bird	Horse
Income	Under $12,500	14	15	16	9
	$12,500 to $24,999	20	20	21	21
	$25,000 to $39,999	24	23	24	25
	$40,000 to $59,999	22	22	21	22
	$60,000 and over	20	20	18	23
	Total	100	100	100	100

a) Do you think the income distributions of the households who own these different animals would be roughly the same? Why or why not?
b) The table shows the percentages of income levels for each type of animal owned. Are these row percentages, column percentages, or table percentages?
c) Do the data support that the pet food company should not target specific market segments based on household income? Explain.

49. Worldwide toy sales. Around the world, toys are sold through different channels. For example, in some parts of the world toys are sold primarily through large toy store chains, while in other countries department stores sell more toys. The following table shows the percentages by region of the distribution of toys sold through various channels in Europe and America in 2003, accumulated by the International Council of Toy Industries (www.toy-icti.org).

a) Are these row percentages, column percentages, or table percentages?
b) Can you tell what percent of toys sold by mail order in both Europe and America are sold in Europe? Why or why not?
c) Use a graphical display to compare the distribution of channels between Europe and America.
d) Summarize the distribution of toy sales by channel in a few sentences. What are the biggest differences between these two continents?

50. Internet piracy. Illegal downloading of copyrighted movies is an international problem estimated to have cost the international movie industry more than $18 billion in 2005. The typical pirate worldwide is a 16 to 24-year old male living in an urban area, according to a study by the international strategy consulting firm LEK (www.mpaa.org/researchStatistics.asp). The following table compares the age distribution of the U.S. pirate to the rest of the world.

		Age			
		16–24	25–29	30–39	Over 40
Region	United States	71	11	7	11
	Rest of World	58	15	18	9

a) Are these row percentages, column percentages, or table percentages?
b) Can you tell what percent of pirates worldwide are in the 16 to 24 age group?
c) Use a graphical display to compare the age distribution of pirates in the United States to the distribution in the rest of the world.
d) Summarize the distribution of *Age* by *Region* in a few sentences. What are the biggest differences between these two regions?

51. Insurance company, part 2. An insurance company that provides medical insurance is concerned with recent data. They suspect that patients who undergo surgery at large hospitals have their discharges delayed for various reasons—which results in increased medical costs to the insurance company. The recent data for area hospitals and two types of surgery (major and minor) are shown in the following table.

		Discharge Delayed	
		Large Hospital	Small Hospital
Procedure	Major surgery	120 of 800	10 of 50
	Minor surgery	10 of 200	20 of 250

		Channel					
		General Merchandise	Toy Specialists	Department Stores	Mass Merchant Discounters & Food Hypermarkets	Mail Order	Other
Location	America	9%	25%	3%	51%	4%	8%
	Europe	13%	36%	7%	24%	5%	15%

Table for Exercise 49

a) Overall, for what percent of patients was discharge delayed?

b) Were the percentages different for major and minor surgery?

c) Overall, what were the discharge delay rates at each hospital?

d) What were the delay rates at each hospital for each kind of surgery?

e) The insurance company is considering advising their clients to use large hospitals for surgery to avoid postsurgical complications. Do you think they should do this?

f) Explain, in your own words, why this confusion occurs.

52. Delivery service. A company must decide which of two delivery services they will contract with. During a recent trial period, they shipped numerous packages with each service and have kept track of how often deliveries did not arrive on time. Here are the data.

Delivery Service	Type of Service	Number of Deliveries	Number of Late Packages
Pack Rats	Regular	400	12
	Overnight	100	16
Boxes R Us	Regular	100	2
	Overnight	400	28

a) Compare the two services' overall percentage of late deliveries.

b) Based on the results in part a, the company has decided to hire Pack Rats. Do you agree they deliver on time more often? Why or why not? Be specific.

c) The results here are an instance of what phenomenon?

53. Graduate admissions. A 1975 article in the magazine *Science* examined the graduate admissions process at Berkeley for evidence of gender bias. The following table shows the number of applicants accepted to each of four graduate programs.

Program	Males Accepted (of Applicants)	Females Accepted (of Applicants)
1	511 of 825	89 of 108
2	352 of 560	17 of 25
3	137 of 407	132 of 375
4	22 of 373	24 of 341
Total	**1022 of 2165**	**262 of 849**

a) What percent of total applicants were admitted?

b) Overall, were a higher percentage of males or females admitted?

c) Compare the percentage of males and females admitted in each program.

d) Which of the comparisons you made do you consider to be the most valid? Why?

54. Simpson's Paradox. Develop your own table of data that is a business example of Simpson's Paradox. Explain the conflict between the conclusions made from the conditional and marginal distributions.

Just Checking Answers

1 50.0%

2 40.0%

3 25.0%

4 15.6% Nearsighted, 56.3% Farsighted, 28.1% Need Bifocals

5 18.8% Nearsighted, 62.5% Farsighted, 18.8% Need Bifocals

6 40% of the nearsighted customers are female, while 50% of customers are female.

7 Since nearsighted customers appear less likely to be female, it seems that they may not be independent. (But the numbers are small.)

Answers

SECTION EXERCISE ANSWERS

1. a)   Frequency table:

None	AA	BA	MA	PhD
164	42	225	52	29

b)   Relative frequency table (divide each number by 512 and multiply by 100):

None	AA	BA	MA	PhD
32.03%	8.20%	43.95%	10.16%	5.66%

3. a)

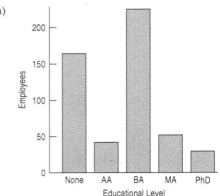

b)

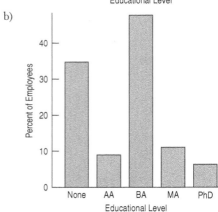

c)

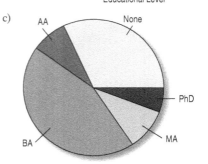

5. a)   The vast majority of employees have either no college degree or a bachelor's degree (44% and 32%, respectively). About 10% have master's degrees, 8% have associate's degrees, and nearly 6% have PhDs.

b)   I would not be comfortable generalizing this to any other division or company. These data were collected only from my division. Other companies might have vastly different educational distributions.

7. a)

	Totals
<1 year	95
1–5 years	205
more than 5 years	212

b)   Yes

None	AA	BA	MA	PhD
164	42	225	52	29

9. a)

(%)	None	AA	BA	MA	PhD
<1 year	6.1	7.1	22.2	38.5	41.4
1–5 years	25.6	21.4	49.8	51.9	51.7
more than 5 years	68.3	71.4	28	9.6	6.9

b)   No. The distributions look quite different. More than 2/3 of those with no college degree have been with the company longer than 5 years, but almost none of the PhDs (less than 7%) have been there that long.

c)

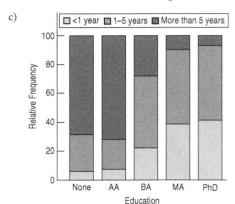

d)   It's possible to see it in the table, but the stacked bar chart makes the differences much clearer.

CHAPTER EXERCISE ANSWERS

11. Answers will vary.

13. Answers will vary.

15. a)   Yes, the categories divide a whole.
b)   Coca-Cola.

17. a)   The pie chart does a better job of showing portions of a whole.
b)   There is no bar for "Other."

19. a)   Yes, it is reasonable to assume that heart and respiratory disease caused approximately 38% of U.S. deaths in this year, since there is no possibility for overlap. Each person could only have one cause of death.
b)   Since the percentages listed add up to 73.7%, other causes must account for 26.3% of U.S. deaths.
c)   A bar graph or pie chart would be appropriate if a category for Other with 26.3% were added.

21. WebEx Communications, Inc. has the majority of the market share for web conferencing (58.4%), and Microsoft has approximately a quarter of the market share. There appears to be room for both to grow, because other companies comprise about 15% of market share. A pie chart or bar chart would be appropriate.

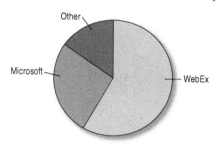

23. a) They total more than 100%; overlapping categories.

b)

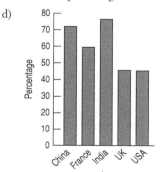

c) No because the percentages do not total 100%.

d) (Answers will vary). More than 50% of business owners say that they have either updated their computers or made other noncomputer capital investments (or both). Smaller percentages of business owners (from 10 to 37%) made changes in either their hiring or salary structure.

25. The bar chart shows that grounding is the most frequent cause of oil spillage for these 312 spills, and allows the reader to rank the other types as well. If being able to differentiate between these close counts is required, use the bar chart. The pie chart is also acceptable as a display, but it's difficult to tell whether, for example, there is a greater percentage of spills caused by grounding or collisions. To showcase the causes of oil spills as a fraction of all 312 spills, use the pie chart.

27. a) 31%

b) It looks like India's percentage is about 6 times as big, but it's not even twice as big.

c) Start the percentages at 0% on the vertical axis, not 40%.

d)

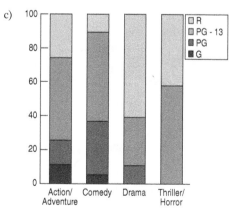

e) The percentage of people who say that wealth is important to them is highest in China and India (around 70%), followed by France (around 60%) and then the U.S. and U.K. where the percentage was only about 45%.

29. a) They must be column percentages because the sums are greater than 100% across the rows and all the columns add to 100%.

b)

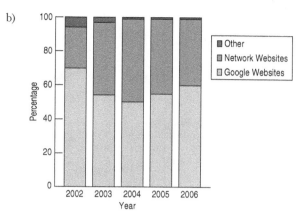

c) The main source of revenue for Google is from their own websites, which in 2002 was 70%, dropped down to 50% in 2004, and by 2006 was back up to 60%. The second largest source is from other network websites. Licensing and other revenue was 6% in 2002, but since 2004 has been only 1%.

31. a) 62.5%
b) 35%
c) 15%
d) 50%
e) 61%
f) 65%
g) There does not appear to be any relationship between the performance of a stock on a single day and its performance over the prior year.

33. a) 10.2%; 13.2%
b) 1.8%; 1.5%
c) Residential sales decreased by 3.3%.

35. a) 11.4% G; 14.3% PG; 48.6% PG-13; 25.7% R
b) 0% G; 0% PG%; 57.9% PG-13; 42.1% R

c)

d) *Genre* and *Rating* are not independent. Thriller/Horror movie are all PG-13 or R and Drama are nearly so. Comedy moves are nearly 40% G and PG and only 10% R. Action/Adventure movies are nearly 15% G and 15% PG.

37. a) 62.7%
b) 62.8%
c) 62.5%
d) 23.9% from Asia, 1.9% Europe, 7.8% Latin America, 3.7% Middle East, and 62.7% North America.
e) The column percentages are given in the table.

89

		MBA Program		
		Two-Yr	Evening	Total
Origin	Asia	18.90	31.73	23.88
	urope	3.05	0.00	1.87
	Latin America	12.20	0.96	7.84
	Middle East	3.05	4.81	3.73
	North America	62.80	62.50	62.69
	Total	**100.00**	**100.00**	**100.00**

f) No. The distributions appear to be different. For example, the percentage from Latin America among those in Two-Yr. programs is nearly 20% while for those in Evening programs it is less than 1%.

39. a) 6%
b) 5%
c) 3.5%
d) 56.7%
e) 73.8%
f) Here are row percentages:

					Total
2004–2008	6%	23%	57%	14%	100.0%
1999–2003	6%	19%	53%	22%	100.0%

The distributions are quite similar, although there were fewer R rated films in the second half of the period (14% of 20 top films, compared to 22%). The increase was in both PG and PG-13 films.

41. The study by the University of Texas Southwestern Medical Center provides evidence of an association between having a tattoo and contracting hepatitis C. Around 33% of the subjects who were tattooed in a commercial parlor had hepatitis C, compared with 13% of those tattooed elsewhere, and only 3.5% of those with no tattoo. If having a tattoo and having hepatitis C were independent, we would have expected these percentages to be roughly the same.

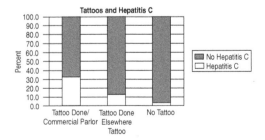

43. a) 8%
b) No, because we're not given counts or totals.
c) 92%
d) There appears to be little, if any, relationship between revenue category and education level of the women CEOs.

45. a) 14.5% Hispanic, 12.5% African-American, and 73.0% Caucasian.
b) For 2006, 15.7% Hispanic, 12.0% African-American, 72.3% Caucasian.

c)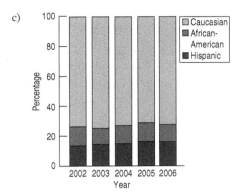

d) The (conditional) distribution of *Ethnicity* is almost the same across the five *Years*, however there seems to be a slight increase in the percentage of Hispanics who go to the movies from 13.1% in 2002 to 15.7% in 2006.

47. a) Row percentages.
b) A slightly higher percentage of urban women's business centers are established (at least 5 years old).

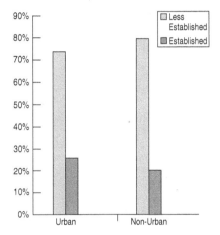

49. a) Row percentages.
b) No. We are given only the conditional distributions. We have no idea how much are sold in either Europe or America.
c)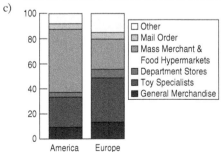

d) In America more than 50% of all toys are sold by large mass merchant discounters and food hypermarkets and only 25% are sold in toy specialty stores. In Europe 36% of all toys are sold in toy specialty stores while a relatively small 24% are sold in the large discount and hypermarket chains.

51. a) The marginal totals have been added to the table:

		Hospital Size		
		Large	**Small**	**Total**
Procedure	**Major surgery**	120 of 800	10 of 50	**130 of 850**
	Minor surgery	0 of 200	20 of 250	**30 of 450**
	Total	**130 of 1000**	**30 of 300**	**160 of 1300**

160 of 1300, or about 12.3% of the patients had a delayed discharge.

b) Major surgery patients were delayed 15.3% of the time. Minor Surgery patients were delayed 6.7% of the time.

c) Large Hospital had a delay rate of 13%.
Small Hospital had a delay rate of 10%.
The small hospital has the lower overall rate of delayed discharge.

d) Large Hospital: Major Surgery 15% and Minor Surgery 5%.
Small Hospital: Major Surgery 20% and Minor Surgery 8%.
Even though the small hospital had the lower overall rate of delayed discharge, the large hospital had a lower rate of delayed discharge for each type of surgery.

e) Yes. While the overall rate of delayed discharge is lower for the small hospital, the large hospital did better with *both* major surgery and minor surgery.

f) The small hospital performs a higher percentage of minor surgeries than major surgeries. 250 of 300 surgeries at the small hospital were minor (83%). Only 200 of the large hospital's 1000 surgeries were minor (20%). Minor surgery had a lower delay rate than major surgery (6.7% to 15.3%), so the small hospital's overall rate was artificially inflated. The larger hospital is the better hospital when comparing discharge delay rates.

53. a) 1284 applicants were admitted out of a total of 3014 applicants. 1284/3014 = 42.6%

		Males Accepted (of applicants)	Females Accepted (of applicants)	Total
Program	1	511 of 825	89 of 108	**600 of 933**
	2	352 of 560	17 of 25	**369 of 585**
	3	137 of 407	132 of 375	**269 of 782**
	4	22 of 373	24 of 341	**46 of 714**
	Total	**1022 of 2165**	**262 of 849**	**1284 of 3014**

b) 1022 of 2165 (47.2%) of males were admitted. 262 of 849 (30.9%) of females were admitted.

c) Since there are four comparisons to make, the table below organizes the percentages of males and females accepted in each program. Females are accepted at a higher rate in every program.

Program	Males	Females
1	61.9%	82.4%
2	62.9%	68.0%
3	33.7%	35.2%
4	5.9%	7.0%

d) The comparison of acceptance rate within each program is most valid. The overall percentage is an unfair average. It fails to take the different numbers of applicants and different acceptance rates of each program. Women tended to apply to the programs in which gaining acceptance was difficult for everyone. This is an example of Simpson's Paradox.

Displaying
and Describing
Quantitative Data

DigitalVision

Andrew Scheck/Shutterstock

Ivan Mateev/iStockphoto

Pali Rao/iStockphoto

AIG

The American International Group (AIG) was once the 18th largest corporation in the world. AIG was founded nearly 100 years ago by Cornelius Vander Starr who opened an insurance agency in Shanghai, China. As the first Westerner to sell insurance to the Chinese, Starr grew his business rapidly until 1949 when Mao Zedong and the People's Liberation Army took over Shanghai. Starr moved the company to New York City, where it continued to grow, expanding its markets worldwide. In 2004, AIG stock hit an all-time high of $76.77, putting its market value at nearly $300 billion.

According to its own website, "By early 2007 AIG had assets of $1 trillion, $110 billion in revenues, 74 million customers and 116,000 employees in 130 countries and jurisdictions. Yet just 18 months later, AIG found itself on the brink of failure and in need of emergency government assistance." AIG was one of the largest beneficiaries of the U.S. government's Troubled Asset Relief Program (TARP), established in 2008 during the financial crisis to purchase assets and equity from financial institutions. TARP was an attempt to strengthen the financial sector and avoid a repeat of a depression as severe as the 1930s. Many banks quickly repaid the government part or all of the money given to them under the TARP program, but AIG, which received $170 billion, did not.

From Chapter 5 of *Business Statistics*, Second Edition, Norean R. Sharpe, Richard D. De Veaux, Paul F. Velleman.

By 2009, AIG stock had lost more than 99% of its value, hitting $0.35 in early March. That same month AIG became embroiled in controversy when it disclosed that it had paid $218 million in bonuses to employees of its financial services division. AIG's drop in stock price represented a loss of nearly $300 billion for investors. Portfolio managers typically examine stock prices and volumes to determine stock volatility and to help them decide which stocks to buy and sell. Were there early warning signs in AIG's data?

To learn more about the behavior and volatility of AIG's stock, let's start by looking at Table 1, which gives the monthly average stock price (in dollars) for the six years leading up to the company's crisis.

	Jan.	Feb.	Mar.	Apr.	May	June	July	Aug.	Sept.	Oct.	Nov.	Dec.
2002	77.26	72.95	73.72	71.57	68.42	65.99	61.22	64.10	58.04	60.26	65.03	59.96
2003	59.74	49.57	49.41	54.38	56.52	57.88	59.80	61.51	59.39	60.93	58.73	62.37
2004	69.02	73.25	72.06	74.21	70.93	72.61	69.85	69.58	70.67	62.31	62.17	65.33
2005	66.74	68.96	61.55	51.77	53.81	55.66	60.27	60.86	60.54	62.64	67.06	66.72
2006	68.33	67.02	67.15	64.29	63.14	59.74	59.40	62.00	65.25	67.02	69.86	71.35
2007	70.45	68.99	68.14	68.25	71.78	71.75	68.64	65.21	66.02	66.12	56.86	58.13

| Table 1   Monthly stock price in dollars of AIG stock for the period 2002 through 2007.

It's hard to tell very much from tables of values like this. You might get a rough idea of how much the stock cost—usually somewhere around $60 or so, but that's about it.

1   Displaying Quantitative Variables

Instead, let's follow the first rule of data analysis and make a picture. What kind of picture should we make? It can't be a bar chart or a pie chart. Those are only for categorical variables, and AIG's stock price is a *quantitative* variable, whose units are dollars.

WHO	Months
WHAT	Monthly average price for AIG's stock (in dollars)
WHEN	2002 through 2007
WHERE	New York Stock Exchange
WHY	To examine AIG stock volatility

Histograms

Here are the monthly prices of AIG stock displayed in a histogram.

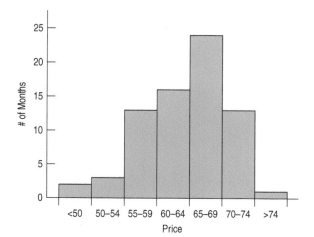

Figure 1   Monthly average prices of AIG stock. The histogram displays the distribution of prices by showing for each "bin" of prices, the number of months having prices in that bin.

Like a bar chart, a **histogram** plots the bin counts as the heights of bars. It counts the number of cases that fall into each bin, and displays that count as the height of the corresponding bar. In this histogram of monthly average prices, each bin has a width of $5, so, for example, the height of the tallest bar says that there were 24 months whose average price of AIG stock was between $65 and $70. In this way, the histogram displays the entire distribution of prices at a glance. Unlike a bar chart, which puts gaps between bars to separate the categories, there are no gaps between the bars of a histogram unless there are actual gaps in the data. **Gaps** indicate a region where there are no values. Gaps can be important features of the distribution so watch out for them and point them out.

For categorical variables, each category got its own bar. The only choice was whether to combine categories for ease of display. For quantitative variables, we have to choose the width of the bins.

- **Making a Histogram by Hand** Although you'll rarely make a histogram by hand, it can be instructive to see how it might be done. Some of the same choices that you have to make by hand will either be made by software automatically, or with input from you.

Step 1. Organize your data into a table. Divide the data into equal intervals or bins so that all values are covered. The number of bins depends on how many data values you have. For small (fewer than 25 or so values) data sets, 5 bins is fine. For large data sets you may need 20 or more.

You will probably want the width of intervals to be aesthetically pleasing (bins that have widths that end with 5's or 0's are popular—for example, 35–40,40–45, 45–50, etc). Now create two columns—one for the bins and the other for the frequencies. This creates a frequency distribution much like that for a categorical variable, but here instead of categories, we have bins of equal width. You'll have to decide whether to put values that lie at the end points of the bin into the left or right bin. Most software histogram programs put values into the bin on the right with the larger values, so 40 would go into the bin 40–45, not in the bin 35–40, but

Price Bin	# of Months
45–50	2
50–55	3
55–60	13
60–65	16
65–70	24
70–75	13
75–80	1

either choice is possible. In fact, Excel chooses to put the values to the left, so that 5 goes into the bin 0–5 not the bin 5–10.

Step 2. On a sheet of paper, mark the bins on the *x*-axis (horizontal axis) with no spaces between the bins. Mark the frequencies on the *y*-axis (vertical axis) over the center of each bin.

Step 3. Plot your data. For each bin, draw a horizontal line at the appropriate frequency over the bin. Then, draw vertical bars on the sides of each bin, reaching up to the corresponding frequency.

From the histogram, we can see that in these months a typical AIG stock price was near $60 or so. We can see that although they vary, most of the monthly prices were between $55 and $75. Only in a very few months was the average price below $55. It's important to note that the histogram is a static picture. We have treated these prices simply as a collection of months, with no sense of time, and shown their distribution. Later in the chapter we will add time to the story.

Does the distribution look as you expected? It's often a good idea to imagine what the distribution might look like before making the display. That way you're less likely to be fooled by errors either in your display or in the data themselves.

If our focus is on the overall pattern of how the values are distributed rather than on the counts themselves, it can be useful to make a relative frequency histogram, replacing the counts on the vertical axis with the percentage of the total number of cases falling in each bin (simply divide the counts in each bin by the total number of data values). The shape of the histogram is exactly the same; only the labels are different. A **relative frequency histogram** is faithful to the area principle by displaying the *percentage* of cases in each bin instead of the count.

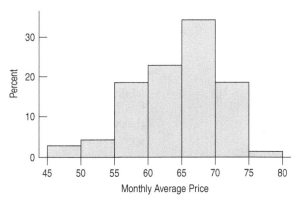

Figure 2　A relative frequency histogram looks just like a frequency histogram except that the *y*-axis now shows the percentage of months in each bin.

For Example   Creating a histogram

1. As the chief financial officer of a music download site, you've just secured the rights to offer downloads of a new album. You'd like to see how well it's selling, so you collect the number of downloads per hour for the past 24 hours:

Hour	Downloads	Hour	Downloads
12:00 a.m.	36	12:00 p.m.	25
1:00 a.m.	28	1:00 p.m.	22
2:00 a.m.	19	2:00 p.m.	17
3:00 a.m.	10	3:00 p.m.	18
4:00 a.m.	5	4:00 p.m.	20
5:00 a.m.	3	5:00 p.m.	23
6:00 a.m.	2	6:00 p.m.	21
7:00 a.m.	6	7:00 p.m.	18
8:00 a.m.	12	8:00 p.m.	24
9:00 a.m.	14	9:00 p.m.	30
10:00 a.m.	20	10:00 p.m.	27
11:00 a.m.	18	11:00 p.m.	30

Question: Make a histogram for this variable.

Answer: Create a frequency table of bins of width five from 0 to 40 and put values at the ends of bins into the right bin:

Downloads	Number OF Hours
0–5	2
5–10	2
10–15	3
15–20	5
20–25	6
25–30	3
30–35	2
35–40	1
Total	**24**

The histogram looks like this:

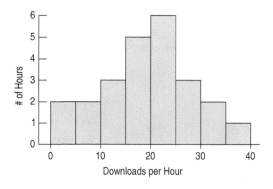

*Stem-and-Leaf Displays

Histograms provide an easy-to-understand summary of the distribution of a quantitative variable, but they don't show the data values themselves. **Stem-and-leaf displays** are like histograms, but they also give the individual values. They are easy to make by hand for data sets that aren't too large, so they're a great way to look at a small batch of values quickly.[1] Here's a stem-and-leaf display for the AIG stock data, alongside a histogram of the same data.

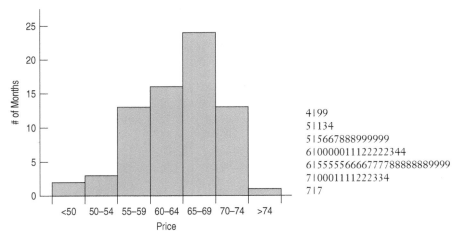

4|99
5|134
5|5667888999999
6|0000011122222344
6|55555666677778888889999
7|0001111222334
7|7

Figure 3 The AIG monthly average stock prices displayed both by a histogram (left) and stem-and-leaf display (right). Stem-and-leaf displays are typically made by hand, so we are most likely to use them for small data sets. For much larger data sets, we use a histogram.

- **How do stem-and-leaf displays work?** A stem-and-leaf display breaks each number into two parts: the stem shown to the left of the solid line and the leaf, to the right. For the AIG data, each price change, for example $67.02 is first truncated to two digits, $67. Then it is split into its two components: 6|7. The line 5|134 therefore, shows the values $51, $53, and $54 and corresponds to the histogram bin from $50 to $55. The stem-and-leaf in Figure 3 uses a bin width of 5. Another choice would be to increase the bin size and put all the prices from $50 to $60 on one line:

  5|1345667888999999

  That would decrease the number of bins to 4, but makes the bin from $60 to $70 too crowded:

  4|99
  5|1345667888999999
  6|0000011122222344555556666777788888889999
  7|00011112223347

  Sometimes the stem-and-leaf display puts the higher numbers on top:

  7|7
  7|00001111222334
  6|55555666677778888889999
  6|0000011122222344
  5|5667888999999
  5|134
  4|99

  Either choice is possible, although putting the lower numbers on top makes the correspondence between histogram and stem-and-leaf easier to see.

---

[1]The authors like to make stem-and-leaf displays whenever data are presented (without a suitable display) at committee meetings or working groups. The insights from just that quick look at the distribution are often quite valuable.

You should already have learned to check the Categorical Data Condition Zbefore making a pie chart or a bar chart. Now, by contrast, before making a stem-and-leaf display, or a histogram, you need to check the **Quantitative Data Condition**: The data are values of a quantitative variable whose units are known.

Although a bar chart and a histogram may look similar, they're not the same display. You can't display categorical data in a histogram or quantitative data in a bar chart. Always check the condition that confirms what type of data you have before making your display.

2 Shape

Once you've displayed the distribution in a histogram or stem-and-leaf display, what can you say about it? When you describe a distribution, you should pay attention to three things: its **shape**, its **center**, and its **spread**.

We describe the shape of a distribution in terms of its modes, its symmetry, and whether it has any gaps or outlying values.

Mode

Does the histogram have a single, central hump (or peak) or several, separated humps? These humps are called **modes**.[2] Formally, the mode is the single, most frequent value, but we rarely use the term that way. Sometimes we talk about the mode as being the value of the variable at the center of this hump. The AIG stock prices have a single mode around $65 (Figure 1). We often use modes to describe the shape of the distribution. A distribution whose histogram has one main hump, such as the one for the AIG stock prices, is called **unimodal**; distributions whose histograms have two humps are **bimodal**, and those with three or more are called **multimodal**. For example, here's a bimodal distribution.

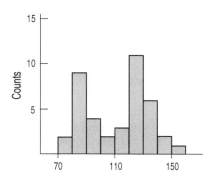

Figure 4 A bimodal distribution has two apparent modes.

A bimodal histogram is often an indication that there are two groups in the data. It's a good idea to investigate when you see bimodality.

A distribution whose histogram doesn't appear to have any mode and in which all the bars are approximately the same height is called **uniform**.

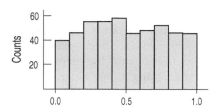

Figure 5 In a uniform distribution, bars are all about the same height. The histogram doesn't appear to have a mode.

---

[2]Technically, the mode is the value on the *x*-axis of the histogram below the highest peak, but informally we often refer to the peak or hump itself as a mode.

Symmetry

Could you fold the histogram along a vertical line through the middle and have the edges match pretty closely, as in Figure 6, or are more of the values on one side, as in the histograms in Figure 7? A distribution is **symmetric** if the halves on either side of the center look, at least approximately, like mirror images.

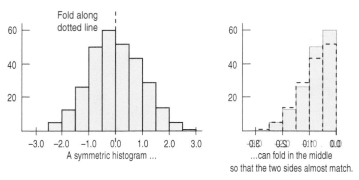

Figure 6   A symmetric histogram can fold in the middle so that the two sides almost match.

The (usually) thinner ends of a distribution are called the **tails**. If one tail stretches out farther than the other, the distribution is said to be **skewed** to the side of the longer tail.

> Amounts of things (dollars, employees, waiting times) can't be negative and have no natural upper limit. So, they often have distributions that are skewed to the right.

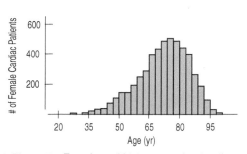 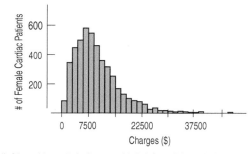

Figure 7   Two skewed histograms showing the age (left) and hospital charges (right) for all female heart attack patients in New York State in one year. The histogram of Age (in blue) is skewed to the left, while the histogram of Charges (in purple) is skewed to the right.

Outliers

Do any features appear to stick out? Often such features tell us something interesting or exciting about the data. You should always point out any stragglers or **outliers** that stand off away from the body of the distribution. For example, if you're studying the personal wealth of Americans and Bill Gates is in your sample, he would certainly be an outlier. Because his wealth would be so obviously atypical, you'd want to point it out as a special feature.

Outliers can affect almost every method we discuss in this text, so we'll always be on the lookout for them. An outlier can be the most informative part of your data, or it might just be an error. Either way, you shouldn't throw it away without comment. Treat it specially and discuss it when you report your conclusions about your data. (Or find the error and fix it if you can.) We'll soon learn a rule of thumb for how we can decide if and when a value might be considered to be an outlier and some advice for what to do when you encounter them.

- **Using Your Judgment.** How you characterize a distribution is often a judgment call. Does the gap you see in the histogram really reveal that you have two subgroups, or will it go away if you change the bin width slightly? Are those observations at the high end of the histogram truly unusual, or are they just the largest ones at the end of a long tail? These are matters of judgment on which different people can legitimately disagree. There's no automatic calculation or rule of thumb that can make the decision for you. Understanding your data and how they arose can help. What should guide your decisions is an honest desire to understand what is happening in the data.

   Looking at a histogram at several different bin widths can help you to see how persistent some of the features are. Some technologies offer ways to change the bin width interactively to get multiple views of the histogram. If the number of observations in each bin is small enough so that moving a couple of values to the next bin changes your assessment of how many modes there are, be careful. Be sure to think about the data, where they came from, and what kinds of questions you hope to answer from them.

For Example   Describing the shape of a distribution

Question: Describe the shape of the distribution of downloads from the example earlier in this chapter.

Answer: It is symmetric and unimodal with no outliers.

---

3 Center

Look again at the AIG prices in Figure 1. If you had to pick one number to describe a *typical* price, what would you pick? When a histogram is unimodal and fairly symmetric, most people would point to the center of the distribution, where the histogram peaks. The typical price is around $65.00.

If we want to be more precise and *calculate* a number, we can *average* the data. In the AIG example, the average monthly prices is $64.48, about what we might expect from the histogram. You already know how to average values, but this is a good place to introduce notation that we'll use throughout the text. We'll call the generic variable y, and use the Greek capital letter sigma, Σ, to mean "sum" (sigma is "S" in Greek), and write[3]:

$$\bar{y} = \frac{Total}{n} = \frac{\Sigma y}{n}.$$

According to this formula, we add up all the values of the variable, y, and divide that sum (*Total*, or Σy) by the number of data values, n. We call the resulting value the **mean** of y.[4]

Notation Alert! ———

A bar over any symbol indicates the mean of that quantity.

---

[3]You may also see the variable called x and the equation written $\bar{x} = \frac{Total}{n} = \frac{\Sigma x}{n}$. We prefer to call a single variable y instead of x, because x will later be used to name a variable that predicts another (which we'll call y), but when you have only one variable either name is common. Most calculators call a single variable x.

[4]Once you've averaged the data, you might logically expect the result to be called the *average*. But average is used too colloquially as in the "average" home buyer, where we don't sum up anything. Even though average *is* sometimes used in the way we intend, as in the Dow Jones Industrial Average (which is actually a weighted average) or a batting average, we'll usually use the term *mean* throughout the text.

Although the mean is a natural summary for unimodal, symmetric distributions, it can be misleading for skewed data or for distributions with gaps or outliers. The histogram of AIG monthly prices in Figure 1 is unimodal, and nearly symmetric, with a slight left skew. A look at the total volume of stocks sold each month for the same 6 years tells a very different story. Figure 8 shows a unimodal but strongly right-skewed distribution with two gaps. The mean monthly volume was 170.1 million shares. Locate that value on the histogram. Does it seem a little high as a summary of a typical month's volume? In fact, more than two out of three months have volumes that are less than that value. It might be better to use the **median—** the value that splits the histogram into two equal *areas*. We find the median by counting in from the ends of the data until we reach the middle value. The median is commonly used for variables such as cost or income, which are likely to be skewed. That's because the median is *resistant* to unusual observations and to the shape of the distribution. For the AIG monthly trading volumes, the median is 135.9 million shares, which seems like a more appropriate summary.

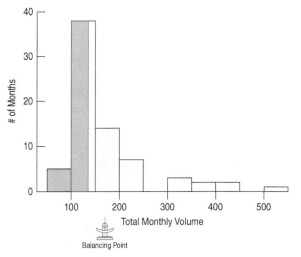

Figure 8 The median splits the area of the histogram in half at 135.9 million shares. Because the distribution is skewed to the right, the mean 170.1 million shares is *higher* than the median. The points at the right have pulled the mean toward them, away from the median.

Does it really make a difference whether we choose a mean or a median? The mean monthly price for the AIG stock is $64.48. Because the distribution of the prices is roughly symmetric, we'd expect the mean and median to be close. In fact, we compute the median to be $65.23. But for variables with skewed distributions, the story is quite different. For a right-skewed distribution like the monthly volumes in Figure 8, the mean is larger than the median: 170.1 compared to 135.9. The two give quite different summaries. The difference is due to the overall shape of the distributions.

By Hand

Finding the Median

Finding the median of a batch of *n* numbers is easy as long as you remember to order the values first. If *n* is odd, the median is the middle value.

Counting in from the ends, we find this value in the $\frac{n + 1}{2}$ position.

> When n is even, there are two middle values. So, in this case, the median is the average of the two values in positions $\frac{n}{2}$ and $\frac{n}{2} + 1$.
>   Here are two examples:
>   Suppose the batch has the values 14.1, 3.2, 25.3, 2.8, −17.5, 13.9, and 45.8. First we order the values: −17.5, 2.8, 3.2, 13.9, 14.1, 25.3, and 45.8. There are 7 values, so the median is the $(7 + 1)/2 = 4$th value counting from the top or bottom: 13.9.
>   Suppose we had the same batch with another value at 35.7. Then the ordered values are −17.5, 2.8, 3.2, 13.9, 14.1, 25.3, 35.7, and 45.8. The median is the average of the 8/2, or 4th, and the $(8/2) + 1$, or 5th, values. So the median is $(13.9 + 14.1)/2 = 14.0$.

The mean is the point at which the histogram would balance. Just like a child who moves away from the center of a see-saw, a bar of the histogram far from the center has more leverage, pulling the mean in its direction. It's hard to argue that a summary that's been pulled aside by only a few outlying values or by a long tail is what we mean by the center of the distribution. That's why the median is usually a better choice for skewed data.

However, when the distribution is unimodal and symmetric, the mean offers better opportunities to calculate useful quantities and draw more interesting conclusions. It will be the summary value we work with much more throughout the rest of the text.

For Example   Finding the mean and median

Question: From the data earlier in this chapter, what is a typical number of downloads per hour?

Answer: The mean number is 18.7 downloads per hour. The median is 19.5 downloads per hour. Because the distribution is unimodal and roughly symmetric, we shouldn't be surprised that the two are close. There are a few more hours (in the middle of the night) with small numbers of downloads that pull the mean lower than the median, but either one seems like a reasonable summary to report.

4   Spread of the Distribution

We know that the typical price of the AIG stock is around $65, but knowing the mean or median alone doesn't tell us about the entire distribution. A stock whose price doesn't move away from its center isn't very interesting.[5] The more the data vary, the less a measure of center can tell us. We need to know how spread out the data are as well.

One simple measure of spread is the **range**, defined as the difference between the extremes:

$$\text{Range} = max - min.$$

For the AIG price data, the range is $77.26 − $49.41 = $27.85. Notice that the range is *a single number* that describes the spread of the data, not an interval of values—as you might think from its use in common speech. If there are any unusual

---

[5]And not much of an investment, either.

observations in the data, the range is not resistant and will be influenced by them. Concentrating on the middle of the data avoids this problem.

The **quartiles** are the values that frame the middle 50% of the data. One quarter of the data lies below the lower quartile, Q1, and one quarter of the data lies above the upper quartile, Q3. The **interquartile range (IQR)** summarizes the spread by focusing on the middle half of the data. It's defined as the difference between the two quartiles:

$$IQR = Q3 - Q1.$$

By Hand

Finding Quartiles

Quartiles are easy to find in theory, but more difficult in practice. The three quarties, Q1 (lower quartile), Q2 (the median) and Q3 (the upper quartile) split the sorted data values into quarters. So, for example, 25% of the data values will lie at or below Q1. The problem lies in the fact that unless your sample size divides nicely by 4, there isn't just one way to split the data into quarters. The statistical software package SAS offers at least five different ways to compute quartiles. The differences are usually small, but can be annoying. Here are two of the most common methods for finding quartiles by hand or with a calculator:

1. The Tukey Method

   Split the sorted data at the median. (If n is odd, include the median with each half). Then find the median of each of these halves—use these as the quartiles.

   Example: The data set {14.1, 3.2, 25.3, 2.8, −17.5, 13.9, 45.8}

   First we order the values: {−17.5, 2.8, 3.2, 13.9, 14.1, 25.3, 45.8}. We found the median to be 13.9, so form two data sets: {−17.5, 2.8, 3.2, 13.9} and { 13.9, 14.1, 25.3, 45.8}. The medians of these are $3.0 = (2.8 + 3.2)/2$ and $19.7 = (14.1 + 25.3)/2$. So we let Q1 = 3.0 and Q3 = 19.7.

2. The TI calculator method

   The same as the Tukey method, except we *don't* include the median with each half. So for {14.1, 3.2, 25.3, 2.8, −17.5, 13.9, and 45.8} we find the two data sets:

   {−17.5, 2.8, 3.2} and {14.1, 25.3, 45.8} by not including the median in either.

   Now the medians of these are Q1 = 2.8 and Q3 = 25.3.

   Notice the effect on the IQR. For Tukey:
   IQR = Q3−Q1 = 19.7−3.0 = 16.7, but for TI,
   IQR = 25.3−2.8 = 22.5.

For both of these methods, notice that the quartiles are either data values, or the average of two adjacent values. In Excel, and other software, the quartiles are *interpolated*, so they may not be simple averages of two values. Be aware that there may be differences, but the idea is the same: the quartiles Q1, Q2, and Q3 split the data roughly into quarters.

For the AIG data, there are 36 values on either side of the median. After ordering the data, we average the 18th and 19th values to find Q1 = (59.96 + 60.26)/2 = \$60.11. We average the 54th and 55th values to find Q3 = (68.99 + 69.02)/2 = \$69.01. So the IQR = Q3 − Q1 = \$69.01 − \$60.11 = \$8.90.

The IQR is usually a reasonable summary of spread, but because it uses only the two quartiles of the data, it ignores much of the information about how individual values vary.

A more powerful measure of spread—and the one we'll use most often—is the standard deviation, which, as we'll see, takes into account how far each value is from the mean. Like the mean, the standard deviation is appropriate only for symmetric data and can be influenced by outlying observations.

As the name implies, the standard deviation uses the *deviations* of each data value from the mean. If we tried to average these deviations, the positive and negative differences would cancel each other out, giving an average deviation of 0—not very useful. Instead, we square each deviation. The average[6] of the *squared* deviations is called the **variance** and is denoted by s^2:

$$s^2 = \frac{\sum (y - \bar{y})^2}{n - 1}.$$

The variance plays an important role in statistics, but as a measure of spread, it has a problem. Whatever the units of the original data, the variance is in *squared* units. We want measures of spread to have the same units as the data, so we usually take the square root of the variance. That gives the **standard deviation**.

$$s = \sqrt{\frac{\sum (y - \bar{y})^2}{n - 1}}.$$

For the AIG stock prices, $s = \$6.12$.

For Example   Describing the spread

Question: For the data earlier in this chapter, describe the spread of the number of downloads per hour.

Answer: The range of downloads is 36 − 2 = 34 downloads per hour.
The quartiles are 13 and 24.5, so the IQR is 24.5 − 13 = 11.5 downloads per hour. The standard deviation is 8.94 downloads per hour.

By Hand

Finding the Standard Deviation

To find the standard deviation, start with the mean, $\bar{y}$. Then find the *deviations* by taking $\bar{y}$ from each value: $(y - \bar{y})$. Square each deviation: $(y - \bar{y})^2$.

Now you're nearly home. Just add these up and divide by $n − 1$. That gives you the variance, s^2. To find the standard deviation, s, take the square root.

Suppose the batch of values is 4, 3, 10, 12, 8, 9, and 3.

(continued)

---

[6]For technical reasons, we divide by $n − 1$ instead of n to take this average.

The mean is $\bar{y} = 7$. So find the deviations by subtracting 7 from each value:

Original Values	Deviations	Squared Deviations
4	$4 - 7 = -3$	$(-3)^2 = 9$
3	$3 - 7 = -4$	$(-4)^2 = 16$
10	$10 - 7 = 3$	9
12	$12 - 7 = 5$	25
8	$8 - 7 = 1$	1
9	$9 - 7 = 2$	4
3	$3 - 7 = -4$	16

Add up the squared deviations:
$9 + 16 + 9 + 25 + 1 + 4 + 16 = 80$.
Now, divide by $n - 1$: $80/6 = 13.33$.
Finally, take the square root: $s = \sqrt{13.33} = 3.65$

Just Checking

Thinking About Variation

1 The U.S. Census Bureau reports the median family income in its summary of census data. Why do you suppose they use the median instead of the mean? What might be the disadvantages of reporting the mean?

2 You've just bought a new car that claims to get a highway fuel efficiency of 31 miles per gallon. Of course, your mileage will "vary." If you had to guess, would you expect the IQR of gas mileage attained by all cars like yours to be 30 mpg, 3 mpg, or 0.3 mpg? Why?

3 A company selling a new MP3 player advertises that the player has a mean lifetime of 5 years. If you were in charge of quality control at the factory, would you prefer that the standard deviation of life spans of the players you produce be 2 years or 2 months? Why?

5   Shape, Center, and Spread—A Summary

What should you report about a quantitative variable? Report the shape of its distribution, and include a center and a spread. But which measure of center and which measure of spread? The guidelines are pretty easy.

- If the shape is skewed, point that out and report the median and IQR. You may want to include the mean and standard deviation as well, explaining why the mean and median differ. The fact that the mean and median do not agree is a sign that the distribution may be skewed. A histogram will help you make the point.

- If the shape is unimodal and symmetric, report the mean and standard deviation and possibly the median and IQR as well. For unimodal symmetric data, the IQR is usually a bit larger than the standard deviation. If that's not true for your data set, look again to make sure the distribution isn't skewed or mutimodal and that there are no outliers.

- If there are multiple modes, try to understand why. If you can identify a reason for separate modes, it may be a good idea to split the data into separate groups.

- If there are any clearly unusual observations, point them out. If you are reporting the mean and standard deviation, report them computed with and without the unusual observations. The differences may be revealing.

- Always pair the median with the IQR and the mean with the standard deviation. It's not useful to report one without the other. Reporting a center without a spread can lead you to think you know more about the distribution than you do. Reporting only the spread omits important information.

For Example   Summarizing data

Question: Report on the shape, center, and spread of the downloads data from For Example: Creating a Histogram.

Answer: The distribution of downloads per hour over the past 24 hours is unimodal and roughly symmetric. The mean number of downloads per hour is 18.7 and the standard deviation is 8.94. There are several hours in the middle of the night with very few downloads, but none seem to be so unusual as to be considered outliers.

---

6   Five-Number Summary and Boxplots

One good way to summarize a distribution with just a few values is with a five-number summary. The **five-number summary** of a distribution reports its median, quartiles, and extremes (maximum and minimum). For example, the five-number summary of the monthly trading volumes of AIG stock for the period 2002 to 2007 looks like this (in millions of shares).

Max	515.62
Q3	182.32
Median	135.87
Q1	121.04
Min	83.91

Table 2   The five-number summary of monthly trading volume of AIG shares (in millions of shares) for the period 2002 to 2007.

The five-number summary provides a good overall look at the distribution. For example, because the quartiles frame the middle half of the data, we can see that on half of the days the volume was between 121.04 and 182.32 million shares. We can also see the extremes of over 500 million shares on the high end and 83.91 million shares on the low end. Were those days extraordinary for some reason or just the busiest and quietest days? To answer that, we'll need to work with the summaries a bit more.

Once we have a five-number summary of a (quantitative) variable, we can display that information in a **boxplot** (see Figure 9).

A boxplot highlights several features of the distribution of a variable. The central box shows the middle half of the data, between the quartiles. Because the top of the box is at the third quartile (Q3) and the bottom is at Q1, the height of the box

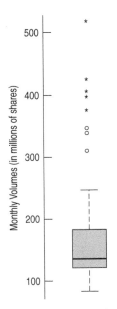

Figure 9 Boxplot of monthly volumes of AIG stock traded in the period 2002–2007 (in millions of shares).

The 1.5 IQR Rule for Nomination Outliers

Designate a point as an outlier if it lies farther than 1.5 IQRs from either the first (Q1) or third (Q3) quartile. Some boxplots also designate points as "far" outliers if they lie more than 3 IQRs from the quartiles. The prominent statistician John W. Tukey, the originator of the boxplot, was asked (by one of the authors) why the outlier nomination rule cut at 1.5 IQRs beyond each quartile. He answered that the reason was that 1 IQR would be too small and 2 IQRs would be too large.

is equal to Q3 − Q1 which is the IQR. (For the AIG data, it's 61.28.) The median is displayed as a horizontal line. If the median is roughly centered between the quartiles, then the middle half of the data is roughly symmetric. If it is not centered, the distribution is skewed. In extreme cases, the median can coincide with one of the quartiles.

The whiskers reach out from the box to the most extreme values that are not considered outliers. The boxplot nominates points as outliers if they fall farther than 1.5 IQRs beyond either quartile (for the AIG data, 1.5 IQR = 1.5 × 61.28 = 91.92). Outliers are displayed individually, both to keep them out of the way for judging skewness and to encourage you to give them special attention. They may be mistakes or they may be the most interesting cases in your data. This rule is not a definition of what makes a point an outlier. It just nominates cases for special attention. But it is not a substitute for careful analysis and thought about whether a value is special.

It's easy to make a boxplot. First locate the median and quartiles on an axis and draw three short lines. For the AIG data, those are at approximately 121 (Q1), 136 (median), and 182 (Q3). The axis is usually vertical (as in Figure 9), but it can be horizontal. Connect the quartile lines to make a box. Identify the "fences" at 1.5 IQR beyond each quartile. For the AIG data, that's 121.04 − 1.5 × 61.28 = 29.12 (lower fence) and 182.32 + 1.5 × 61.28 = 274.24 (upper fence). These fences are not drawn on the final boxplot. They are used to decide which points to display as outliers. Draw whiskers to the most extreme data value not outside the fences. In the AIG data, there are no values below the lower fence since the minimum 83.91 is greater than 29.12, but there are 7 points above the upper fence at 274.24. Finally, draw any outliers individually. Some boxplots use a special symbol for "far" outliers that lie more than 3 IQR's from the fences, as shown in Figure 9.

Some features of the distribution are lost in a boxplot, but as we'll soon see, they are especially useful when comparing several distributions side by side.

From the shape of the box in Figure 9, it looks like the central part of the distribution of volume is skewed to the right (upward here) and the dissimilar length of the two whiskers shows the outer parts of the distribution to be skewed as well. We also see several high volume and some extremely high volume days. Boxplots are particularly good at exhibiting outliers. These extreme days may deserve more attention. (When and why did they occur?)

For Example The boxplot rule for nominating outliers

Question: From the histogram earlier in this chapter, we saw that no points seemed to be so far from the center as to be considered outliers. Use the 1.5 IQR rule to see if it nominates any points as outliers.

Answer: The quartiles are 13 and 24.5 and the IQR is 11.5. 1.5 *IQR = 17.25. A point would have to be larger than 24.5 + 17.25 = 41.25 downloads/hr or smaller than 13 − 17.25 = −4.25. The largest value was 36 downloads/hr and all values must be nonnegative, so there are no points nominated as outliers.

Guided Example   Credit Card Bank Customers

Blend Images/fotolia

To focus on the needs of particular customers, companies often segment their customers into groups with similar needs or spending patterns. A major credit card bank wanted to see how much a particular group of cardholders charged per month on their cards in order to understand the potential growth in their card use. The data for each customer was the amount he or she spent using the card during a three-month period in 2008. Boxplots are especially useful for one variable when combined with a histogram and numerical summaries. Let's summarize the spending of this market segment.

PLAN

Setup Identify the *variable*, the time frame of the data, and the objective of the analysis.

We want to summarize the average monthly charges (in dollars) made by 500 cardholders from a market segment of interest during a three-month period in 2008. The data are quantitative, so we'll use histograms and boxplots, as well as numerical summaries.

DO

Mechanics Select an appropriate display based on the nature of the data and what you want to know about it.

REALITY CHECK It is always a good idea to think about what you expected to see and to check whether the histogram is close to what you expected. Are the data about what you might expect for customers to charge on their cards in a month? A typical value is a few hundred dollars. That seems like the right ballpark.

Note that outliers are often easier to see with boxplots than with histograms, but the histogram provides more details about the shape of the distribution. This computer program "jitters" the outliers in the boxplot so they don't lie on top of each other, making them easier to see.

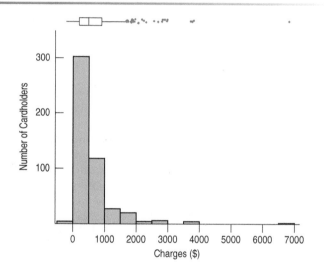

Both graphs show a distribution that is highly skewed to the right with several outliers and an extreme outlier near $7000.

Summary of Monthly Charges	
Count	500
Mean	544.749
Median	370.65
StdDev	661.244
IQR	624.125
Q1	114.54
Q3	738.665

The mean is much larger than the median. The data do not have a symmetric distribution.

(continued)

REPORT

Interpretation Describe the shape, center, and spread of the distribution. Be sure to report on the symmetry, number of modes, and any gaps or outliers.

Recommendation State a conclusion and any recommended actions or analysis.

MEMO

Re: Report on segment spending.

The distribution of charges for this segment during this time period is unimodal and skewed to the right. For that reason, we have summarized the data with the median and interquartile range (IQR).

The median amount charged was $370.65. Half of the cardholders charged between $114.54 and $738.67.

In addition, there are several high outliers, with one extreme value at $6745.

There are also a few negative values. We suspect that these are people who returned more than they charged in a month, but because the values might be data errors, we suggest that they be checked.

Future analyses should look at whether charges during these three months in 2008 were similar to charges in the rest of the year. We would also like to investigate if there is a seasonal pattern and, if so, whether it can be explained by our advertising campaigns or by other factors.

7 Comparing Groups

As we saw earlier, the volume of a stock can vary greatly from month to month or even day to day, but if we step back a bit, we may be able to find patterns that can help us understand, model, and predict it. We started the chapter by looking at monthly summaries of the price and volume of AIG stock. If, instead, we consider the individual daily values, we can group them into periods such as weeks, months, seasons, or years. The picture can change depending on what grouping we use. Comparing the distributions can reveal patterns, differences, and trends.

Let's start with the "big picture." Instead of taking monthly averages, let's look at the daily closing prices for the first two years of our data, 2002 and 2003:

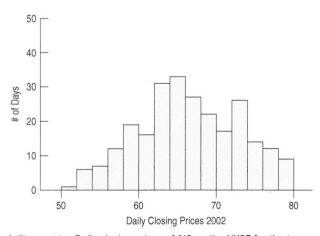
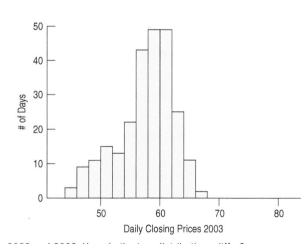

I Figure 10   Daily closing prices of AIG on the NYSE for the two years 2002 and 2003. How do the two distributions differ?

It's not hard to see that prices were generally lower in 2003 than 2002. The price distribution for 2002 appears to be symmetric with a center in the high $60s while the 2003 distribution is left skewed with a center below $60. We were able to make the comparison easily because we displayed the two histograms on the same scale. Histograms with very different centers and spreads may appear similar unless you do that.

Histograms work well for comparing two groups, but what if we want to compare the prices across several years? Histograms are best at displaying one or two distributions. When we compare several groups, boxplots usually do a better job. Boxplots offer an ideal balance of information and simplicity, hiding the details while displaying the overall summary information. And we can plot them side by side, making it easy to compare multiple groups or categories.

When we place boxplots side by side, we can easily see which group has the higher median, which has the greater IQR, where the central 50% of the data is located, and which has the greater overall range. We can also get a general idea of symmetry from whether the medians are centered within their boxes and whether the whiskers extend roughly the same distance on either side of the boxes. Equally important, we can see past any outliers in making these comparisons because they've been displayed separately. We can also begin to look for trends in the medians and in the IQRs.

Guided Example   AIG Stock Price and Volume

What really happened to the AIG stock price from the beginning of the period we've been studying through the financial crisis of 2008/2009? Boxplots of the number of shares traded by month are a good way to see such patterns. We're interested not only in the centers, but also in the spreads. Are volumes equally variable from year to year or are they more spread out in some years?

| PLAN | Setup Identify the variables, report the time frame of the data, and state the objective. | We want to compare the daily price of shares traded from year to year on the NYSE from 2002 through 2009.

The daily price is quantitative and measured in dollars. We can partition the values by year and use side-by-side boxplots to compare the daily prices across years. |
|---|---|---|
| DO | Mechanics Plot the side-by-side boxplots of the data. | |

(continued)

Display any other plots suggested by the previous.

What happened in 2008? We'd better look there with a finer partition. Here are boxplots by month for 2008.

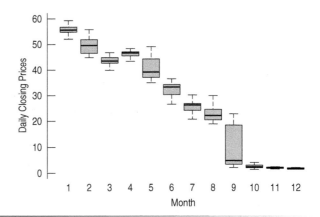

REPORT

Conclusion Report what you've learned about the data and any recommended action or analysis.

MEMO

Re: Research on price of AIG stock

We have examined the daily closing prices of AIG stock on the NYSE for the period 2002 through 2009. As the displays show, prices were relatively stable for the period 2002 through 2007. Prices lowered in 2003 but recovered and stayed generally above $60 for 2004 through 2007. Then in 2008, prices dropped dramatically, and throughout 2009 AIG's stock price was a small fraction of what it had once been. A boxplot by month during 2008 shows that the decline in price was constant throughout the entire year but most noticeable in September 2008. Most analysts point to that month as the beginning of the financial meltdown, but clearly there were signs in the price of AIG that trouble had been brewing for much longer. By October and for the rest of the year, the price was very low with almost no variation.

For Example Comparing boxplots

Question: For the data earlier in this chapter, compare the AM downloads to the PM downloads by displaying the two distributions side-by-side with boxplots.

Answer: There are generally more downloads in the afternoon than in the morning. The median number of afternoon downloads is around 22 as compared with 14 for the morning hours. The PM downloads are also much more consistent. The entire range of the PM hours, 15, is about the size of the IQR for AM hours. Both distributions appear to be fairly symmetric, although the AM hour distribution has some high points which seem to give some asymmetry.

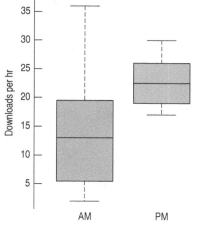

8   Identifying Outliers

We've just seen that the price of AIG shares dropped precipitously during the year 2008. Let's look at a boxplot by month of the daily volumes to see if a similar pattern appears.

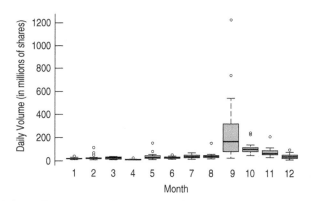

Figure 11   In January, there was a high volume day of 38 million shares that is nominated as an outlier for that month. In February there were three outliers with a maximum of over 100 million shares. In most months one or more high volume days are identified as outliers for their month. But none of these high volume days would have been considered unusual during September, when the median daily volume of AIG stock was 170 million shares. Days that may have seemed ordinary for September if placed in another month would have seemed extraordinary and *vice versa*. That high volume day in January certainly wouldn't stand out in September or even October or November, but for January it was remarkable.

Cases that stand out from the rest of the data deserve our attention. Boxplots have a rule for nominating extreme cases to display as outliers, but that's just a rule of thumb—not a definition. The rule doesn't tell you what to do with them. It's never a substitute for careful thinking about the data and their context.

So, what *should* we do with outliers? The first thing to do is to try to understand them in the context of the data. Once you've identified likely outliers, you should always investigate them. Some outliers are unbelievable and may simply be errors. A decimal point may have been misplaced, digits transposed, or digits repeated or omitted. Sometimes a number is transcribed incorrectly, perhaps copying an adjacent value on the original data sheet. Or, the units may be wrong. If you saw the number of AIG shares traded on the NYSE listed as 2 shares for a particular day, you'd know something was wrong. It could be that it was meant as 2 million shares, but you'd have to check to be sure. If you can identify the error, then you should certainly correct it.

Many outliers are not wrong; they're just different. These are the cases that often repay your efforts to understand them. You may learn more from the extraordinary cases than from summaries of the overall dataset.

What about those two days in September that stand out as extreme even during that volatile month? Those were September 15 and 16, 2008. On the 15th, 740 million shares of AIG stock were traded. That was followed by an incredible volume of over one billion shares of stock from a single company traded the following day. Here's how Barron's described the trading of September 16:

Record Volume for NYSE Stocks, Nasdaq Trades Surge
Beats Its July Record

Yesterday's record-setting volume of 8.14 billion shares traded of all stocks listed on the New York Stock Exchange was pushed aside today by 9.31 billion shares in NYSE Composite volume. The biggest among those trades was the buying and selling of American International Group, with 1.11 billion shares traded as of 4 p.m. today. The AIG trades were 12% of all NYSE Composite volume.

For Example   Identifying outliers and summarizing data

Question: A real estate report lists the following prices for sales of single family homes in a small town in Virginia (rounded to the nearest thousand). Write a couple of sentences describing house prices in this town.

155,000	329,000	172,000	122,000	260,000
139,000	178,000	339,435,000	136,000	330,000
158,000	194,000	279,000	167,000	159,000
149,000	160,000	231,000	136,000	128,000

Answer: A box plot shows an extreme outlier:

That extreme point is a home whose sale price is listed at $339.4 M.

A check on the Internet shows that the most expensive homes ever sold are less than $200 M. This is clearly a mistake.

Setting aside this point, we find the following histogram and summary statistics:

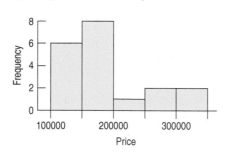

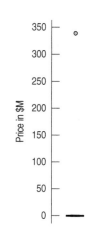

The distribution of prices is strongly skewed to the right. The median price is $160,000. The minimum is $122,000 and the maximum (without the outlier) is $330,000. The middle 50% of house prices lie between $144,000 and $212,500 with an IQR of $68,500.

9 Standardizing

Forbes magazine lists the 258 largest privately held companies in the United States. What do we mean by large? *Forbes* provides two measures: *Revenue* (measured in $B) and number of *Employees*. *Forbes* uses only revenue in its rankings, but couldn't the size of the workforce be a way to measure size as well? How can we compare the two? How does having revenue of $20B compare to having a workforce of 50,000 employees? Which is "larger"? They don't have the same units, so we can't compare them directly. The trick is to standardize each variable first and then compare them. By doing this, we avoid comparing apples to oranges. Over and over during this course (and in many other courses you may take), questions such as "How does this value compare to a typical value?" or "How different are these two values?" will be answered by measuring the distance or difference in standard deviations from the mean.

Here are two companies listed by *Forbes*:

US Foodservice (A diversified food company, ranked #11) with $19.81B revenue and 26,000 employees

Toys "R" Us (the toy chain, ranked #21) with revenues of only $13.72B but 69,000 employees

It's easy to see which company earns more and which has more employees, but which company stands out more relative to others in the Forbes list?

How does standardizing work?

We first need to find the mean and standard deviation of each variable for all 258 companies in the *Forbes* list:

	Mean (all companies)	SD (all companies)
Revenue ($B)	6.23	10.56
Employees	19,629	32,055

Next we measure how *far* each of our values are by subtracting the mean and then dividing by the standard deviation:

$$z = (y - \bar{y})/s$$

Blend Images/fotolia

We call the resulting value a **standardized value** and denote it with the letter z. Usually, we just call it a **z-score**. The z-score tells us how many standard deviations the value is from its mean.

Let's look at revenues first.

To compute the z-score for US Foodservice, take its value (19.81), subtract the mean (6.23) and divide by 10.56:

$$z = (19.81 - 6.23)/10.56 = 1.29$$

That means that US Foodservice's revenue is 1.29 standard deviations *above* the mean. How about employees?

$$z = (26,000 - 19,629)/32,055 = 0.20$$

So US Foodservice's workforce is not nearly as large (relative to the rest of the companies) as their revenue. The number of employees is only 0.20 standard deviations larger than the mean.

What about Toys "R" Us?

For revenue, $z = (13.72 - 6.23)/10.56 = 0.71$ and for employees, $z = (69,000 - 19,629)/32,055 = 1.54$

So who's bigger? If we use revenue, US Foodservice is the winner. If we use workforce, it's Toys "R" Us.

It's not clear which one we should use, but standardizing gives us a way to compare variables even when they're measured in different units. In this case, one could argue that Toys "R" Us is the bigger company. Its revenue z-score is 0.71 compared to US Foodservice's 1.29 but its employee size is 1.54 compared to 0.20 for US Foodservice.

It's not clear how to combine these two variables, although people do this sort of thing all the time. *Fortune* magazine with the help of the Great Places to Work Institute ranks the best companies to work for. In 2009 the software company SAS won. How did they get that honor? Overall, the analysts measured 50 different aspects of the companies. Was SAS better on all 50 variables? Certainly not, but it's almost certain that to combine the variables the analysts had to standardize the variables before combining them, no matter what their methodology.

> **Standardizing into z-Scores:**
>
> - Shifts the mean to 0.
> - Changes the standard deviation to 1.
> - Does not change the shape.
> - Removes the units.

For Example   Comparing values by standardizing

Question: A real estate analyst finds more data from home sales as discussed in the example earlier in this chapter. Of 350 recent sales, the average price was $175,000 with a standard deviation of $55,000. The size of the houses (in square feet) averaged 2100 sq. ft. with a standard deviation of 650 sq. ft. Which is more unusual, a house in this town that costs $340,000, or a 5000 sq. ft. house?

Answer: Compute the z-scores to compare. For the $340,000 house:

$$z = \frac{y - \bar{y}}{s} = \frac{(340,000 - 175,000)}{55,000} = 3.0$$

The house price is 3 standard deviations above the mean.
For the 5000 sq. ft. house:

$$z = \frac{y - \bar{y}}{s} = \frac{(5,000 - 2,100)}{650} = 4.46$$

This house is 4.46 standard deviations above the mean in size. That's more unusual than the house that costs $340,000.

10   Time Series Plots

The price and volume of stocks traded on the NYSE are reported daily. Earlier, we grouped the days into months and years, but we could simply look at the price day by day. A histogram can provide information about the distribution of a variable, but it can't show any pattern over time. Whenever we have time series data, it is a good idea to look for patterns by plotting the data in time order. Figure 12 shows the *daily prices* plotted over time for 2007.

A display of values against time is called a **time series plot**. This plot reflects the pattern that we were unable to see by displaying the entire year's prices in either a histogram or a boxplot. Now we can see that although the price rallied in the spring of 2007, after July there were already signs that the price might not stay above $60. By October, that pattern was clear.

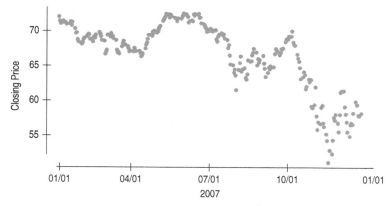

Figure 12   A time series plot of daily closing *prices* of AIG stock shows the overall pattern and changes in variation.

Time series plots often show a great deal of point-to-point variation, as Figure 12 does, and you'll often see time series plots drawn with all the points connected, especially in financial publications.

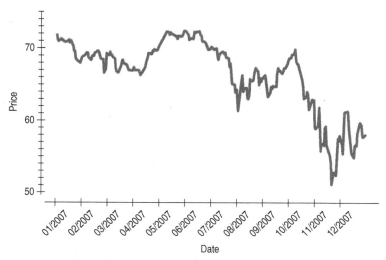

Figure 13   The *daily prices* of Figure 12, drawn by connecting all the points. Sometimes this can help us see the underlying pattern.

Often it is better to try to smooth out the local point-to-point variability. After all, we usually want to see past this variation to understand any underlying trend and think about how the values vary around that trend—the time series version of center and spread. There are many ways for computers to run a smooth trace through a time series plot. Some follow local bumps, others emphasize long-term trends. Some provide an equation that gives a typical value for any given time point, others just offer a smooth trace.

A smooth trace can highlight long-term patterns and help us see them through the more local variation. Figure 14 shows the daily prices of Figures 12 and 13 with a typical smoothing function, available in many statistics programs. With the smooth trace, it's a bit easier to see a pattern. The trace helps our eye follow the main trend and alerts us to points that don't fit the overall pattern.

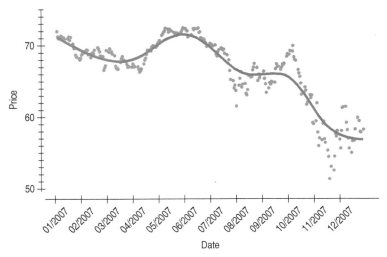

Figure 14   The daily volumes of Figure 12, with a smooth trace added to help your eye see the long-term pattern.

It is always tempting to try to extend what we see in a timeplot into the future. Sometimes that makes sense. Most likely, the NYSE volume follows some regular patterns throughout the year. It's probably safe to predict more volume on triple witching days (when contracts expire) and less activity in the week between Christmas and New Year's Day.

Other patterns are riskier to extend into the future. If a stock's price has been rising, how long will it continue to go up? No stock has ever increased in value indefinitely, and no stock analyst has consistently been able to forecast when a stock's value will turn around. Stock prices, unemployment rates, and other economic, social, or psychological measures are much harder to predict than physical quantities. The path a ball will follow when thrown from a certain height at a given speed and direction is well understood. The path interest rates will take is much less clear.

Unless we have strong (nonstatistical) reasons for doing otherwise, we should resist the temptation to think that any trend we see will continue indefinitely. Statistical models often tempt those who use them to think beyond the data. We'll pay close attention later in this text to understanding when, how, and how much we can justify doing that.

Look at the prices in Figures 12 through 14 and try to guess what happened in the subsequent months. Was that drop from October to December a sign of trouble ahead, or was the increase in December back to around $60 where the stock had comfortably traded for several years a sign that stability had returned to AIG's stock price? Perhaps those who picked up the stock for $51 in early November really got a bargain. Let's look ahead to 2008:

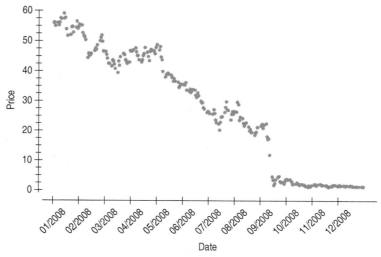

Figure 15 A time series plot of daily AIG *prices* shows what happened to the company in 2008.

Even through the spring of 2008, although the price was gently falling, nothing prepared traders following only the time series plot for what was to follow. In September the stock lost 99% of its value and as of 2010 was still trading below $2 an original share.

For Example Plotting time series data

Question: The downloads from the example earlier in this chapter are a time series. Plot the data by hour of the day and describe any patterns you see.

Answer: For this day, downloads were highest at midnight with about 36 downloads/hr, then dropped sharply until about 5–6 AM when they reached their minimum at 2–3 per hour. They gradually increased to about 20/hr by noon, and then stayed in the twenties until midnight, with a slight increase during the evening hours. When we split the data at midnight and noon, as we did earlier, we missed this pattern entirely.

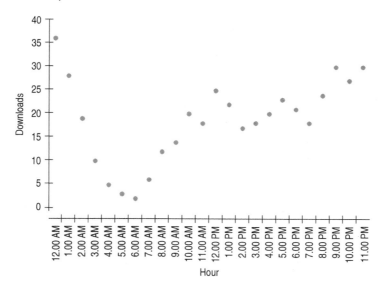

The histogram we saw the beginning of the chapter (Figure 1) summarized the distribution of prices fairly well because during that period the prices were fairly stable. When a time series is **stationary**[7] (without a strong trend or change in variability), a histogram can provide a useful summary, especially in conjunction with a time series plot. However, when the time series is not stationary as was the case for AIG prices after 2007, a histogram is unlikely to capture much of interest. Then, a time series plot is the best graphical display to use in describing the behavior of the data.

11 Transforming Skewed Data

When a distribution is skewed, it can be hard to summarize the data simply with a center and spread, and hard to decide whether the most extreme values are outliers or just part of the stretched-out tail. How can we say anything useful about such data? The secret is to apply a simple function to each data value. One such function that can change the shape of a distribution is the logarithmic function. Let's examine an example in which a set of data is severely skewed.

In 1980, the average CEO made about 42 times the average worker's salary. In the two decades that followed, CEO compensation soared when compared with the average worker's pay; by 2000, that multiple had jumped to 525.[8] What does the distribution of the Fortune 500 companies' CEOs look like? Figure 16 shows a boxplot and a histogram of the 2005 compensation.

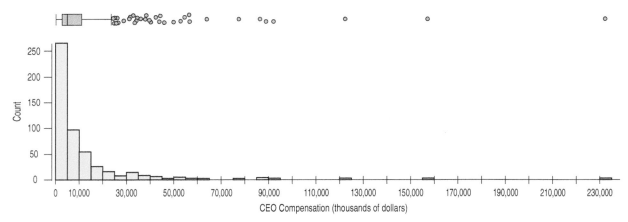

Figure 16 The total compensation for CEOs (in $000) of the 500 largest companies is skewed and includes some extraordinarily large values.

These values are reported in *thousands* of dollars. The boxplot indicates that some of the 500 CEOs received extraordinarily high compensation. The first bin of the histogram, containing about half the CEOs, covers the range $0 to $5,000,000. The reason that the histogram seems to leave so much of the area blank is that the largest observations are so far from the bulk of the data, as we can see from the boxplot. Both the histogram and boxplot make it clear that this distribution is very skewed to the right.

---

[7]Sometimes we separate out the properties and say the series is stationary with respect to the mean (if there is no trend) or stationary with respect to the variance (if the spread doesn't change), but unless otherwise noted, we'll assume that *all the statistical properties* of a stationary series are constant over time.

[8]Sources: United for a Fair Economy, *Business Week* annual CEO pay surveys, Bureau of Labor Statistics, "Average Weekly Earnings of Production Workers, Total Private Sector." Series ID: EEU00500004.

Total compensation for CEOs consists of their base salaries, bonuses, and extra compensation, usually in the form of stock or stock options. Data that add together several variables, such as the compensation data, can easily have skewed distributions. It's often a good idea to separate the component variables and examine them individually, but we don't have that information for the CEOs.

Skewed distributions are difficult to summarize. It's hard to know what we mean by the "center" of a skewed distribution, so it's not obvious what value to use to summarize the distribution. What would you say was a typical CEO total compensation? The mean value is $10,307,000, while the median is "only" $4,700,000. Each tells something different about how the data are distributed.

One way to make a skewed distribution more symmetric is to **re-express**, or **transform**, the data by applying a simple function to all the data values. Variables with a distribution that is skewed to the right often benefit from a re-expression by logarithms or square roots. Those skewed to the left may benefit from squaring the data values. It doesn't matter what base you use for a logarithm.

- **Dealing with logarithms** You probably don't encounter logarithms every day. In this text, we use them to make data behave better by making model assumptions more reasonable. Base 10 logs are the easiest to understand, but natural logs are often used as well. (Either one is fine.) You can think of base 10 logs as roughly one less than the number of digits you need to write the number. So 100, which is the smallest number to require 3 digits, has a $\log_{10}$ of 2. And 1000 has a $\log_{10}$ of 3. The $\log_{10}$ of 500 is between 2 and 3, but you'd need a calculator to find that it's approximately 2.7. All salaries of "six figures" have $\log_{10}$ between 5 and 6. Logs are incredibly useful for making skewed data more symmetric. Fortunately, with technology, remaking a histogram or other display of the data is as easy as pushing a button.

The histogram of the logs of the total CEO compensations in Figure 17 is much more symmetric, so we can see that a typical *log compensation* is between 6.0 and 7.0, which means that it lies between $1 million and $10 million. To be more precise, the mean $\log_{10}$ value is 6.73, while the median is 6.67 (that's $5,370,317 and $4,677,351, respectively). Note that nearly all the values are between 6.0 and 8.0—in other words, between $1,000,000 and $100,000,000 per year. Logarithmic transformations are common, and because computers and calculators are available to do the calculating, you should consider transformation as a helpful tool whenever you have skewed data.

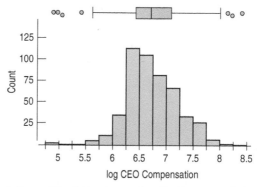

Figure 17 Taking logs makes the histogram of CEO total compensation nearly symmetric.

For Example   Transforming skewed data

Question: Every year *Fortune* magazine publishes a list of the 100 best companies to work for (http://money.cnn.com/magazines/fortune/bestcompanies/2010/). One statistic often looked at is the average annual pay for the most common job title at the company. Can we characterize those pay values? Here is a histogram of the average annual pay values and a histogram of the logarithm of the pay values. Which would provide the better basis for summarizing pay?

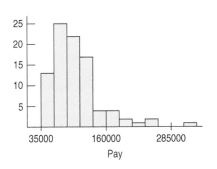
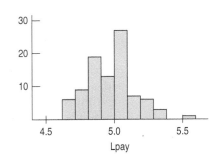

Answer: The pay values are skewed to the high end. The logarithm transformation makes the distribution more nearly symmetric. A symmetric distribution is more appropriate to summarize with a mean and standard deviation.

What Can Go Wrong?

A data display should tell a story about the data. To do that it must speak in a clear language, making plain what variable is displayed, what any axis shows, and what the values of the data are. And it must be consistent in those decisions.

The task of summarizing a quantitative variable requires that we follow a set of rules. We need to watch out for certain features of the data that make summarizing them with a number dangerous. Here's some advice:

- **Don't make a histogram of a categorical variable.** Just because the variable contains numbers doesn't mean it's quantitative. Here's a histogram of the insurance policy numbers of some workers. It's not very informative because the policy numbers are categorical. A histogram or stem-and-leaf display of a categorical variable makes no sense. A bar chart or pie chart may do better.

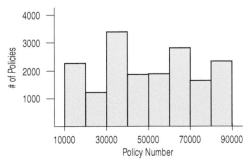

Figure 18   It's not appropriate to display categorical data like policy numbers with a histogram.

- **Choose a scale appropriate to the data.** Computer programs usually do a pretty good job of choosing histogram bin widths. Often, there's an easy way to adjust the width, sometimes interactively. Figure 19 shows the AIG price change histogram with two other choices for the bin size.

- **Avoid inconsistent scales.** Parts of displays should be mutually consistent—no fair changing scales in the middle or plotting two variables on different scales but on the same display. When comparing two groups, be sure to draw them on the same scale.

- **Label clearly.** Variables should be identified clearly and axes labeled so a reader knows what the plot displays.

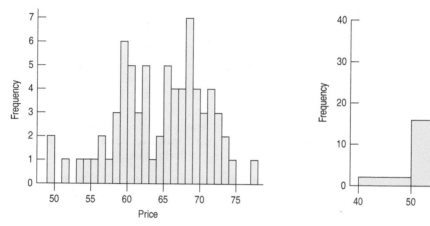

Figure 19   Changing the bin width changes how the histogram looks. The AIG stock prices look very different with these two choices.

Here's a remarkable example of a plot gone wrong. It illustrated a news story about rising college costs. It uses time series plots, but it gives a misleading impression. First, think about the story you're being told by this display. Then try to figure out what has gone wrong.

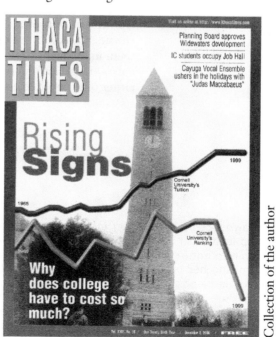

Collection of the author

(continued)

What's wrong? Just about everything.

- The horizontal scales are inconsistent. Both lines show trends over time, but for what years? The tuition sequence starts in 1965, but rankings are graphed from 1989. Plotting them on the same (invisible) scale makes it seem that they're for the same years.

- The vertical axis isn't labeled. That hides the fact that it's using two different scales. Does it graph dollars (of tuition) or ranking (of Cornell University)?

This display violates three of the rules. And it's even worse than that. It violates a rule that we didn't even bother to mention. The two inconsistent scales for the vertical axis don't point in the same direction! The line for Cornell's rank shows that it has "plummeted" from 15th place to 6th place in academic rank. Most of us think that's an *improvement*, but that's not the message of this graph.

- **Do a reality check.** Don't let the computer (or calculator) do your thinking for you. Make sure the calculated summaries make sense. For example, does the mean look like it is in the center of the histogram? Think about the spread. An IQR of 50 mpg would clearly be wrong for a family car. And no measure of spread can be negative. The standard deviation can take the value 0, but only in the very unusual case that all the data values equal the same number. If you see the IQR or standard deviation equal to 0, it's probably a sign that something's wrong with the data.

- **Don't compute numerical summaries of a categorical variable.** The mean zip code or the standard deviation of Social Security numbers is not meaningful. If the variable is categorical, you should instead report summaries such as percentages. It is easy to make this mistake when you let technology do the summaries for you. After all, the computer doesn't care what the numbers mean.

- **Watch out for multiple modes.** If the distribution—as seen in a histogram, for example—has multiple modes, consider separating the data into groups. If you cannot separate the data in a meaningful way, you should not summarize the center and spread of the variable.

- **Beware of outliers.** If the data have outliers but are otherwise unimodal, consider holding the outliers out of the further calculations and reporting them individually. If you can find a simple reason for the outlier (for instance, a data transcription error), you should remove or correct it. If you cannot do either of these, then choose the median and IQR to summarize the center and spread.

Ethics in Action

Beth Tully owns Zenna's Café, an independent coffee shop located in a small midwestern city. Since opening Zenna's in 2002, she has been steadily growing her business and now distributes her custom coffee blends to a number of regional restaurants and markets. She operates a microroaster that offers specialty grade Arabica coffees recognized as some as the best in the area. In addition to providing the highest quality coffees, Beth also wants her business to be socially responsible. Toward that end, she pays fair prices to coffee farmers and donates funds to help charitable causes in Panama, Costa Rica, and Guatemala. In addition, she encourages her employees to get involved in the local community. Recently, one of the well-known multinational coffeehouse chains announced plans to locate shops in her area. This chain is one of the few to offer Certified Free Trade coffee products and work toward social justice in the global community. Consequently, Beth thought it might be a good idea for her to begin communicating Zenna's socially responsible efforts to the public, but with an emphasis on their commitment to the local community. Three months ago she began collecting data on the number of volunteer hours donated by her employees per week. She has a total of 12 employees, of whom 10 are full time. Most employees volunteered less than 2 hours per week, but Beth noticed that one part-time employee volunteered more than 20 hours per week. She discovered that her employees collectively volunteered an average of 15 hours per month (with a median of 8 hours). She planned to report the average number and believed most people would be impressed with Zenna's level of commitment to the local community.

ETHICAL ISSUE *The outlier in the data affects the average in a direction that benefits Beth Tully and Zenna's Café (related to Item C, ASA Ethical Guidelines).*

ETHICAL SOLUTION *Beth's data are highly skewed. There is an outlier value (for a part-time employee) that pulls the average number of volunteer hours up. Reporting the average is misleading. In addition, there may be justification to eliminate the value since it belongs to a part-time employee (10 of the 12 employees are full time). It would be more ethical for Beth to: (1) report the average but discuss the outlier value, (2) report the average for only full-time employees, or (3) report the median instead of the average.*

What Have We Learned?

Learning Objectives

- Make and interpret histograms to display the distribution of a variable.
  - We understand distributions in terms of their shape, center, and spread.

- Describe the shape of a distribution.
  - A **symmetric** distribution has roughly the same shape reflected around the center
  - A **skewed** distribution extends farther on one side than on the other.
  - A **unimodal** distribution has a single major hump or mode; a bimodal distribution has two; multimodal distributions have more.
  - **Outliers** are values that lie far from the rest of the data.

- Compute the mean and median of a distribution, and know when it is best to use each to summarize the center.
  - The **mean** is the sum of the values divided by the count. It is a suitable summary for unimodal, symmetric distributions.
  - The **median** is the middle value; half the values are above and half are below the median. It is a better summary when the distribution is skewed or has outliers.

- Compute the standard deviation and interquartile range (IQR), and know when it is best to use each to summarize the spread.
  - The **standard deviation** is roughly the square root of the average squared difference between each data value and the mean. It is the summary of choice for the spread of unimodal, symmetric variables.
  - The **IQR** is the difference between the quartiles. It is often a better summary of spread for skewed distributions or data with outliers.

- Find a five-number summary and, using it, make a boxplot. Use the boxplot's outlier nomination rule to identify cases that may deserve special attention.
  - A **five-number summary** consists of the median, the quartiles, and the extremes of the data.
  - A **boxplot** shows the quartiles as the upper and lower ends of a central box, the median as a line across the box, and "whiskers" that extend to the most extreme values that are not nominated as outliers.

(continued)

- Boxplots display separately any case that is more than 1.5 IQRs beyond each quartile. These cases should be considered as possible outliers.

■ Use boxplots to compare distributions.
- Boxplots facilitate comparisons of several groups. It is easy to compare centers (medians) and spreads (IQRs).
- Because boxplots show possible outliers separately, any outliers don't affect comparisons.

■ Standardize values and use them for comparisons of otherwise disparate variables.
- We standardize by finding **z-scores**. To convert a data value to its z-score, subtract the mean and divide by the standard deviation.
- z-scores have no units, so they can be compared to z-scores of other variables.
- The idea of measuring the distance of a value from the mean in terms of standard deviations is a basic concept in Statistics and will return many times later in the course.

■ Make and interpret time plots for time series data.
- Look for the trend and any changes in the spread of the data over time.

Terms	
Bimodal	Distributions with two modes.
Boxplot	A boxplot displays the 5-number summary as a central box with whiskers that extend to the nonoutlying values. Boxplots are particularly effective for comparing groups.
Center	The middle of the distribution, usually summarized numerically by the mean or the median.
Distribution	The distribution of a variable gives: • possible values of the variable • frequency or relative frequency of each value
Five-number summary	A five-number summary for a variable consists of: • The minimum and maximum • The quartiles Q1 and Q3 • The median
Histogram (relative frequency histogram)	A histogram uses adjacent bars to show the distribution of values in a quantitative variable. Each bar represents the frequency (relative frequency) of values falling in an interval of values.
Interquartile range (IQR)	The difference between the first and third quartiles. IQR = Q3 − Q1.
Mean	A measure of center found as $\bar{y} = \Sigma y / n$.
Median	The middle value with half of the data above it and half below it.
Mode	A peak or local high point in the shape of the distribution of a variable. The apparent location of modes can change as the scale of a histogram is changed.
Multimodal	Distributions with more than two modes.
Outliers	Extreme values that don't appear to belong with the rest of the data. They may be unusual values that deserve further investigation or just mistakes; there's no obvious way to tell.
Quartile	The lower quartile (Q1) is the value with a quarter of the data below it. The upper quartile (Q3) has a quarter of the data above it. The median and quartiles divide the data into four equal parts.
Range	The difference between the lowest and highest values in a data set: Range = *max − min*.
Re-express or transform	To re-express or transform data, take the logarithm, square root, reciprocal, or some other mathematical operation on all values of the data set. Re-expression can make the distribution of a variable more nearly symmetric and the spread of groups more nearly alike.

Shape	The visual appearance of the distribution. To describe the shape, look for:
	• single vs. multiple modes
	• symmetry vs. skewness
Skewed	A distribution is skewed if one tail stretches out farther than the other.
Spread	The description of how tightly clustered the distribution is around its center. Measures of spread include the IQR and the standard deviation.
Standard deviation	A measure of spread found as $s = \sqrt{\dfrac{\Sigma(y - \bar{y})^2}{n - 1}}$.
Standardized value	We standardize a value by subtracting the mean and dividing by the standard deviation for the variable. These values, called z-scores, have no units.
Stationary	A time series is said to be stationary if its statistical properties don't change over time.
Stem-and-leaf display	A stem-and-leaf display shows quantitative data values in a way that sketches the distribution of the data. It's best described in detail by example.
Symmetric	A distribution is symmetric if the two halves on either side of the center look approximately like mirror images of each other.
Tail	The tails of a distribution are the parts that typically trail off on either side.
Time series plot	Displays data that change over time. Often, successive values are connected with lines to show trends more clearly.
Uniform	A distribution that's roughly flat is said to be uniform.
Unimodal	Having one mode. This is a useful term for describing the shape of a histogram when it's generally mound-shaped.
Variance	The standard deviation squared.
z-score	A standardized value that tells how many standard deviations a value is from the mean; z-scores have a mean of 0 and a standard deviation of 1.

Technology Help: Displaying and Summarizing Quantitative Variables

Almost any program that displays data can make a histogram, but some will do a better job of determining where the bars should start and how they should partition the span of the data (see the art on the next page).

Many statistics packages offer a prepackaged collection of summary measures. The result might look like this:

```
Variable: Weight
N = 234
Mean =143.3      Median = 139
St. Dev = 11.1   IQR = 14
```

Alternatively, a package might make a table for several variables and summary measures:

```
Variable   N     mean    median   stdev   IQR
Weight    234    143.3   139      11.1    14
Height    234    68.3    68.1     4.3     5
Score     234    86      88       9       5
```

It is usually easy to read the results and identify each computed summary. You should be able to read the summary statistics produced by any computer package.

Packages often provide many more summary statistics than you need. Of course, some of these may not be appropriate when the data are skewed or have outliers. It is your responsibility to check a histogram or stem-and-leaf display and decide which summary statistics to use.

It is common for packages to report summary statistics to many decimal places of "accuracy." Of course, it is rare to find data that have such accuracy in the original measurements. The ability to calculate to six or seven digits beyond the decimal point doesn't mean that those digits have any meaning. Generally, it's a good idea to round these values, allowing perhaps one more digit of precision than was given in the original data.

Displays and summaries of quantitative variables are among the simplest things you can do in most statistics packages.

(continued)

The vertical scale may be counts or proportions. Sometimes it isn't clear which. But the shape of the histogram is the same either way.

Most packages choose the number of bars for you automatically. Often you can adjust that choice.

The axis should be clearly labeled so you can tell what "pile" each bar represents. You should be able to tell the lower and upper bounds of each bar.

Run Times

EXCEL   XLSTAT

To make a histogram in Excel 2007 or 2010, use the Data Analysis add-in. If you have not installed that, you must do that first.

- From the Data ribbon, select the Data Analysis add-in.
- From its menu, select Histograms.
- Indicate the range of the data whose histogram you wish to draw.
- Indicate the bin ranges that are up to and including the right end points of each bin.
- Check **Labels** if your columns have names in the first cell.
- Check **Chart output** and click **OK**.
- Right-click on any bar of the resulting graph and, from the menu that drops down, select **Format Data Series . . .**
- In the dialog box that opens, select **Series Options** from the sidebar.
- Slide the Gap Width slider to **No Gap**, and click **Close**.
- In the pivot table on the left, use your pointing tool to slide the bottom of the table up to get rid of the "more" bin.
- Edit the bin names in Column A to properly identify the contents of each bin.

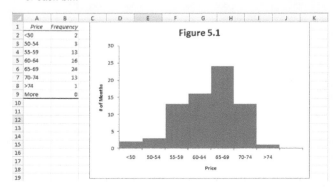

- You can right click on the legend or axis names to edit or remove them.
- Following these instructions, you can reproduce Figure 1 using the data set AIG.

    Alternatively, you can set up your own bin boundaries and count the observations falling within each bin using an Excel function such as FREQUENCY (Data array, Bins array). Consult your Excel manual or help files for details of how to do this.

JMP

To make a histogram and find summary statistics:

- Choose **Distribution** from the **Analyze** menu.
- In the **Distribution** dialog, drag the name of the variable that you wish to analyze into the empty window beside the label "**Y, Columns.**"
- Click **OK**. JMP computes standard summary statistics along with displays of the variables.

To make boxplots:

- Choose **Fit y By x**. Assign a continuous response variable to **Y, Response** and a nominal group variable holding the group names to **X, Factor,** and click **OK**. JMP will offer (among other things) dotplots of the data. click the red triangle and, under **Display Options**, select Boxplots. Note: If the variables are of the wrong type, the display options might not offer boxplots.

MINITAB

To make a histogram:

- Choose **Histogram** from the **Graph** menu.
- Select "Simple" for the type of graph and click **OK**.
- Enter the name of the quantitative variable you wish to display in the box labeled "Graph variables." Click **OK**.

To make a boxplot:

- Choose **Boxplot** from the **Graph** menu and specify your data format.

To calculate summary statistics:

- Choose **Basic Statistics** from the **Stat** menu. From the **Basic Statistics** submenu, choose **Display Descriptive Statistics**.
- Assign variables from the variable list box to the Variables box. MINITAB makes a Descriptive Statistics table.

SPSS

To make a histogram or boxplot in SPSS open the Chart Builder from the Graphs menu.

- Click the **Gallery** tab.

- Choose **Histogram** or **Boxplot** from the list of chart types.
- Drag the icon of the plot you want onto the canvas.
- Drag a scale variable to the y-axis drop zone.
- Click **OK**.

  To make side-by-side boxplots, drag a categorical variable to the x-axis drop zone and click **OK**.

  To calculate summary statistics:

- Choose **Explore** from the **Descriptive Statistics** submenu of the **Analyze** menu. In the Explore dialog, assign one or more variables from the source list to the Dependent List and click the **OK** button.

Brief CASE

Klaas Lingbeek-van Kranen/iStockphoto

Aimin Tang/iStockphoto

Hotel Occupancy Rates

Many properties in the hospitality industry experience strong seasonal fluctuations in demand. To be successful in this industry it is important to anticipate such fluctuations and to understand demand patterns. The file **Occupancy_Rates**, which can be found at www.pearsonhighered.com/sharpe, contains data on monthly *Hotel Occupancy Rates* (in % capacity) for Honolulu, Hawaii, from January 2000 to December 2007.

Examine the data and prepare a report for the manager of a hotel chain in Honolulu on patterns in *Hotel Occupancy* during this period. Include both numerical summaries and graphical displays and summarize the patterns that you see. Discuss any unusual features of the data and explain them if you can, including a discussion of whether the manager should take these features into account for future planning.

Value and Growth Stock Returns

Investors in the stock market have choices of how aggressive they would like to be with their investments. To help investors, stocks are classified as "growth" or "value" stocks. Growth stocks are generally shares in high quality companies that have demonstrated consistent performance and are expected to continue to do well. Value stocks on the other hand are stocks whose prices seem low compared to their inherent worth (as measured by the book to price ratio). Managers invest in these hoping that their low price is simply an overreaction to recent negative events.

In the data set **Returns**[9] (also on the website) be are the monthly returns of 2500 stocks classified as Growth and Value for the time period January 1975 to June 1997. Examine the distributions of the two types of stocks and discuss the advantages and disadvantages of each. Is it clear which type of stock offers the best investment? Discuss briefly.

---

[9]Source: Independence International Associates, Inc. maintains a family of international style indexes covering 22 equity markets. The highest book-to-price stocks are selected one by one from the top of the list. The top half of these stocks become the constituents of the "value index," and the remaining stocks become the "growth index."

Exercises

SECTION 1

1. As part of the marketing team at an Internet music site, you want to understand who your customers are. You send out a survey to 25 customers (you use an incentive of $50 worth of downloads to guarantee a high response rate) asking for demographic information. One of the variables is the customer's age. For the 25 customers the ages are:

20	32	34	29	30
30	30	14	29	11
38	22	44	48	26
25	22	32	35	32
35	42	44	44	48

a) Make a histogram of the data using a bar width of 10 years.
b) Make a histogram of the data using a bar width of 5 years.
c) Make a relative frequency histogram of the data using a bar width of 5 years.
d) *Make a stem-and-leaf plot of the data using 10s as the stems and putting the youngest customers on the top of the plot.

2. As the new manager of a small convenience store, you want to understand the shopping patterns of your customers. You randomly sample 20 purchases from yesterday's records (all purchases in U.S. dollars):

39.05	2.73	32.92	47.51
37.91	34.35	64.48	51.96
56.95	81.58	47.80	11.72
21.57	40.83	38.24	32.98
75.16	74.30	47.54	65.62

a) Make a histogram of the data using a bar width of $20.
b) Make a histogram of the data using a bar width of $10.
c) Make a relative frequency histogram of the data using a bar width of $10.
d) *Make a stem-and-leaf plot of the data using $10 as the stems and putting the smallest amounts on top.

SECTION 2

3. For the histogram you made in Exercise 1a,

a) Is the distribution unimodal or multimodal?
b) Where is (are) the mode(s)?
c) Is the distribution symmetric?
d) Are there any outliers?

4. For the histogram you made in Exercise 2a:

a) Is the distribution unimodal or multimodal?
b) Where is (are) the mode(s)?
c) Is the distribution symmetric?
d) Are there any outliers?

SECTION 3

5. For the data in Exercise 1:

a) Would you expect the mean age to be smaller than, bigger than, or about the same size as the median? Explain.
b) Find the mean age.
c) Find the median age.

6. For the data in Exercise 2:

a) Would you expect the mean purchase to be smaller than, bigger than, or about the same size as the median? Explain.
b) Find the mean purchase.
c) Find the median purchase.

SECTION 4

7. For the data in Exercise 1:

a) Find the quartiles using your calculator.
b) Find the quartiles using the method.
c) Find the IQR using the quartiles from part b.
d) Find the standard deviation.

8. For the data in Exercise 2:

a) Find the quartiles using your calculator.
b) Find the quartiles using the method.
c) Find the IQR using the quartiles from part b.
d) Find the standard deviation.

SECTION 5

9. The histogram shows the December charges (in $) for 5000 customers from one marketing segment from a credit card company. (Negative values indicate customers who received more credits than charges during the month.)

a) Write a short description of this distribution (shape, center, spread, unusual features).
b) Would you expect the mean or the median to be larger? Explain.
c) Which would be a more appropriate summary of the center, the mean or the median? Explain.

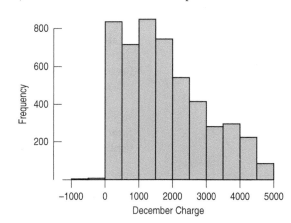

10. Adair Vineyard is a 10-acre vineyard in New Paltz, New York. The winery itself is housed in a 200-year-old historic Dutch barn, with the wine cellar on the first floor and the tasting room and gift shop on the second. Since they are relatively small and considering an expansion, they are curious about how their size compares to that of other vineyards. The histogram shows the sizes (in acres) of 36 wineries in upstate New York.

a) Write a short description of this distribution (shape, center, spread, unusual features).

b) Would you expect the mean or the median to be larger? Explain.

c) Which would be a more appropriate summary of the center, the mean or the median? Explain.

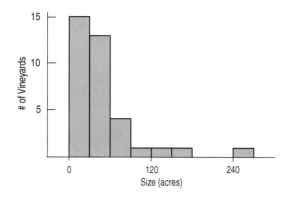

SECTION 6

11. For the data in Exercise 1:

a) Draw a boxplot using the quartiles from Exercise 7b.
b) Does the boxplot nominate any outliers?
c) What age would be considered a high outlier?

12. For the data in Exercise 2:

a) Draw a boxplot using the quartiles from Exercise 8b.
b) Does the boxplot nominate any outliers?
c) What purchase amount would be considered a high outlier?

13. Here are summary statistics for the sizes (in acres) of upstate New York vineyards from Exercise 10.

Variable	N	Mean	StDev	Minimum	Q1	Median	Q3	Maximum
Acres	36	46.50	47.76	6	18.50	33.50	55	250

a) From the summary statistics, would you describe this distribution as symmetric or skewed? Explain.

b) From the summary statistics, are there any outliers? Explain.

c) Using these summary statistics, sketch a boxplot. What additional information would you need to complete the boxplot?

14. A survey of major universities asked what percentage of incoming freshmen usually graduate "on time" in 4 years. Use the summary statistics given to answer these questions.

	% on time
Count	48
Mean	68.35
Median	69.90
StdDev	10.20
Min	43.20
Max	87.40
Range	44.20
25th %tile	59.15
75th %tile	74.75

a) Would you describe this distribution as symmetric or skewed?
b) Are there any outliers? Explain.
c) Create a boxplot of these data.

SECTION 7

15. The survey from Exercise 1 had also asked the customers to say whether they were male or female. Here are the data:

Age	Sex	Age	Sex	Age	Sex	Age	Sex	Age	Sex
20	M	32	F	34	F	29	M	30	M
30	F	30	M	14	M	29	M	11	M
38	F	22	M	44	F	48	F	26	F
25	M	22	M	32	F	35	F	32	F
35	F	42	F	44	F	44	F	48	F

Construct boxplots to compare the ages of men and women and write a sentence summarizing what you find.

16. The store manager from Exercise 2 has collected data on purchases from weekdays and weekends. Here are some summary statistics (rounded to the nearest dollar):

Weekdays n = 230

Min = 4, Q1 = 28, Median = 40, Q3 = 68, Max = 95

Weekend n = 150

Min = 10, Q1 = 35, Median = 55, Q3 = 70, Max = 100

From these statistics, construct side-by-side boxplots and write a sentence comparing the two distributions.

17. Here are boxplots of the weekly sales (in $ U.S.) over a two-year period for a regional food store for two locations. Location #1 is a metropolitan area that is known to be residential where shoppers walk to the store. Location #2 is a suburban area where shoppers drive to the store. Assume that the two towns have similar populations and that the two stores are similar in square footage. Write a brief report discussing what these data show.

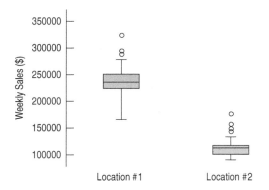

18. Recall the distributions of the weekly sales for the regional stores in Exercise 17. Following are boxplots of weekly sales for this same food store chain for three stores of similar size and location for two different states: Massachusetts (MA) and Connecticut (CT). Compare the distribution of sales for the two states and describe in a report.

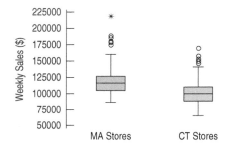

SECTION 9

19. Using the ages from Exercise 1:

a) Standardize the minimum and maximum ages using the mean from Exercise 5b and the standard deviation from Exercise 7d.
b) Which has the more extreme z-score, the min or the max?
c) How old would someone with a z-score of 3 be?

20. Using the purchases from Exercise 2:

a) Standardize the minimum and maximum purchase using the mean from Exercise 6b and the standard deviation from Exercise 8d.
b) Which has the more extreme z-score, the min or the max?
c) How large a purchase would a purchase with a z-score of 3.5 be?

SECTION 11

21. When analyzing data on the number of employees in small companies in one town, a researcher took square roots of the counts. Some of the resulting values, which are reasonably symmetric, were:

4, 4, 6, 7, 7, 8, 10

What were the original values, and how are they distributed?

22. You wish to explain to your boss what effect taking the base-10 logarithm of the salary values in the company's database will have on the data. As simple, example values, you compare a salary of $10,000 earned by a part-time shipping clerk, a salary of $100,000 earned by a manager, and the CEO's $1,000,000 compensation package. Why might the average of these values be a misleading summary? What would the logarithms of these three values be?

CHAPTER EXERCISES

23. Statistics in business. Find a histogram that shows the distribution of a variable in a business publication (e.g., *The Wall Street Journal, Business Week,* etc.).

a) Does the article identify the W's?
b) Discuss whether the display is appropriate for the data.
c) Discuss what the display reveals about the variable and its distribution.
d) Does the article accurately describe and interpret the data? Explain.

24. Statistics in business, part 2. Find a graph other than a histogram that shows the distribution of a quantitative variable in a business publication (e.g., *The Wall Street Journal, Business Week,* etc.).

a) Does the article identify the W's?
b) Discuss whether the display is appropriate for the data.
c) Discuss what the display reveals about the variable and its distribution.
d) Does the article accurately describe and interpret the data? Explain.

25. Two-year college tuition. The histogram shows the distribution of average tuitions charged by each of the 50 U.S. states for public two-year colleges in the 2007–2008

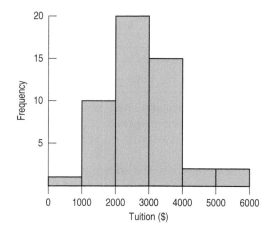

academic year. Write a short description of this distribution (shape, center, spread, unusual features).

26. Gas prices. The website MSN auto (www.autos.msn .com) provides prices of gasoline at stations all around the United States. This histogram shows the price of regular gas (in $/gallon) for 57 stations in the Los Angeles area during the week before Christmas 2007. Describe the shape of this distribution (shape, center, spread, unusual features).

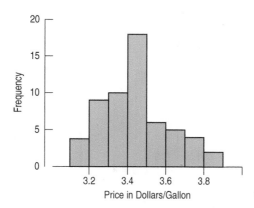

27. Mutual funds. The histogram displays the 12-month returns (in percent) for a collection of mutual funds in 2007. Give a short summary of this distribution (shape, center, spread, unusual features).

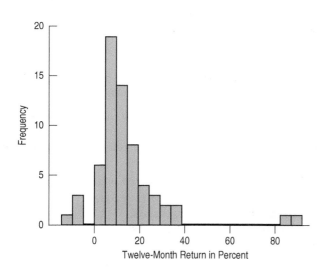

28. Car discounts. A researcher, interested in studying gender differences in negotiations, collects data on the prices that men and women pay for new cars. Here is a histogram of the discounts (the amount in $ below the list price) that men and women received at one car dealership for the last 100 transactions (54 men and 46 women). Give a short summary of this distribution (shape, center, spread, unusual features). What do you think might account for this particular shape?

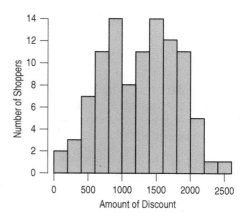

29. Mutual funds, part 2. Use the data set of Exercise 27 to answer the following questions.

a) Find the five-number summary for these data.
b) Find appropriate measures of center and spread for these data.
c) Create a boxplot for these data.
d) What can you see, if anything, in the histogram that isn't clear in the boxplot?

30. Car discounts, part 2. Use the data set of Exercise 28 to answer the following questions.

a) Find the five-number summary for these data.
b) Create a boxplot for these data.
c) What can you see, if anything, in the histogram of Exercise 28 that isn't clear in the boxplot?

*31. Vineyards. The data set provided contains the data from Exercises 10 and 13. Create a stem-and-leaf display of the sizes of the vineyards in acres. Point out any unusual features of the data that you can see from the stem-and-leaf.

*32. Gas prices, again. The data set provided contains the data from Exercise 26 on the price of gas for 57 stations around Los Angeles in December 2007. Round the data to the nearest penny (e.g., 3.459 becomes 3.46) and create a stem-and-leaf display of the data. Point out any unusual features of the data that you can see from the stem-and-leaf.

33. Gretzky. During his 20 seasons in the National Hockey League, Wayne Gretzky scored 50% more points than anyone else who ever played professional hockey. He accomplished this amazing feat while playing in 280 fewer games than Gordie Howe, the previous record holder. Here are the number of games Gretzky played during each season:

79, 80, 80, 80, 74, 80, 80, 79, 64, 78, 73, 78, 74, 45, 81, 48, 80, 82, 82, 70

*a) Create a stem-and-leaf display.
b) Sketch a boxplot.

c) Briefly describe this distribution.

d) What unusual features do you see in this distribution? What might explain this?

34. McGwire. In his 16-year career as a player in major league baseball, Mark McGwire hit 583 home runs, placing him eighth on the all-time home run list (as of 2008). Here are the number of home runs that McGwire hit for each year from 1986 through 2001:

3, 49, 32, 33, 39, 22, 42, 9, 9, 39, 52, 58, 70, 65, 32, 29

a) *Create a stem-and-leaf display.

b) Sketch a boxplot.

c) Briefly describe this distribution.

d) What unusual features do you see in this distribution? What might explain this?

35. Gretzky returns. Look once more at data of hockey games played each season by Wayne Gretzky, seen in Exercise 33.

a) Would you use the mean or the median to summarize the center of this distribution? Why?

b) Without actually finding the mean, would you expect it to be lower or higher than the median? Explain.

c) A student was asked to make a histogram of the data in Exercise 33 and produced the following. Comment.

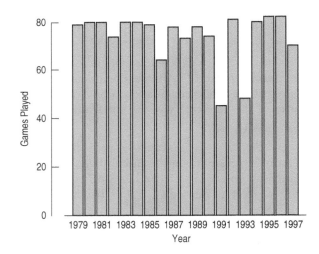

36. McGwire, again. Look once more at data of home runs hit by Mark McGwire during his 16-year career as seen in Exercise 34.

a) Would you use the mean or the median to summarize the center of this distribution? Why?

b) Find the median.

c) Without actually finding the mean, would you expect it to be lower or higher than the median? Explain.

d) A student was asked to make a histogram of the data in Exercise 34 and produced the following. Comment.

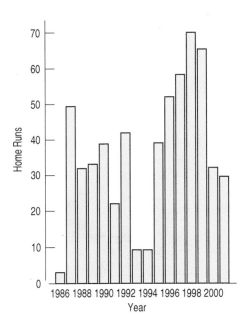

37. Pizza prices. The weekly prices of one brand of frozen pizza over a three-year period in Dallas are provided in the data file. Use the price data to answer the following questions.

a) Find the five-number summary for these data.

b) Find the range and IQR for these data.

c) Create a boxplot for these data.

d) Describe this distribution.

e) Describe any unusual observations.

38. Pizza prices, part 2. The weekly prices of one brand of frozen pizza over a three-year period in Chicago are provided in the data file. Use the price data to answer the following questions.

a) Find the five-number summary for these data.

b) Find the range and IQR for these data.

c) Create a boxplot for these data.

d) Describe the shape (center and spread) of this distribution.

e) Describe any unusual observations.

39. Gasoline usage. The U.S. Department of Transportation collects data on the amount of gasoline sold in each state and the District of Columbia. The following data show the per capita (gallons used per person) consumption in the year 2005. Write a report on the gasoline usage by state in the year 2005, being sure to include appropriate graphical displays and summary statistics.

State	Gasoline Usage	State	Gasoline Usage
Alabama	556.91	Montana	486.15
Alaska	398.99	Nebraska	439.46
Arizona	487.52	Nevada	484.26
Arkansas	491.85	New Hampshire	521.45
California	434.11	New Jersey	481.79
Colorado	448.33	New Mexico	482.33
Connecticut	441.39	New York	283.73
Delaware	514.78	North Carolina	491.07
District of Columbia	209.47	North Dakota	513.16
Florida	485.73	Ohio	434.65
Georgia	560.90	Oklahoma	501.12
Hawaii	352.02	Oregon	415.67
Idaho	414.17	Pennsylvania	402.85
Illinois	392.13	Rhode Island	341.67
Indiana	497.35	South Carolina	570.24
Iowa	509.13	South Dakota	498.36
Kansas	399.72	Tennessee	509.77
Kentucky	511.30	Texas	505.39
Louisiana	489.84	Utah	409.93
Maine	531.77	Vermont	537.94
Maryland	471.52	Virginia	518.06
Massachusetts	427.52	Washington	423.32
Michigan	470.89	West Virginia	444.22
Minnesota	504.03	Wisconsin	440.45
Mississippi	539.39	Wyoming	589.18
Missouri	530.72		

40. **OECD** Established in Paris in 1961, the Organisation for Economic Co-operation and Development (OECD) (www.oced.org) collects information on many economic and social aspects of countries around the world. Here are the 2005 gross domestic product (GDP) growth rates (in percentages) of 30 industrialized countries. Write a brief report on the 2005 GDP growth rates of these countries being sure to include appropriate graphical displays and summary statistics.

Country	Growth Rate
Turkey	0.074
Czech Republic	0.061
Slovakia	0.061
Iceland	0.055
Ireland	0.055
Hungary	0.041
Korea, Republic of (South Korea)	0.040
Luxembourg	0.040
Greece	0.037

Country	Growth Rate
Poland	0.034
Spain	0.034
Denmark	0.032
United States	0.032
Mexico	0.030
Canada	0.029
Finland	0.029
Sweden	0.027
Japan	0.026
Australia	0.025
New Zealand	0.023
Norway	0.023
Austria	0.020
Switzerland	0.019
United Kingdom	0.019
Belgium	0.015
The Netherlands	0.015
France	0.012
Germany	0.009
Portugal	0.004
Italy	0.000

41. **Golf courses.** A start-up company is planning to build a new golf course. For marketing purposes, the company would like to be able to advertise the new course as one of the more difficult courses in the state of Vermont. One measure of the difficulty of a golf course is its length: the total distance (in yards) from tee to hole for all 18 holes. Here are the histogram and summary statistics for the lengths of all the golf courses in Vermont.

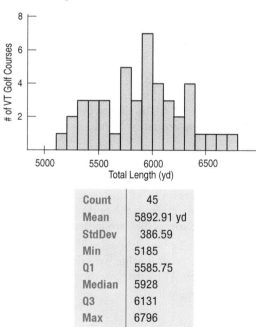

Count	45
Mean	5892.91 yd
StdDev	386.59
Min	5185
Q1	5585.75
Median	5928
Q3	6131
Max	6796

135

a) What is the range of these lengths?
b) Between what lengths do the central 50% of these courses lie?
c) What summary statistics would you use to describe these data?
d) Write a brief description of these data (shape, center, and spread).

42. Real estate. A real estate agent has surveyed houses in 20 nearby zip codes in an attempt to put together a comparison for a new property that she would like to put on the market. She knows that the size of the living area of a house is a strong factor in the price, and she'd like to market this house as being one of the biggest in the area. Here is a histogram and summary statistics for the sizes of all the houses in the area.

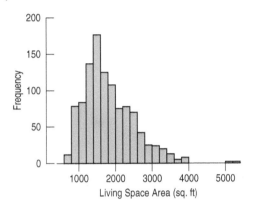

Count	1057
Mean	1819.498 sq. ft
Std Dev	662.9414
Min	672
Q1	1342
Median	1675
Q3	2223
Max	5228
Missing	0

a) What is the range of these sizes?
b) Between what sizes do the central 50% of these houses lie?
c) What summary statistics would you use to describe these data?
d) Write a brief description of these data (shape, center, and spread).

43. Food sales. Sales (in $) for one week were collected for 18 stores in a food store chain in the northeastern United States. The stores and the towns they are located in vary in size.

a) Make a suitable display of the sales from the data provided.
b) Summarize the central value for sales for this week with a median and mean. Why do they differ?

c) Given what you know about the distribution, which of these measures does the better job of summarizing the stores' sales? Why?
d) Summarize the spread of the sales distribution with a standard deviation and with an IQR.
e) Given what you know about the distribution, which of these measures does the better job of summarizing the spread of stores' sales? Why?
f) If we were to remove the outliers from the data, how would you expect the mean, median, standard deviation, and IQR to change?

44. Insurance profits. Insurance companies don't know whether a policy they've written is profitable until the policy matures (expires). To see how they've performed recently, an analyst looked at mature policies and investigated the net profit to the company (in $).

a) Make a suitable display of the profits from the data provided.
b) Summarize the central value for the profits with a median and mean. Why do they differ?
c) Given what you know about the distribution, which of these measures might do a better job of summarizing the company's profits? Why?
d) Summarize the spread of the profit distribution with a standard deviation and with an IQR.
e) Given what you know about the distribution, which of these measures might do a better job of summarizing the spread in the company's profits? Why?
f) If we were to remove the outliers from the data, how would you expect the mean, median, standard deviation, and IQR to change?

45. iPod failures. MacInTouch (www.macintouch.com/reliability/ipodfailures.html) surveyed readers about the reliability of their iPods. Of the 8926 iPods owned, 7510 were problem-free while the other 1416 failed. From the data on the CD, compute the failure rate for each of the 17 iPod models. Produce an appropriate graphical display of the failure rates and briefly describe the distribution. (To calculate the failure rate, divide the number failed by the sum of the number failed and the number OK for each model and then multiply by 100.)

46. Unemployment. The data set provided contains 2008 unemployment rates for 23 developed countries (www.oecd.org). Produce an appropriate graphical display and briefly describe the distribution of unemployment rates.

47. Gas prices, part 2. Below are boxplots of weekly gas prices at a service station in the Midwest United States (prices in $ per gallon).

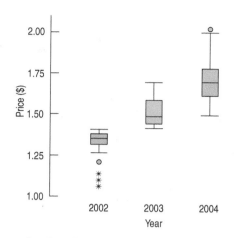

a) Compare the distribution of prices over the three years.

b) In which year were the prices least stable (most volatile)? Explain.

48. Fuel economy. American automobile companies are becoming more motivated to improve the fuel efficiency of the automobiles they produce. It is well known that fuel efficiency is impacted by many characteristics of the car. Describe what these boxplots tell you about the relationship between the number of cylinders a car's engine has and the car's fuel economy (mpg).

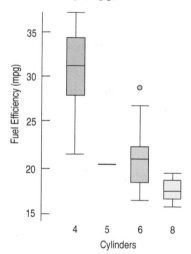

49. Wine prices. The boxplots display case prices (in dollars) of wines produced by vineyards along three of the Finger Lakes in upstate New York.

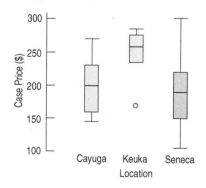

a) Which lake region produces the most expensive wine?

b) Which lake region produces the cheapest wine?

c) In which region are the wines generally more expensive?

d) Write a few sentences describing these prices.

50. Ozone. Ozone levels (in parts per billion, ppb) were recorded at sites in New Jersey monthly between 1926 and 1971. Here are boxplots of the data for each month (over the 46 years) lined up in order (January = 1).

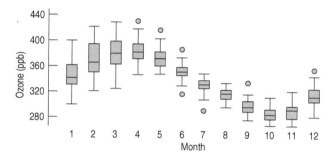

a) In what month was the highest ozone level ever recorded?

b) Which month has the largest IQR?

c) Which month has the smallest range?

d) Write a brief comparison of the ozone levels in January and June.

e) Write a report on the annual patterns you see in the ozone levels.

51. Derby speeds. How fast do horses run? Kentucky Derby winners top 30 miles per hour, as shown in the graph. This graph shows the percentage of Kentucky Derby winners that have run *slower* than a given speed. Note that few have won running less than 33 miles per hour, but about 95% of the winning horses have run less than 37 miles per hour. (A cumulative frequency graph like this is called an **ogive**.)

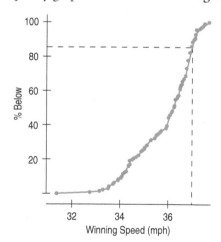

a) Estimate the median winning speed.

b) Estimate the quartiles.

c) Estimate the range and the IQR.

d) Create a boxplot of these speeds.

e) Write a few sentences about the speeds of the Kentucky Derby winners.

52. Mutual fund, part 3. Here is an ogive of the distribution of monthly returns for a group of aggressive (or high growth) mutual funds over a period of 25 years from 1975 to 1999. (Recall from Exercise 51 that an ogive, or cumulative relative frequency graph, shows the percent of cases at or below a certain value. Thus this graph always begins at 0% and ends at 100%.)

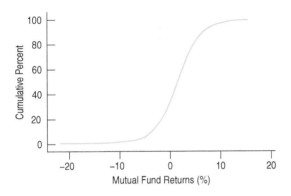

a) Estimate the median.
b) Estimate the quartiles.
c) Estimate the range and the IQR.
d) Create a boxplot of these returns.

53. Test scores. Three Statistics classes all took the same test. Here are histograms of the scores for each class.

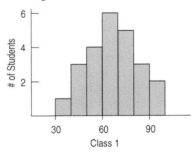

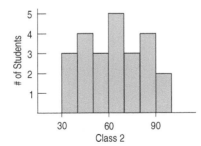

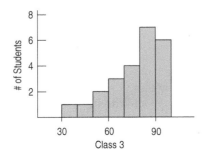

a) Which class had the highest mean score?
b) Which class had the highest median score?
c) For which class are the mean and median most different? Which is higher? Why?
d) Which class had the smallest standard deviation?
e) Which class had the smallest IQR?

54. Test scores, again. Look again at the histograms of test scores for the three Statistics classes in Exercise 53.

a) Overall, which class do you think performed better on the test? Why?
b) How would you describe the shape of each distribution?
c) Match each class with the corresponding boxplot.

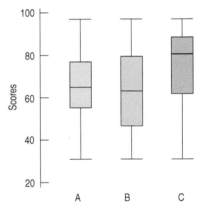

55. Quality control holes. Engineers at a computer production plant tested two methods for accuracy in drilling holes into a PC board. They tested how fast they could set the drilling machine by running 10 boards at each of two different speeds. To assess the results, they measured the distance (in inches) from the center of a target on the board to the center of the hole. The data and summary statistics are shown in the table.

	Fast	Slow
	0.000101	0.000098
	0.000102	0.000096
	0.000100	0.000097
	0.000102	0.000095
	0.000101	0.000094
	0.000103	0.000098
	0.000104	0.000096
	0.000102	0.975600
	0.000102	0.000097
	0.000100	0.000096
Mean	0.000102	0.097647
StdDev	0.000001	0.308481

Write a report summarizing the findings of the experiment. Include appropriate visual and verbal displays of the distributions, and make a recommendation to the engineers if they are most interested in the accuracy of the method.

56. Fire sale. A real estate agent notices that houses with fireplaces often fetch a premium in the market and wants to assess the difference in sales price of 60 homes that recently sold. The data and summary are shown in the table.

	No Fireplace	Fireplace
	142,212	134,865
	206,512	118,007
	50,709	138,297
	108,794	129,470
	68,353	309,808
	123,266	157,946
	80,248	173,723
	135,708	140,510
	122,221	151,917
	128,440	235,105,000
	221,925	259,999
	65,325	211,517
	87,588	102,068
	88,207	115,659
	148,246	145,583
	205,073	116,289
	185,323	238,792
	71,904	310,696
	199,684	139,079
	81,762	109,578
	45,004	89,893
	62,105	132,311
	79,893	131,411
	88,770	158,863
	115,312	130,490
	118,952	178,767
		82,556
		122,221
		84,291
		206,512
		105,363
		103,508
		157,513
		103,861
Mean	**116,597.54**	**7,061,657.74**
Median	**112,053**	**136,581**

Write a report summarizing the findings of the investigation. Include appropriate visual and verbal displays of the distributions, and make a recommendation to the agent about the average premium that a fireplace is worth in this market.

57. Customer database. A philanthropic organization has a database of millions of donors that they contact by mail to raise money for charities. One of the variables in the database, *Title*, contains the title of the person or persons printed on the address label. The most common are Mr., Ms., Miss, and Mrs., but there are also Ambassador and Mrs., Your Imperial Majesty, and Cardinal, to name a few others. In all there are over 100 different titles, each with a corresponding numeric code. Here are a few of them.

Code	Title
000	MR.
001	MRS.
1002	MR. and MRS.
003	MISS
004	DR.
005	MADAME
006	SERGEANT
009	RABBI
010	PROFESSOR
126	PRINCE
127	PRINCESS
128	CHIEF
129	BARON
130	SHEIK
131	PRINCE AND PRINCESS
132	YOUR IMPERIAL MAJESTY
135	M. ET MME.
210	PROF.
⋮	⋮

An intern who was asked to analyze the organization's fundraising efforts presented these summary statistics for the variable *Title*.

Mean	54.41
StdDev	957.62
Median	1
IQR	2
n	94649

a) What does the mean of 54.41 mean?
b) What are the typical reasons that cause measures of center and spread to be as different as those in this table?
c) Is that why these are so different?

58. CEOs. For each CEO, a code is listed that corresponds to the industry of the CEO's company. Here are a few of the codes and the industries to which they correspond.

Industry	Industry Code	Industry	Industry Code
Financial services	1	Energy	12
Food/drink/tobacco	2	Capital goods	14
Health	3	Computers/ communications	16
Insurance	4	Entertainment/ information	17
Retailing	6	Consumer non- durables	18
Forest products	9	Electric utilities	19
Aerospace/defense	11		

A recently hired investment analyst has been assigned to examine the industries and the compensations of the CEOs. To start the analysis, he produces the following histogram of industry codes.

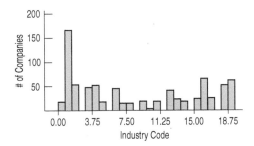

a) What might account for the gaps seen in the histogram?
b) What advice might you give the analyst about the appropriateness of this display?

59. Mutual funds types. The 64 mutual funds of Exercise 27 are classified into three types: U.S. Domestic Large Cap Funds, U.S. Domestic Small/Mid Cap Funds, and International Funds. Compare the 3-month return of the three types of funds using an appropriate display and write a brief summary of the differences.

60. Car discounts, part 3. The discounts negotiated by the car buyers in Exercise 28 are classified by whether the buyer was Male (code = 0) or Female (code = 1). Compare the discounts of men vs. women using an appropriate display and write a brief summary of the differences.

61. Houses for sale. Each house listed on the multiple listing service (MLS) is assigned a sequential ID number. A recently hired real estate agent decided to examine the MLS numbers in a recent random sample of homes for sale by one real estate agency in nearby towns. To begin the analysis, the agent produces the following histogram of ID numbers.

a) What might account for the distribution seen in the histogram?
b) What advice might you give the analyst about the appropriateness of this display?

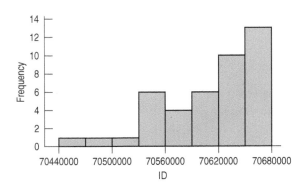

62. Zip codes. Holes-R-Us, an Internet company that sells piercing jewelry, keeps transaction records on its sales. At a recent sales meeting, one of the staff presented the following histogram and summary statistics of the zip codes of the last 500 customers, so that the staff might understand where sales are coming from. Comment on the usefulness and appropriateness of this display.

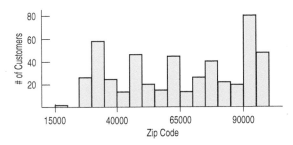

*63. Hurricanes. Buying insurance for property loss from hurricanes has become increasingly difficult since hurricane Katrina caused record property loss damage. Many companies have refused to renew policies or write new ones. The data set provided contains the total number of hurricanes by every full decade from 1851 to 2000 (from the National Hurricane Center). Some scientists claim that there has been an increase in the number of hurricanes in recent years.

a) Create a histogram of these data.
b) Describe the distribution.
c) Create a time series plot of these data.
d) Discuss the time series plot. Does this graph support the claim of these scientists, at least up to the year 2000?

*64. Hurricanes, part 2. Using the hurricanes data set, examine the number of major hurricanes (category 3, 4, or 5) by every full decade from 1851 to 2000.

a) Create a histogram of these data.
b) Describe the distribution.
c) Create a timeplot of these data.
d) Discuss the timeplot. Does this graph support the claim of scientists that the number of major hurricanes has been increasing (at least up through the year 2000)?

65. Productivity study. The National Center for Productivity releases information on the efficiency of workers. In a recent report, they included the following graph showing a rapid rise in productivity. What questions do you have about this?

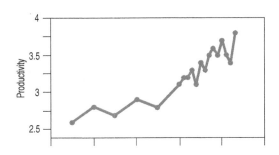

66. Productivity study revisited. A second report by the National Center for Productivity analyzed the relationship between productivity and wages. Comment on the graph they used.

67. Real estate, part 2. The 1057 houses described in Exercise 42 have a mean price of $167,900, with a standard deviation of $77,158. The mean living area is 1819 sq. ft., with a standard deviation of 663 sq. ft. Which is more unusual, a house in that market that sells for $400,000 or a house that has 4000 sq. ft of living area? Explain.

68. Tuition, 2008. The data set provided contains the average tuition of private four-year colleges and universities as well as the average 2007–2008 tuitions for each state seen in Exercise 25. The mean tuition charged by a public two-year college was $2763, with a standard deviation of $988. For private four-year colleges the mean was $21,259, with a standard deviation of $6241. Which would be more unusual: a state whose average public two-year college is $700 or a state whose average private four-year college tuition was $10,000? Explain.

69. Food consumption. FAOSTAT, the Food and Agriculture Organization of the United Nations, collects information on the production and consumption of more than

Country	Alcohol	Meat	Country	Alcohol	Meat
Australia	29.56	242.22	Luxembourg	34.32	197.34
Austria	40.46	242.22	Mexico	13.52	126.50
Belgium	34.32	197.34	Netherlands	23.87	201.08
Canada	26.62	219.56	New Zealand	25.22	228.58
Czech Republic	43.81	166.98	Norway	17.58	129.80
Denmark	40.59	256.96	Poland	20.70	155.10
Finland	25.01	146.08	Portugal	33.02	194.92
France	24.88	225.28	Slovakia	26.49	121.88
Germany	37.44	182.82	South Korea	17.60	93.06
Greece	17.68	201.30	Spain	28.05	259.82
Hungary	29.25	179.52	Sweden	20.07	155.32
Iceland	15.94	178.20	Switzerland	25.32	159.72
Ireland	55.80	194.26	Turkey	3.28	42.68
Italy	21.68	200.64	United Kingdom	30.32	171.16
Japan	14.59	93.28	United States	26.36	267.30

200 food and agricultural products for 200 countries around the world. Here are two tables, one for meat consumption (per capita in kg per year) and one for alcohol consumption (per capita in gallons per year). The United States leads in meat consumption with 267.30 pounds, while Ireland is the largest alcohol consumer at 55.80 gallons.

Using z-scores, find which country is the larger consumer of both meat and alcohol together.

70. World Bank. The World Bank, through their Doing Business project (www.doingbusiness.org), ranks nearly 200 economies on the ease of doing business. One of their rankings measures the ease of starting a business and is made up (in part) of the following variables: number of required start-up procedures, average start-up time (in days), and average start-up cost (in % of per capita income). The following table gives the mean and standard deviations of these variables for 95 economies.

	Procedures (#)	Time (Days)	Cost (%)
Mean	7.9	27.9	14.2
SD	2.9	19.6	12.9

Here are the data for three countries.

	Procedures	Time	Cost
Spain	10	47	15.1
Guatemala	11	26	47.3
Fiji	8	46	25.3

a) Use z-scores to combine the three measures.
b) Which country has the best environment after combining the three measures? Be careful—a lower rank indicates a better environment to start up a business.

*71. Regular gas. The data set provided contains U.S. regular retail gasoline prices (cents/gallon) from August 20, 1990 to May 28, 2007, from a national sample of gasoline stations obtained from the U.S. Department of Energy.

a) Create a histogram of the data and describe the distribution.
b) Create a time series plot of the data and describe the trend.
c) Which graphical display seems the more appropriate for these data? Explain.

*72. Home price index. Standard and Poor's Case-Shiller® Home Price Index measures the residential housing market in 20 metropolitan regions across the United States. The national index is a composite of the 20 regions and can be found in the data set provided.

a) Create a histogram of the data and describe the distribution.
b) Create a time series plot of the data and describe the trend.
c) Which graphical display seems the more appropriate for these data? Explain.

*73. Unemployment rate, 2010. The histogram shows the monthly U.S. unemployment rate from January 2001 to January 2010.

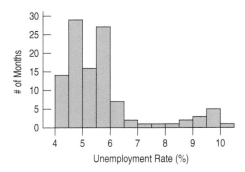

Here is the time series plot for the same data.

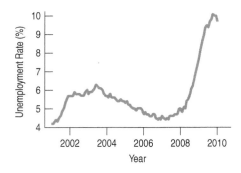

a) What features of the data can you see in the histogram that aren't clear in the time series plot?
b) What features of the data can you see in the time series plot that aren't clear in the histogram?
c) Which graphical display seems the more appropriate for these data? Explain.
d) Write a brief description of unemployment rates over this time period in the United States.

*74. Mutual fund performance. The following histogram displays the monthly returns for a group of mutual funds considered aggressive (or high growth) over a period of 22 years from 1975 to 1997.

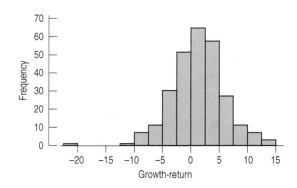

Here is the time series plot for the same data.

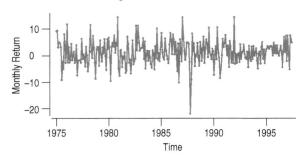

a) What features of the data can you see in the histogram that aren't clear from the time series plot?
b) What features of the data can you see in the time series plot that aren't clear in the histogram?
c) Which graphical display seems the more appropriate for these data? Explain.
d) Write a brief description of monthly returns over this time period.

75. Assets. Here is a histrogram of the assets (in millions of dollars) of 79 companies chosen from the *Forbes* list of the nation's top corporations.

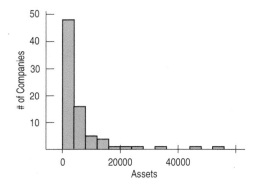

a) What aspect of this distribution makes it difficult to summarize, or to discuss, center and spread?
b) What would you suggest doing with these data if we want to understand them better?

76. Assets, again. Here are the same data you saw in Exercise 75 after re-expressions as the square root of assets and the logarithm of assets.

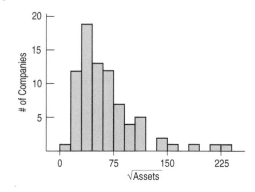

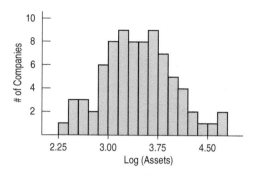

a) Which re-expression do you prefer? Why?

b) In the square root re-expression, what does the value 50 actually indicate about the company's assets?

Just Checking Answers

1 Incomes are probably skewed to the right and not symmetric, making the median the more appropriate measure of center. The mean will be influenced by the high end of family incomes and not reflect the "typical" family income as well as the median would. It will give the impression that the typical income is higher than it is.

2 An IQR of 30 mpg would mean that only 50% of the cars get gas mileages in an interval 30 mpg wide. Fuel economy doesn't vary that much. 3 mpg is reasonable. It seems plausible that 50% of the cars will be within about 3 mpg of each other. An IQR of 0.3 mpg would mean that the gas mileage of half the cars varies little from the estimate. It's unlikely that cars, drivers, and driving conditions are that consistent.

3 We'd prefer a standard deviation of 2 months. Making a consistent product is important for quality. Customers want to be able to count on the MP3 player lasting somewhere close to 5 years, and a standard deviation of 2 years would mean that life spans were highly variable.

Answers

1. a)

b)

c)

d) 1|14
   2|0225699
   3|0002224558
   4|244488

3. a) Unimodal.
   b) Around 35 years old.
   c) Fairly symmetric.
   d) No outliers.

5. a) About the same. The distribution is fairly symmetric.
   b) 31.84 years.
   c) 32 years.

7. a) Q1 26; Q3 38 (Answers may vary slightly.)
   b) Q1 26; Q3 38
   c) IQR = 12 years
   d) sd = 9.84 years

9. a) The distribution is skewed to the right. There are a few negative values. The range is about $6000.
   b) The mean will be larger because the distribution is right skewed.
   c) Because of the skewness, the median is a better summary.

11. a)

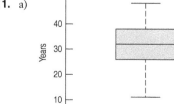

b) No.
c) 32 + 1.5*12 = 50 years old

13. a) Skewed to the right, since the mean is much greater than the median.
b) Yes, at least one high outlier, since 250 is far greater than Q3 + 1.5 IQRs.
c) We don't know how far the high whisker should go because we don't know the largest value inside the fence.

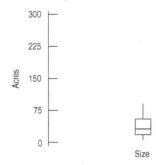

15. The ages of the women are generally higher than the men by about 10 years. As the boxplot shows, more than 3/4 of the women are older than all the men.

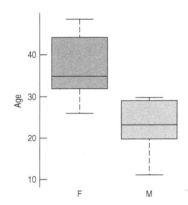

17. Sales in Location #1 were higher than sales in Location #2 in every week. The company might want to compare other stores in locations like these to see if this phenomenon holds true for other locations.

19. a) 11 has a z-score of −2.12; 48 has a z-score of +1.64.
b) The min, 11, is more extreme.
c) 61.36 years old.

21. 16, 16, 36, 49, 49, 64, 100
Skewed to the high end.

23. Answers will vary.

25. This distribution is nearly symmetric and unimodal, centered at around $2500. The range is about $6000. Most of the tuitions lie between $1000 and $4000.

27. The distribution is unimodal and skewed to the right with two high outliers. The median is near 10%.

29. a) Five-Number Summary (Answers may vary depending on software.)

Min.	1st Qu.	Median	3rd Qu.	Max.
−10.820	7.092	11.270	17.330	94.940

b) Median = 11.275%; IQR = 10.24%
c)

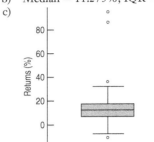

d) The histogram makes the skewness of the distribution clear.

31. The stem-and-leaf display shows that many of the acreage values end in 0 or 5. Perhaps this is evidence that they are rounding or estimating the value. There is a high outlier near 240.

```
24 | 0
22 |
20 |
18 |
16 |
14 | 0
12 | 0
10 | 0
 8 | 0
```
```
6 | 920
4 | 553500
2 | 8655210987520
0 | 751000086
```
Key: 8|0 = 80 acres

33. a) Wayne Gretzky—Games played per season

```
8 | 000000122
7 | 8899
7 | 0344
6 |
6 | 4
5 |
5 |
4 | 58
4 |
```
Key: 7|8 = 78 games

b)

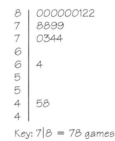

c) The distribution of the number of games played per season by Wayne Gretzky is skewed to the low end and has low outliers. The median is 78, and the range is 37 games.

d) There are two outlier seasons with 45 and 48 games. He may have been injured. The season with 64 games is also separated by a gap.

35. a) The median because the distribution is skewed.
b) Lower, because the distribution is skewed toward the low end.
c) That display is not a histogram. It's a time series plot using bars to represent each point. The histogram should split up the number of home runs into bins, not display the number of home runs over time.

37. a) Descriptive Statistics: Price ($)

Minimum	Q1	Median	Q3	Maximum
2.21	2.51	2.61	2.72	3.05

b) Range = max − min = 3.05 − 2.21 = $0.84; IQR = Q3 − Q1 = 2.72 − 2.51 = $0.21

c)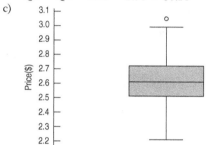

d) Symmetric with one high outlier. The mean is $2.62, with a standard deviation of $0.156.
e) There is one unusually high price that is greater than $3.00 per frozen pizza.

39. As we can see from the histogram and boxplot, the distribution of gasoline use is unimodal and skewed to the left with two low outliers, the District of Columbia and New York State. D.C. is a city, and New York may be dominated by New York City. Because of public transportation, gasoline usage is lower per capita in cities. The median usage is 485.7 gal./yr per capita with an IQR of about 81.75 gal./yr (values from different software may vary slightly). The minimum is D.C. with 209.5, and the maximum is Wyoming with 589.18 gal./yr.

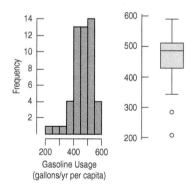

41. a) 1611 yards.
b) Between Quartile 1 = 5585.75 yards, and Quartile 3 = 6131 yards.
c) The distribution of golf course lengths appears roughly symmetric, so the mean and SD are appropriate.

d) The distribution of the lengths of all the golf courses in Vermont is roughly unimodal and symmetric. The mean length of the golf courses is approximately 5900 yards and the standard deviation is 386.6 yd.

43. a) A boxplot is shown. A histogram would also be appropriate.

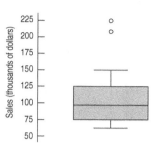

b) Descriptive Statistics: Sales ($) (Different statistics software may yield different results.)

Variable	N	Mean	SE Mean	StDev	Minimum
Sales ($)	18	107845	11069	46962	62006

Q1	Median	Q3	Maximum
173422.5	95975	112330.0	224504

The mean sale is $107,845, and the median is $95,975. The mean is higher because the outliers pull it up.
c) The median because the distribution has outliers.
d) The standard deviation of the distribution is $46,962, and the IQR is $38,907.50 (answers may vary due to different quartile algorithms).
e) The IQR because the outliers inflate the standard deviation.
f) The mean would decrease. The standard deviation would decrease. The median and IQR would be relatively unaffected.

45. A histogram shows that the distribution is unimodal and skewed to the left. There do not appear to be any outliers. The median failure rate for these 17 models is 16.2%. The middle 50% of the models have failure rates between 10.87% and 21.2%. The best rate is 3.17% for the 60GB Video model, and the worst is the 40GB Click Wheel at 29.85%.

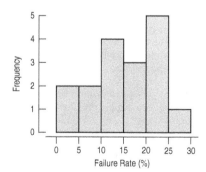

47. a) Gas prices increased over the three-year period, and the spread increased as well. The distribution of prices in 2002 was skewed to the left with several low outliers. Since then, the distribution has been increasingly skewed to the right. There is a high outlier in 2004, although it appears to be pretty close to the upper fence.
b) The distribution of gas prices in 2004 shows the greatest range and the biggest IQR, so the prices varied a great deal.

49. a) Seneca Lake.
   b) Seneca Lake.
   c) Keuka Lake.
   d) Cayuga Lake vineyards and Seneca Lake vineyards have approximately the same average case price, of about $200, while a typical Keuka Lake vineyard has a case price of about $260. Keuka Lake vineyards have consistently high case prices, between $240 and $280, with one low outlier at about $170 per case. Cayuga Lake vineyards have case prices from $140 to $270, and Seneca Lake vineyards have highly variable case prices, from $100 to $300.

51. a) The median speed is the speed at which 50% of the winning horses ran slower. Find 50% on the left, move straight over to the graph and down to a speed of about 36 mph.
   b) Q1 = 34.5 mph, and Q3 = 36.5 mph.
   c) Range = 7 mph
      IRQ = 2 mph.
   d)

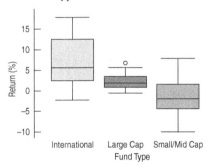

   e) The distribution of winning speeds in the Kentucky Derby is skewed to the left. The lowest winning speed is just under 31 mph, and the fastest speed is about 37.5 mph. The median speed is approximately 36 mph, and 75% of winning speeds are above 34.5 mph. Only a few percent of winners have had speeds below 33 mph.

53. a) Class 3.
   b) Class 3.
   c) Class 3 because it is the most highly skewed.
   d) Class 1.
   e) Probably Class 1. But without the actual scores, it is impossible to calculate the exact IQRs.

55. There is an extreme outlier for the slow-speed drilling. One hole was drilled almost an inch away from the center of the target! If that distance is correct, the engineers at the computer production plant should investigate the slow-speed drilling process closely. It may be plagued by extreme, intermittent inaccuracy. The outlier in the slow-speed drilling process is so extreme that no graphical display can display the distribution in a meaningful way while including that outlier. That distance should be removed before looking at a plot of the drilling distances.

With the outlier removed, we can see that the slow drilling process is more accurate. The greatest distance from the target for the slow drilling process, 0.000098 inches, is still more accurate than the smallest distance for the fast drilling process, 0.000100 inches.

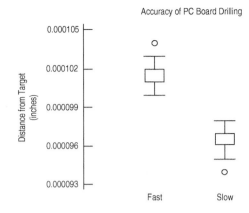

57. a) The mean of 54.41 is meaningless. These are categorical values.
   b) Typically, the mean and standard deviation are influenced by outliers and skewness.
   c) No. Summary statistics are only appropriate for quantitative data.

59. Over this 3-month period, International Funds generally outperformed the other two. Almost half of the International Funds outperformed all the funds in the other two categories. U.S. Domestic Large Cap Funds did better than U.S. Domestic Small/Mid Cap Funds in general. Large Cap funds had the least variation of the three types.

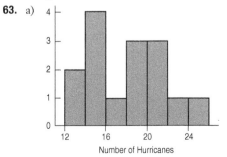

61. a) Even though MLS ID numbers are categorical identifiers, they are assigned sequentially, so this graph has some information. Most of the houses listed long ago have sold and are no longer listed.
   b) A histogram is generally not an appropriate display for categorical data.

63. a)

b) The distribution is fairly uniform. There do not appear to be any decades that would be considered to be outliers.

c)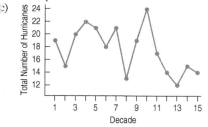

d) This graph does not support the claim that the number of hurricanes has increased in recent decades.

What is the *x*-axis? If it is time, what are the units? Months? Years? Decades? How is "productivity" measured?

The house that sells for $400,000 has a *z*-score of $(400000 - 267900)/77158 = 3.01$, but the house with 4000 sq. ft. of living space has a *z*-score of $(4000 - 1819)/663 = 3.29$. So it's even more unusual.

U.S. *z*-scores are -0.04 and 1.63, total $= 1.59$. Ireland *z*-scores are 0.25 and 2.77, total 3.02. So Ireland "wins" the consumption battle.

a) The histogram shows that the distribution of prices is strongly skewed to the right.

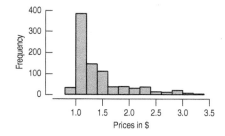

b) Prices were relatively stable until the late 1990s, when they started increasing. Since 2005, the prices have been higher and unstable.

c) The time series plot because the prices change over time.

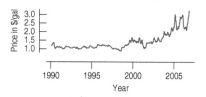

73. a) The bimodality of the distribution.

b) The trend over time.

c) The time series plot because it reveals much more of the structure of the data.

d) Unemployment decreased steadily from about 5.6% in 1995 to below 4.0% by 2000, and then increased sharply to between 5.5 and 6.0% from 2002 to 2004.

75. a) The distribution is skewed. That makes it difficult to estimate anything meaningful from the graph.

b) Transform these data using either square roots or logs.

Correlation and Linear Regression

Lowe's

In 1921 Lucius S. Lowe opened a hardware store in North Wilkesboro, North Carolina. After his death, his son Jim and son-in-law Carl Buchan took over the store. After World War II, the company expanded under Buchan's leadership. By purchasing materials directly from manufacturers, Lowe's was able to offer lower prices to its customers, most of whom were contractors. By 1955 Lowe's had six stores. Most had a small retail floor with limited inventory and a lumberyard out back near the railroad tracks. By the late 1960s, Lowe's had grown to more than 50 stores and sales of about $100 million. When new home construction almost stopped in the later part of the 1970s, Lowe's researched the market and found that stores that served do-it-yourself homeowners did well even during home-building slumps. So they began to shift their focus and expand their stores.

By the late 1980s Lowe's had more than 300 stores, but those stores still averaged barely more than 20,000 square feet, and The Home Depot had shot past Lowe's, pioneering a new big-box era. Lowe's studied that market and, in 1989, committed to developing big-box stores, taking a $71.3 million restructuring charge in 1991 to cover the costs of closing, relocating, and remodeling about half of the company's stores. By 1996 there were

From Chapter 6 of *Business Statistics*, Second Edition, Norean R. Sharpe, Richard D. De Veaux, Paul F. Velleman.

more than 400 Lowe's stores, now averaging more than 75,000 square feet per unit. Sales grew rapidly after the restructuring, increasing from $3.1 billion to $8.6 billion. Net earnings reached $292.2 million in 1996. The company has continued to grow rapidly, working to bolster its number two position and to cut into The Home Depot's lead.

In 2000, Bob Tillman, Chairman and CEO of Lowe's, released a policy promising that all wood products sold would not be sourced from rainforests. Lowe's was awarded the Energy Star retail partner of the year in 2004 for its outstanding contribution to reducing greenhouse gas emissions and in 2007 Lowe's won an Environmental Excellence Award from the U.S. Environmental Protection Agency SmartWay Transport Partnership.

WHO	Years
WHAT	Lowe's Net *Sales* and U.S. Expenditures on Residential *Improvements* and Repairs
UNITS	Both in $M
WHEN	1985–2007
WHERE	United States
WHY	To assess Lowe's sales relative to the home improvement market

Lowe's sells to both contractors and homeowners. Perhaps knowing how much Americans spend on home improvement nationally can help us predict Lowe's sales. Here's a plot showing Lowe's annual net sales against the U.S. Census Bureau's measure of the amount spent by homeowners on residential improvement and repairs.[1]

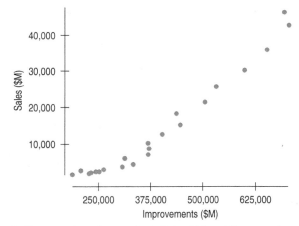

Figure 1   Lowe's annual net *Sales* ($M) and the amount spent annually on residential *Improvements* and Repairs ($M) from 1985–2007.

If you were asked to summarize this relationship, what would you say? Clearly Lowe's sales grew when home improvement expenses grew. This plot is an example of a **scatterplot**, which plots one quantitative variable against another. Just by looking at a scatterplot, you can see patterns, trends, relationships, and even the occasional unusual values standing apart from the others. Scatterplots are the best way to start observing the relationship between two *quantitative* variables.

---

[1]www.census.gov/const/C50/histtab1.pdf. The census bureau gives quarterly values. We've combined them to obtain annual totals.

Relationships between variables are often at the heart of what we'd like to learn from data.

- Is consumer confidence related to oil prices?
- What happens to customer satisfaction as sales increase?
- Is an increase in money spent on advertising related to sales?
- What is the relationship between a stock's sales volume and its price?

Questions such as these relate two quantitative variables and ask whether there is an association between them. Scatterplots are the ideal way to picture such associations.

1 Looking at Scatterplots

WHO	Cities in the United States
WHAT	*Congestion Cost* Per Person and Peak Period *Freeway Speed*
UNITS	*Congestion Cost* Per Person ($ per person per year); Peak Period *Freeway Speed* (mph)
WHEN	2000
WHERE	United States
WHY	To examine the relationship between congestion on the highways and its impact on society and business

The Texas Transportation Institute, which studies the mobility provided by the nation's transportation system, issues an annual report on traffic congestion and its costs to society and business. Figure 2 shows a scatterplot of the annual *Congestion Cost* Per Person of traffic delays (in dollars) in 65 cities in the United States against the Peak Period *Freeway Speed* (mph).

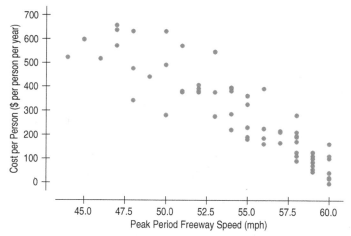

Figure 2 Congestion Cost Per Person ($ per year) of traffic delays against Peak Period Freeway Speed (mph) for 65 U.S. cities.

Everyone looks at scatterplots. But, if asked, many people would find it hard to say what to look for in a scatterplot. What do *you* see? Try to describe the scatterplot of *Congestion Cost* against *Freeway Speed*.

You might say that the **direction** of the association is important. As the peak freeway speed goes up, the cost of congestion goes down. A pattern that runs from the upper left to the lower right is said to be **negative**. A pattern running the other way is called **positive**.

The second thing to look for in a scatterplot is its **form**. If there is a straight line relationship, it will appear as a cloud or swarm of points stretched out in a generally consistent, straight form. For example, the scatterplot of traffic congestion has an underlying **linear** form, although some points stray away from it.

Scatterplots can reveal many different kinds of patterns. Often they will not be straight, but straight line patterns are both the most common and the most useful for statistics.

> Look for **Direction**: What's the sign—positive, negative, or neither?

If the relationship isn't straight, but curves gently, while still increasing or decreasing steadily, we can often find ways to straighten it out. But if

Look for Form: Straight, curved, something exotic, or no pattern?

it curves sharply—up and then down, for example, —then you'll need more advanced methods.

The third feature to look for in a scatterplot is the **strength** of the relationship.

At one extreme, do the points appear tightly clustered in a single stream (whether straight, curved, or bending all over the place)? Or, at the other extreme, do the points seem to be so variable and spread out that we can barely discern any

Look for Strength: How much scatter?

trend or pattern? The traffic congestion plot shows moderate scatter around a generally straight form. That indicates that there's a moderately strong linear relationship between cost and speed.

Finally, always look for the unexpected. Often the most interesting discovery in a scatterplot is something you never thought to look for. One example of such a surprise is an unusual observation, or **outlier**, standing away from the overall pattern of the scatterplot. Such a point is almost always interesting and deserves special attention. You may see entire clusters or subgroups that stand away or show a trend in a different direction than the rest of the plot. That should raise questions about why they are different. They may be a clue that you should split the data into subgroups instead of looking at them all together.

Look for Unusual Features: Are there unusual observations or subgroups?

For Example   Creating a scatterplot

The first automobile crash in the United States occurred in New York City in 1896, when a motor vehicle collided with a "pedal-cycle" rider. Cycle/car accidents are a serious concern for insurance companies. About 53,000 cyclists have died in traffic crashes in the United States since 1932. Demographic information such as this is often available from government agencies. It can be useful to insurers, who use it to set appropriate rates, and to retailers, who must plan what safety equipment to stock and how to present it to their customers. This becomes a more pressing concern when the demographic profiles change over time.

Here's data on the mean age of cyclists killed each year during the decade from 1998 to 2008. (Source: National Highway Transportation Safety Agency, http://www-nrd.nhtsa.dot.gov/Pubs/811156.PDF)

Year	Mean Age
1998	32
1999	33
2000	35
2001	36
2002	37
2003	36
2004	39
2005	39
2006	41
2007	40
2008	41

Question: Make a scatterplot and summarize what it says.

Answer:

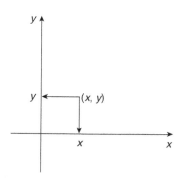

The mean age of cyclist traffic deaths has been increasing almost linearly during this period. The trend is a strong one.

Descartes was a philosopher, famous for his statement cogito, ergo sum: I think, therefore I am.

2 Assigning Roles to Variables in Scatterplots

Scatterplots were among the first modern mathematical displays. The idea of using two axes at right angles to define a field on which to display values can be traced back to René Descartes (1596–1650), and the playing field he defined in this way is formally called a *Cartesian plane*, in his honor.

The two axes Descartes specified characterize the scatterplot. The axis that runs up and down is, by convention, called the *y*-axis, and the one that runs from side to side is called the *x*-axis. These terms are standard.[2]

To make a scatterplot of two quantitative variables, assign one to the *y*-axis and the other to the *x*-axis. As with any graph, be sure to label the axes clearly, and indicate the scales of the axes with numbers. Scatterplots display *quantitative* variables. Each variable has units, and these should appear with the display—usually near each axis. Each point is placed on a scatterplot at a position that corresponds to values of these two variables. Its horizontal location is specified by its *x*-value, and its vertical location is specified by its *y*-value variable. Together, these are known as *coordinates* and written (x, y).

Scatterplots made by computer programs (such as the two we've seen in this chapter) often do not—and usually should not—show the *origin*, the point at $x = 0$, $y = 0$ where the axes meet. If both variables have values near or on both sides of zero, then the origin will be part of the display. If the values are far from zero, though, there's no reason to include the origin. In fact, it's far better to focus on the part of the Cartesian plane that contains the data. In our example about freeways,

---

[2]The axes are also called the "ordinate" and the "abscissa"—but we can never remember which is which because statisticians don't generally use these terms. In Statistics (and in all statistics computer programs) the axes are generally called "*x*" (abscissa) and "*y*" (ordinate) and are usually labeled with the names of the corresponding variables.

none of the speeds was anywhere near 0 mph, so the computer drew the scatterplot in Figure 2 with axes that don't quite meet.

Which variable should go on the *x*-axis and which on the *y*-axis? What we want to know about the relationship can tell us how to make the plot. We often have questions such as:

- Is Lowe's employee satisfaction related to productivity?
- Are increased sales at Lowe's reflected in the stock price?
- What other factors besides residential improvements are related to Lowe's sales?

In all of these examples, one variable plays the role of the **explanatory** or **predictor variable**, while the other takes on the role of the **response variable**. We place the explanatory variable on the *x*-axis and the response variable on the *y*-axis. When you make a scatterplot, you can assume that those who view it will think this way, so choose which variables to assign to which axes carefully.

The roles that we choose for variables have more to do with how we *think* about them than with the variables themselves. Just placing a variable on the *x*-axis doesn't necessarily mean that it explains or predicts *anything*, and the variable on the *y*-axis may not respond to it in any way. We plotted *Congestion Cost* Per Person against peak *Freeway Speed*, thinking that the slower traffic moves, the more it costs in delays. But maybe *spending* $500 per person in freeway improvement would increase speed. If we were examining that option, we might choose to plot *Congestion Cost* Per Person as the explanatory variable and *Freeway Speed* as the response.

The *x*- and *y*-variables are sometimes referred to as the **independent** and **dependent** variables, respectively. The idea is that the *y*-variable *depends* on the *x*-variable and the *x*-variable acts *independently* to make *y* respond. These names, however, conflict with other uses of the same terms in Statistics. Instead, we'll sometimes use the terms "explanatory" or "predictor variable" and "response variable" when we're discussing roles, but we'll often just say *x-variable* and *y-variable*.

Notation Alert!

So *x* and *y* are reserved letters as well, but not just for labeling the axes of a scatterplot. In Statistics, the assignment of variables to the *x*- and *y*-axes (and choice of notation for them in formulas) often conveys information about their roles as predictor or response.

For Example   Assigning roles to variables

Question: When examining the ages of victims in cycle/car accidents, why does it make the most sense to plot *year* on the *x*-axis and *mean age* on the *y*-axis?

Answer: We are interested in how the age of accident victims might change over time, so we think of the year as the basis for prediction and the mean age of victims as the variable that is predicted.

3   Understanding Correlation

WHO	Quarters
WHAT	Expenditures for *Improvement* and *Replacement* of residences
UNITS	Both in $M
WHEN	1985–2004
WHERE	United States
WHY	To understand components of the U.S. Census Bureau's total expenditures for residential maintenance

The U.S. Census Bureau reports separate components of their quarterly home improvement expenditure data. For example, they categorize some expenditures as *Improvement* and others as *Replacement*. How are these related to each other? Figure 3 shows the scatterplot.

As you might expect, expenses for both improvement and replacement tend to rise and fall together. There is a clear positive association, and the scatterplot looks linear. But how strong is the association? If you had to put a number (say, between 0 and 1) on the strength of the association, what would it be? Your measure shouldn't depend on the choice of units for the variables. After all, if sales had been recorded in euros instead of dollars or maintenance expenditures in billions of dollars rather than millions, the scatterplot would look the same. The direction, form, and strength won't change, so neither should our measure of the association's strength.

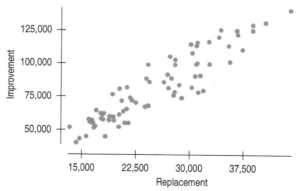

Figure 3 Quarterly expenditures on *Improvement* and *Replacement* in residential maintenance and repairs from 1985 to 2004, both in $M.

We saw a way to remove the units previously. We can standardize each of the variables, finding $z_x = \left(\dfrac{x - \bar{x}}{s_x}\right)$ and $z_y = \left(\dfrac{y - \bar{y}}{s_y}\right)$. With these, we can compute a measure of strength that you've probably heard of: the **correlation coefficient**:

$$r = \frac{\sum z_x z_y}{n - 1}.$$

Keep in mind that the x's and y's are paired. For each quarter, we have a replacement expenditure and an improvement expenditure. To find the correlation we multiply each standardized value by the standardized value it is paired with and add up those *crossproducts*. Then we divide the total by the number of pairs minus one, $n - 1$.[3]

For residential *Improvement* and *Replacement*, the correlation coefficient is 0.92.

There are alternative formulas for the correlation in terms of the variables x and y. Here are two of the more common:

$$r = \frac{\sum (x - \bar{x})(y - \bar{y})}{\sqrt{\sum (x - \bar{x})^2 \sum (y - \bar{y})^2}} = \frac{\sum (x - \bar{x})(y - \bar{y})}{(n - 1)s_x s_y}.$$

These formulas can be more convenient for calculating correlation by hand, but the form given using z-scores is best for understanding what correlation means.

Correlation Conditions

Correlation measures the strength of the *linear* association between two *quantitative* variables. Before you use correlation, you must check three *conditions*:

- **Quantitative Variables Condition:** Correlation applies only to quantitative variables. Don't apply correlation to categorical data masquerading as quantitative. Check that you know the variables' units and what they measure.

- **Linearity Condition:** Sure, you can *calculate* a correlation coefficient for any pair of variables. But correlation measures the strength only of the *linear* association and will be misleading if the relationship is not straight enough. What is "straight enough"? This question may sound too informal for a statistical condition, but that's really the point. We can't verify whether a relationship is linear or not. Very

---

[3]The same $n - 1$ we used for calculating the standard deviation.

Notation Alert! ————

The letter r is always used for correlation, so you can't use it for anything else in Statistics. Whenever you see an "r," it's safe to assume it's a correlation.

few relationships between variables are perfectly linear, even in theory, and scatterplots of real data are never perfectly straight. How nonlinear looking would the scatterplot have to be to fail the condition? This is a judgment call that you just have to think about. Do you think that the underlying relationship is curved? If so, then summarizing its strength with a correlation would be misleading.

- **Outlier Condition:** Unusual observations can distort the correlation and can make an otherwise small correlation look big or, on the other hand, hide a large correlation. It can even give an otherwise positive association a negative correlation coefficient (and vice versa). When you see an outlier, it's often a good idea to report the correlation both with and without the point.

Each of these conditions is easy to check with a scatterplot. Many correlations are reported without supporting data or plots. You should still think about the conditions. You should be cautious in interpreting (or accepting others' interpretations of) the correlation when you can't check the conditions for yourself.

By Hand

Finding the correlation coefficient

To find the correlation coefficient by hand, we'll use a formula in original units, rather than z-scores. This will save us the work of having to standardize each individual data value first. Start with the summary statistics for both variables: $\bar{x}, \bar{y}, s_x,$ and s_y. Then find the deviations as we did for the standard deviation, but now in both x and y: $(x - \bar{x})$ and $(y - \bar{y})$. For each data pair, multiply these deviations together: $(x - \bar{x}) \times (y - \bar{y})$. Add the products up for all data pairs. Finally, divide the sum by the product of $(n - 1) \times s_x \times s_y$ to get the correlation coefficient.

Here we go.

Suppose the data pairs are:

x	6	10	14	19	21
y	5	3	7	8	12

Then $\bar{x} = 14, \bar{y} = 7, s_x = -6.20,$ and $s_y = 3.39$

Deviations in x	Deviations in y	Product
$6 - 14 = -8$	$5 - 7 = -2$	$-8 \times -2 = 16$
$10 - 14 = -4$	$3 - 7 = -4$	16
$14 - 14 = 0$	$7 - 7 = 0$	0
$19 - 14 = 5$	$8 - 7 = 1$	5
$21 - 14 = 7$	$12 - 7 = 5$	35

Add up the products: $16 + 16 + 0 + 5 + 35 = 72$
Finally, we divide by $(n - 1) \times s_x \times s_y = (5 - 1) \times 6.20 \times 3.39 = 84.07$
The ratio is the correlation coefficient:

$$r = 72/84.07 = 0.856$$

Just Checking

For the years 1992 to 2002, the quarterly stock price of the semiconductor companies Cypress and Intel have a correlation of 0.86.

1 Before drawing any conclusions from the correlation, what would you like to see? Why?

2 If your coworker tracks the same prices in euros, how will this change the correlation? Will you need to know the exchange rate between euros and U.S. dollars to draw conclusions?

3 If you standardize both prices, how will this affect the correlation?

4 In general, if on a given day the price of Intel is relatively low, is the price of Cypress likely to be relatively low as well?

5 If on a given day the price of Intel stock is high, is the price of Cypress stock definitely high as well?

Guided Example   Customer Spending

Shutterstock

A major credit card company sends an incentive to its best customers in hope that the customers will use the card more. They wonder how often they can offer the incentive. Will repeated offerings of the incentive result in repeated increased credit card use? To examine this question, an analyst took a random sample of 184 customers from their highest use segment and investigated the charges in the two months in which the customers had received the incentive.

PLAN

Setup State the objective. Identify the quantitative variables to examine. Report the time frame over which the data have been collected and define each variable. (State the W's.)

Our objective is to investigate the association between the amount that a customer charges in the two months in which they received an incentive. The customers have been randomly selected from among the highest use segment of customers. The variables measured are the total credit card charges (in $) in the two months of interest.

✓ **Quantitative Variable Condition.** Both variables are quantitative. Both charges are measured in dollars.

Make the scatterplot and clearly label the axes to identify the scale and units.

Because we have two quantitative variables measured on the same cases, we can make a scatterplot.

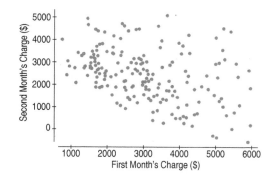

Check the conditions.

✓ **Linearity Condition.** The scatterplot is straight enough.

✓ **Outlier Condition.** There are no obvious outliers.

(continued)

DO	Mechanics Once the conditions are satisfied, calculate the correlation with technology.	The correlation is −0.391. The negative correlation coefficient confirms the impression from the scatterplot.
REPORT	Conclusion Describe the direction, form, and the strength of the plot, along with any unusual points or features. Be sure to state your interpretation in the proper context.	MEMO **Re: Credit Card Spending** We have examined some of the data from the incentive program. In particular, we looked at the charges made in the first two months of the program. We noted that there was a negative association between charges in the second month and charges in the first month. The correlation was −0.391, which is only moderately strong, and indicates substantial variation. We've concluded that although the observed pattern is negative, these data do not allow us to find the causes of this behavior. It is likely that some customers were encouraged by the offer to increase their spending in the first month, but then returned to former spending patterns. It is possible that others didn't change their behavior until the second month of the program, increasing their spending at that time. Without data on the customers' pre-incentive spending patterns it would be hard to say more. We suggest further research, and we suggest that the next trial extend for a longer period of time to help determine whether the patterns seen here persist.

Correlation Properties

Because correlation is so widely used as a measure of association it's a good idea to remember some of its basic properties. Here's a useful list of facts about the correlation coefficient:

<table>
<tr><td>

How Strong Is Strong?

There's little agreement on what the terms "weak," "moderate," and "strong" mean. The same correlation might be strong in one context and weak in another. A correlation of 0.7 between an economic index and stock market prices would be exciting, but finding "only" a correlation of 0.7 between a drug dose and blood pressure might be seen as a failure by a pharmaceutical company. Use these terms cautiously and be sure to report the correlation and show a scatterplot so others can judge the strength for themselves.

</td></tr>
</table>

- **The sign of a correlation coefficient gives the direction of the association.**

- **Correlation is always between −1 and +1.** Correlation *can* be exactly equal to −1.0 or +1.0, but watch out. These values are unusual in real data because they mean that all the data points fall *exactly* on a single straight line.

- **Correlation treats x and y symmetrically.** The correlation of x with y is the same as the correlation of y with x.

- **Correlation has no units.** This fact can be especially important when the data's units are somewhat vague to begin with (customer satisfaction, worker efficiency, productivity, and so on).

- **Correlation is not affected by changes in the center or scale of either variable.** Changing the units or baseline of either variable has no effect on the correlation coefficient because the correlation depends only on the z-scores.

- **Correlation measures the strength of the *linear* association between the two variables.** Variables can be strongly associated but still have a small correlation if the association is not linear.

- **Correlation is sensitive to unusual observations.** A single outlier can make a small correlation large or make a large one small.

Correlation Tables

Sometimes you'll see the correlations between each pair of variables in a data set arranged in a table. The rows and columns of the table name the variables, and the cells hold the correlations.

	Volume	Close	Net earnings
Volume	1.000		
Close	0.396	1.000	
Net earnings	0.477	0.464	1.000

Table 1   A correlation table for some other variables measured quarterly during the period 1985 to 2007. *Volume* = number of shares of Lowe's traded, *Close* = closing price of Lowe's stock, *Net Earnings* = Lowe's reported net earnings for the quarter.

Correlation tables are compact and give a lot of summary information at a glance. They can be an efficient way to start to look at a large data set. The diagonal cells of a correlation table always show correlations of exactly 1.000, and the upper half of the table is symmetrically the same as the lower half (can you see why?), so by convention, only the lower half is shown. A table like this can be convenient, but be sure to check for linearity and unusual observations or the correlations in the table may be misleading or meaningless. Can you be sure, looking at Table 1, that the variables are linearly associated? Correlation tables are often produced by statistical software packages. Fortunately, these same packages often offer simple ways to make all the scatterplots you need to look at.[4]

For Example   Finding the correlation coefficient

Question: What is the correlation of *mean age* and *year* for the cyclist accident data?

Answer: Working by hand following the method in the sidebar:

$$\bar{x} = 2003, s_x = 3.32$$
$$\bar{y} = 37.18, s_y = 3.09$$

The sum of the cross-product of the deviations is found as follows:

$$\sum (x - \bar{x})(y - \bar{y}) = 99$$

Putting the sum of the cross-products in the numerator and $(n - 1) \times s_x \times s_y$ in the denominator, we get

$$\frac{99}{(11 - 1) \times 3.32 \times 3.09} = 0.965$$

For *mean age* and *year*, the correlation coefficient is 0.965. That indicates a strong linear association. Because this is a time series, it indicates a strong trend.

---

[4]A table of scatterplots arranged just like a correlation table is sometimes called a *scatterplot matrix*, or SPLOM, and is easily created using a statistics package.

Shutterstock

4 Lurking Variables and Causation

An educational researcher finds a strong association between height and reading ability among elementary school students in a nationwide survey. Taller children tend to have higher reading scores. Does that mean that students' height *causes* their reading scores to go up? No matter how strong the correlation is between two variables, there's no simple way to show from observational data that one variable causes the other. A high correlation just increases the temptation to think and to say that the *x*-variable *causes* the *y*-variable. Just to make sure, let's repeat the point again.

No matter how strong the association, no matter how large the *r* value, no matter how straight the form, there is no way to conclude from a high correlation *alone* that one variable causes the other. There's always the possibility that some third variable—a **lurking variable**—is affecting both of the variables you have observed. In the reading score example, you may have already guessed that the lurking variable is the age of the child. Older children tend to be taller and have stronger reading skills. But even when the lurking variable isn't as obvious, resist the temptation to think that a high correlation implies causation. Here's another example.

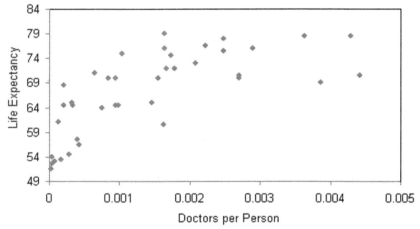

Figure 4   *Life Expectancy* and numbers of *Doctors per Person* in 40 countries shows a fairly strong, positive linear relationship with a correlation of 0.705. (Scatterplot created in **Excel**.)

The scatterplot shows the *Life Expectancy* (average of men and women, in years) for each of 40 countries of the world, plotted against the number of *Doctors per Person* in each country. The strong positive association ($r = 0.705$) seems to confirm our expectation that more *Doctors per Person* improves health care, leading to longer lifetimes and a higher *Life Expectancy*. Perhaps we should send more doctors to developing countries to increase life expectancy.

If we increase the number of doctors, will the life expectancy increase? That is, would adding more doctors *cause* greater life expectancy? Could there be another explanation of the association? Figure 5 shows another scatterplot. *Life Expectancy* is still the response, but this time the predictor variable is not the number of doctors, but the number of *Televisions per Person* in each country. The positive association in this scatterplot looks even *stronger* than the association in the previous plot. If we wanted to calculate a correlation, we should straighten the plot first, but even from this plot, it's clear that higher life expectancies are associated with more televisions per person. Should we conclude that increasing the number of televisions extends lifetimes? If so, we should send televisions instead of doctors to developing

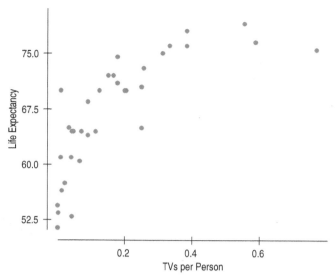

Figure 5 *Life Expectancy* and number of *Televisions per Person* shows a strong, positive (although clearly not linear) relationship.

countries. Not only is the association with life expectancy stronger, but televisions are cheaper than doctors.

What's wrong with this reasoning? Maybe we were a bit hasty earlier when we concluded that doctors *cause* greater life expectancy. Maybe there's a lurking variable here. Countries with higher standards of living have both longer life expectancies *and* more doctors. Could higher living standards cause changes in the other variables? If so, then improving living standards might be expected to prolong lives, increase the number of doctors, and increase the number of televisions. From this example, you can see how easy it is to fall into the trap of mistakenly inferring causality from a correlation. For all we know, doctors (or televisions) *do* increase life expectancy. But we can't tell that from data like these no matter how much we'd like to. Resist the temptation to conclude that *x* causes *y* from a correlation, no matter how obvious that conclusion seems to you.

For Example   Understanding causation

Question: An insurance company analyst suggests that the data on ages of cyclist accident deaths are actually due to the entire population of cyclists getting older and not to a change in the safe riding habits of older cyclists. What would we call the *mean cyclist age* if we had that variable available?

Answer: It would be a lurking variable. If the entire population of cyclists is aging then that would lead to the average age of cyclists in accidents increasing.

5   The Linear Model

Let's return to the relationship between Lowe's sales and home improvement expenditures between 1985 and 2007. In Figure 1 (repeated here) we saw a strong, positive, linear relationship, so we can summarize its strength with a correlation. For this relationship, the correlation is 0.976.

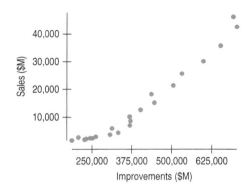

That's quite strong, but the strength of the relationship is only part of the picture. Lowe's management might want to predict sales based on the census bureau's estimate of residential improvement expenditures for the next year. That's a reasonable business question, but to answer it we'll need a model for the trend. The correlation says that there seems to be a strong linear association between the variables, but it doesn't tell us what that association is.

Of course, we can say more. We can model the relationship with a line and give the equation. For Lowe's, we can find a linear model to describe the relationship we saw in Figure 1 between Lowe's *Sales* and residential *Improvements*. A **linear model** is just an equation of a straight line through the data. The points in the scatterplot don't all line up, but a straight line can summarize the general pattern with only a few parameters. This model can help us understand how the variables are associated.

Residuals

We know the model won't be perfect. No matter what line we draw, it won't go through many of the points. The best line might not even hit any of the points. Then how can it be the "best" line? We want to find the line that somehow comes *closer* to all the points than any other line. Some of the points will be above the line and some below. A linear model can be written as $\hat{y} = b_0 + b_1 x$, where b_0 and b_1 are numbers estimated from the data and $\hat{y}$ (pronounced y-hat) is the **predicted value**. We use the *hat* to distinguish the predicted value from the observed value *y*. The difference between these two is called the **residual**:

$$e = y - \hat{y}.$$

The residual value tells us how far the model's prediction is from the observed value at that point. To find the residuals, we always subtract the predicted values from the observed ones.

Our question now is how to find the right line.

The Line of "Best Fit"

When we draw a line through a scatterplot, some residuals are positive, and some are negative. We can't assess how well the line fits by adding up all the residuals—the positive and negative ones would just cancel each other out. We need to find the line that's closest to all the points, and to do that, we need to make all the distances positive. We faced the same issue when we calculated a standard deviation to measure spread. And we deal with it the same way here: by squaring the residuals to make them positive. The sum of all the squared residuals tells us how well the line we drew fits the data—the smaller the sum, the better the fit. A different line will produce a different sum, maybe bigger, maybe smaller. The **line of best fit** is the line for which the sum of the squared residuals is smallest—often called the **least squares line**.

Positive or Negative?

A *negative* residual means the predicted value is too big—an overestimate. A *positive* residual shows the model makes an underestimate. These may actually seem backwards at first.

Notation Alert!

"Putting a hat on it" is standard Statistics notation to indicate that something has been predicted by a model. Whenever you see a hat over a variable name or symbol, you can assume it is the predicted version of that variable or symbol.

---

[5]Stigler, Steven M., "Gauss and the Invention of Least Squares," **Annals of Statistics, 9, (3)**, 1981, pp. 465-474.

This line has the special property that the variation of the data around the model, as seen in the residuals, is the smallest it can be for any straight line model for these data. No other line has this property. Speaking mathematically, we say that this line minimizes the sum of the squared residuals. You might think that finding this "least squares line" would be difficult. Surprisingly, it's not, although it was an exciting mathematical discovery when Legendre published it in 1805.

For Example   Interpreting the equation of a linear model

Question: The data on cyclist accident deaths show a linear pattern. Find and interpret the equation of a linear model for that pattern. Refer to the values given in the answer to the example "Finding the correlation coefficient."

Answer:

$$b = 0.965 \times \frac{3.09}{3.32} = 0.90$$

$$a = 37.18 - 0.90 \times 2003 = -1765.52$$

$$MeanAge = -1765.52 + 0.90\, Year$$

The mean age of cyclists killed in vehicular accidents has increased by about 0.9 years of age (about 11 months) per year during the decade observed by these data.

---

6   Correlation and the Line

Any straight line can be written as:

$$y = b_0 + b_1 x.$$

If we were to plot all the (x, y) pairs that satisfy this equation, they'd fall exactly on a straight line. We'll use this form for our linear model. Of course, with real data, the points won't all fall on the line. So, we write our model as $\hat{y} = b_0 + b_1 x$, using $\hat{y}$ for the predicted values, because it's the predicted values (not the data values) that fall on the line. If the model is a good one, the data values will scatter closely around it.

For the Lowe's sales data, the line is:

$$\widehat{Sales} = -19{,}679 + 0.346\, Improvements.$$

What does this mean? The **slope,** 0.346, says that we can expect a year in which residential improvement spending is 1 million dollars higher to be one in which Lowe's sales will be about 0.346 \$M (\$346,000) higher. Slopes are always expressed in y-units per x-units. They tell you how the response variable changes for a one unit step in the predictor variable. So we'd say that the slope is 0.346 million dollars of *Sales* per million dollars of *Improvements*.

The **intercept,** $-19{,}679$, is the value of the line when the x-variable is zero. What does it mean here? The intercept often serves just as a starting value for our predictions. We don't interpret it unless a 0 value for the predictor variable would really mean something under the circumstances. The Lowe's model is based on years in which annual spending on residential improvements is between 50 and 100 billion dollars. It's unlikely to be appropriate if there were no such spending at all. In this case, we wouldn't interpret the intercept.

How do we find the slope and intercept of the least squares line? The formulas are simple. The model is built from the summary statistics we've used before. We'll need the correlation (to tell us the strength of the linear association), the standard deviations (to give us the units), and the means (to tell us where to locate the line).

Who Was First?

One of history's most famous disputes of authorship was between Gauss and Legendre over the method of "least squares." Legendre was the first to publish the solution to finding the best fit line through data in 1805, at which time Gauss claimed to have known it for years. There is some evidence that, in fact, Gauss may have been right, but he hadn't bothered to publish it, and had been unable to communicate its importance to other scientists[5]. Gauss later referred to the solution as "*our* method" (principium *nostrum*), which certainly didn't help his relationship with Legendre.

Just Checking

A scatterplot of sales per month (in thousands of dollars) vs. number of employees for all the outlets of a large computer chain shows a relationship that is straight, with only moderate scatter and no outliers. The correlation between *Sales* and *Employees* is 0.85, and the equation of the least squares model is:

$$\widehat{Sales} = 9.564 + 122.74\ Employees$$

6 What does the slope of 122.74 mean?

7 What are the units of the slope?

8 The outlet in Dallas, Texas, has 10 more employees than the outlet in Cincinnati. How much more *Sales* do you expect it to have?

The slope of the line is computed as:

$$b_1 = r\frac{s_y}{s_x}.$$

We've already seen that the correlation tells us the sign and the strength of the relationship, so it should be no surprise to see that the slope inherits this sign as well. If the correlation is positive, the scatterplot runs from lower left to upper right, and the slope of the line is positive.

Correlations don't have units, but slopes do. How *x* and *y* are measured—what units they have—doesn't affect their correlation, but does change the slope. The slope gets its units from the ratio of the two standard deviations. Each standard deviation has the units of its respective variable. So, the units of the slope are a ratio, too, and are always expressed in units of *y* per unit of *x*.

How do we find the intercept? If you had to predict the *y*-value for a data point whose *x*-value was average, what would you say? The best fit line predicts $\bar{y}$ for points whose *x*-value is $\bar{x}$. Putting that into our equation and using the slope we just found gives:

$$\bar{y} = b_0 + b_1\bar{x}$$

and we can rearrange the terms to find:

$$b_0 = \bar{y} - b_1\bar{x}.$$

Finding the Regression Coefficients for the Lowe's Data

Summary statistics:

$$Sales: \bar{y} = 13,564.17;\ s_y = 14,089.61$$

$$Improvements: \bar{x} = 96,009.8;\ s_x = 39,036.8$$

$$Correlation = 0.976$$

So, $b_1 = r\dfrac{s_y}{s_x} = (0.976)\dfrac{14,089.61}{39,036.8}$

$\quad = 0.352$ ($M Sales per $M Improvement expenditures)

And

$$b_0 = \bar{y} - b_1\bar{x} = 13,564.17 - (0.352)96,009.8 = -20,231.3$$

The equation from the computer output has slope 0.346 and intercept −19,679. The differences are due to rounding error. We've shown the calculation using rounded summary statistics, but if you are doing this by hand, you should always keep all digits in intermediate steps.

It's easy to use the estimated linear model to predict Lowe's *Sales* for any amount of national spending on residential *Improvements*. For example, in 2007 the total was $172,150(M). To estimate Lowe's *Sales*, we substitute this value for x in the model:

$$\widehat{Sales} = -19{,}679 + 0.346 \times 172{,}150 = 39{,}885$$

Sales actually were 46,927 ($M), so the residual of $46{,}927 - 39{,}885 = 7{,}042$ ($M) tells us how much better Lowe's did than the model predicted.

Least squares lines are commonly called **regression** lines. Although this name is an accident of history (as we'll soon see), "regression" almost always means "the linear model fit by least squares." Clearly, regression and correlation are closely related. We'll need to check the same conditions for regression as we did for correlation:

1. **Quantitative Variables Condition**
2. **Linearity Condition**
3. **Outlier Condition**

A little later in the chapter we'll add two more.

Understanding Regression from Correlation

The slope of a regression line depends on the units of both x and y. Its units are the units of y per unit of x. The units are expressed in the slope because $b_1 = r\dfrac{s_y}{s_x}$. The correlation has no units, but each standard deviation is measured in the units of its respective variable. For our regression of Lowe's *Sales* on home *Improvements*, the slope was millions of dollars of sales *per* million dollars of improvement expenditure.

It can be useful to see what happens to the regression equation if we were to standardize both the predictor and response variables and regress z_y on z_x. For both these standardized variables, the standard deviation is 1 and the means are zero. That means that the slope is just r, and the intercept is 0 (because both $\bar{y}$ and $\bar{x}$ are now 0).

This gives us the simple equation for the regression of standardized variables:

$$\hat{z}_y = rz_x.$$

Although we don't usually standardize variables for regression, it can be useful to think about what this means. Thinking in z-scores is a good way to understand what the regression equation is doing. The equation says that for every standard deviation we deviate from the mean in x, we predict that y will be r standard deviations away from the mean in y.

Let's be more specific. For the Lowe's example, the correlation is 0.976. So, we know immediately that:

$$\hat{z}_{Sales} = 0.976 \, z_{Improvements}.$$

That means that a change of one standard deviation in expenditures on *Improvements* corresponds in our model to a 0.976 standard deviation change in *Sales*.

7 Regression to the Mean

Suppose you were told that a new male student was about to join the class and you were asked to guess his height in inches. What would be your guess? A good guess would be the mean height of male students. Now suppose you are also told that this student had a grade point average (GPA) of 3.9—about 2 SDs above the mean

GPA. Would that change your guess? Probably not. The correlation between GPA and height is near 0, so knowing the GPA value doesn't tell you anything and doesn't move your guess. (And the standardized regression equation, $\hat{z}_y = rz_x$, tells us that as well, since it says that we should move 0×2 SDs from the mean.)

On the other hand, if you were told that, measured in centimeters, the student's height was 2 SDs above the mean, you'd know his height in inches. There's a perfect correlation between *Height* in inches and *Height* in centimeters ($r = 1$), so you know he's 2 SDs above mean height in inches as well.

What if you were told that the student was 2 SDs above the mean in shoe size? Would you still guess that he's of average height? You might guess that he's taller than average, since there's a positive correlation between height and shoe size. But would you guess that he's 2 SDs above the mean? When there was no correlation, we didn't move away from the mean at all. With a perfect correlation, we moved our guess the full 2 SDs. Any correlation between these extremes should lead us to move somewhere between 0 and 2 SDs above the mean. (To be exact, our best guess would be to move $r \times 2$ standard deviations away from the mean.)

Notice that if x is 2 SDs above its mean, we won't ever move more than 2 SDs away for y, since r can't be bigger than 1.0. So each predicted y tends to be closer to its mean (in standard deviations) than its corresponding x was. This property of the linear model is called **regression to the mean**. This is why the line is called the regression line.

Losevsky Pavel/Shutterstock

Sir Francis Galton was the first to speak of "regression," although others had fit lines to data by the same method.

The First Regression

Sir Francis Galton related the heights of sons to the heights of their fathers with a regression line. The slope of his line was less than 1. That is, sons of tall fathers were tall, but not as much above the average height as their fathers had been above their mean. Sons of short fathers were short, but generally not as far from their mean as their fathers. Galton interpreted the slope correctly as indicating a "regression" toward the mean height—and "regression" stuck as a description of the method he had used to find the line.

Math Box

Equation of the line of best fit

Where does the equation of the line of best fit come from? To write the equation of any line, we need to know a point on the line and the slope. It's logical to expect that an average x will correspond to an average y, and, in fact, the line does pass through the point $(\bar{x}, \bar{y})$. (This is not hard to show as well.)

To think about the slope, we look once again at the z-scores. We need to remember a few things.

1. The mean of any set of z-scores is 0. This tells us that the line that best fits the z-scores passes through the origin $(0, 0)$.

2. The standard deviation of a set of z-scores is 1, so the variance is also 1. This means that $\dfrac{\sum(z_y - \bar{z}_y)^2}{n-1} = \dfrac{\sum(z_y - 0)^2}{n-1} = \dfrac{\sum z_y^2}{n-1} = 1$, a fact that will be important soon.

3. The correlation is $r = \dfrac{\sum z_x z_y}{n-1}$, also important soon.

Remember that our objective is to find the slope of the best fit line. Because it passes through the origin, the equation of the best fit line will be of the form $\hat{z}_y = mz_x$. We want to find the value for m that will minimize the sum of the squared errors. Actually we'll divide that sum by $n - 1$ and minimize this mean squared error (MSE). Here goes:

Minimize: $\qquad\qquad MSE = \dfrac{\sum(z_y - \hat{z}_y)^2}{n-1}$

Since $\hat{z}_y = mz_x$: $\qquad MSE = \dfrac{\sum(z_y - mz_x)^2}{n-1}$

$$\text{Square the binomial:} \qquad = \frac{\sum (z_y^2 - 2m z_x z_y + m^2 z_x^2)}{n - 1}$$

$$\text{Rewrite the summation:} \qquad = \frac{\sum z_y^2}{n - 1} - 2m \frac{\sum z_x z_y}{n - 1} + m^2 \frac{\sum z_x^2}{n - 1}$$

4. Substitute from (2) and (3): $\quad = 1 - 2mr + m^2$

This last expression is a quadratic. A parabola in the form $y = ax^2 + bx + c$ reaches its minimum at its turning point, which occurs when $x = \frac{-b}{2a}$. We can minimize the mean of squared errors by choosing

$$m = \frac{-(-2r)}{2(1)} = r.$$

The slope of the best fit line for z-scores is the correlation, r. This fact leads us immediately to two important additional results:

A slope with value r for z-scores means that a difference of 1 standard deviation in z_x corresponds to a difference of r standard deviations in $\hat{z}_y$. Translate that back to the original x and y values: "Over one standard deviation in x, up r standard deviations in $\hat{y}$."

The slope of the regression line is $b = \dfrac{r s_y}{s_x}$.

We know choosing $m = r$ minimizes the sum of the squared errors (SSE), but how small does that sum get? Equation (4) told us that the mean of the squared errors is $1 - 2mr + m^2$. When $m = r$, $1 - 2mr + m^2 = 1 - 2r^2 + r^2 = 1 - r^2$. This is the percentage of variability *not* explained by the regression line. Since $1 - r^2$ of the variability is *not* explained, the percentage of variability in y that *is* explained by x is r^2. This important fact will help us assess the strength of our models.

And there's still another bonus. Because r^2 is the percent of variability explained by our model, r^2 is at most 100%. If $r^2 \leq 1$, then $-1 \leq r \leq 1$, proving that correlations are always between -1 and $+1$.

Why *r* for *Correlation*?

In his original paper on correlation, Galton used r for the "index of correlation"—what we now call the correlation coefficient. He calculated it from the regression of y on x or of x on y after standardizing the variables, just as we have done. It's fairly clear from the text that he used r to stand for (standardized) regression.

8   Checking the Model

The linear regression model is perhaps the most widely used model in all of Statistics. It has everything we could want in a model: two easily estimated parameters, a meaningful measure of how well the model fits the data, and the ability to predict new values. It even provides a self-check in plots of the residuals to help us avoid all kinds of mistakes. Most models are useful only when specific **assumptions** are true. Of course, assumptions are hard—often impossible—to check. That's why we *assume* them. But we should check to see whether the assumptions are *reasonable*. Fortunately, we can often check *conditions* that provide information about the assumptions. For the linear model, we start by checking the same ones we checked earlier in this chapter for using correlation.

Linear models only make sense for quantitative data. The **Quantitative Data Condition** is pretty easy to check, but don't be fooled by categorical data recorded as numbers. You probably don't want to predict zip codes from credit card account numbers.

The regression model *assumes* that the relationship between the variables is, in fact, linear. If you try to model a curved relationship with a straight line, you'll usually get what you deserve. We can't ever verify that the underlying relationship between two variables is truly linear, but an examination of the scatterplot will let you decide whether the **Linearity Assumption** is reasonable. The **Linearity Condition** we used for correlation is designed to do precisely that and is satisfied if the scatterplot looks reasonably straight. If the scatterplot is not straight enough, stop. You can't use a linear model for just *any* two variables, even if they are related. The two variables must have a *linear* association, or the model won't mean a thing. Some nonlinear relationships can be saved by re-expressing the data to make the scatterplot more linear.

Watch out for outliers. The linearity assumption also requires that no points lie far enough away to distort the line of best fit. Check the **Outlier Condition** to make sure no point needs special attention. Outlying values may have large residuals, and squaring makes their influence that much greater. Outlying points can dramatically change a regression model. Unusual observations can even change the sign of the slope, misleading us about the direction of the underlying relationship between the variables.

Another assumption that is usually made when fitting a linear regression is that the residuals are independent of each other. We don't strictly need this assumption to fit the line, but to generalize from the data it's a crucial assumption and one that we'll come back to when we discuss inference. As with all assumptions, there's no way to be sure that **Independence Assumption** is true. However, we could check that the cases are a random sample from the population.

We can also check displays of the regression residuals for evidence of patterns, trends, or clumping, any of which would suggest a failure of independence. In the special case when we have a time series, a common violation of the Independence Assumption is for the errors to be correlated with each other (autocorrelation). The error our model makes today may be similar to the one it made yesterday. We can check this violation by plotting the residuals against time (usually *x* for a time series) and looking for patterns.

When our goal is just to explore and describe the relationship, independence isn't essential (and so we won't insist that the conditions relating to it be formally checked). However, when we want to go beyond the data at hand and make inferences for other situations this will be a crucial assumption, so it's good practice to think about it even now, especially for time series.

We always check conditions with a scatterplot of the data, but we can learn even more after we've fit the regression model. There's extra information in the residuals that we can use to help us decide how reasonable our model is and how well the model fits. So, we plot the residuals and check the conditions again.

The residuals are the part of the data that *hasn't* been modeled. We can write

$$Data = Predicted + Residual$$

or, equivalently,

$$Residual = Data - Predicted.$$

Or, as we showed earlier, in symbols:

$$e = y - \hat{y}.$$

A scatterplot of the residuals versus the *x*-values should be a plot without patterns. It shouldn't have any interesting features—no direction, no shape. It should stretch horizontally, showing no bends, and it should have no outliers. If you see nonlinearities, outliers, or clusters in the residuals, find out what the regression model missed.

Make a Picture

Check the scatterplot. The shape must be linear, or you can't use regression for the variables in their current form. And watch out for outliers.

Why e for *Residual?*

The easy answer is that *r* is already taken for correlation, but the truth is that *e* stands for "error." It's not that the data point is a mistake but that statisticians often refer to variability not explained by a model as error.

Let's examine the residuals from our regression of Lowe's *Sales* on residential *Improvement* expenditures.[6]

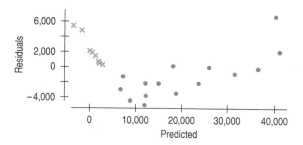

Figure 6 Residuals of the regression model predicting Lowe's *Sales* from Residential *Improvement* expenses 1985–2007. Now we can see that there are really two groups. Can we identify them?

These residuals hold a surprise. They seem to fall into two groups, one with a steeply declining trend (indicating sales that did not increase with residential improvements as fast as the regression model predicts) and one with an increasing trend. If we identify the two groups, we find that the red **x**'s are for the years 1985–1992 and the green dots are for the years 1993–2007. Recall that in 1991 Lowe's started a re-structuring plan to convert to big-box stores. This analysis suggests that it was a successful business decision but that we ought to fit a separate linear model to the years 1993–2007 where the linearity condition holds.

Not only can the residuals help check the conditions, but they can also tell us how well the model performs. The better the model fits the data, the less the residuals will vary around the line. The standard deviation of the residuals, s_e, gives us a measure of how much the points spread around the regression line. Of course, for this summary to make sense, the residuals should all share the same underlying spread. So we must *assume* that the standard deviation around the line is the same wherever we want the model to apply.

This new assumption about the standard deviation around the line gives us a new condition, called the **Equal Spread Condition**. The associated question to ask is does the plot have a consistent spread or does it fan out? We check to make sure that the spread of the residuals is about the same everywhere. We can check that either in the original scatterplot of y against x or in the scatterplot of residuals (or, preferably, in both plots). We estimate the **standard deviation of the residuals** in almost the way you'd expect:

$$s_e = \sqrt{\frac{\sum e^2}{n-2}}.$$

We don't need to subtract the mean of the residuals because $\bar{e} = 0$. Why divide by $n - 2$ rather than $n - 1$? We used $n - 1$ for s when we estimated the mean. Now we're estimating both a slope and an intercept. Looks like a pattern—and it is. We subtract one more for each parameter we estimate.

If we predict Lowe's *Sales* in 1999 when home *Improvements* totaled 100,250 $M, the regression model gives a predicted value of 15,032 $M. The actual value was about 12,946 $M. So our residual is 12,946 − 15,032 = −2,086. The value of s_e from the regression is 3170, so our residual is only 2086/3170 = 0.66 standard deviations away from the actual value. That's a fairly typical size for a residual because it's within two standard deviations.

Equal Spread Condition

This condition requires that the scatter is about equal for all *x*-values. It's often checked using a plot of residuals against predicted values. The underlying assumption of equal variance is also called *homoscedasticity*.

---

[6]Most computer statistics packages plot the residuals as we did in Figure 6, against the predicted values, rather than against x. When the slope is positive, the scatterplots are virtually identical except for the axes labels. When the slope is negative, the two versions are mirror images. Since all we care about is the patterns (or, better, lack of patterns) in the plot, either plot is useful.

For Example   Examining the residuals

Here is a scatterplot of the residuals for the linear model found in the example earlier in this chapter plotted against the predicted values:

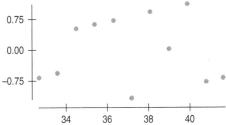

Question: Show how the plotted values were calculated. What does the plot suggest about the model?

Answer: The predicted values are the values of $\widehat{MeanAge}$ found for each year by substituting the year value in the linear model. The residuals are the differences between the actual mean ages and the predicted values for each year.

The plot shows some remaining pattern in the form of three nearly parallel trends. A further analysis may want to determine the reason for this pattern.

9   Variation in the Model and R^2

The variation in the residuals is the key to assessing how well the model fits. Let's compare the variation of the response variable with the variation of the residuals. Lowe's *Sales* has a standard deviation of 14,090 ($M). The standard deviation of the residuals is only 3,097 ($M). If the correlation were 1.0 and the model predicted the *Sales* values perfectly, the residuals would all be zero and have no variation. We couldn't possibly do any better than that.

On the other hand, if the correlation were zero, the model would simply predict 13,564 ($M) (the mean) for all menu items. The residuals from that prediction would just be the observed *Sales* values minus their mean. These residuals would

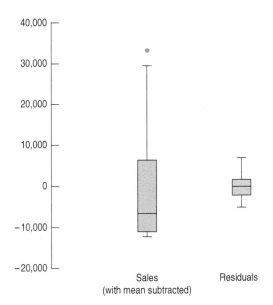

Figure 7   Compare the variability of *Sales* with the variability of the residuals from the regression. The means have been subtracted to make it easier to compare spreads. The variation left in the residuals is unaccounted for by the model, but it's less than the variation in the original data.

r and R²

Is a correlation of 0.80 twice as strong as a correlation of 0.40? Not if you think in terms of R^2. A correlation of 0.80 means an R^2 of $0.80^2 = 64\%$. A correlation of 0.40 means an R^2 of $0.40^2 = 16\%$—only a quarter as much of the variability accounted for. A correlation of 0.80 gives an R^2 *four* times as strong as a correlation of 0.40 and accounts for four times as much of the variability.

Some Extreme Tales

One major company developed a method to differentiate between proteins. To do so, they had to distinguish between regressions with R^2 of 99.99% and 99.98%. For this application, 99.98% was not high enough.

The president of a financial services company reports that although his regressions give R^2 below 2%, they are highly successful because those used by his competition are even lower.

have the same variability as the original data because, as we know, just subtracting the mean doesn't change the spread.

How well does the regression model do? Look at the boxplots in Figure 7. The variation in the residuals is smaller than in the data, but bigger than zero. That's nice to know, but how much of the variation is still left in the residuals? If you had to put a number between 0% and 100% on the fraction of the variation left in the residuals, what would you say?

All regression models fall somewhere between the two extremes of zero correlation and perfect correlation. We'd like to gauge where our model falls. Can we use the correlation to do that? Well, a regression model with correlation −0.5 is doing as well as one with correlation +0.5. They just have different directions. But if we *square* the correlation coefficient, we'll get a value between 0 and 1, and the direction won't matter. The squared correlation, r^2, gives the fraction of the data's variation accounted for by the model, and $1 - r^2$ is the fraction of the original variation left in the residuals. For the Lowe's *Sales* model, $r^2 = 0.976^2 = 0.952$ and $1 - r^2$ is 0.048, so only 4.8% of the variability in *Sales* has been left in the residuals.

All regression analyses include this statistic, although by tradition, it is written with a capital letter, R^2, and pronounced "*R*-squared." An R^2 of 0 means that none of the variance in the data is in the model; all of it is still in the residuals. It would be hard to imagine using that model for anything.

Because R^2 is a fraction of a whole, it is often given as a percentage.[7] For the Lowe's *Sales* data, R^2 is 95.2%.

When interpreting a regression model, you need to report what R^2 means. According to our linear model, 95.2% of the variability in Lowe's *Sales* is accounted for by variation in residential *Improvement* expenditures.

- **How can we see that R^2 is really the fraction of variance accounted for by the model?** It's a simple calculation. The variance of *Sales* is $14089.6^2 = 198,516,828$. If we treat the residuals as data, the variance of the residuals is $9,592,072$.[8] As a fraction of the variance of *Sales*, that's 0.483 or 4.83%. That's the fraction of the variance that is *not* accounted for by the model. The fraction that *is* accounted for is $100\% - 4.83\% = 95.2$, just the value we got for R^2.

How Big Should R^2 Be?

The value of R^2 is always between 0% and 100%. But what is a "good" R^2 value? The answer depends on the kind of data you are analyzing and on what you want to do with it. Just as with correlation, there is no value for R^2 that automatically

Just Checking

Let's go back to our regression of sales ($000) on number of employees again.

$$\widehat{Sales} = 9.564 + 122.74\ Employees$$

The R^2 value is reported as 71.4%.

9 What does the R^2 value mean about the relationship of *Sales* and *Employees*?

10 Is the correlation of *Sales* and *Employees* positive or negative? How do you know?

11 If we measured the *Sales* in thousands of euros instead of thousands of dollars, would the R^2 value change? How about the slope?

[7] By contrast, we usually give correlation coefficients as decimal values between −1.0 and 1.0.
[8] This isn't quite the same as squaring s_e which we discussed previously, but it's very close.

> **Sums of Squares**
>
> The sum of the squared residuals $\Sigma(y - \hat{y})^2$ is sometimes written as SSE (sum of squared errors). If we call $\Sigma(y - \bar{y})^2$ SST (for total sum of squares) then
>
> $$R^2 = 1 - \frac{\text{SSE}}{\text{SST}}.$$

determines that the regression is "good." Data from scientific experiments often have R^2 in the 80% to 90% range and even higher. Data from observational studies and surveys, though, often show relatively weak associations because it's so difficult to measure reliable responses. An R^2 of 30% to 50% or even lower might be taken as evidence of a useful regression. The standard deviation of the residuals can give us more information about the usefulness of the regression by telling us how much scatter there is around the line.

As we've seen, an R^2 of 100% is a perfect fit, with no scatter around the line. The s_e would be zero. All of the variance would be accounted for by the model with none left in the residuals. This sounds great, but it's too good to be true for real data.[9]

For Example   Understanding R^2

Question: Find and interpret the R^2 for the regression of cyclist death ages vs. time found in the example earlier in this chapter. (Hint: The calculation is a simple one.)

Answer: We are given the correlation, $r = 0.965$. R^2 is the square of this, or 0.9312. It tells us that 93.1% of the variation in the mean age of cyclist deaths can be accounted for by the trend of increasing age over time.

10   Reality Check: Is the Regression Reasonable?

Statistics don't come out of nowhere. They are based on data. The results of a statistical analysis should reinforce common sense. If the results are surprising, then either you've learned something new about the world or your analysis is wrong.

Whenever you perform a regression, think about the coefficients and ask whether they make sense. Is the slope reasonable? Does the direction of the slope seem right? The small effort of asking whether the regression equation is plausible will be repaid whenever you catch errors or avoid saying something silly or absurd about the data. It's too easy to take something that comes out of a computer at face value and assume that it makes sense.

Always be skeptical and ask yourself if the answer is reasonable.

Guided Example   Home Size and Price

Shutterstock

Real estate agents know the three most important factors in determining the price of a house are *location*, *location*, and *location*. But what other factors help determine the price at which a house should be listed? Number of bathrooms? Size of the yard? A student amassed publicly available data on thousands of homes in upstate New York. We've drawn a random sample of 1057 homes to examine house pricing. Among the variables she collected were the total living area (in square feet), number of bathrooms, number of bedrooms, size of lot (in acres), and age of house (in years). We will investigate how well the size of the house, as measured by living area, can predict the selling price.

---

[9]If you see an R^2 of 100%, it's a good idea to investigate what happened. You may have accidentally regressed two variables that measure the same thing.

PLAN

Setup State the objective of the study.

Identify the variables and their context.

Model We need to check the same conditions for regression as we did for correlation. To do that, make a picture. Never fit a regression without looking at the scatterplot first.

Check the Linearity, Equal Spread, and Outlier Conditions.

We want to find out how well the living area of a house in upstate NY can predict its selling price.

We have two quantitative variables: the living area (in square feet) and the selling price ($). These data come from public records in upstate New York in 2006.

✓ **Quantitative Variables Condition**

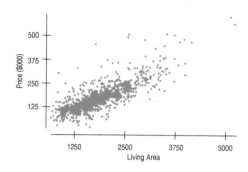

✓ **Linearity Condition** The scatterplot shows two variables that appear to have a fairly strong positive association. The plot appears to be fairly linear.

✓ **Equal Spread Condition** The scatterplot shows a consistent spread across the x-values.

✓ **Outlier Condition** There appear to be a few possible outliers, especially among large, relatively expensive houses. A few smaller houses are expensive for their size. We will check their influence on the model later.

We have two quantitative variables that appear to satisfy the conditions, so we will model this relationship with a regression line.

DO

Mechanics Find the equation of the regression line using a statistics package. Remember to write the equation of the model using meaningful variable names.

Once you have the model, plot the residuals and check the Equal Spread Condition again.

Our software produces the following output.

```
Dependent variable is: Price
1057 total cases
R squared = 62.43%
s = 57930 with 1000 − 2 = 998 df
Variable          Coefficient
Intercept         6378.08
Living Area       115.13
```

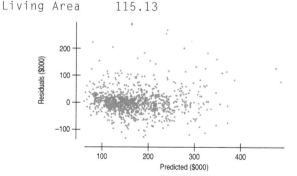

(continued)

The residual plot appears generally patternless. The few relatively expensive small houses are evident, but setting them aside and refitting the model did not change either the slope or intercept very much so we left them in. There is a slight tendency for cheaper houses to have less variation, but the spread is roughly the same throughout.

REPORT

Conclusion Interpret what you have found in the proper context.

MEMO

Re: Report on housing prices.

We examined how well the size of a house could predict its selling price. Data were obtained from recent sales of 1057 homes in upstate New York. The model is:

$$\widehat{Price} = \$6376.08 + 115.13 \times \text{Living Area}$$

In other words, from a base of \$6376.08, houses cost about \$115.13 per square foot in upstate NY.

This model appears reasonable from both a statistical and real estate perspective. Although we know that size is not the only factor in pricing a house, the model accounts for 62.4% of the variation in selling price.

As a reality check, we checked with several real estate pricing sites (www.realestateabc.com, www.zillow.com) and found that houses in this region were averaging \$100 to \$150 per square foot, so our model is plausible.

Of course, not all house prices are predicted well by the model. We computed the model without several of these houses, but their impact on the regression model was small. We believe that this is a reasonable place to start to assess whether a house is priced correctly for this market. Future analysis might benefit by considering other factors.

11   Nonlinear Relationships

Everything we've discussed in this chapter requires that the underlying relationship between two variables be linear. But what should we do when the relationship is nonlinear and we can't use the correlation coefficient or a linear model? There are three basic approaches, each with its advantages and disadvantages.

Let's consider an example. The Human Development Index (HDI) was developed by the United Nations as a general measure of quality of life in countries around the world. It combines economic information (GDP), life expectancy, and education. The growth of cell phone usage has been phenomenal worldwide. Is cell phone usage related to the developmental state of a country? Figure 8 shows a scatterplot of number of cell phones vs. HDI for 152 countries of the world.

We can look at the scatterplot and see that cell phone usage increases with increasing HDI. But the relationship is not straight. In Figure 8, we can easily see the bend in the form. But that doesn't help us summarize or model the relationship.

You might think that we should just fit some curved function such as an exponential or quadratic to a shape like this. But using curved functions is complicated, and the resulting model can be difficult to interpret. And many of the convenient

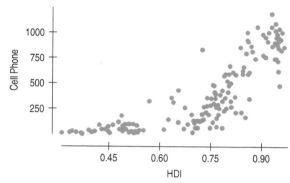

Figure 8   The scatterplot of number of cell phones (000s) vs. HDI for countries shows a bent relationship not suitable for correlation or regression.

associated statistics are not appropriate for such models. So this approach isn't often used.

Another approach allows us to summarize the strength of the association between the variables even when we don't have a linear relationship. The **Spearman rank correlation**[10] works with the *ranks* of the data rather than their values. To find the ranks we simply count from the lowest value to the highest so that rank 1 is assigned to the lowest value, rank 2 to the next lowest, and so on. Using ranks for both variables generally straightens out the relationship, as Figure 9 shows.

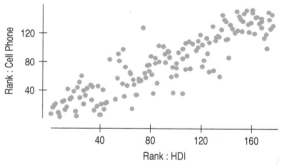

Figure 9   Plotting the ranks results in a plot with a straight relationship.

Now we can calculate a correlation on the ranks. The resulting correlation[11] summarizes the degree of relationship between two variables—but not, of course, of the degree of *linear* relationship. The Spearman correlation for these variables is 0.876. That says there's a reasonably strong relationship between cell phones and HDI. We don't usually fit a linear model to the ranks because that would be difficult to interpret and because the supporting statistics wouldn't be appropriate.

A third approach to a nonlinear relationship is to transform or re-express one or both of the variables by a function such as the square root, logarithm, or reciprocal. We saw that a transformation can improve the symmetry of the distribution of a single variable. In the same way—and often with the same transforming function—transformations can make a relationship more nearly linear.

---

[10]Due to Charles Spearman, a psychologist who did pioneering work in intelligence testing.

[11]Spearman rank correlation is a *nonparametric* statistical method.

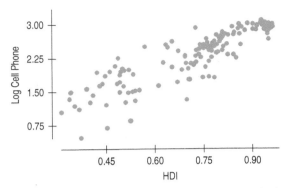

Figure 10   Taking the logarithm of Cell Phones results in a more nearly linear relationship.

Figure 10, for example, shows the relationship between the log of the number of cell phones and the HDI for the same countries.

The advantage of re-expressing variables is that we *can* use regression models, along with all the supporting statistics still to come. The disadvantage is that we must interpret our results in terms of the re-expressed data, and it can be difficult to explain what we mean by the logarithm of the number of cell phones in a country. We can, of course, reverse the transformation to transform a predicted value or residual back to the original units. (In the case of a logarithmic transformation, calculate 10^y to get back to the original units.)

Which approach you choose is likely to depend on the situation and your needs. Statisticians, economists, and scientists generally prefer to transform their data, and many of their laws and theories include transforming functions.[12] But for just understanding the shape of a relationship, a scatterplot does a fine job, and as a summary of the strength of a relationship, a Spearman correlation is a good general-purpose tool.

For Example   Re-expressing for linearity

Consider the relationship between a company's *Assets* and its *Sales* as reported in annual financial statements. Here's a scatterplot of those variables for 79 of the largest companies:

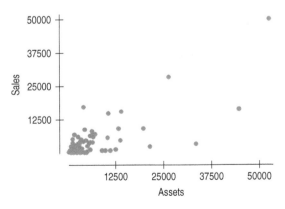

---

[12]In fact, the HDI itself includes such transformed variables in its construction.

The Pearson correlation is 0.746, and the Spearman rank correlation is 0.50. Taking the logarithm of both variables produces the following scatterplot:

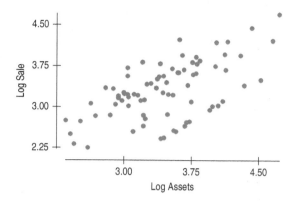

Question: What should we say about the relationship between Assets and Sales?

Answer: The Pearson correlation is not appropriate because the scatterplot of the data is not linear. The Spearman correlation is a more appropriate summary. The scatterplot of the log transformed variables is linear and shows a strong pattern. We could find a linear model for this relationship, but we'd have to interpret it in terms of log Sales and log Assets.

What Can Go Wrong?

- **Don't say "correlation" when you mean "association."** How often have you heard the word "correlation"? Chances are pretty good that when you've heard the term, it's been misused. It's one of the most widely misused Statistics terms, and given how often Statistics are misused, that's saying a lot. One of the problems is that many people use the specific term *correlation* when they really mean the more general term *association*. Association is a deliberately vague term used to describe the relationship between two variables.

    Correlation is a precise term used to describe the strength and direction of a linear relationship between quantitative variables.

- **Don't correlate categorical variables.** Be sure to check the Quantitative Variables Condition. It makes no sense to compute a correlation of categorical variables.

- **Make sure the association is linear.** Not all associations between quantitative variables are linear. Correlation can miss even a strong nonlinear association. And linear regression models are never appropriate for relationships that are not linear. A company, concerned that customers might use ovens with imperfect temperature controls, performed a series of experiments[13] to assess the effect of baking temperature on the quality of brownies made from their freeze-dried reconstituted brownies. The company wants to understand the sensitivity of brownie quality to variation in oven temperatures around the recommended baking temperature of 325°F. The lab reported a correlation of −0.05 between the scores awarded by a panel of trained taste-testers and baking

(continued)

---

[13]Experiments designed to assess the impact of environmental variables outside the control of the company on the quality of the company's products were advocated by the Japanese quality expert Dr. Genichi Taguchi starting in the 1980s in the United States.

temperature and a regression slope of −0.02, so they told management that there is no relationship. Before printing directions on the box telling customers not to worry about the temperature, a savvy intern asks to see the scatterplot.

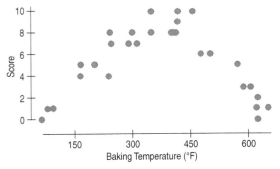

Figure 11   The relationship between brownie taste score and baking temperature is strong, but not linear.

The plot actually shows a strong association—but not a linear one. Don't forget to check the Linearity Condition.

• **Beware of outliers.** You can't interpret a correlation coefficient or a regression model safely without a background check for unusual observations. Here's an example. The relationship between IQ and shoe size among comedians shows a surprisingly strong positive correlation of 0.50. To check assumptions, we look at the scatterplot.

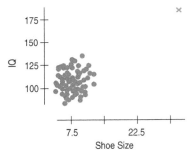

| Figure 12   IQ vs. Shoe Size.

From this "study," what can we say about the relationship between the two? The correlation is 0.50. But who *does* that point in the upper right-hand corner belong to? The outlier is Bozo the Clown, known for his large shoes and widely acknowledged to be a comic "genius." Without Bozo the correlation is near zero.

Even a single unusual observation can dominate the correlation value. That's why you need to check the Unusual Observations Condition.

• **Don't confuse correlation with causation.** Once we have a strong correlation, it's tempting to try to explain it by imagining that the predictor variable has *caused* the response to change. Putting a regression line on a scatterplot tempts us even further. Humans are like that; we tend to see causes and effects in everything. Just because two variables are related does not mean that one *causes* the other.

Does cancer cause smoking?

Even if the correlation of two variables is due to a causal relationship, the correlation itself cannot tell us what causes what.

Sir Ronald Aylmer Fisher (1890–1962) was one of the greatest statisticians of the 20th century. Fisher testified in court (paid by the tobacco companies) that a causal relationship might underlie the correlation of smoking and cancer:

> "Is it possible, then, that lung cancer . . . is one of the causes of smoking cigarettes? I don't think it can be excluded . . . the pre-cancerous condition is one involving a certain amount of slight chronic inflammation . . .
>
> A slight cause of irritation . . . is commonly accompanied by pulling out a cigarette, and getting a little compensation for life's minor ills in that way. And . . . is not unlikely to be associated with smoking more frequently."

Ironically, the proof that smoking indeed is the cause of many cancers came from experiments conducted following the principles of experiment design and analysis that Fisher himself developed.

Scatterplots, correlation coefficients, and regression models *never* prove causation. This is, for example, partly why it took so long for the U.S. Surgeon General to get warning labels on cigarettes. Although there was plenty of evidence that increased smoking was *associated* with increased levels of lung cancer, it took years to provide evidence that smoking actually *causes* lung cancer. (The tobacco companies used this to great advantage.)

Shutterstock

- **Watch out for lurking variables.** A scatterplot of the damage (in dollars) caused to a house by fire would show a strong correlation with the number of firefighters at the scene. Surely the damage doesn't cause firefighters. And firefighters actually do cause damage, spraying water all around and chopping holes, but does that mean we shouldn't call the fire department? Of course not. There is an underlying variable that leads to both more damage and more firefighters—the size of the blaze. A hidden variable that stands behind a relationship and determines it by simultaneously affecting the other two variables is called a **lurking variable**. You can often debunk claims made about data by finding a lurking variable behind the scenes.

- **Don't fit a straight line to a nonlinear relationship.** Linear regression is suited only to relationships that are, in fact, linear.

- **Beware of extraordinary points.** Data values can be extraordinary or unusual in a regression in two ways. They can have *y*-values that stand off from the linear pattern suggested by the bulk of the data. These are what we have been calling outliers; although with regression, a point can be an outlier by being far from the linear pattern even if it is not the largest or smallest *y*-value. Points can also be extraordinary in their *x*-values. Such points can exert a strong influence on the line. Both kinds of extraordinary points require attention.

- **Don't extrapolate far beyond the data. A linear model will often do a reasonable job of summarizing a relationship in the range of observed *x*-values.** Once we have a working model for the relationship, it's tempting to use it. But beware of predicting *y*-values for *x*-values that lie too far outside the range of the original data. The model may no longer hold there, so such extrapolations too far from the data are dangerous.

(continued)

- **Don't choose a model based on R^2 alone.** Although R^2 measures the *strength* of the linear association, a high R^2 does not demonstrate the *appropriateness* of the regression. A single unusual observation, or data that separate into two groups, can make the R^2 seem quite large when, in fact, the linear regression model is simply inappropriate. Conversely, a low R^2 value may be due to a single outlier. It may be that most of the data fall roughly along a straight line, with the exception of a single point. Always look at the scatterplot.

Ethics in Action

An ad agency hired by a well-known manufacturer of dental hygiene products (electric toothbrushes, oral irrigators, etc.) put together a creative team to brainstorm ideas for a new ad campaign. Trisha Simes was chosen to lead the team as she has had the most experience with this client to date. At their first meeting, Trisha communicated to her team the client's desire to differentiate themselves from their competitors by not focusing their message on the cosmetic benefits of good dental care. As they brainstormed ideas, one member of the team, Brad Jonns, recalled a recent CNN broadcast that reported a "correlation" between flossing teeth and reduced risk of heart disease. Seeing potential in promoting the health benefits of proper dental care, the team agreed to pursue this idea further. At their next meeting several team members commented on how surprised they were to find so many articles, medical, scientific, and popular, that seemed to claim good dental hygiene resulted in good health. One member noted that he found articles that linked gum disease not only to heart attacks and strokes but to diabetes and even cancer. Although Trisha puzzled over why their client's competitors had not yet capitalized on these research findings, her team was on a roll and had already begun to focus on designing the campaign around this core message.

ETHICAL ISSUE *Correlation does not imply causation. The possibility of lurking variables is not explored. For example, it is likely that those who take better care of themselves would floss regularly and also have less risk of heart disease (related to Item C, ASA Ethical Guidelines).*

ETHICAL SOLUTION *Refrain from implying cause and effect from correlation results.*

Jill Hathway is looking for a career change and is interested in starting a franchise. After spending the last 20 years working as a mid-level manager for a major corporation, Jill wants to indulge her entrepreneurial spirit and strike out on her own. She currently lives in a small southwestern city and is considering a franchise in the health and fitness industry. She is considering several possibilities including *Pilates One*, for which she requested a franchise packet. Included in the packet information were data showing how various regional demographics (age, gender, income) related to franchise success (revenue, profit, return on investment). *Pilates One* is a relatively new franchise with only a few scattered locations. Nonetheless, the company reported various graphs and data analysis results to help prospective franchisers in their decision-making process. Jill was particularly interested in the graph and the regression analysis that related the proportion of women over the age of 40 within a 20-mile radius of a *Pilates One* location to return on investment for the franchise. She noticed that there was a positive relationship. With a little research, she discovered that the proportion of women over the age of 40 in her city was higher than for any other *Pilates One* location (attributable, in part, to the large number of retirees relocating to the southwest). She then used the regression equation to project return on investment for a *Pilates One* located in her city and was very pleased with the result. With such objective data, she felt confident that *Pilates One* was the franchise for her.

ETHICAL ISSUE *Pilates One is reporting analysis based on only a few observations. Jill is extrapolating beyond the range of x-values (related to Item C, ASA Ethical Guidelines).*

ETHICAL SOLUTION *Pilates One should include a disclaimer that the analysis was based on very few observations and that the equation should not be used to predict success at other locations or beyond the range of x-values used in the analysis.*

What Have We Learned?

Learning Objectives

- Make a scatterplot to display the relationship between two quantitative variables.
  - Look at the direction, form, and strength of the relationship, and any outliers that stand away from the overall pattern.

- Provided the form of the relationship is linear, summarize its strength with a correlation, r.
  - The sign of the correlation gives the direction of the relationship.
  - $-1 \leq r \leq 1$; A correlation of 1 or -1 is a perfect linear relationship. A correlation of 0 is a lack of linear relationship.
  - Correlation has no units, so shifting or scaling the data, standardizing, or even swapping the variables has no effect on the numerical value.
  - A large correlation is not a sign of a causal relationship

- Model a linear relationship with a least squares regression model.
  - The regression (best fit) line doesn't pass through all the points, but it is the best compromise in the sense that the sum of squares of the residuals is the smallest possible.
  - The slope tells us the change in y per unit change in x.
  - The R^2 gives the fraction of the variation in y accounted for by the linear regression model.

- Recognize regression to the mean when it occurs in data.
  - A deviation of one standard deviation from the mean in one variable is predicted to correspond to a deviation of r standard deviations from the mean in the other. Because r is never more than 1, we predict a change toward the mean.

- Examine the residuals from a linear model to assess the quality of the model.
  - When plotted against the predicted values, the residuals should show no pattern and no change in spread.

Terms

Association
- **Direction:** A positive direction or association means that, in general, as one variable increases, so does the other. When increases in one variable generally correspond to decreases in the other, the association is negative.
- **Form:** The form we care about most is straight, but you should certainly describe other patterns you see in scatterplots.
- **Strength:** A scatterplot is said to show a strong association if there is little scatter around the underlying relationship.

Correlation coefficient
A numerical measure of the direction and strength of a linear association.

$$r = \frac{\sum z_x z_y}{n - 1}$$

Explanatory or independent variable (x-variable)
The variable that accounts for, explains, predicts, or is otherwise responsible for the y-variable.

Intercept
The intercept, b_0, gives a starting value in y-units. It's the $\hat{y}$ value when x is 0.

$$b_0 = \bar{y} - b_1 \bar{x}$$

(continued)

181

Least squares	A criterion that specifies the unique line that minimizes the variance of the residuals or, equivalently, the sum of the squared residuals.
Linear model (Line of best fit)	The linear model of the form $\hat{y} = b_0 + b_1 x$ fit by least squares. Also called the regression line. To interpret a linear model, we need to know the variables and their units.
Lurking variable	A variable other than x and y that simultaneously affects both variables, accounting for the correlation between the two.
Outlier	A point that does not fit the overall pattern seen in the scatterplot.
Predicted value	The prediction for y found for each x-value in the data. A predicted value, $\hat{y}$, is found by substituting the x-value in the regression equation. The predicted values are the values on the fitted line; the points $(x, \hat{y})$ lie exactly on the fitted line.
Re-expression or transformation	Re-expressing one or both variables using functions such as log, square root, or reciprocal can improve the straightness of the relationship between them.
Residual	The difference between the actual data value and the corresponding value predicted by the regression model—or, more generally, predicted by any model.
Spearman rank correlation	The correlation between the ranks of two variables may be an appropriate measure of the strength of a relationship when the form isn't straight.
Regression line	The particular linear equation that satisfies the least squares criterion, often called the line of best fit.
Regression to the mean	Because the correlation is always less than 1.0 in magnitude, each predicted y tends to be fewer standard deviations from its mean than its corresponding x is from its mean.
Response or dependent variable (y-variable)	The variable that the scatterplot is meant to explain or predict.
R^2	• The square of the correlation between y and x • The fraction of the variability of y accounted for by the least squares linear regression on x • An overall measure of how successful the regression is in linearly relating y to x
Scatterplot	A graph that shows the relationship between two quantitative variables measured on the same cases.
Standard deviation of the residuals	s_e is found by: $$s_e = \sqrt{\frac{\sum e^2}{n-2}}.$$
Slope	The slope, b_1, is given in y-units per x-unit. Differences of one unit in x are associated with differences of b_1 units in predicted values of y: $$b_1 = r\frac{s_y}{s_x}$$

Technology Help: Correlation and Regression

All statistics packages make a table of results for a regression. These tables may differ slightly from one package to another, but all are essentially the same—and all include much more than we need to know for now. Every computer regression table includes a section that looks something like this:

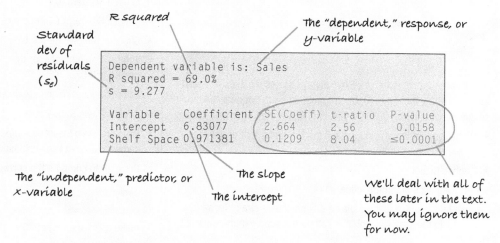

The slope and intercept coefficient are given in a table such as this one. Usually the slope is labeled with the name of the *x*-variable, and the intercept is labeled "Intercept" or "Constant." So the regression equation shown here is

$$\widehat{Sales} = 6.83077 + 0.97138 \; Shelf \; Space.$$

EXCEL   XLSTAT

To make a scatterplot in Excel 2007 or Excel 2010,

- From the Data ribbon, select the Data Analysis add-in.
- From its menu, select **Regression**.
- Indicate the range of the data whose scatterplot you wish to draw.
- Check the Labels box if your data columns have names in the first cell.
- Check the **Line Fit Plots** box, and click **OK**.

- Excel will place regression output and the scatterplot on a new sheet.
- The correlation is in cell B4.
- The slope and *y*-intercept are in cells B18 and B17 respectively.
- You can edit or remove any part of the scatterplot by right clicking on the part you want to edit.
- For example, to remove the Predicted Values, right click on one of the points and **Delete**.
- To add the Least Squares Regression Line, right click on the data and **Add Trendline . . .**

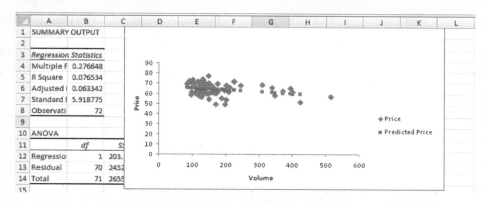

(continued)

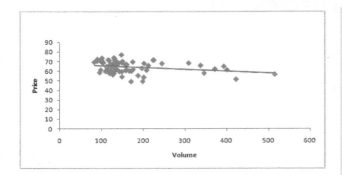

But we aren't quite done yet. Excel always scales the axes of a scatterplot to show the origin (0, 0). But most data are not near the origin, so you may get a plot that, like this one, is bunched up in one corner.

- Right-click on the *y*-axis labels. From the menu that drops down, choose Format axis. . .
- Choose Scale.
- Set the *y*-axis minimum value.

One useful trick is to use the dialog box itself as a straightedge to read over to the *y*-axis so you can estimate a good minimum value. Here 75 seems appropriate.

- Repeat the process with the *x*-axis.

JMP

To make a scatterplot and compute correlation

- Choose Fit Y by X from the Analyze menu.
- In the Fit Y by X dialog, drag the Y variable into the "Y, Response" box, and drag the X variable into the "X, Factor" box.
- Click the OK button.

Once JMP has made the scatterplot, click on the red triangle next to the plot title to reveal a menu of options.

- Select Density Ellipse and select .95. JMP draws an ellipse around the data and reveals the Correlation tab.
- Click the blue triangle next to Correlation to reveal a table containing the correlation coefficient.

To compute a regression,

- Choose Fit Y by X from the Analyze menu. Specify the *y*-variable in the — Select Columns box and click the "Y, Response" button.
- Specify the *x*-variable and click the "X, Factor" button.
- Click OK to make a scatterplot.

- In the scatterplot window, click on the red triangle beside the heading labeled "Bivariate Fit. . ." and choose "Fit Line." JMP draws the least squares regression line on the scatterplot and displays the results of the regression in tables below the plot.

MINITAB

To make a scatterplot,

- Choose Scatterplot from the Graph menu.
- Choose "Simple" for the type of graph. Click OK.
- Enter variable names for the *Y*-variable and *X*-variable into the table. Click OK.

To compute a correlation coefficient,

- Choose Basic Statistics from the Stat menu.
- From the Basic Statistics submenu, choose Correlation. Specify the names of at least two quantitative variables in the "Variables" box.
- Click OK to compute the correlation table.

SPSS

To make a scatterplot in SPSS, open the Chart Builder from the Graphs menu. Then

- Click the Gallery tab.
- Choose Scatterplot from the list of chart types.
- Drag the scatterplot onto the canvas.
- Drag a scale variable you want as the response variable to the *y*-axis drop zone.
- Drag a scale variable you want as the factor or predictor to the *x*-axis drop zone.
- Click OK.

To compute a correlation coefficient,

- Choose Correlate from the Analyze menu.
- From the Correlate submenu, choose Bivariate.
- In the Bivariate Correlations dialog, use the arrow button to move variables between the source and target lists. Make sure the Pearson option is selected in the Correlation Coefficients field.

To compute a regression, from the Analyze menu, choose

- Regression > Linear . . . In the Linear Regression dialog, specify the Dependent (*y*), and Independent (*x*) variables.
- Click the Plots button to specify plots and Normal Probability Plots of the residuals. Click OK.

Brief CASE

Pali Rao/
iStockphoto

Klaas Lingbeek-van Kranen/iStockphoto

Fuel Efficiency

With the ever increasing price of gasoline, both drivers and auto companies are motivated to raise the fuel efficiency of cars. Recent information posted by the U.S. government proposes some simple ways to increase fuel efficiency (see www.fueleconomy.gov): avoid rapid acceleration, avoid driving over 60 mph, reduce idling, and reduce the vehicle's weight. An extra 100 pounds can reduce fuel efficiency (mpg) by up to 2%. A marketing executive is studying the relationship between the fuel efficiency of cars (as measured in miles per gallon) and their weight to design a new compact car campaign. In the data set **Fuel_Efficiency** you'll find data on the variables below.[14]

- Make of Car
- Model of Car
- Engine Size (L)
- Cylinders
- MSRP (Manufacturer's Suggested Retail Price in $)

- City (mpg)
- Highway (mpg)
- Weight (pounds)
- Type and Country of manufacturer

Describe the relationship of Weight, MSRP, and Engine Size with fuel efficiency (both City and Highway) in a written report. Only in the U.S. is fuel efficiency measured in miles per gallon. The rest of the world uses liters per 100 kilometers. To convert mpg to l/100km, compute 235.215/mpg. Try that form of the variable and compare the resulting models. Be sure to plot the residuals.

The U.S. Economy and the Home Depot Stock Prices

The file **Home_Depot**, which can be found at www.pearsonhighered.com/sharpe, contains economic variables, as well as stock market data for The Home Depot. Economists, investors, and corporate executives use measures of the U.S. economy to evaluate the impact of inflationary pressures and employment fluctuations on the stock market. Inflation is often tracked through interest rates. Although there are many different types of interest rates, here we include the monthly values for the bank prime loan rate, a rate posted by a majority of the top 25 (based on assets) insured U.S.-chartered commercial banks. The prime rate is often used by banks to price short-term business loans. In addition, we provide the interest rates on 6-month CDs, the unemployment rates (seasonally adjusted), and the rate on Treasury bills. Investigate the relationships between *Closing Price* for The Home Depot stock and the following variables from 2006 to 2008:[15]

- Unemployment Rate (%)
- Bank Prime Rate (Interest Rate in %)
- CD Rate (%)
- Treasury Bill Rate (%)

---

[14]Data are from the 2004 model year and were compiled from www.Edmonds.com.

[15]Sources: Unemployment rate—U.S. Bureau of Labor Statistics. See unemployment page at www.bls.gov/cps/home.htm#data. Interest rates—Federal Reserve. See www.federalreserve.gov/releases/H15/update/. Home Depot stock prices on HD/Investor Relations website. See ir.homedepot.com/quote.cfm.

(continued)

Describe the relationship of each of these variables with The Home Depot *Closing Price* in a written report. Be sure to use scatterplots and correlation tables in your analysis and transform variables, if necessary.

Cost of Living

The Mercer Human Resource Consulting website (www.mercerhr.com) lists prices of certain items in selected cities around the world. They also report an overall cost-of-living index for each city compared to the costs of hundreds of items in New York City. For example, London at 110.6 is 10.6% more expensive than New York. You'll find the 2006 data for 16 cities in the data set **Cost_of_living_vs_cost_of_items** also available at www.pearsonhighered.com/sharpe. Included are the 2006 cost of living index, cost of a luxury apartment (per month), price of a bus or subway ride, price of a compact disc, price of an international newspaper, price of a cup of coffee (including service), and price of a fast-food hamburger meal. All prices are in U.S. dollars.

Examine the relationship between the overall cost of living and the cost of each of these individual items. Verify the necessary conditions and describe the relationship in as much detail as possible. (Remember to look at direction, form, and strength.) Identify any unusual observations.

Based on the correlations and linear regressions, which item would be the best predictor of overall cost in these cities? Which would be the worst? Are there any surprising relationships? Write a short report detailing your conclusions.

Mutual Funds

According to the U.S. Securities and Exchange Commission (SEC), a mutual fund is a professionally-managed collection of investments for a group of investors in stocks, bonds, and other securities. The fund manager manages the investment portfolio and tracks the wins and losses. Eventually the dividends are passed along to the individual investors in the mutual fund. The first group fund was founded in 1924, but the spread of these types of funds was slowed by the stock market crash in 1929. Congress passed the Securities Act in 1933 and the Securities Exchange Act in 1934 to require that investors be provided disclosures about the fund, the securities, and the fund manager. The SEC drafted the Investment Company Act, which provided guidelines for registering all funds with the SEC. By the end of the 1960s, funds reported $48 billion in assets and, by October 2007 there were over 8,000 mutual funds with combined assets under management of over $12 trillion.

Investors often choose mutual funds on the basis of past performance, and many brokers, mutual fund companies, and other websites offer such data. In the file **Mutual_funds_returns**, you'll find the 3-month return, the annualized 1 yr, 5 yr, and 10 yr returns, and the return since inception of 64 funds of various types. Which data from the past provides the best predictions of the recent 3 months? Examine the scatterplots and regression models for predicting 3-month returns and write a short report containing your conclusions.

Correlation and Linear Regression

The calculations for correlation and regression models can be very sensitive to how intermediate results are rounded. If you find your answers using a calculator and writing down intermediate results, you may obtain slightly different answers that you would have had you used statistics software. Different programs can also yield different results. So your answers may differ in the trailing digits from those in the Appendix. That should not concern you. The meaningful digits are the first few; the trailing digits may be essentially random results of the rounding of intermediate results.

Exercises

SECTION 1

1. Consider the following data from a small bookstore.

Number of sales people working	Sales (in $1000)
2	10
3	11
7	13
9	14
10	18
10	20
12	20
15	22
16	22
20	26
$\bar{x} = 10.4$	$\bar{y} = 17.6$
$SD(x) = 5.64$	$SD(y) = 5.34$

a) Prepare a scatterplot of *Sales* against *Number of sales people* working.
b) What can you say about the direction of the association?
c) What can you say about the form of the relationship?
d) What can you say about the strength of the relationship?
e) Does the scatterplot show any outliers?

2. Disk drives have been getting larger. Their capacity is now often given in *terabytes* (TB) where 1 TB = 1000 gigabytes, or about a trillion bytes. A survey of prices for external disk drives found the following data:

Capacity (in TB)	Price (in $)
.080	29.95
.120	35.00
.200	299.00
.250	49.95
.320	69.95
1.0	99.00
2.0	205.00
4.0	449.00

a) Prepare a scatterplot of *Price* against *Capacity*.
b) What can you say about the direction of the association?
c) What can you say about the form of the relationship?

d) What can you say about the strength of the relationship?
e) Does the scatterplot show any outliers?

SECTION 2

3. The human resources department at a large multinational corporation wants to be able to predict average salary for a given number of years experience. Data on salary (in $1000's) and years of experience were collected for a sample of employees.

a) Which variable is the explanatory or predictor variable?
b) Which variable is the response variable?
c) Which variable would you plot on the *y* axis?

4. A company that relies on Internet-based advertising linked to key search terms wants to understand the relationship between the amount it spends on this advertising and revenue (in $).

a) Which variable is the explanatory or predictor variable?
b) Which variable is the response variable?
c) Which variable would you plot on the *x* axis?

SECTION 3

5. If we assume that the conditions for correlation are met, which of the following are true? If false, explain briefly.

a) A correlation of –0.98 indicates a strong, negative association.
b) Multiplying every value of *x* by 2 will double the correlation.
c) The units of the correlation are the same as the units of *y*.

6. If we assume that the conditions for correlation are met, which of the following are true? If false, explain briefly.

a) A correlation of 0.02 indicates a strong positive association.
b) Standardizing the variables will make the correlation 0.
c) Adding an outlier can dramatically change the correlation.

SECTION 4

7. A larger firm is considering acquiring the bookstore of Exercise 1. An analyst for the firm, noting the relationship seen in Exercise 1, suggests that when they acquire the store they should hire more people because that will drive higher sales. Is his conclusion justified? What alternative explanations can you offer? Use appropriate statistics terminology.

8. A study finds that during blizzards, online sales are highly associated with the number of snow plows on the road; the more plows, the more online purchases. The director of an association of online merchants suggests that the organization should encourage municipalities to send out more plows whenever it snows because, he says, that will increase business. Comment.

SECTION 5

9. True or False. If False, explain briefly.

a) We choose the linear model that passes through the most data points on the scatterplot.
b) The residuals are the observed y-values minus the y-values predicted by the linear model.
c) Least squares means that the square of the largest residual is as small as it could possibly be.

10. True or False. If False, explain briefly.

a) Some of the residuals from a least squares linear model will be positive and some will be negative.
b) Least Squares means that some of the squares of the residuals are minimized.
c) We write $\hat{y}$ to denote the predicted values and y to denote the observed values.

SECTION 6

11. For the bookstore sales data in Exercise 1, the correlation is 0.965.

a) If the number of people working is 2 standard deviations above the mean, how many standard deviations above or below the mean do you expect sales to be?
b) What value of sales does that correspond to?
c) If the number of people working is 1 standard deviation below the mean, how many standard deviations above or below the mean do you expect sales to be?
d) What value of sales does that correspond to?

12. For the hard drive data in Exercise 2, some research on the prices discovered that the 200 GB hard drive was a special "hardened" drive designed to resist physical shocks and work under water. Because it is completely different from the other drives, it was removed from the data. The correlation is now 0.994 and other summary statistics are:

Capacity (in TB)	Price (in $)
$\bar{x} = 1.110$	$\bar{y} = 133.98$
$SD(x) = 1.4469$	$SD(y) = 151.26$

a) If a drive has a capacity of 2.55669 TB (or 1 SD above the mean of 1.100 TB), how many standard deviations above or below the mean price of $133.98 do you expect the drive to cost?
b) What price does that correspond to?

13. For the bookstore of Exercise 1, the manager wants to predict *Sales* from *Number of Sales People Working*.

a) Find the slope estimate, b_1.
b) What does it mean, in this context?
c) Find the intercept, b_0.
d) What does it mean, in this context? Is it meaningful?
e) Write down the equation that predicts *Sales* from *Number of Sales People Working*.
f) If 18 people are working, what *Sales* do you predict?
g) If sales are actually $25,000, what is the value of the residual?
h) Have we overestimated or underestimated the sales?

14. For the disk drives in Exercise 2 (as corrected in Exercise 12), we want to predict *Price* from *Capacity*.

a) Find the slope estimate, b_1.
b) What does it mean, in this context?
c) Find the intercept, b_0.
d) What does it mean, in this context? Is it meaningful?
e) Write down the equation that predicts *Price* from *Capacity*.
f) What would you predict for the price of a 3.0 TB disk?
g) You have found a 3.0 TB drive for $300. Is this a good buy? How much would you save compared to what you expected to pay?
h) Does the model overestimate or underestimate the price?

SECTION 7

15. A CEO complains that the winners of his "rookie junior executive of the year" award often turn out to have less impressive performance the following year. He wonders whether the award actually encourages them to slack off. Can you offer a better explanation?

16. An online investment blogger advises investing in mutual funds that have performed badly the past year because "regression to the mean tells us that they will do well next year." Is he correct?

SECTION 8

17. Here are the residuals for a regression of *Sales* on *Number of Sales People Working* for the bookstore of Exercise 1:

Sales People Working	Residual
2	0.07
3	0.16
7	−1.49
9	−2.32
10	0.77
10	2.77
12	0.94
15	0.20
16	−0.72
20	−0.37

a) What are the units of the residuals?
b) Which residual contributes the most to the sum that was minimized according to the Least Squares Criterion to find this regression?
c) Which residual contributes least to that sum?

18. Here are residual plots (residuals plotted against predicted values) for three linear regression models. Indicate which condition appears to be violated (linearity, outlier or equal spread) in each case.

a)

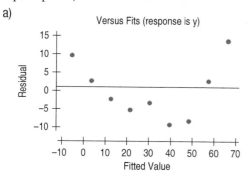

b)

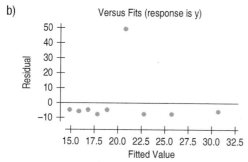

c)

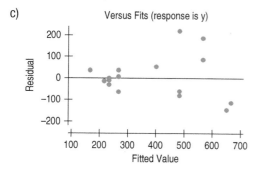

SECTION 9

19. For the regression model for the bookstore of Exercise 1, what is the value of R^2 and what does it mean?

20. For the disk drive data of Exercise 2 (as corrected in Exercise 12), find and interpret the value of R^2.

SECTION 11

21. When analyzing data on the number of employees in small companies in one town, a researcher took square roots of the counts. Some of the resulting values, which were reasonably symmetric were:

$$4, 4, 6, 7, 7, 8, 10$$

What were the original values, and how are they distributed?

22. You wish to explain to your boss what effect taking the base-10 logarithm of the salary values in the company's database will have on the data. As simple, example values, you compare a salary of \$10,000 earned by a part-time shipping clerk, a salary of \$100,000 earned by a manager, and the CEO's \$1,000,000 compensation package. Why might the average of these values be a misleading summary? What would the logarithms of these three values be?

CHAPTER EXERCISES

23. Association. Suppose you were to collect data for each pair of variables. You want to make a scatterplot. Which variable would you use as the explanatory variable and which as the response variable? Why? What would you expect to see in the scatterplot? Discuss the likely direction and form.

a) Cell phone bills: number of text messages, cost.
b) Automobiles: Fuel efficiency (mpg), sales volume (number of autos).
c) For each week: Ice cream cone sales, air conditioner sales.
d) Product: Price (\$), demand (number sold per day).

24. Association, part 2. Suppose you were to collect data for each pair of variables. You want to make a scatterplot. Which variable would you use as the explanatory variable and which as the response variable? Why? What would you expect to see in the scatterplot? Discuss the likely direction and form.

a) T- shirts at a store: price each, number sold.
b) Real estate: house price, house size (square footage).
c) Economics: Interest rates, number of mortgage applications.
d) Employees: Salary, years of experience.

25. Scatterplots. Which of the scatterplots show:

a) Little or no association?
b) A negative association?
c) A linear association?
d) A moderately strong association?
e) A very strong association?

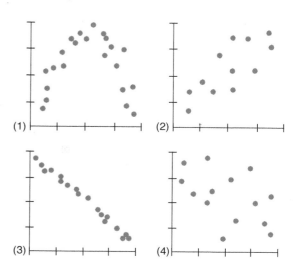

26. Scatterplots, part 2. Which of the scatterplots show:

a) Little or no association?
b) A negative association?
c) A linear association?
d) A moderately strong association?
e) A very strong association?

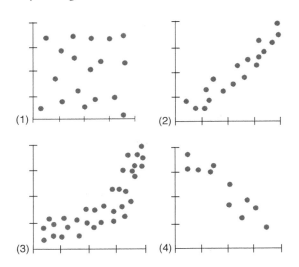

(1) (2) (3) (4)

27. Manufacturing. A ceramics factory can fire eight large batches of pottery a day. Sometimes a few of the pieces break in the process. In order to understand the problem better, the factory records the number of broken pieces in each batch for three days and then creates the scatterplot shown.

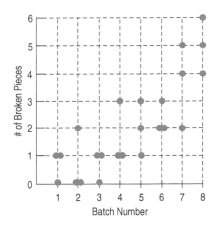

a) Make a histogram showing the distribution of the number of broken pieces in the 24 batches of pottery examined.
b) Describe the distribution as shown in the histogram. What feature of the problem is more apparent in the histogram than in the scatterplot?

c) What aspect of the company's problem is more apparent in the scatterplot?

28. Coffee sales. Owners of a new coffee shop tracked sales for the first 20 days and displayed the data in a scatterplot (by day).

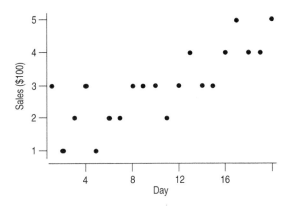

a) Make a histogram of the daily sales since the shop has been in business.
b) State one fact that is obvious from the scatterplot, but not from the histogram.
c) State one fact that is obvious from the histogram, but not from the scatterplot.

29. Matching. Here are several scatterplots. The calculated correlations are −0.923, −0.487, 0.006, and 0.777. Which is which?

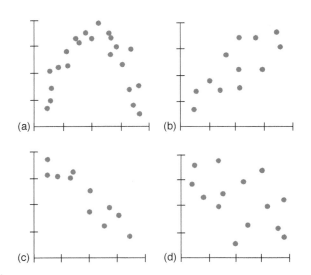

(a) (b) (c) (d)

30. **Matching, part 2.** Here are several scatterplots. The calculated correlations are −0.977, −0.021, 0.736, and 0.951. Which is which?

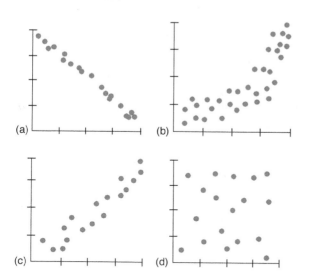

31. **Pizza sales and price.** A linear model fit to predict weekly *Sales* of frozen pizza (in pounds) from the average *Price* ($/unit) charged by a sample of stores in the city of Dallas in 39 recent weeks is:

$$\widehat{Sales} = 141{,}865.53 - 24{,}369.49 \ Price.$$

a) What is the explanatory variable?
b) What is the response variable?
c) What does the slope mean in this context?
d) What does the *y*-intercept mean in this context? Is it meaningful?
e) What do you predict the sales to be if the average price charged was $3.50 for a pizza?
f) If the sales for a price of $3.50 turned out to be 60,000 pounds, what would the residual be?

32. **Used Saab prices.** A linear model to predict the *Price* of a 2004 Saab 9-3 (in $) from its *Mileage* (in miles) was fit to 38 cars that were available during the week of January 11, 2008 (Kelly's Blue Book, www.kbb.com). The model was:

$$\widehat{Price} = 24{,}356.15 - 0.0151 \ Mileage.$$

a) What is the explanatory variable?
b) What is the response variable?
c) What does the slope mean in this context?
d) What does the *y*-intercept mean in this context? Is it meaningful?
e) What do you predict the price to be for a car with 100,000 miles on it?
f) If the price for a car with 100,000 miles on it was $24,000, what would the residual be?

33. **Football salaries.** Is there a relationship between total team salary and the performance of teams in the National Football League (NFL)? For the 2006 season, a linear model

predicting *Wins* (out of 16 regular season games) from the total team *Salary* ($M) for the 32 teams in the league is:

$$\widehat{Wins} = 1.783 + 0.062 \ Salary.$$

a) What is the explanatory variable?
b) What is the response variable?
c) What does the slope mean in this context?
d) What does the *y*-intercept mean in this context? Is it meaningful?
e) If one team spends $10 million more than another on salary, how many more games on average would you predict them to win?
f) If a team spent $50 million on salaries and won 8 games, would they have done better or worse than predicted?
g) What would the residual of the team in part f be?

34. **Baseball salaries.** In 2007, the Boston Red Sox won the World Series and spent $143 million on salaries for their players (benfry.com/salaryper). Is there a relationship between salary and team performance in Major League Baseball? For the 2007 season, a linear model fit to the number of *Wins* (out of 162 regular season games) from the team *Salary* ($M) for the 30 teams in the league is:

$$\widehat{Wins} = 70.097 + 0.132 \ Salary.$$

a) What is the explanatory variable?
b) What is the response variable?
c) What does the slope mean in this context?
d) What does the *y*-intercept mean in this context? Is it meaningful?
e) If one team spends $10 million more than another on salaries, how many more games on average would you predict them to win?
f) If a team spent $110 million on salaries and won half (81) of their games, would they have done better or worse than predicted?
g) What would the residual of the team in part f be?

35. **Pizza sales and price, part 2.** For the data in Exercise 31, the average *Sales* was 52,697 pounds (SD = 10,261 pounds), and the correlation between *Price* and *Sales* was = −0.547.

If the *Price* in a particular week was one SD higher than the mean *Price*, how much pizza would you predict was sold that week?

36. **Used Saab prices, part 2.** The 38 cars in Exercise 32 had an average *Price* of $23,847 (SD = $923), and the correlation between *Price* and *Mileage* was = −0.169.

If the *Mileage* of a 2004 Saab was 1 SD below the average number of miles, what *Price* would you predict for it?

37. **Packaging.** A CEO announces at the annual shareholders meeting that the new see-through packaging for the company's flagship product has been a success. In fact, he says, "There is a strong correlation between packaging and sales." Criticize this statement on statistical grounds.

38. Insurance. Insurance companies carefully track claims histories so that they can assess risk and set rates appropriately. The National Insurance Crime Bureau reports that Honda Accords, Honda Civics, and Toyota Camrys are the cars most frequently reported stolen, while Ford Tauruses, Pontiac Vibes, and Buick LeSabres are stolen least often. Is it reasonable to say that there's a correlation between the type of car you own and the risk that it will be stolen?

39. Sales by region. A sales manager for a major pharmaceutical company analyzes last year's sales data for her 96 sales representatives, grouping them by region (1 = East Coast U.S.; 2 = Mid West U.S.; 3 = West U.S.; 4 = South U.S.; 5 = Canada; 6 = Rest of World). She plots *Sales* (in $1000) against *Region* (1–6) and sees a strong negative correlation.

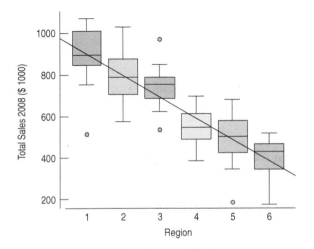

She fits a regression to the data and finds:

$$\widehat{Sales} = 1002.5 - 102.7 \, Region.$$

The R^2 is 70.5%.

Write a few sentences interpreting this model and describing what she can conclude from this analysis.

40. Salary by job type. At a small company, the head of human resources wants to examine salary to prepare annual reviews. He selects 28 employees at random with job types ranging from 01 = Stocking clerk to 99 = President. He plots *Salary* ($) against *Job Type* and finds a strong linear relationship with a correlation of 0.96.

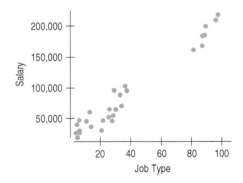

The regression output gives:

$$\widehat{Salary} = 15827.9 + 1939.1 \, Job \, Type$$

Write a few sentences interpreting this model and describing what he can conclude from this analysis.

41. Carbon footprint. The scatterplot shows, for 2008 cars, the carbon footprint (tons of CO_2 per year) vs. the new Environmental Protection Agency (EPA) highway mileage for 82 family sedans as reported by the U.S. government (www.fueleconomy.gov/feg/byclass.htm). The car with the highest highway mpg and lowest carbon footprint is the Toyota Prius.

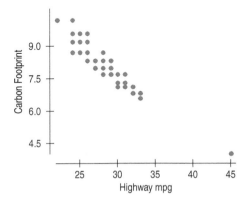

a) The correlation is −0.947. Describe the association.
b) Are the assumptions and conditions met for computing correlation?
c) Using technology, find the correlation of the data when the Prius is not included with the others. Can you explain why it changes in that way?

42. EPA mpg. In 2008, the EPA revised their methods for estimating the fuel efficiency (mpg) of cars—a factor that plays an increasingly important role in car sales. How do the new highway and city estimated mpg values relate to each other? Here's a scatterplot for 83 family sedans as reported by the U.S. government. These are the same cars as in Exercise 41 except that the Toyota Prius has been removed from the data and two other hybrids, the Nissan Altima and Toyota Camry, are included in the data (and are the cars with highest city mpg).

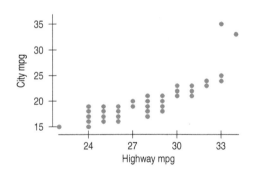

a) The correlation of these two variables is 0.823. Describe the association.

b) If the two hybrids were removed from the data, would you expect the correlation to increase, decrease, or stay the same? Try it using technology. Report and discuss what you find.

43. Real estate. Is the number of total rooms in the house associated with the price of a house? Here is the scatterplot of a random sample of homes for sale:

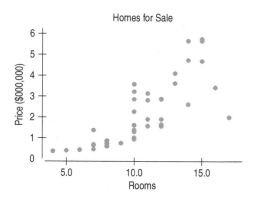

Homes for Sale

a) Is there an association?

b) Check the assumptions and conditions for correlation.

44. Economic analysis. An economics student is studying the American economy and finds that the correlation between the inflation adjusted Dow Jones Industrial Average and the Gross Domestic Product (GDP) (also inflation adjusted) is 0.77 (www.measuringworth.com). From that he concludes that there is a strong linear relationship between the two series and predicts that a drop in the GDP will make the stock market go down. Here is a scatterplot of the adjusted DJIA against the GDP (in year 2000 $). Describe the relationship and comment on the student's conclusions.

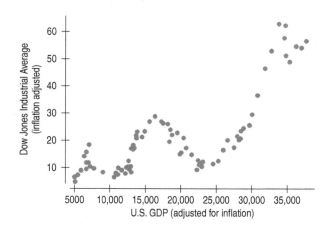

45. GDP growth. Is economic growth in the developing world related to growth in the industrialized countries? Here's a scatterplot of the growth (in % of Gross Domestic

Product) of the developing countries vs. the growth of developed countries for 180 countries as grouped by the World Bank (www.ers.usda.gov/data/macroeconomics). Each point represents one of the years from 1970 to 2007. The output of a regression analysis follows.

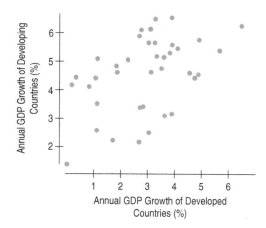

```
Dependent variable: GDP Growth Developing
Countries
R² = 20.81%
s = 1.244
Variable                      Coefficient
Intercept                     3.46
GDP Growth Developed          0.433
Countries
```

a) Check the assumptions and conditions for the linear model.

b) Explain the meaning of R^2 in this context.

c) What are the cases in this model?

46. European GDP growth. Is economic growth in Europe related to growth in the United States? Here's a scatterplot of the average growth in 25 European countries (in % of Gross Domestic Product) vs. the growth in the United States. Each point represents one of years from 1970 to 2007.

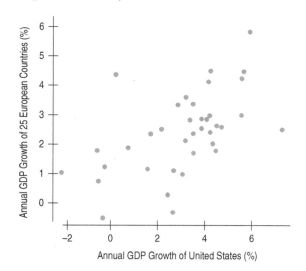

```
Dependent variable: 25 European Countries GDP
Growth
R² = 29.65%
s = 1.156
Variable            Coefficient
Intercept           1.330
U.S. GDP Growth     0.3616
```

a) Check the assumptions and conditions for the linear model.
b) Explain the meaning of R^2 in this context.

47. GDP growth, part 2. From the linear model fit to the data on GDP growth in Exercise 45.

a) Write the equation of the regression line.
b) What is the meaning of the intercept? Does it make sense in this context?
c) Interpret the meaning of the slope.
d) In a year in which the developed countries grow 4%, what do you predict for the developing world?
e) In 2007, the developed countries experienced a 2.65% growth, while the developing countries grew at a rate of 6.09%. Is this more or less than you would have predicted?
f) What is the residual for this year?

48. European GDP growth, part 2. From the linear model fit to the data on GDP growth of Exercise 46.

a) Write the equation of the regression line.
b) What is the meaning of the intercept? Does it make sense in this context?
c) Interpret the meaning of the slope.
d) In a year in which the United States grows at 0%, what do you predict for European growth?
e) In 2007, the United States experienced a 3.20% growth, while Europe grew at a rate of 2.16%. Is this more or less than you would have predicted?
f) What is the residual for this year?

49. Attendance 2006. American League baseball games are played under the designated hitter rule, meaning that weak-hitting pitchers do not come to bat. Baseball owners believe that the designated hitter rule means more runs scored,

which in turn means higher attendance. Is there evidence that more fans attend games if the teams score more runs? Data collected from American League games during the 2006 season have a correlation of 0.667 between *Runs Scored* and the number of people at the game (www.mlb.com).

a) Does the scatterplot indicate that it's appropriate to calculate a correlation? Explain.
b) Describe the association between attendance and runs scored.
c) Does this association prove that the owners are right that more fans will come to games if the teams score more runs?

50. Attendance 2006, part 2. Perhaps fans are just more interested in teams that win. Here are displays of other variables in the dataset of exercise 49 (espn.go.com). Are the teams that win necessarily those that score the most runs?

	Correlation		
	Wins	Runs	Attend
Wins	1.000		
Runs	0.605	1.000	
Attend	0.697	0.667	1.000

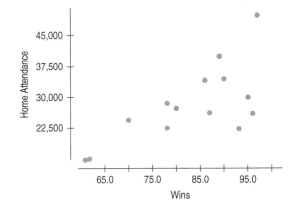

a) Do winning teams generally enjoy greater attendance at their home games? Describe the association.
b) Is attendance more strongly associated with winning or scoring runs? Explain.
c) How strongly is scoring more runs associated with winning more games?

51. Tuition 2008. All 50 states offer public higher education through four-year colleges and universities and two-year colleges (often called community colleges). Tuition charges by different states vary widely for both types. Would you expect to find a relationship between the tuition states charge for the two types?

a) Using the data on the CD, make a scatterplot of the average tuition for four-year colleges against the tuition charged for two-year colleges. Describe the relationship.

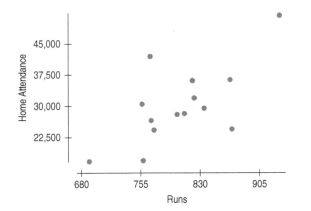

b) Is the direction of the relationship what you expected?

c) What is the regression equation for predicting the tuition at a four-year college from the tuition at a two-year college in the same state?

d) Is a linear model appropriate?

e) How much more do states charge on average in yearly tuition for four-year colleges compared to two-year colleges according to this model?

f) What is the R^2 value for this model? Explain what it says.

52. Tuition 2008, part 2. Exercise 51 examined the relationship between the tuition charged by states for four-year colleges and universities compared to the tuition for two-year colleges. Now, examine the relationship between private and public four-year colleges and universities in the states.

a) Would you expect the relationship between tuition ($ per year) charged by private and public four-year colleges and universities to be as strong as the relationship between public four-year and two-year institutions?

b) Using the data on the CD, examine a scatterplot of the average tuition for four-year private institutions against the tuition charged for four-year public institutions. Describe the relationship.

c) What is the regression equation for predicting the tuition at a four-year private institution from the tuition at a four-year public institution in the same state?

d) Is a linear model appropriate?

e) Interpret the regression equation. How much more is the tuition for four-year private institutions compared to four-year public institutions in the same state according to this model?

f) What is the R^2 value for this model? Explain what it says.

53. Mutual fund flows. As the nature of investing shifted in the 1990s (more day traders and faster flow of information using technology), the relationship between mutual fund monthly performance (*Return*) in percent and money flowing (*Flow*) into mutual funds ($ million) shifted. Using only the values for the 1990s, answer the following questions. (You may assume that the assumptions and conditions for regression are met.)

The least squares linear regression is:

$$\widehat{Flow} = 9747 + 771 \; Return.$$

a) Interpret the intercept in the linear model.

b) Interpret the slope in the linear model.

c) What is the predicted fund *Flow* for a month that had a market *Return* of 0%?

d) If during this month, the recorded fund *Flow* was $5 billion, what is the residual using this linear model? Did the model provide an underestimate or overestimate for this month?

54. Online clothing purchases. An online clothing retailer examined their transactional database to see if total yearly *Purchases* ($) were related to customers' *Incomes* ($). (You may assume that the assumptions and conditions for regression are met.)

The least squares linear regression is:

$$\widehat{Purchases} = -31.6 + 0.012 \; Income.$$

a) Interpret the intercept in the linear model.

b) Interpret the slope in the linear model.

c) If a customer has an *Income* of $20,000, what is his predicted total yearly *Purchases*?

d) This customer's yearly *Purchases* were actually $100. What is the residual using this linear model? Did the model provide an underestimate or overestimate for this customer?

55. Residual plots. Tell what each of the following residual plots indicates about the appropriateness of the linear model that was fit to the data.

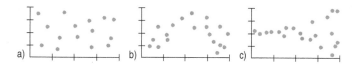

56. Residual plots, again. Tell what each of the following residual plots indicates about the appropriateness of the linear model that was fit to the data.

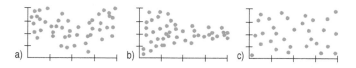

57. Consumer spending. An analyst at a large credit card bank is looking at the relationship between customers' charges to the bank's card in two successive months. He selects 150 customers at random, regresses charges in *March* ($) on charges in *February* ($), and finds an R^2 of 79%. The intercept is $730.20, and the slope is 0.79. After verifying all the data with the company's CPA, he concludes that the model is a useful one for predicting one month's charges from the other. Examine the data on the CD and comment on his conclusions.

58. Insurance policies. An actuary at a mid-sized insurance company is examining the sales performance of the company's sales force. She has data on the average size of the policy ($) written in two consecutive years by 200 salespeople. She fits a linear model and finds the slope to be 3.00 and the R^2 is 99.92%. She concludes that the predictions for next year's policy size will be very accurate. Examine the data on the CD and comment on her conclusions.

59. What slope? If you create a regression model for predicting the sales ($ million) from money spent on advertising the prior month ($ thousand), is the slope most likely to be 0.03, 300 or 3000? Explain.

60. What slope, part 2? If you create a regression model for estimating a student's business school GPA (on a scale of 1–5) based on his math SAT (on a scale of 200–800), is the slope most likely to be 0.01, 1, or 10? Explain.

61. Misinterpretations. An advertising agent who created a regression model using amount spent on *Advertising* to predict annual *Sales* for a company made these two statements. Assuming the calculations were done correctly, explain what is wrong with each interpretation.
a) My R^2 of 93% shows that this linear model is appropriate.
b) If this company spends $1.5 million on advertising, then annual sales will be $10 million.

62. More misinterpretations. An economist investigated the association between a country's *Literacy Rate* and *Gross Domestic Product (GDP)* and used the association to draw the following conclusions. Explain why each statement is incorrect. (Assume that all the calculations were done properly.)
a) The *Literacy Rate* determines 64% of the *GDP* for a country.
b) The slope of the line shows that an increase of 5% in *Literacy Rate* will produce a $1 billion improvement in *GDP*.

63. Business admissions. An analyst at a business school's admissions office claims to have developed a valid linear model predicting success (measured by starting salary ($) at time of graduation) from a student's undergraduate performance (measured by GPA). Describe how you would check each of the four regression conditions in this context.

64. School rankings. A popular magazine annually publishes rankings of both U.S. business programs and international business programs. The latest issue claims to have developed a linear model predicting the school's ranking (with "1" being the highest ranked school) from its financial resources (as measured by size of the school's endowment). Describe how you would apply each of the four regression conditions in this context.

65. Used BMW prices. A business student needs cash, so he decides to sell his car. The car is a valuable BMW 840 that was only made over the course of a few years in the late 1990s. He would like to sell it on his own, rather than through a dealer so he'd like to predict the price he'll get for his car's model year.
a) Make a scatterplot for the data on used BMW 840s provided.
b) Describe the association between year and price.
c) Do you think a linear model is appropriate?
d) Computer software says that $R^2 = 57.4\%$. What is the correlation between year and price?
e) Explain the meaning of R^2 in this context.
f) Why doesn't this model explain 100% of the variability in the price of a used BMW 840?

66. Used BMW prices, part 2. Use the advertised prices for BMW 840s given in Exercise 65 to create a linear model for the relationship between a car's *Year* and its *Price*.
a) Find the equation of the regression line.
b) Explain the meaning of the slope of the line.
c) Explain the meaning of the intercept of the line.
d) If you want to sell a 1997 BMW 840, what price seems appropriate?
e) You have a chance to buy one of two cars. They are about the same age and appear to be in equally good condition. Would you rather buy the one with a positive residual or the one with a negative residual? Explain.

67. Cost of living index. The *Worldwide Cost of Living Survey City Rankings* determine the cost of living in the most expensive cities in the world as an index. This index scales New York City as 100 and expresses the cost of living in other cities as a percentage of the New York cost. For example, in 2007, the cost of living index in Tokyo was 122.1, which means that it was 22% higher than New York. The scatterplot shows the index for 2007 plotted against the 2006 index for the 15 most expensive cities of 2007.

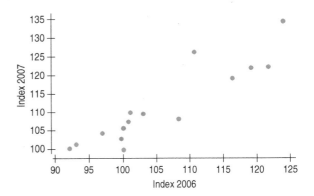

a) Describe the association between cost of living indices in 2007 and 2006.
b) The R^2 for the regression equation is 0.837. Interpret the value of R^2.
c) Using the data provided, find the correlation.
d) Predict the 2007 cost of living of Moscow and find its residual.

68. Lobster prices. Over the past few decades both the demand for lobster and the price of lobster have continued to increase. The scatterplot shows this increase in the *Price* of Maine lobster (*Price*/pound) since 1990.
a) Describe the increase in the *Price* of lobster since 1990.
b) The R^2 for the regression equation is 88.5%. Interpret the value of R^2.
c) Find the correlation.
d) Find the linear model and examine the plot of residuals versus predicted values. Is the Equal Spread Condition satisfied? (Use time starting at 1990 so that 1990 = 0.)

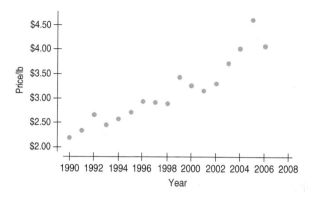

69. El Niño. Concern over the weather associated with El Niño has increased interest in the possibility that the climate on Earth is getting warmer. The most common theory relates an increase in atmospheric levels of carbon dioxide (CO_2), a greenhouse gas, to increases in temperature. Here is a scatterplot showing the mean annual CO_2 concentration in the atmosphere, measured in parts per million (ppm) at the top of Mauna Loa in Hawaii, and the mean annual air temperature over both land and sea across the globe, in degrees Celsius (C).

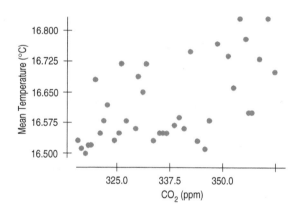

A regression predicting *Mean Temperature* from CO_2 produces the following output table (in part).

```
Dependent variable: Temperature
R-squared = 33.4%

Variable              Coefficient
Intercept             15.3066
CO2                   0.004
```

a) What is the correlation between CO_2 and *Mean Temperature*?
b) Explain the meaning of *R*-squared in this context.
c) Give the regression equation.
d) What is the meaning of the slope in this equation?
e) What is the meaning of the intercept of this equation?
f) Here is a scatterplot of the residuals vs. CO_2. Does this plot show evidence of the violations of any of the assumptions of the regression model? If so, which ones?

g) CO_2 levels may reach 364 *ppm* in the near future. What *Mean Temperature* does the model predict for that value?

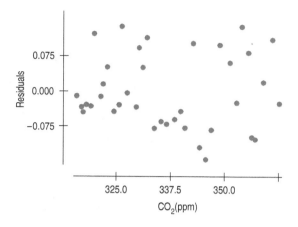

70. U.S. birthrates. The table shows the number of live births per 1000 women aged 15–44 years in the United States, starting in 1965. (National Center for Health Statistics, www.cdc.gov/nchs/)

Year	1965	1970	1975	1980	1985
Rate	19.4	18.4	14.8	15.9	15.6

Year	1990	1995	2000	2005
Rate	16.4	14.8	14.4	14.0

a) Make a scatterplot and describe the general trend in *Birthrates*. (Enter *Year* as years since 1900: 65, 70, 75, etc.)
b) Find the equation of the regression line.
c) Check to see if the line is an appropriate model. Explain.
d) Interpret the slope of the line.
e) The table gives rates only at 5-year intervals. Estimate what the rate was in 1978.
f) In 1978, the birthrate was actually 15.0. How close did your model come?
g) Predict what the *Birthrate* will be in 2010. Comment on your faith in this prediction.
h) Predict the *Birthrate* for 2025. Comment on your faith in this prediction.

71. Dirt bikes. Off-road motorcycles, commonly called "dirt bikes," are engineered for a particular kind of performance. One measure of the power of the engine is its displacement, measured in cubic centimeters. The first scatterplot shows the relationship between *Displacement* and *Total Weight* for a selection of 4-stroke off-road bikes. The other scatterplot plots $\sqrt{Displacement}$ instead.

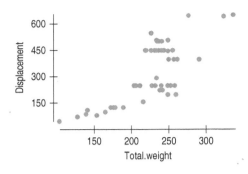

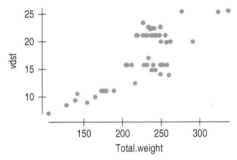

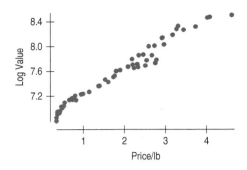

a) Is the Pearson correlation appropriate for either of these relationships? If not, what would you use? Explain.

b) Would it be appropriate to fit a linear model by least squares to either of these relationships? Explain.

a) What statistic would be appropriate to summarize the strength of the association between *Displacement* and *Total Weight*? Explain.

b) Which form would be the best choice if you wanted to fit a linear model to the relationship? Explain.

72. Lobsters. The Maine lobster fishery is closely monitored, and statistics about the lobster business are published annually. Here are plots relating the total value ($M) of lobsters harvested between 1950 and 2006 to the price of lobster ($ per pound) and the *LogValue* offered as an alternative transformation.

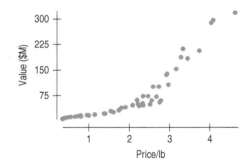

Just Checking Answers

1. We know the scores are quantitative. We should check to see if the *Linearity Condition* and the *Outlier Condition* are satisfied by looking at a scatterplot of the two scores.

2. It won't change.

3. It won't change.

4. They are more likely to do poorly. The positive correlation means that low closing prices for Intel are associated with low closing prices for Cypress.

5. No, the general association is positive, but daily closing prices may vary.

6. For each additional employee, monthly sales increase, on average, $122,740.

7. Thousands of $ per employee.

8. $1,227,400 per month.

9. Differences in the number of employees account for about 71.4% of the variation in the monthly sales.

10. It's positive. The correlation and the slope have the same sign.

11. R^2, No. Slope, Yes.

Answers

1. a)

b) Positive.
c) Linear.
d) Strong.
e) No.

3. a) Years of experience.
b) Salary.
c) Salary.

5. a) True.
b) False. It will not change the correlation.
c) False. Correlation has no units.

7. Correlation does not demonstrate causation. The analyst's argument is that sales staff cause sales. However, the data may reflect the store hiring more people as sales increase, so any causation would run the other way.

9. a) False. The line usually touches none of the points. We minimize the sum of the squared errors.
b) True.
c) False. It is the sum of the squares of all the residuals that is minimized.

11. a) $2 \times 0.965 = 1.93$ SDs.
b) $17.6 + 1.93 \times 5.34 = 27.906$ or $27,906.
c) 0.965 SDs below the mean.
d) $12,447.

13. a) $b_1 = 0.914$ if found by hand. $b_1 = 0.913$ if found by technology. (Difference is due to rounding error.)
b) It means that an additional 0.914 ($1000) or $914 of sales is associated with each additional sales person working.
c) $b_0 = 8.10$
d) It would mean that, on average, we expect sales of 8.10 ($1000) or $8100 with 0 sales people working. Doesn't really make sense in this context.
e) $\widehat{Sales} = 8.10 + 0.914$ *Number of Sales People Working*.
f) $24.55 ($1000) or $24,550. (24,540 if using the technology solution.)
g) 0.45 ($1000) or $450. ($460 with technology.)
h) Underestimated.

15. The winners may be suffering from regression to the mean. Perhaps they weren't really better than other rookie executives, but just happened to have a lucky year.

17. a) Thousands of dollars.
b) 2.77 (the largest residual in magnitude).
c) 0.07 (the smallest residual in magnitude).

19. $R^2 = 93.12\%$ About 93% of the variance in *Sales* can be accounted for by the regression of *Sales* on *Number of Sales Workers*.

21. 16, 16, 36, 49, 49, 64, 100.
They are skewed to the high end.

23. a) Number of text messages: explanatory; cost: response. To predict cost from number of text messages. Positive direction. Linear shape. Possibly an outlier for contracts with fixed cost for texting.
b) Fuel efficiency: explanatory; sales volume: response. To predict sales from fuel efficiency. There may be no association between mpg and sales volume. Environmentalists hope that a higher mpg will encourage higher sales, which would be a positive association. We have no information about the shape of the relationship.
c) Neither variable is explanatory. Both are responses to the lurking variable of temperature.
d) Price: explanatory variable; demand: response variable. To predict demand from price. Negative direction. Linear shape in a narrow range, but curved over a larger range of prices.

25. a) None
b) 3 and 4
c) 2, 3, and 4
d) 1 and 2
e) 3 and 1

27. a)

b) Unimodal, skewed to the right. The skewness.
c) The positive, somewhat linear relation between batch number and broken pieces.

29. a) 0.006
b) 0.777
c) −0.923
d) −0.487

31. a) *Price*
b) *Sales*
c) Sales decrease by 24,369.49 pounds per dollar.
d) It is just a base value. It means nothing because stores won't set their price to $0.
e) 56,572.32 pounds
f) 3427.69 pounds

33. a) *Salary*
b) *Wins*
c) On average, teams win 0.062 more games per million dollars in salary.
d) Number of wins predicted for a team that spends $0 on salaries. This is not meaningful here.
e) 0.62 games more
f) 4.883 games. Better.
g) 3.117 games

35. 47,084.23 pounds

37. "Packaging" isn't a variable. At best, it is a category. There's no basis for computing a correlation.

39. The model is meaningless because the variable Region is not quantitative. The slope makes no sense because Region has no units. The boxplot comparisons are fine, but the regression is meaningless.

41. a) There is a strong negative linear association between Carbon Footprint and Highway mpg.
b) Quantitative variables, straight enough. The Prius is far from the rest of the data. But it is in line with the linear pattern. It is correct to regard it as an outlier or not; that's a matter of judgment.
c) $r = -0.94$; Removing the Prius reduces the correlation. Data values far from the main body of the data and in line with the linear trend tend to increase correlation and may make it misleading.

43. a) Positive association.
b) Plot is not linear, violating the linearity condition. There may be an outlier at 17 rooms.

45. a) The variables are both quantitative (with units % of GDP), the plot is reasonably straight, there are no outliers, and the spread is roughly constant (although the spread is large).
b) About 21% of the variation in the growth rates of developing countries is accounted for by the growth rates of developed countries.
c) Years 1970–2007

47. a) $\overline{Growth\ (Developing\ Countries)} = 3.46 + 0.433\ Growth\ (Developed\ Countries)$
b) The predicted growth of developing countries in years of 0 growth in developed countries. Yes, this makes sense.
c) On average, GDP in developed countries increased 0.433% for a 1% increase in growth in developed countries.
d) 5.192%
e) More; we would predict 4.61%.
f) 1.48%

49. a) Yes, the scatterplot is straight enough, variables are quantitative and there are no outliers.
b) Teams that score more runs generally have higher attendance.
c) There is a positive association, but correlation doesn't imply causation.

51. a) Positive, roughly straight (slight bending at the upper right), and moderately strong.
b) Yes (although answers may vary). It makes sense that a state's finances would influence both amounts in the same way.
c) $\overline{Public.4yr} = 2826.00 + 1.216\ Public.2yr$
d) Yes
e) A public four-year education costs, on average, $2826 + 1.216 \times$ average tuition at two-year colleges.
f) 44.29% of the variation in the average tuition of four-yr state colleges is accounted for by the regression on two-yr college tuition.

53. a) The predicted value of the money *Flow* if the *Return* was 0%.
b) An increase of 1% in mutual fund return was associated with an increase of $771 million in money flowing into mutual funds.
c) $9747 million
d) −$4747 million; Overestimated

55. a) Model seems appropriate. Residual plot looks fine.
b) Model not appropriate. Relationship is nonlinear.
c) Model not appropriate. Spread is increasing.

57. There are two outliers that inflate the R^2 value and affect the slope and intercept. Without those two points, the R^2 drops from

79% to about 31%. The analyst should set aside those two customers and refit the model.

59. 0.03

61. a) R^2 is an indication of the strength of the model, not the appropriateness of the model.
b) The student should have said, "The model predicts that quarterly sales will be $10 million when $1.5 million is spent on advertising."

63. a) Quantitative variable condition: Both variables are quantitative (*GPA* and *Starting Salary*).
b) Linearity condition: Examine a scatterplot of *Starting Salary* by *GPA*.
c) Outlier condition: Examine the scatterplot.
d) Equal spread condition: Plot the regression residuals versus predicted values.

65. a)

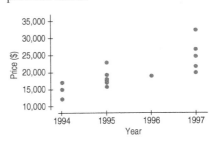

b) There is a strong, positive, linear association between *Price* and *Year* of used BMW 840s.
c) Yes
d) 0.757
e) 57.4% of the variability in *Price* of a used BMW 840 can be accounted for by the *Year* the car was made.
f) The relationship is not perfect. Other factors, such as options, condition, and mileage, may account for some of the variability in price.

67. a) The association between cost of living in 2007 and 2006 is linear, positive, and strong. The linearity of the scatterplot indicates that the linear model is appropriate.
b) 83.7% of the variability in cost of living in 2007 can be explained by variability in cost of living in 2006.
c) 0.915
d) Moscow had a cost of living of 123.9% of New York's in 2006. According to the model, Moscow is predicted to have a cost of living in 2007 that is about 128.8% of New York's. Moscow actually had a cost of living in 2007 that was 134.4% of New York's, so its residual was about 5.6%.

69. a) 0.578
b) CO_2 levels account for 33.4% of the variation in mean temperature.
c) $\overline{Mean\ Temperature} = 15.3066 + 0.004\ CO_2$
d) The predicted mean temperature has been increasing at an average rate of 0.004 degrees (C)/ppm of CO_2.
e) One *could* say that with no CO_2 in the atmosphere, there would be a temperature of 15.3066 degrees Celsius, but this is extrapolation to a nonsensical point.
f) No
g) Predicted 16.7626 degrees C.

71. a) Spearman's rank correlation would be more appropriate because the relationship is not straight.
b) The relationship with the square root of *Displacement* is more nearly linear and would be more appropriate for fitting a linear model.

Randomness and Probability

Phillip Spears/Photodisc/
Getty Images

Sean Russell/fStop/Getty Images

DreamPictures/Getty Images

Frank Bean/UpperCut Images/Getty Images

Credit Reports and the Fair Isaacs Corporation

You've probably never heard of the Fair Isaacs Corporation, but they probably know you. Whenever you apply for a loan, a credit card, or even a job, your credit "score" will be used to determine whether you are a good risk. And because the most widely used credit scores are Fair Isaacs' FICO® scores, the company may well be involved in the decision. The Fair Isaacs Corporation (FICO) was founded in 1956, with the idea that data, used intelligently, could improve business decision-making. Today, Fair Isaacs claims that their services provide companies around the world with information for more than 180 billion business decisions a year.

Your credit score is a number between 350 and 850 that summarizes your credit "worthiness." It's a snapshot of credit risk today based on your credit history and past behavior. Lenders of all kinds use credit scores to predict behavior, such as how likely you are to make your loan payments on time or to default on a loan. Lenders use the score to determine not only whether to give credit, but also the cost of the credit that they'll offer. There are no established boundaries, but generally scores over 750 are considered excellent, and applicants with those scores get the best rates. An applicant with a score below 620 is generally considered to be a poor risk. Those with very low scores may be denied credit outright or only offered "subprime" loans at substantially higher rates.

From Chapter 7 of *Business Statistics*, Second Edition, Norean R. Sharpe, Richard D. De Veaux, Paul F. Velleman.

It's important that you be able to verify the information that your score is based on, but until recently, you could only hope that your score was based on correct information. That changed in 2000, when a California law gave mortgage applicants the right to see their credit scores. Today, the credit industry is more open about giving consumers access to their scores and the U.S. government, through the Fair and Accurate Credit Transaction Act (FACTA), now guarantees that you can access your credit report at no cost, at least once a year.[1]

C ompanies have to manage risk to survive, but by its nature, risk carries uncertainty. A bank can't know for certain that you'll pay your mortgage on time—or at all. What can they do with events they can't predict? They start with the fact that, although individual outcomes cannot be anticipated with certainty, random phenomena do, in the long run, settle into patterns that are consistent and predictable. It's this property of random events that makes Statistics practical.

1 Random Phenomena and Probability

When a customer calls the 800 number of a credit card company, he or she is asked for a card number before being connected with an operator. As the connection is made, the purchase records of that card and the demographic information of the customer are retrieved and displayed on the operator's screen. If the customer's FICO score is high enough, the operator may be prompted to "cross-sell" another service— perhaps a new "platinum" card for customers with a credit score of at least 750.

Of course, the company doesn't know which customers are going to call. Call arrivals are an example of a random phenomenon. With **random phenomena**, we can't predict the individual outcomes, but we can hope to understand characteristics of their long-run behavior. We don't know whether the *next* caller will qualify for the platinum card, but as calls come into the call center, the company will find that the percentage of platinum-qualified callers who qualify for cross-selling will settle into a pattern, like that shown in the graph in Figure 1.

As calls come into the call center, the company might record whether each caller qualifies. The first caller today qualified. Then the next five callers' qualifications were no, yes, yes, no, and no. If we plot the percentage who qualify against the call number, the graph would start at 100% because the first caller qualified (1 out of 1, for 100%). The next caller didn't qualify, so the accumulated percentage dropped to 50% (1 out of 2). The third caller qualified (2 out of 3, or 67%), then yes again (3 out of 4, or 75%), then no twice in a row (3 out of 5, for 60%, and then 3 out of 6, for 50%), and so on (Table 1). With each new call, the new datum is a smaller fraction of the accumulated experience, so, in the long run, the graph settles down. As it settles down, it appears that, in fact, the fraction of customers who qualify is about 35%.

When talking about long-run behavior, it helps to define our terms. For any random phenomenon, each attempt, or **trial**, generates an **outcome**. For the call center, each call is a trial. Something happens on each trial, and we call whatever happens the outcome. Here the outcome is whether the caller qualifies or not.

---

[1]However, the score you see in your report will be an "educational" score intended to show consumers how scoring works. You still have to pay a "reasonable fee" to see your FICO score.

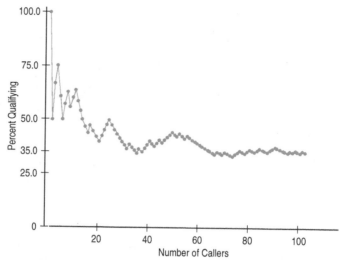

Figure 1 The percentage of credit card customers who qualify for the premium card.

Call	FICO Score	Qualify?	% Qualify
1	750	Yes	100
2	640	No	50
3	765	Yes	66.7
4	780	Yes	75
5	680	No	60
6	630	No	50
⋮	⋮		⋮

Table 1 Data on the first six callers showing their FICO score, whether they qualified for the platinum card offer, and a running percentage of number of callers who qualified.

> A **phenomenon** consists of **trials**. Each trial has an **outcome**. Outcomes combine to make **events**.

We use the more general term **event** to refer to outcomes or combinations of outcomes. For example, suppose we categorize callers into 6 risk categories and number these outcomes from 1 to 6 (of increasing credit worthiness). The three outcomes 4, 5, or 6 could make up the event "caller is at least a category 4."

We sometimes talk about the collection of *all possible outcomes*, a special event that we'll refer to as the **sample space**. We denote the sample space **S**; you may also see the Greek letter Ω used. But whatever symbol we use, the sample space is the set that contains all the possible outcomes. For the calls, if we let Q = qualified and N = not qualified, the sample space is simple: **S** = {Q, N}. If we look at two calls together, the sample space has four outcomes: **S** = {QQ, QN, NQ, NN}. If we were interested in at least one qualified caller from the two calls, we would be interested in the event (call it **A**) consisting of the three outcomes QQ, QN, and NQ, and we'd write **A** = {QQ, QN, NQ}.

Although we may not be able to predict a *particular* individual outcome, such as which incoming call represents a potential upgrade sale, we can say a lot about the long-run behavior. Look back at Figure 1. If you were asked for the probability that a random caller will qualify, you might say that it was 35% because, in the *long run*, the percentage of the callers who qualify is about 35%. And, that's exactly what we mean by **probability**.

> The **probability** of an event is its long-run relative frequency. A relative frequency is a fraction, so we can write it as $\frac{35}{100}$, as a decimal, 0.35, or as a percentage, 35%.

That seems simple enough, but do random phenomena always behave this well? Couldn't it happen that the frequency of qualified callers never settles down, but just bounces back and forth between two numbers? Maybe it hovers around 45% for awhile, then goes down to 25%, and then back and forth forever. When we think about what happens with a series of trials, it really simplifies things if the individual trials are independent. Roughly speaking, **independence** means that the outcome of one trial doesn't influence or change the outcome of another. Recall that we called two variables *independent* if the value of one categorical variable did not influence the value of another categorical variable. (We checked for independence by comparing relative frequency distributions across variables.) There's no reason to think that whether the one caller qualifies influences whether another caller qualifies, so these are independent trials. We'll see a more formal definition of independence later in the chapter.

Fortunately, for independent events, we can depend on a principle called the **Law of Large Numbers (LLN)**, which states that if the events are independent, then as the number of calls increases, over days or months or years, the long-run relative frequency of qualified calls gets closer and closer to a single value. This gives us the guarantee we need and makes probability a useful concept.

Because the LLN guarantees that relative frequencies settle down in the long run, we know that the value we called the probability is legitimate and the number it settles down to is called the probability of that event. For the call center, we can write $P(\text{qualified}) = 0.35$. Because it is based on repeatedly observing the event's outcome, this definition of probability is often called **empirical probability**.

---

2 The Nonexistent Law of Averages

The Law of Large Numbers says that the relative frequency of a random event settles down to a single number in the long run. But, it is often misunderstood to be a "law of averages," perhaps because the concept of "long run" is hard to grasp. Many people believe, for example, that an outcome of a random event that hasn't occurred in many trials is "due" to occur. The original "dogs of the Dow" strategy for buying stocks recommended buying the 10 worst performing stocks of the 30 that make up the Dow Jones Industrial Average, figuring that these "dogs" were bound to do better next year. After all, we know that in the long run, the relative frequency will settle down to the probability of that outcome, so now we have some "catching up" to do, right? Wrong. In fact, Louis Rukeyser (the former host of *Wall Street Week*) said of the "dogs of the Dow" strategy, "that theory didn't work as promised."

Actually, we know very little about the behavior of random events in the short run. The fact that we are seeing independent random events makes each individual result impossible to predict. Relative frequencies even out *only* in the long run. And, according to the LLN, the long run is really long (infinitely long, in fact). The "Large" in the law's name means *infinitely* large. Sequences of random events don't compensate in the short run and don't need to do so to get back to the right long-run probability. Any short-run deviations will be overwhelmed in the long run. If the probability of an outcome doesn't change and the events are independent, the probability of any outcome in another trial is always what it was, no matter what has happened in other trials.

Many people confuse the Law of Large numbers with the so-called Law of Averages that would say that things have to even out in the short run. But even though the Law of Averages doesn't exist at all, you'll hear people talk about it as if it does. Is a good hitter in baseball who has struck out the last six times due for a hit his next time up? If the stock market has been down for the last three sessions, is it due to increase today? No. This isn't the way random phenomena work. There is no Law of Averages for short runs—no "Law of Small Numbers." A belief in such a "law" can lead to poor business decisions.

Law of Large Numbers

The *long-run relative frequency* of repeated, independent events eventually produces the *true relative frequency* as the number of trials increases.

"Slump? I ain't in no slump. I just ain't hittin'."

—YOGI BERRA

St. Andrews University/The MacTutor History of Mathematics Archive

You may think it's obvious that the frequency of repeated events settles down in the long run to a single number. The discoverer of the Law of Large Numbers thought so, too. The way he put it was: *"For even the most stupid of men is convinced that the more observations have been made, the less danger there is of wandering from one's goal."*

—JACOB BERNOULLI, 1713

Jean-Loup Gautreau/AFP/
Getty Images

Keno and the Law of Averages

Of course, sometimes an apparent drift from what we expect means that the probabilities are, in fact, *not* what we thought. If you get 10 heads in a row, maybe the coin has heads on both sides!

Keno is a simple casino game in which numbers from 1 to 80 are chosen. The numbers, as in most lottery games, are supposed to be equally likely. Payoffs are made depending on how many of those numbers you match on your card. A group of graduate students from a Statistics department decided to take a field trip to Reno. They (*very* discreetly) wrote down the outcomes of the games for a couple of days, then drove back to test whether the numbers were, in fact, equally likely. It turned out that some numbers were *more likely* to come up than others. Rather than bet on the Law of Averages and put their money on the numbers that were "due," the students put their faith in the LLN—and all their (and their friends') money on the numbers that had come up before. After they pocketed more than $50,000, they were escorted off the premises and invited never to show their faces in that casino again. Not coincidentally, the ringleader of that group currently makes his living on Wall Street.

"In addition, in time, if the roulette-betting fool keeps playing the game, the bad histories [outcomes] will tend to catch up with him."

—NASSIM NICHOLAS TALEB IN
FOOLED BY RANDOMNESS

You've just flipped a fair coin and seen six heads in a row. Does the coin "owe" you some tails? Suppose you spend that coin and your friend gets it in change. When she starts flipping the coin, should we expect a run of tails? Of course not. Each flip is a new event. The coin can't "remember" what it did in the past, so it can't "owe" any particular outcomes in the future. Just to see how this works in practice, we simulated 100,000 flips of a fair coin on a computer. In our 100,000 "flips," there were 2981 streaks of at least 5 heads. The "Law of Averages" suggests that the next flip after a run of 5 heads should be tails more often to even things out. Actually, the next flip was heads more often than tails: 1550 times to 1431 times. That's 51.9% heads. You can perform a similar simulation easily.

Just Checking

1 It has been shown that the stock market fluctuates randomly. Nevertheless, some investors believe that they should buy right after a day when the market goes down because it is bound to go up soon. Explain why this is faulty reasoning.

3 Different Types of Probability

Model-Based (Theoretical) Probability

We've discussed *empirical probability*—the relative frequency of an event's occurrence as the probability of an event. There are other ways to define probability as well. Probability was first studied extensively by a group of French mathematicians who were interested in games of chance. Rather than experiment with the games and risk losing their money, they developed mathematical models of probability. To make things simple (as we usually do when we build models), they started by looking at games in which the different outcomes were equally likely. Fortunately, many games of chance are like that. Any of 52 cards is equally likely to be the next one dealt from a well-shuffled deck. Each face of a die is equally likely to land up (or at least it should be).

We can write:

$$P(\mathbf{A}) = \frac{\text{\# of outcomes in } \mathbf{A}}{\text{total \# of outcomes}}$$

and call this the **(theoretical) probability** of the event.

When outcomes are equally likely, their probability is easy to compute—it's just 1 divided by the number of possible outcomes. So the probability of rolling a 3 with a fair die is one in six, which we write as 1/6. The probability of picking the ace of spades from the top of a well-shuffled deck is 1/52.

It's almost as simple to find probabilities for events that are made up of several equally likely outcomes. We just count all the outcomes that the event contains. The probability of the event is the number of outcomes in the event divided by the total number of possible outcomes.

For example, Pew Research[2] reports that of 10,190 randomly generated working phone numbers called for a survey, the initial results of the calls were as follows:

Result	Number of Calls
No Answer	311
Busy	61
Answering Machine	1336
Callbacks	189
Other Non-Contacts	893
Contacted Numbers	7400

The phone numbers were generated randomly, so each was equally likely. To find the probability of a contact, we just divide the number of contacts by the number of calls: 7400/10,190 = 0.7262.

But don't get trapped into thinking that random events are always equally likely. The chance of winning a lottery—especially lotteries with very large payoffs—is small. Regardless, people continue to buy tickets.

Personal Probability

What's the probability that gold will sell for more than $1000 an ounce at the end of next year? You may be able to come up with a number that seems reasonable. Of course, no matter how confident you feel about your prediction, your probability should be between 0 and 1. How did you come up with this probability? In our discussion of probability, we've defined probability in two ways: 1) in terms of the relative frequency—or the fraction of times—that an event occurs in the long run or 2) as the number of outcomes in the event divided by the total number of outcomes. Neither situation applies to your assessment of gold's chances of selling for more than $1000.

We use the *language* of probability in everyday speech to express a degree of uncertainty without basing it on long-run relative frequencies. Your personal assessment of an event expresses your uncertainty about the outcome. That uncertainty may be based on your knowledge of commodities markets, but it can't be based on long-run behavior. We call this kind of probability a subjective, or **personal probability**.

Although personal probabilities may be based on experience, they are not based either on long-run relative frequencies or on equally likely events. Like the two other probabilities we defined, they need to satisfy the same rules as both empirical and theoretical probabilities that we'll discuss in the next section.

---

[2]www.pewinternet.org/pdfs/PIP_Digital_Footprints.pdf.

4   Probability Rules

For some people, the phrase "50/50" means something vague like "I don't know" or "whatever." But when we discuss probabilities, 50/50 has the precise meaning that two outcomes are *equally likely.* Speaking vaguely about probabilities can get you into trouble, so it's wise to develop some formal rules about how probability works. These rules apply to probability whether we're dealing with empirical, theoretical, or personal probability.

*"Baseball is 90% mental.
The other half is physical."*

—YOGI BERRA

Rule 1. If the probability of an event occurring is 0, the event can't occur; likewise if the probability is 1, the event *always* occurs. Even if you think an event is very unlikely, its probability can't be negative, and even if you're sure it will happen, its probability can't be greater than 1. So we require that:

> **A probability is a number between 0 and 1.**
> **For any event A, $0 \leq P(A) \leq 1$.**

Rule 2. If a random phenomenon has only one possible outcome, it's not very interesting (or very random). So we need to distribute the probabilities among all the outcomes a trial can have. How can we do that so that it makes sense? For example, consider the behavior of a certain stock. The possible daily outcomes might be:

A: The stock price goes up.
B: The stock price goes down.
C: The stock price remains the same.

When we assign probabilities to these outcomes, we should be sure to distribute all of the available probability. Something always occurs, so the probability of *something* happening is 1. This is called the **Probability Assignment Rule**:

> **The probability of the set of all possible outcomes must be 1.**
> $$P(S) = 1$$

where **S** represents the set of all possible outcomes and is called the **sample space**.

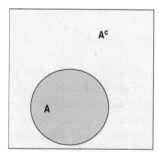

The set **A** and its complement **A**^C. Together, they make up the entire sample space **S**.

Rule 3. Suppose the probability that you get to class on time is 0.8. What's the probability that you don't get to class on time? Yes, it's 0.2. The set of outcomes that are *not* in the event **A** is called the "complement" of **A**, and is denoted **A**^C. This leads to the **Complement Rule**:

> **The probability of an event occurring is 1 minus the probability that it doesn't occur.**
> $$P(A) = 1 - P(A^C)$$

For Example   Applying the complement rule

Lee's Lights sells lighting fixtures. Some customers are there only to browse, so Lee records the behavior of all customers for a week to assess how likely it is that a customer will make a purchase. Lee finds that of 1000 customers entering the store during the week, 300 make purchases. Lee concludes that the probability of a customer making a purchase is 0.30.

Question: If $P(\text{purchase}) = 0.30$, what is the probability that a customer *doesn't* make a purchase?

Answer: Because "no purchase" is the complement of "purchase,"

$$P(\text{no purchase}) = 1 - P(\text{purchase})$$
$$= 1 - 0.30 = 0.70$$

There is a 70% chance a customer won't make a purchase.

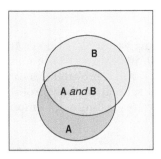

Two sets **A** and **B** that are not disjoint. The event (**A** and **B**) is their intersection.

Rule 4. Whether or not a caller qualifies for a platinum card is a random outcome. Suppose the probability of qualifying is 0.35. What's the chance that the next two callers qualify? The **Multiplication Rule** says that to find the probability that two independent events occur, we multiply the probabilities:

> **For two independent events A and B, the probability that both A *and* B occur is the product of the probabilities of the two events. *P*(A and B) = *P*(A) × *P*(B), provided that A and B are independent.**

Thus if **A** = {customer 1 qualifies} and **B** = {customer 2 qualifies}, the chance that both qualify is:

$$0.35 \times 0.35 = 0.1225$$

Of course, to calculate this probability, we have used the assumption that the two events are independent. We'll expand the multiplication rule to be more general later in this chapter.

For Example   Using the multiplication rule

Lee knows that the probability that a customer will make a purchase is 30%.

Question: If we can assume that customers behave independently, what is the probability that the next two customers entering Lee's Lights make purchases?

Answer: Because the events are independent, we can use the multiplication rule.

P(first customer makes a purchase *and* second customer makes a purchase)

= *P*(purchase) × *P*(purchase)

= 0.30 × 0.30 = 0.09

There's about a 9% chance that the next two customers will both make purchases.

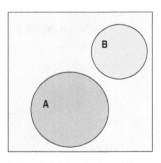

Two disjoint sets, **A** and **B**.

Rule 5. Suppose the card center operator has more options. She can **A:** offer a special travel deal, **B:** offer a platinum card, or **C:** decide to send information about a new affinity card. If she can do one, but only one, of these, then these outcomes are **disjoint** (or **mutually exclusive**). To see whether two events are disjoint, we separate them into their component outcomes and check whether they have any outcomes in common. For example, if the operator can choose to both offer the travel deal and send the affinity card information, those would not be disjoint. The **Addition Rule** allows us to add the probabilities of disjoint events to get the probability that *either* event occurs:

$$P(\text{A or B}) = P(\text{A}) + P(\text{B}).$$

Thus the probability that the caller *either* is offered a platinum card *or* is sent the affinity card information is the sum of the two probabilities, since the events are disjoint.

For Example   Using the addition rule

Some customers prefer to see the merchandise but then make their purchase later using Lee's Lights' new Internet site. Tracking customer behavior, Lee determines that there's an 8% chance of a customer making a purchase in this way. We know that about 30% of customers make purchases when they enter the store.

Question: What is the probability that a customer who enters the store makes no purchase at all?

Answer: We can use the Addition Rule because the alternatives "no purchase," "purchase in the store," and "purchase online" are disjoint events.

$$P(\text{purchase in the store } or \text{ online}) = P(\text{purchase in store}) + P(\text{purchase online})$$
$$= 0.30 + 0.09 = 0.39$$

$$P(\text{no purchase}) = P(\text{not } P(\text{purchase in the store } or \text{ purchase online}))$$
$$= 1 - P(\text{in store } or \text{ online})$$
$$= 1 - 0.39 = 0.61$$

Notation Alert! ————

You may see the event (**A** or **B**) written as (**A** $\cup$ **B**). The symbol $\cup$ means "union" and represents the outcomes in event **A** or event **B**. Similarly the symbol $\cap$ means intersection and represents outcomes that are in *both* event **A** and event **B**. You may see the event (**A** and **B**) written as (**A** $\cap$ **B**).

Rule 6. Suppose we would like to know the probability that either of the next two callers is qualified for a platinum card? We know $P(\mathbf{A}) = P(\mathbf{B}) = 0.35$, but $P(\mathbf{A} \text{ or } \mathbf{B})$ is not simply the sum $P(\mathbf{A}) + P(\mathbf{B})$ because the events **A** and **B** are not disjoint in this case. Both customers could qualify. So we need a new probability rule.

We can't simply add the probabilities of **A** and **B** because that would count the outcome of *both* customers qualifying twice. So, if we started by adding the two probabilities, we could compensate by subtracting out the probability of that outcome. In other words,

$P(\text{customer A } or \text{ customer B qualifies}) =$

$P(\text{customer A qualifies}) + P(\text{customer B qualifies}) - P(\text{both customers qualify})$

$= (0.35) + (0.35) - (0.35 \times 0.35) \text{ (since events are independent)}$

$= (0.35) + (0.35) - (0.1225)$

$= 0.5775$

It turns out that this method works in general. We add the probabilities of two events and then subtract out the probability of their intersection. This gives us the **General Addition Rule**, which does not require disjoint events:

$$P(\mathbf{A} \text{ or } \mathbf{B}) = P(\mathbf{A}) + P(\mathbf{B}) - P(\mathbf{A} \text{ and } \mathbf{B})$$

For Example — Using the general addition rule

Lee notices that when two customers enter the store together, their behavior isn't independent. In fact, there's a 20% chance they'll *both* make a purchase.

Question: When two customers enter the store together, what is the probability that *at least one* of them will make a purchase?

Answer: Now we know that the events are not independent, so we must use the General Addition Rule

$$P(\text{Both purchase}) = P(\text{A purchases } or \text{ B purchases})$$
$$= P(\text{A purchases}) + P(\text{B purchases}) - P(\text{A and B both purchase})$$
$$= 0.30 + 0.30 - 0.20 = 0.40$$

Just Checking

2 MP3 players have relatively high failure rates for a consumer product, especially those models that contain a disk drive as opposed to those that have less storage but no drive. The worst failure rate for all iPod models was the 40GB Click wheel (as reported by MacIntouch.com) at 30%. If a store sells this model and failures are independent,

   a) What is the probability that the next one they sell will have a failure?

   b) What is the probability that there will be failures on *both* of the next two?

   c) What is the probability that the store's first failure problem will be with the third one they sell?

   d) What is the probability the store will have a failure problem with at least one of the next five that they sell?

Guided Example   M&M's Modern Market Research

Adam Rountree/AP Images

In 1941, when M&M's® milk chocolate candies were introduced to American GIs in World War II, there were six colors: brown, yellow, orange, red, green, and violet. Mars®, the company that manufactures M&M's, has used the introduction of a new color as a marketing and advertising event several times in the years since then. In 1980, the candy went international adding 16 countries to their markets. In 1995, the company conducted a "worldwide survey" to vote on a new color. Over 10 million people voted to add blue. They even got the lights of the Empire State Building in New York City to glow blue to help announce the addition. In 2002, they used the Internet to help pick a new color. Children from over 200 countries were invited to respond via the Internet, telephone, or mail. Millions of voters chose among purple, pink, and teal. The global winner was purple, and for a brief time, purple M&M's could be found in packages worldwide (although in 2010, the colors were brown, yellow, red, blue, orange, and green). In the United States, 42% of those who voted said purple, 37% said teal, and only 19% said pink. But in Japan the percentages were 38% pink, 36% teal, and only 16% purple. Let's use Japan's percentages to ask some questions.

1. What's the probability that a Japanese M&M's survey respondent selected at random preferred either pink or teal?

2. If we pick two respondents at random, what's the probability that they *both* selected purple?

3. If we pick three respondents at random, what's the probability that *at least one* preferred purple?

PLAN

Setup The probability of an event is its long-term relative frequency. This can be determined in several ways: by looking at many replications of an event, by deducing it from equally likely events, or by using some other information. Here, we are told the relative frequencies of the three responses.

The M&M's website reports the proportions of Japanese votes by color. These give the probability of selecting a voter who preferred each of the colors:

$P(\text{pink}) = 0.38$
$P(\text{teal}) = 0.36$
$P(\text{purple}) = 0.16$

Make sure the probabilities are legitimate. Here, they're not. Either there was a mistake or the other voters must have chosen a color other than the three given. A check of other countries shows a similar deficit, so probably we're seeing those who had no preference or who wrote in another color.

Each is between 0 and 1, but these don't add up to 1. The remaining 10% of the voters must have not expressed a preference or written in another color. We'll put them together into "other" and add $P(\text{other}) = 0.10$.

With this addition, we have a legitimate assignment of probabilities.

Question 1. What's the probability that a Japanese M&M's survey respondent selected at random preferred either pink or teal?

PLAN

Setup Decide which rules to use and check the conditions they require.

The events "pink" and "teal" are individual outcomes (a respondent can't choose both colors), so they are disjoint. We can apply the General Addition Rule anyway.

DO	Mechanics Show your work.	$P(\text{pink or teal}) = P(\text{pink}) + P(\text{teal})$ $\qquad\qquad\qquad - P(\text{pink and teal})$ $\qquad = 0.38 + 0.36 - 0 = 0.74$ The probability that both pink and teal were chosen is zero, since respondents were limited to one choice.
REPORT	Conclusion Interpret your results in the proper context.	The probability that the respondent said pink or teal is 0.74.

Question 2. If we pick two respondents at random, what's the probability that they both said purple?

PLAN	Setup The word "both" suggests we want $P(\mathbf{A} \text{ and } \mathbf{B})$, which calls for the Multiplication Rule. Check the required condition.	**Independence** It's unlikely that the choice made by one respondent affected the choice of the other, so the events seem to be independent. We can use the Multiplication Rule.
DO	Mechanics Show your work. For both respondents to pick purple, each one has to pick purple.	$P(\text{both purple})$ $\quad = P(\text{first respondent picks purple and}$ $\qquad\quad \text{second respondent picks purple})$ $\quad = P(\text{first respondent picks purple})$ $\qquad\quad \times P(\text{second respondent picks purple})$ $\quad = 0.16 \times 0.16 = 0.0256$
REPORT	Conclusion Interpret your results in the proper context.	The probability that both respondents pick purple is 0.0256.

Question 3. If we pick three respondents at random, what's the probability that at least one preferred purple?

PLAN	Setup The phrase "at least one" often flags a question best answered by looking at the complement, and that's the best approach here. The complement of "at least one preferred purple" is "none of them preferred purple." Check the conditions.	$P(\text{at least one picked purple})$ $\quad = P(\{\text{none picked purple}\}^c)$ $\quad = 1 - P(\text{none picked purple}).$ **Independence.** These are independent events because they are choices by three random respondents. We can use the Multiplication Rule.
DO	Mechanics We calculate $P(\text{none purple})$ by using the Multiplication Rule.	$P(\text{none picked purple}) = P(\text{first not purple})$ $\qquad\qquad\qquad\quad \times P(\text{second not purple})$ $\qquad\qquad\qquad\quad \times P(\text{third not purple})$ $\qquad\qquad\qquad = [P(\text{not purple})]^3.$ $P(\text{not purple}) = 1 - P(\text{purple})$ $\qquad\qquad\qquad = 1 - 0.16 = 0.84.$

(continued)

	Then we can use the Complement Rule to get the probability we want.	So $P(\text{none picked purple}) = (0.84)^3 = 0.5927.$
		$P(\text{at least 1 picked purple})$
		$= 1 - P(\text{none picked purple})$
		$= 1 - 0.5927 = 0.4073.$
REPORT	**Conclusion** Interpret your results in the proper context.	There's about a 40.7% chance that at least one of the respondents picked purple.

5 Joint Probability and Contingency Tables

As part of a Pick Your Prize Promotion, a chain store invited customers to choose which of three prizes they'd like to win (while providing name, address, phone number, and e-mail address). At one store, the responses could be placed in the contingency table in Table 2.

		Prize preference			
		MP3	**Camera**	**Bike**	**Total**
Sex	**Man**	117	50	60	**227**
	Woman	130	91	30	**251**
	Total	**247**	**141**	**90**	**478**

| Table 2 Prize preference for 478 customers.

> A **marginal probability** uses a marginal frequency (from either the Total row or Total column) to compute the probability.

If the winner is chosen at random from these customers, the probability we select a woman is just the corresponding relative frequency (since we're equally likely to select any of the 478 customers). There are 251 women in the data out of a total of 478, giving a probability of:

$$P(\text{woman}) = 251/478 = 0.525$$

This is called a **marginal probability** because it depends only on totals found in the margins of the table. The same method works for more complicated events. For example, what's the probability of selecting a woman whose preferred prize is the camera? Well, 91 women named the camera as their preference, so the probability is:

$$P(\text{woman } and \text{ camera}) = 91/478 = 0.190$$

Probabilities such as these are called **joint probabilities** because they give the probability of two events occurring together.

The probability of selecting a customer whose preferred prize is a bike is:

$$P(\text{bike}) = 90/478 = 0.188$$

Lee suspects that men and women make different kinds of purchases at Lee's Lights. The table shows the purchases made by the last 100 customers.

	Utility Lighting	Fashion Lighting	Total
Men	40	20	60
Women	10	30	40
Total	50	50	100

Question: What's the probability that one of Lee's customers is a woman? What is the probability that a random customer is a man who purchases fashion lighting?

Answer: From the marginal totals we can see that 40% of Lee's customers are women, so the probability that a customer is a woman is 0.40. The cell of the table for Men who purchase Fashion lighting has 20 of the 100 customers, so the probability of that event is 0.20.

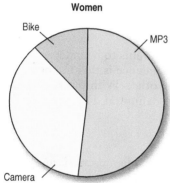

Women

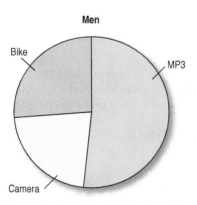

Men

Figure 2   Conditional distributions of *Prize Preference* for *Women* and for *Men*.

Notation Alert! ——————

$P(\mathbf{B}|\mathbf{A})$ is the conditional probability of $\mathbf{B}$ *given* $\mathbf{A}$.

6   Conditional Probability

Since our sample space is these 478 customers, we can recognize the relative frequencies as probabilities. What if we are given the information that the selected customer is a woman? Would that change the probability that the selected customer's preferred prize is a bike? You bet it would! The pie charts show that women are much less likely to say their preferred prize is a bike than are men. When we restrict our focus to women, we look only at the women's row of the table, which gives the conditional distribution of preferred prizes given "woman." Of the 251 women, only 30 of them said their preferred prize was a bike. We write the probability that a selected customer wants a bike *given* that we have selected a woman as:

$$P(\text{bike}|\text{woman}) = 30/251 = 0.120$$

For men, we look at the conditional distribution of preferred prizes given "man" shown in the top row of the table. There, of the 227 men, 60 said their preferred prize was a bike. So, $P(\text{bike}|\text{man}) = 60/227 = 0.264$, more than twice the women's probability (see Figure 2).

In general, when we want the probability of an event from a *conditional* distribution, we write $P(\mathbf{B}|\mathbf{A})$ and pronounce it "the probability of $\mathbf{B}$ *given* $\mathbf{A}$." A probability that takes into account a given *condition* such as this is called a **conditional probability**.

Let's look at what we did. We worked with the counts, but we could work with the probabilities just as well. There were 30 women who selected a bike as a prize, and there were 251 women customers. So we found the probability to be 30/251. To find the probability of the event $\mathbf{B}$ *given* the event $\mathbf{A}$, we restrict our attention to the outcomes in $\mathbf{A}$. We then find in what fraction of *those* outcomes $\mathbf{B}$ also occurred. Formally, we write:

$$P(\mathbf{B}|\mathbf{A}) = \frac{P(\mathbf{A} \text{ and } \mathbf{B})}{P(\mathbf{A})}$$

We can use the formula directly with the probabilities derived from the contingency table (Table 2) to find:

$$P(\text{bike}|\text{woman}) = \frac{P(\text{bike } and \text{ woman})}{P(\text{woman})} = \frac{30/478}{251/478} = \frac{0.063}{0.525} = 0.120 \text{ as before.}$$

The formula for conditional probability requires one restriction. The formula works only when the event that's given has probability greater than 0. The formula doesn't work if $P(\mathbf{A})$ is 0 because that would mean we had been "given" the fact that $\mathbf{A}$ was true even though the probability of $\mathbf{A}$ is 0, which would be a contradiction.

Rule 7. Remember the Multiplication Rule for the probability of $\mathbf{A}$ *and* $\mathbf{B}$? It said

$$P(\mathbf{A} \text{ and } \mathbf{B}) = P(\mathbf{A}) \times P(\mathbf{B})$$

when $\mathbf{A}$ and $\mathbf{B}$ are independent. Now we can write a more general rule that doesn't require independence. In fact, we've already written it. We just need to rearrange the equation a bit.

The equation in the definition for conditional probability contains the probability of $\mathbf{A}$ *and* $\mathbf{B}$. Rearranging the equation gives the **General Multiplication Rule** for compound events that does not require the events to be independent:

$$P(\mathbf{A} \text{ and } \mathbf{B}) = P(\mathbf{A}) \times P(\mathbf{B}|\mathbf{A})$$

The probability that two events, $\mathbf{A}$ and $\mathbf{B}$, both occur is the probability that event $\mathbf{A}$ occurs multiplied by the probability that event $\mathbf{B}$ *also* occurs—that is, by the probability that event $\mathbf{B}$ occurs given that event $\mathbf{A}$ occurs.

Of course, there's nothing special about which event we call $\mathbf{A}$ and which one we call $\mathbf{B}$. We should be able to state this the other way around. Indeed we can. It is equally true that:

$$P(\mathbf{A} \text{ and } \mathbf{B}) = P(\mathbf{B}) \times P(\mathbf{A}|\mathbf{B}).$$

Let's return to the question of just what it means for events to be independent. We said informally before that what we mean by independence is that the outcome of one event does not influence the probability of the other. With our new notation for conditional probabilities, we can write a formal definition. Events $\mathbf{A}$ and $\mathbf{B}$ are **independent** whenever:

$$P(\mathbf{B}|\mathbf{A}) = P(\mathbf{B}).$$

Now we can see that the Multiplication Rule for independent events is just a special case of the General Multiplication Rule. The general rule says

$$P(\mathbf{A} \text{ and } \mathbf{B}) = P(\mathbf{A}) \times P(\mathbf{B}|\mathbf{A})$$

whether the events are independent or not. But when events $\mathbf{A}$ and $\mathbf{B}$ are independent, we can write $P(\mathbf{B})$ for $P(\mathbf{B}|\mathbf{A})$ and we get back our simple rule:

$$P(\mathbf{A} \text{ and } \mathbf{B}) = P(\mathbf{A}) \times P(\mathbf{B}).$$

Sometimes people use this statement as the definition of independent events, but we find the other definition more intuitive. Either way, the idea is that the probabilities of independent events don't change when you find out that one of them has occurred.

Using our earlier example, is the probability of the event *choosing a bike* independent of the sex of the customer? We need to check whether

$$P(\text{bike}|\text{man}) = \frac{P(\text{bike and man})}{P(\text{man})} = \frac{0.126}{0.475} = 0.265$$

is the same as $P(\text{bike}) = 0.189$.

Because these probabilities aren't equal, we can say that prize preference is *not* independent of the sex of the customer. Whenever at least one of the joint probabilities in the table is *not* equal to the product of the marginal probabilities, we say that the variables are not independent.

> **Independence**
>
> If we had to pick one key idea in this chapter that you should understand and remember, it's the definition and meaning of independence.

- **Independent *vs.* Disjoint.** Are disjoint events independent? Both concepts seem to have similar ideas of separation and distinctness about them, but in fact disjoint events *cannot* be independent.[3] Let's see why. Consider the two disjoint events {you get an A in this course} and {you get a B in this course}. They're disjoint because they have no outcomes in common. Suppose you learn that you *did* get an A in the course. Now what is the probability that you got a B? You can't get both grades, so it must be 0.

    Think about what that means. Knowing that the first event (getting an A) occurred changed your probability for the second event (down to 0). So these events aren't independent.

    Mutually exclusive events can't be independent. They have no outcomes in common, so knowing that one occurred means the other didn't. A common error is to treat disjoint events as if they were independent and apply the Multiplication Rule for independent events. Don't make that mistake.

For Example   Conditional probability

Question: Using the table from the example earlier in this chapter, if customer purchases a Fashion light, what is the probability that customer is a woman?

Answer: $P(\text{woman}\,|\,\text{Fashion}) = P(\text{Woman }and\text{ Fashion})/P(\text{Fashion})$

$$= 0.30/0.50 = 0.60$$

7   Constructing Contingency Tables

LM Productions/Digital Visions/ Getty Images

Sometimes we're given probabilities without a contingency table. You can often construct a simple table to correspond to the probabilities.

A survey of real estate in upstate New York classified homes into two price categories (Low—less than $175,000 and High—over $175,000). It also noted whether the houses had at least 2 bathrooms or not (True or False). We are told that 56% of the houses had at least 2 bathrooms, 62% of the houses were Low priced, and 22% of the houses were both. That's enough information to fill out the table. Translating the percentages to probabilities, we have:

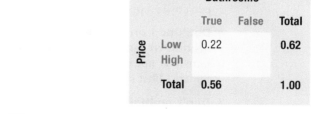

		At least 2 Bathrooms		
		True	False	Total
Price	Low	0.22		0.62
	High			
	Total	0.56		1.00

The 0.56 and 0.62 are marginal probabilities, so they go in the margins. What about the 22% of houses that were both Low priced and had at least 2 bathrooms? That's a *joint* probability, so it belongs in the interior of the table.

Because the cells of the table show disjoint events, the probabilities always add to the marginal totals going across rows or down columns.

---

[3]Technically two disjoint events *can* be independent, but only if the probability of one of the events is 0. For practical purposes, we can ignore this case, since we don't anticipate collecting data about things that can't possibly happen.

		At least 2 Bathrooms		
		True	**False**	**Total**
Price	**Low**	0.22	0.40	**0.62**
	High	0.64	0.04	**0.38**
	Total	**0.56**	**0.44**	**1.00**

Now, finding any other probability is straightforward. For example, what's the probability that a high-priced house has at least 2 bathrooms?

$$P(\text{at least 2 bathrooms} \mid \text{high-priced})$$
$$= P(\text{at least 2 bathrooms } and \text{ high-priced})/P(\text{high-priced})$$
$$= 0.34/0.38 = 0.895 \text{ or } 89.5\%.$$

Just Checking

3 Suppose a supermarket is conducting a survey to find out the busiest time and day for shoppers. Survey respondents are asked 1) whether they shopped at the store on a weekday or on the weekend and 2) whether they shopped at the store before or after 5 p.m. The survey revealed that:

- 48% of shoppers visited the store before 5 p.m.
- 27% of shoppers visited the store on a weekday (Mon.–Fri.)

- 7% of shoppers visited the store before 5 p.m. on a weekday.

a) Make a contingency table for the variables *time of day* and *day of week*.
b) What is the probability that a randomly selected shopper who shops before 5 p.m. also shops on a weekday?
c) Are time and day of the week disjoint events?
d) Are time and day of the week independent events?

What Can Go Wrong?

- **Beware of probabilities that don't add up to 1.** To be a legitimate assignment of probability, the sum of the probabilities for all possible outcomes must total 1. If the sum is less than 1, you may need to add another category ("other") and assign the remaining probability to that outcome. If the sum is more than 1, check that the outcomes are disjoint. If they're not, then you can't assign probabilities by counting relative frequencies.

- **Don't add probabilities of events if they're not disjoint.** Events must be disjoint to use the Addition Rule. The probability of being under 80 *or* a female is not the probability of being under 80 *plus* the probability of being female. That sum may be more than 1.

- **Don't multiply probabilities of events if they're not independent.** The probability of selecting a customer at random who is over 70 years old *and* retired is not the probability the customer is over 70 years old *times* the probability the customer is retired. Knowing that the customer is over 70 changes the probability of his or her being retired. You can't multiply these probabilities. The multiplication of probabilities of events that are not independent is one of the most common errors people make in dealing with probabilities.

- **Don't confuse disjoint and independent.** Disjoint events *can't* be independent. If **A** = {you get a promotion} and **B** = {you don't get a promotion}, **A** and **B** are disjoint. Are they independent? If you find out that **A** is true, does that change the probability of **B**? You bet it does! So they can't be independent.

216

Ethics in Action

A national chain of hair salons is considering the inclusion of some spa services. A management team is organized to investigate the possibility of entering the spa market via two offerings: facials or massages. One member of the team, Sherrie Trapper, found some results published by a spa industry trade journal regarding the probability of salon customers purchasing these types of services: There is an 80% chance that a customer visiting a hair salon that offers spa services is there for hair styling services. Of those, 50% will also purchase facials. On the other hand, 90% of customers visiting salons that offer spa services will be there for hair styling services

or massages. Sherry wasn't quite sure how to interpret all the numbers, but argued in favor of offering massages rather than facials on their initial spa menu since 90% is greater than 50%.

ETHICAL ISSUE *Sherrie does not understand what she is reporting and consequently should not use this information to persuade others on the team (related to Item A, ASA Ethical Guidelines).*

ETHICAL SOLUTION *Sherrie should share all details of the published results with the management team. The probabilities she is reporting are not comparable (one is conditional and the other is the probability of a union).*

What Have We Learned?

Learning Objectives

■ Apply the facts about probability to determine whether an assignment of probabilities is legitimate.
- Probability is long-run relative frequency.
- Individual probabilities must be between 0 and 1.
- The sum of probabilities assigned to all outcomes must be 1.

■ Understand the Law of Large Numbers and that the common understanding of the "Law of Averages" is false.

■ Know the rules of probability and how to apply them.
- The **Complement Rule** says that $P(\text{not }\mathbf{A}) = P(\mathbf{A}^C) = 1 - P(\mathbf{A})$.
- The **Multiplication Rule** for independent events says that $P(\mathbf{A}\text{ }and\text{ }\mathbf{B}) = P(\mathbf{A}) \times P(\mathbf{B})$ provided events $\mathbf{A}$ and $\mathbf{B}$ are independent.
- The **General Multiplication Rule** says that $P(\mathbf{A}\text{ }and\text{ }\mathbf{B}) = P(\mathbf{A}) \times P(\mathbf{B}|\mathbf{A})$.
- The **Addition Rule** for disjoint events says that $P(\mathbf{A}\text{ }or\text{ }\mathbf{B}) = P(\mathbf{A}) + P(\mathbf{B})$ provided events A and B are disjoint.
- The **General Addition Rule** says that $P(\mathbf{A}\text{ }or\text{ }\mathbf{B}) = P(\mathbf{A}) + P(\mathbf{B}) - P(\mathbf{A}\text{ }and\text{ }\mathbf{B})$.

■ Know how to construct and read a contingency table.

■ Know how to define and use independence.
- Events A and B are independent if $P(\mathbf{A}|\mathbf{B}) = P(\mathbf{A})$.

Terms

Addition Rule

If $\mathbf{A}$ and $\mathbf{B}$ are disjoint events, then the probability of $\mathbf{A}$ or $\mathbf{B}$ is

$$P(\mathbf{A}\text{ }or\text{ }\mathbf{B}) = P(\mathbf{A}) + P(\mathbf{B}).$$

Complement Rule

The probability of an event occurring is 1 minus the probability that it doesn't occur:

$$P(\mathbf{A}) = 1 - P(\mathbf{A}^C).$$

Conditional probability	$$P(\mathbf{B}|\mathbf{A}) = \frac{P(\mathbf{A} \text{ and } \mathbf{B})}{P(\mathbf{A})}.$$
	$P(\mathbf{B}|\mathbf{A})$ is read "the probability of $\mathbf{B}$ *given* $\mathbf{A}$."
Disjoint (or Mutually Exclusive) Events	Two events are disjoint if they share no outcomes in common. If $\mathbf{A}$ and $\mathbf{B}$ are disjoint, then knowing that $\mathbf{A}$ occurs tells us that $\mathbf{B}$ cannot occur. Disjoint events are also called "mutually exclusive."
Empirical probability	When the probability comes from the long-run relative frequency of the event's occurrence, it is an empirical probability.
Event	A collection of outcomes. Usually, we identify events so that we can attach probabilities to them. We denote events with bold capital letters such as $\mathbf{A}$, $\mathbf{B}$, or $\mathbf{C}$.
General Addition Rule	For any two events, $\mathbf{A}$ and $\mathbf{B}$, the probability of $\mathbf{A}$ *or* $\mathbf{B}$ is: $$P(\mathbf{A} \text{ or } \mathbf{B}) = P(\mathbf{A}) + P(\mathbf{B}) - P(\mathbf{A} \text{ and } \mathbf{B}).$$
General Multiplication Rule	For any two events, $\mathbf{A}$ and $\mathbf{B}$, the probability of $\mathbf{A}$ and $\mathbf{B}$ is: $$P(\mathbf{A} \text{ and } \mathbf{B}) = P(\mathbf{A}) \times P(\mathbf{B}|\mathbf{A}).$$
Independence (informally)	Two events are *independent* if the fact that one event occurs does not change the probability of the other.
Independence (used formally)	Events $\mathbf{A}$ and $\mathbf{B}$ are independent when $P(\mathbf{B}|\mathbf{A}) = P(\mathbf{B})$.
Joint probabilities	The probability that two events both occur.
Law of Large Numbers (LLN)	The Law of Large Numbers states that the *long-run relative frequency* of repeated, independent events settles down to the *true relative frequency* as the number of trials increases.
Marginal probability	In a joint probability table a marginal probability is the probability distribution of either variable separately, usually found in the rightmost column or bottom row of the table.
Multiplication Rule	If $\mathbf{A}$ and $\mathbf{B}$ are independent events, then the probability of $\mathbf{A}$ *and* $\mathbf{B}$ is: $$P(\mathbf{A} \text{ and } \mathbf{B}) = P(\mathbf{A}) \times P(\mathbf{B}).$$
Outcome	The outcome of a trial is the value measured, observed, or reported for an individual instance of that trial.
Personal probability	When the probability is subjective and represents your personal degree of belief, it is called a personal probability.
Probability	The probability of an event is a number between 0 and 1 that reports the likelihood of the event's occurrence. A probability can be derived from a model (such as equally likely outcomes), from the long-run relative frequency of the event's occurrence, or from subjective degrees of belief. We write $P(\mathbf{A})$ for the probability of the event $\mathbf{A}$.
Probability Assignment Rule	The probability of the entire sample space must be 1: $$P(S) = 1.$$
Random phenomenon	A phenomenon is random if we know what outcomes could happen, but not which particular values will happen.
Sample space	The collection of all possible outcome values. The sample space has a probability of 1.
Theoretical probability	When the probability comes from a mathematical model (such as, but not limited to, equally likely outcomes), it is called a theoretical probability.
Trial	A single attempt or realization of a random phenomenon.

Brief CASE

Market Segmentation

The data from the "Chicago Female Fashion Study"[4] were collected using a self-administered survey of a sample of homes in the greater Chicago metropolitan area. Marketing managers want to know how important quality is to their customers. A consultant reports that based on past research, 30% of all consumers nationwide are more interested in quantity than quality. The marketing manager of a particular department store suspects that customers from her store are different, and that customers of different ages might have different views as well. Using conditional probabilities, marginal probabilities, and joint probabilities constructed from the data in the file **Market_Segmentation**,[5] write a report to the manager on what you find.

Keep in mind: The manager may be more interested in the opinions of "frequent" customers than those who never or hardly ever shop at her store. These "frequent" customers contribute a disproportionate amount of profit to the store. Keep that in mind as you do your analysis and write up your report.

Martin Mcelligott/
iStockphoto

Jacob Wackerhausen/iStockphoto

VARIABLE AND QUESTION	CATEGORIES
Age *Into which of the following age categories do you belong?*	18–24 yrs old 25–34 35–44 45–54 55–64 65 or over
Frequency *How often do you shop for women's clothing at [department store X]?*	0. Never–hardly ever 1–2 times per year 3–4 times per year 5 times or more
Quality *For the same amount of money, I will generally buy one good item than several of lower price and quality.*	1. Definitely Disagree 2. Generally Disagree 3. Moderately Disagree 4. Moderately Agree 5. Generally Agree 6. Definitely Agree

Exercises

SECTION 1

1. Indicate which of the following represent independent events. Explain briefly.

a) The gender of customers using an ATM machine.

b) The last digit of the social security numbers of students in a class.

c) The scores you receive on the first midterm, second midterm, and the final exam of a course.

2. Indicate which of the following represent independent events. Explain briefly.

a) Prices of houses on the same block.

b) Successive measurements of your heart rate as you exercise on a treadmill.

c) Measurements of the heart rates of all students in the gym.

---

[4]Original *Market Segmentation Exercise* prepared by K. Matsuno, D. Kopcso, and D. Tigert, Babson College in 1997 (Babson Case Series #133-C97A-U).

[5]For a version with the categories coded as integers see **Market_Segmentation_Coded**.

SECTION 2

3. In many state lotteries you can choose which numbers to play. Consider a common form in which you choose 5 numbers. Which of the following strategies can improve your chance of winning? If the method works, explain why. If not, explain why using appropriate statistics terms.

a) Always play 1, 2, 3, 4, 5.
b) Generate random numbers using a computer or calculator and play those.

4. For the same kind of lottery as in Exercise 3, which of the following strategies can improve your chance of winning? If the method works, explain why. If not, explain why using appropriate statistics terms.

a) Choose randomly from among the numbers that have *not* come up in the last 3 lottery drawings.
b) Choose the numbers that did come up in the most recent lottery drawing.

SECTION 4

5. You and your friend decide to get your cars inspected. You are informed that 75% of cars pass inspection. If the event of your car's passing is independent of your friend's car,

a) What is the probability that your car passes inspection?
b) What is the probability that your car doesn't pass inspection?
c) What is the probability that both of the cars pass?
d) What is the probability that at least one of the two cars passes?

6. At your school, 10% of the class are marketing majors. If you are randomly assigned to two partners in your statistics class,

a) What is the probability that the first partner will be a marketing major?
b) What is the probability that the first partner won't be a marketing major?
c) What is the probability that both will be marketing majors?
d) What is the probability that one or the other will be marketing majors?

SECTION 5

7. The following contingency table shows opinion about global warming (nonissue vs. serious concern) among registered voters, broken down by political party affiliation (Democratic, Republican, and Independent).

		Opinion on Global Warming		
		Nonissue	Serious Concern	Total
Political Party	Democratic	60	440	500
	Republican	290	210	500
	Independent	90	110	200
	Total	**440**	**760**	**1200**

a) What is the probability that a registered voter selected at random believes that global warming is a serious issue?
b) What type of probability did you find in part a?
c) What is the probability that a registered voter selected at random is a Republican and believes that global warming is a serious issue?
d) What type of probability did you find in part c?

8. Multigenerational families can be categorized as having two adult generations such as parents living with adult children, "skip" generation families, such as grandparents living with grandchildren, and three or more generations living in the household. Pew Research surveyed multigenerational households. This table is based on their reported results.

	2 Adult Gens	2 Skip Gens	3 or More Gens	
White	509	55	222	**786**
Hispanic	139	11	142	**292**
Black	119	32	99	**250**
Asian	61	1	48	**110**
	828	**99**	**511**	**1438**

a) What is the probability that a multigenerational family is Hispanic?
b) What is the probability that a multigenerational family selected at random is a Black, two-adult-generation family?
c) What type of probability did you find in parts a and b?

SECTION 6

9. Using the table from Exercise 7,

a) What is the probability that a randomly selected registered voter who is a Republican believes that global warming is a serious issue?
b) What is the probability that a randomly selected registered voter is a Republican given that he or she believes global warming is a serious issue?
c) What is $P(\text{Serious Concern} \mid \text{Democratic})$?

10. Using the table from Exercise 8,

a) What is the probability that a randomly selected Black multigenerational family is a two-generation family?

b) What is the probability that a randomly selected multigenerational family is White, given that it is a "skip" generation family?

c) What is *P*(3 or more Generations | Asian)?

SECTION 7

11. A national survey indicated that 30% of adults conduct their banking online. It also found that 40% are under the age of 50, and that 25% are under the age of 50 and conduct their banking online.

a) What percentage of adults do not conduct their banking online?

b) What type of probability is the 25% mentioned above?

c) Construct a contingency table showing all joint and marginal probabilities.

d) What is the probability that an individual conducts banking online given that the individual is under the age of 50?

e) Are *Banking online* and *Age* independent? Explain.

12. Facebook reports that 70% of their users are from outside the United States and that 50% of their users log on to Facebook every day. Suppose that 20% of their users are United States users who log on every day.

a) What percentage of Facebook's users are from the United States?

b) What type of probability is the 20% mentioned above?

c) Construct a contingency table showing all the joint and marginal probabilities.

d) What is the probability that a user is from the United States given that he or she logs on every day?

e) Are *From United States* and *Log on Every Day* independent? Explain.

CHAPTER EXERCISES

13. What does it mean? part 1. Respond to the following questions:

a) A casino claims that its roulette wheel is truly random. What should that claim mean?

b) A reporter on *Market Place* says that there is a 50% chance that the Federal Reserve Bank will cut interest rates by a quarter point at their next meeting. What is the meaning of such a phrase?

14. What does it mean? part 2. Respond to the following questions:

a) After an unusually dry autumn, a radio announcer is heard to say, "Watch out! We'll pay for these sunny days later on this winter." Explain what he's trying to say, and comment on the validity of his reasoning.

b) A batter who had failed to get a hit in seven consecutive times at bat then hits a game-winning home run. When talking to reporters afterward, he says he was very confident that last time at bat because he knew he was "due for a hit." Comment on his reasoning.

15. Airline safety. Even though commercial airlines have excellent safety records, in the weeks following a crash, airlines often report a drop in the number of passengers, probably because people are afraid to risk flying.

a) A travel agent suggests that since the law of averages makes it highly unlikely to have two plane crashes within a few weeks of each other, flying soon after a crash is the safest time. What do you think?

b) If the airline industry proudly announces that it has set a new record for the longest period of safe flights, would you be reluctant to fly? Are the airlines due to have a crash?

16. Economic predictions. An investment newsletter makes general predictions about the economy to help their clients make sound investment decisions.

a) Recently they said that because the stock market had been up for the past three months in a row that it was "due for a correction" and advised their client to reduce their holdings. What "law" are they applying? Comment.

b) They advised buying a stock that had gone down in the past four sessions because they said that it was clearly "due to bounce back." What "law" are they applying? Comment.

17. Fire insurance. Insurance companies collect annual payments from homeowners in exchange for paying to rebuild houses that burn down.

a) Why should you be reluctant to accept a $300 payment from your neighbor to replace his house should it burn down during the coming year?

b) Why can the insurance company make that offer?

18. Casino gambling. Recently, the International Gaming Technology company issued the following press release:

(LAS VEGAS, Nev.)—Cynthia Jay was smiling ear to ear as she walked into the news conference at the Desert Inn Resort in Las Vegas today, and well she should. Last night, the 37-year-old cocktail waitress won the world's largest slot jackpot— $34,959,458—on a Megabucks machine. She said she had played $27 in the machine when the jackpot hit. Nevada Megabucks has produced 49 major winners in its 14-year history. The top jackpot builds from a base amount of $7 million and can be won with a 3-coin ($3) bet.

a) How can the Desert Inn afford to give away millions of dollars on a $3 bet?

b) Why did the company issue a press release? Wouldn't most businesses want to keep such a huge loss quiet?

19. Toy company. A toy company manufactures a spinning game and needs to decide what probabilities are involved in the game. The plastic arrow on the spinner stops rotating to point at a color that will determine what happens next. Knowing these probabilities will help determine how easy or difficult it is for a person to win the game and helps to determine how long the average game will last. Are each of the following probability assignments possible? Why or why not?

	Probabilities of ...			
	Red	Yellow	Green	Blue
a)	0.25	0.25	0.25	0.25
b)	0.10	0.20	0.30	0.40
c)	0.20	0.30	0.40	0.50
d)	0	0	1.00	0
e)	0.10	0.20	1.20	−1.50

20. Store discounts. Many stores run "secret sales": Shoppers receive cards that determine how large a discount they get, but the percentage is revealed by scratching off that black stuff (what *is* that?) only after the purchase has been totaled at the cash register. The store is required to reveal (in the fine print) the distribution of discounts available. Are each of these probability assignments plausible? Why or why not?

	Probabilities of ...			
	10% off	20% off	30% off	50% off
a)	0.20	0.20	0.20	0.20
b)	0.50	0.30	0.20	0.10
c)	0.80	0.10	0.05	0.05
d)	0.75	0.25	0.25	−0.25
e)	1.00	0	0	0

21. Quality control. A tire manufacturer recently announced a recall because 2% of its tires are defective. If you just bought a new set of four tires from this manufacturer, what is the probability that at least one of your new tires is defective?

22. Pepsi promotion. For a sales promotion, the manufacturer places winning symbols under the caps of 10% of all Pepsi bottles. If you buy a six-pack of Pepsi, what is the probability that you win something?

23. Auto warranty. In developing their warranty policy, an automobile company estimates that over a 1-year period 17% of their new cars will need to be repaired once, 7% will need repairs twice, and 4% will require three or more repairs. If you buy a new car from them, what is the probability that your car will need:

a) No repairs?
b) No more than one repair?
c) Some repairs?

24. Consulting team. You work for a large global management consulting company. Of the entire work force of analysts, 55% have had no experience in the telecommunications

industry, 32% have had limited experience (less than 5 years), and the rest have had extensive experience (5 years or more). On a recent project, you and two other analysts were chosen at random to constitute a team. It turns out that part of the project involves telecommunications. What is the probability that the first teammate you meet has:

a) Extensive telecommunications experience?
b) Some telecommunications experience?
c) No more than limited telecommunications experience?

25. Auto warranty, part 2. Consider again the auto repair rates described in Exercise 23. If you bought two new cars, what is the probability that:

a) Neither will need repair?
b) Both will need repair?
c) At least one car will need repair?

26. Consulting team, part 2. You are assigned to be part of a team of three analysts of a global management consulting company as described in Exercise 24. What is the probability that of your other two teammates:

a) Neither has any telecommunications experience?
b) Both have some telecommunications experience?
c) At least one has had extensive telecommunications experience?

27. Auto warranty, again. You used the Multiplication Rule to calculate repair probabilities for your cars in Exercise 23.

a) What must be true about your cars in order to make that approach valid?
b) Do you think this assumption is reasonable? Explain.

28. Final consulting team project. You used the Multiplication Rule to calculate probabilities about the telecommunications experience of your consulting teammates in Exercise 24.

a) What must be true about the groups in order to make that approach valid?
b) Do you think this assumption is reasonable? Explain.

29. Real estate. Real estate ads suggest that 64% of homes for sale have garages, 21% have swimming pools, and 17% have both features. What is the probability that a home for sale has:

a) A pool or a garage?
b) Neither a pool nor a garage?
c) A pool but no garage?

30. Human resource data. Employment data at a large company reveal that 72% of the workers are married, 44% are college graduates, and half of the college grads are married. What's the probability that a randomly chosen worker is:

a) Neither married nor a college graduate?
b) Married but not a college graduate?
c) Married or a college graduate?

31. Market research on energy. A Gallup Poll in March 2007 asked 1005 U.S. adults whether increasing domestic energy production or protecting the environment should be given higher priority. Here are the results.

Response	Number
Increase Production	342
Protect the Environment	583
Equally Important	50
No Opinion	30
Total	**1005**

If we select a person at random from this sample of 1005 adults:

a) What is the probability that the person responded "Increase Production"?

b) What is the probability that the person responded "Equally Important" or had "No Opinion"?

32. More market research on energy. Exercise 31 shows the results of a Gallup Poll about energy. Suppose we select three people at random from this sample.

a) What is the probability that all three responded "Protect the Environment"?

b) What is the probability that none responded "Equally Important"?

c) What assumption did you make in computing these probabilities?

d) Explain why you think that assumption is reasonable.

33. Telemarketing contact rates. Marketing research firms often contact their respondents by sampling random telephone numbers. Although interviewers currently reach about 76% of selected U.S. households, the percentage of those contacted who agree to cooperate with the survey has fallen. Assume that the percentage of those who agree to cooperate in telemarketing surveys is now only 38%. Each household is assumed to be independent of the others.

a) What is the probability that the next household on the list will be contacted but will refuse to cooperate?

b) What is the probability of failing to contact a household or of contacting the household but not getting them to agree to the interview?

c) Show another way to calculate the probability in part b.

34. Telemarketing contact rates, part 2. According to Pew Research, the contact rate (probability of contacting a selected household) in 1997 was 69%, and in 2003, it was 76%. However, the cooperation rate (probability of someone at the contacted household agreeing to be interviewed) was 58% in 1997 and dropped to 38% in 2003.

a) What is the probability (in 2003) of obtaining an interview with the next household on the sample list? (To obtain an interview, an interviewer must both contact the household and then get agreement for the interview.)

b) Was it more likely to obtain an interview from a randomly selected household in 1997 or in 2003?

35. Mars product information. The Mars company says that before the introduction of purple, yellow made up 20% of their plain M&M candies, red made up another 20%, and orange, blue, and green each made up 10%. The rest were brown.

a) If you picked an M&M at random from a pre-purple bag of candies, what is the probability that it was:

   i) Brown?
   ii) Yellow or orange?
   iii) Not green?
   iv) Striped?

b) Assuming you had an infinite supply of M&M's with the older color distribution, if you picked three M&M's in a row, what is the probability that:

   i) They are all brown?
   ii) The third one is the first one that's red?
   iii) None are yellow?
   iv) At least one is green?

36. American Red Cross. The American Red Cross must track their supply and demand for various blood types. They estimate that about 45% of the U.S. population has Type O blood, 40% Type A, 11% Type B, and the rest Type AB.

a) If someone volunteers to give blood, what is the probability that this donor:

   i) Has Type AB blood?
   ii) Has Type A or Type B blood?
   iii) Is not Type O?

b) Among four potential donors, what is the probability that:

   i) All are Type O?
   ii) None have Type AB blood?
   iii) Not all are Type A?
   iv) At least one person is Type B?

37. More Mars product information. In Exercise 35, you calculated probabilities of getting various colors of M&M's.

a) If you draw one M&M, are the events of getting a red one and getting an orange one disjoint or independent or neither?

b) If you draw two M&M's one after the other, are the events of getting a red on the first and a red on the second disjoint or independent or neither?

c) Can disjoint events ever be independent? Explain.

38. American Red Cross, part 2. In Exercise 36, you calculated probabilities involving various blood types.

a) If you examine one donor, are the events of the donor being Type A and the donor being Type B disjoint or independent or neither? Explain your answer.
b) If you examine two donors, are the events that the first donor is Type A and the second donor is Type B disjoint or independent or neither?
c) Can disjoint events ever be independent? Explain.

39. Tax accountant. A recent study of IRS audits showed that, for estates worth less than $5 million, about 1 out of 7 of all estate tax returns are audited, but that probability increases to 50% for estates worth over $5 million. Suppose a tax accountant has three clients who have recently filed returns for estates worth more than $5 million. What are the probabilities that:

a) All three will be audited?
b) None will be audited?
c) At least one will be audited?
d) What did you assume in calculating these probabilities?

40. Casinos. Because gambling is big business, calculating the odds of a gambler winning or losing in every game is crucial to the financial forecasting for a casino. A standard slot machine has three wheels that spin independently. Each has 10 equally likely symbols: 4 bars, 3 lemons, 2 cherries, and a bell. If you play once, what is the probability that you will get:

a) 3 lemons?
b) No fruit symbols?
c) 3 bells (the jackpot)?
d) No bells?
e) At least one bar (an automatic loser)?

41. Information technology. A company has recently replaced their e-mail server because previously mail was interrupted on about 15% of workdays. To see how bad the situation was, calculate the probability that during a 5-day work week, there would be an e-mail interruption.

a) On Monday and again on Tuesday?
b) For the first time on Thursday?
c) Every day?
d) At least once during the week?

42. Information technology, part 2. At a mid-sized Web design and maintenance company, 57% of the computers are PCs, 29% are Macs, and the rest are Unix-based machines. Assuming that users of each of the machines are equally likely to call in to the information technology help line, what is the probability that of the next three calls:

a) All are Macs?
b) None are PCs?
c) At least one is a Unix machine?
d) All are Unix machines?

43. Casinos, part 2. In addition to slot machines, casinos must understand the probabilities involved in card games. Suppose you are playing at the blackjack table, and the dealer shuffles a deck of cards. The first card shown is red. So is the second and the third. In fact, you are surprised to see 5 red cards in a row. You start thinking, "The next one is due to be black!"

a) Are you correct in thinking that there's a higher probability that the next card will be black than red? Explain.
b) Is this an example of the Law of Large Numbers? Explain.

44. Inventory. A shipment of road bikes has just arrived at The Spoke, a small bicycle shop, and all the boxes have been placed in the back room. The owner asks her assistant to start bringing in the boxes. The assistant sees 20 identical-looking boxes and starts bringing them into the shop at random. The owner knows that she ordered 10 women's and 10 men's bicycles, and so she's surprised to find that the first six are all women's bikes. As the seventh box is brought in, she starts thinking, "This one is bound to be a men's bike."

a) Is she correct in thinking that there's a higher probability that the next box will contain a men's bike? Explain.
b) Is this an example of the Law of Large Numbers? Explain.

45. International food survey. A GfK Roper Worldwide survey in 2005 asked consumers in five countries whether they agreed with the statement "I am worried about the safety of the food I eat." Here are the responses classified by the age of the respondent.

	Agree	Neither Agree nor Disagree	Disagree	Don't Know/ No Response	Total
13–19	661	368	452	32	1513
20–29	816	365	336	16	1533
30–39	871	355	290	9	1525
40–49	914	335	266	6	1521
50+	966	339	283	10	1598
Total	**4228**	**1762**	**1627**	**73**	**7690**

If we select a person at random from this sample:

a) What is the probability that the person agreed with the statement?
b) What is the probability that the person is younger than 50 years old?
c) What is the probability that the person is younger than 50 *and* agrees with the statement?
d) What is the probability that the person is younger than 50 *or* agrees with the statement?

46. Cosmetics marketing. A GfK Roper Worldwide survey asked consumers in five countries whether they agreed with the statement "I follow a skin care routine every day." Here are the responses classified by the country of the respondent.

		Agree	Disagree	Don't know	Total
		Response			
Country	China	361	988	153	**1502**
	France	695	763	81	**1539**
	India	828	689	18	**1535**
	U.K.	597	898	62	**1557**
	USA	668	841	48	**1557**
	Total	**3149**	**4179**	**362**	**7690**

If we select a person at random from this sample:

a) What is the probability that the person agreed with the statement?
b) What is the probability that the person is from China?
c) What is the probability that the person is from China *and* agrees with the statement?
d) What is the probability that the person is from China *or* agrees with the statement?

47. E-commerce. Suppose an online business organizes an e-mail survey to find out if online shoppers are concerned with the security of business transactions on the Web. Of the 42 individuals who respond, 24 are concerned, and 18 are not concerned. Eight of those concerned about security are male and 6 of those not concerned are male. If a respondent is selected at random, find each of the following conditional probabilities:

a) The respondent is male, given that the respondent is not concerned about security.
b) The respondent is not concerned about security, given that she is female.
c) The respondent is female, given that the respondent is concerned about security.

48. Automobile inspection. Twenty percent of cars that are inspected have faulty pollution control systems. The cost of repairing a pollution control system exceeds $100 about 40% of the time. When a driver takes her car in for inspection, what's the probability that she will end up paying more than $100 to repair the pollution control system?

49. Pharmaceutical company. A U.S. pharmaceutical company is considering manufacturing and marketing a pill that will help to lower both an individual's blood pressure and cholesterol. The company is interested in understanding the demand for such a product. The joint probabilities that an adult American man has high blood pressure and/or high cholesterol are shown in the table.

		Blood Pressure	
		High	OK
Cholesterol	High	0.11	0.21
	OK	0.16	0.52

a) What's the probability that an adult American male has both conditions?
b) What's the probability that an adult American male has high blood pressure?
c) What's the probability that an adult American male with high blood pressure also has high cholesterol?
d) What's the probability that an adult American male has high blood pressure if it's known that he has high cholesterol?

50. International relocation. A European department store is developing a new advertising campaign for their new U.S. location, and their marketing managers need to better understand their target market. Based on survey responses, a joint probability table that an adult shops at their new U.S. store classified by their age is shown below.

		Shop		
		Yes	No	Total
Age	< 20	0.26	0.04	**0.30**
	20–40	0.24	0.10	**0.34**
	> 40	0.12	0.24	**0.36**
	Total	**0.62**	**0.38**	**1.00**

a) What's the probability that a survey respondent will shop at the U.S. store?
b) What is the probability that a survey respondent will shop at the store given that they are younger than 20 years old?
c) What is the probability that a survey respondent who is older than 40 shops at the store?
d) What is the probability that a survey respondent is younger than 20 or will shop at the store?

51. Pharmaceutical company, again. Given the table of probabilities compiled for marketing managers in Exercise 49, are high blood pressure and high cholesterol independent? Explain.

52. International relocation, again. Given the table of probabilities compiled for a department store chain in Exercise 50, are age and shopping at the department store independent? Explain.

53. International food survey, part 2. Look again at the data from the GfK Roper Worldwide survey on food attitudes in Exercise 45.

a) If we select a respondent at random, what's the probability we choose a person between 13 and 19 years old who agreed with the statement?

b) Among the 13- to 19-year-olds, what is the probability that a person responded "Agree"?

c) What's the probability that a person who agreed was between 13 and 19?

d) If the person responded "Disagree," what is the probability that they are at least 50 years old?

e) What's the probability that a person 50 years or older disagreed?

f) Are response to the question and age independent?

54. Cosmetics marketing, part 2. Look again at the data from the GfK Roper Worldwide survey on skin care in Exercise 46.

a) If we select a respondent at random, what's the probability we choose a person from the U.S.A. who agreed with the statement?

b) Among those from the U.S.A., what is the probability that a person responded "Agree"?

c) What's the probability that a person who agreed was from the U.S.A.?

d) If the person responded "Disagree," what is the probability that they are from the U.S.A.?

e) What's the probability that a person from the U.S.A. disagreed?

f) Are response to the question and Country independent?

55. Real estate, part 2. In the real estate research described in Exercise 29, 64% of homes for sale have garages, 21% have swimming pools, and 17% have both features.

a) What is the probability that a home for sale has a garage, but not a pool?

b) If a home for sale has a garage, what's the probability that it has a pool, too?

c) Are having a garage and a pool independent events? Explain.

d) Are having a garage and a pool mutually exclusive? Explain.

56. Employee benefits. Fifty-six percent of all American workers have a workplace retirement plan, 68% have health insurance, and 49% have both benefits. If we select a worker at random:

a) What's the probability that the worker has neither employer-sponsored health insurance nor a retirement plan?

b) What's the probability that the worker has health insurance if they have a retirement plan?

c) Are having health insurance and a retirement plan independent? Explain.

d) Are having these two benefits mutually exclusive? Explain.

57. Telemarketing. Telemarketers continue to attempt to reach consumers by calling landline phone numbers. According to estimates from a national 2003 survey,

based on face-to-face interviews in 16,677 households, approximately 58.2% of U.S. adults have both a landline in their residence and a cell phone, 2.8% have only cell phone service but no land line, and 1.6% have no telephone service at all.

a) Polling agencies won't phone cell phone numbers because customers object to paying for such calls. What proportion of U.S. households can be reached by a landline call?

b) Are having a cell phone and having a landline independent? Explain.

58. Snoring. According to the British United Provident Association (BUPA), a major health care provider in the U.K., snoring can be an indication of sleep apnea which can cause chronic illness if left untreated. In the U.S.A., the National Sleep Foundation reports that 36.8% of the 995 adults they surveyed snored. Of the respondents, 81.5% were over the age of 30, and 32% were both over the age of 30 and snorers.

a) What percent of the respondents were 30 years old or younger and did not snore?

b) Is snoring independent of age? Explain.

59. Selling cars. A recent ad campaign for a major automobile manufacturer is clearly geared toward an older demographic. You are surprised, so you decide to conduct a quick survey of your own. A random survey of autos parked in the student and staff lots at your university classified the brands by country of origin, as seen in the table. Is country of origin independent of type of driver?

		Driver	
		Student	Staff
Origin	American	107	105
	European	33	12
	Asian	55	47

60. Fire sale. A survey of 1056 houses in the Saratoga Springs, New York, area found the following relationship between price (in $) and whether the house had a fireplace in 2006. Is the price of the house independent of whether it has a fireplace?

		Fireplace	
		No	Yes
House Price	Low—less than $112,000	198	66
	Med Low ($112 to $152K)	133	131
	Med High ($152 to $207K)	65	199
	High—over $207,000	31	233

61. Used cars. A business student is searching for a used car to purchase, so she posts an ad to a website saying she wants to buy a used Jeep between $18,000 and $20,000. From Kelly's BlueBook.com, she learns that there are 149 cars matching that description within a 30-mile radius of her home. If we assume that those are the people who will call her and that they are equally likely to call her:

a) What is the probability that the first caller will be a Jeep Liberty owner?

b) What is the probability that the first caller will own a Jeep Liberty that costs between $18,000 and $18,999?

c) If the first call offers her a Jeep Liberty, what is the probability that it costs less than $19,000?

d) Suppose she decides to ignore calls with cars whose cost is ≥ $19,000. What is the probability that the first call she takes will offer to sell her a Jeep Liberty?

		Price		
Make		$18,000–$18,999	$19,000–$19,999	**Total**
	Commander	3	6	9
	Compass	6	1	7
Car	Grand Cherokee	33	33	66
	Liberty	17	6	23
	Wrangler	33	11	44
	Total	**92**	**57**	**149**

62. CEO relocation. The CEO of a mid-sized company has to relocate to another part of the country. To make it easier, the company has hired a relocation agency to help purchase a house. The CEO has 5 children and so has specified that the house have at least 5 bedrooms, but hasn't put any other constraints on the search. The relocation agency has narrowed the search down to the houses in the table and has selected one house to showcase to the CEO and family on their trip out to the new site. The agency doesn't know it, but the family has its heart set on a Cape Cod house with a fireplace. If the agency selected the house at random, without regard to this:

		Fireplace?		
		No	Yes	**Total**
	Cape Cod	7	2	9
House Type	Colonial	8	14	22
	Other	6	5	11
	Total	**21**	**21**	**42**

a) What is the probability that the selected house is a Cape Cod?

b) What is the probability that the house is a Colonial with a fireplace?

c) If the house is a Cape Cod, what is the probability that it has a fireplace?

d) What is the probability that the selected house is what the family wants?

Just Checking Answers

1. The probability of going up on the next day is not affected by the previous day's outcome.

2. a) 0.30
   b) $0.30(0.30) = 0.09$
   c) $(1 - 0.30)^2(0.30) = 0.147$
   d) $1 - (1 - 0.30)^5 = 0.832$

3. a)

		Weekday		
		Yes	No	**Total**
Before Five	Yes	0.07	0.41	**0.48**
	No	0.20	0.32	**0.52**
	Total	**0.27**	**0.73**	**1.00**

   b) $P(\mathbf{BF}|\mathbf{WD}) = P(\mathbf{BF} \text{ and } \mathbf{WD})/P(\mathbf{WD}) = 0.07/0.27 = .259$

   c) No, shoppers can do both (and 7% do).

   d) To be independent, we'd need $P(\mathbf{BF}|\mathbf{WD}) = P(\mathbf{BF})$. $P(\mathbf{BF}|\mathbf{WD}) = 0.259$, but $P(\mathbf{BF}) = \mathbf{0.48}$. They do not appear to be independent.

Answers

SECTION EXERCISE ANSWERS

1. a) Independent (unless a large group of one gender comes to the ATM machine together).
b) Independent. The last digit of one student's SS number provides no information about another.
c) Not independent. How you perform on one test provides information about other tests.

3. a) Won't work, but won't hurt. Each number drawn is equally likely and independent of the others, so this set of numbers is just as likely as any other in the next drawing.
b) Won't work, but won't hurt. Each number drawn is equally likely and independent of the others, so randomly generated numbers are just as likely as any others in the next drawing.

5. a) 0.75
b) 0.25
c) $0.75^2 = 0.5625$
d) $0.75 + 0.75 - (0.5625) = 0.9375$ or $1 - (0.25^2) = 0.9375$

7. a) $760/1200 = 0.63$
b) Marginal.
c) $210/1200 = 0.175$
d) Joint.

9. a) $210/500 = 0.42$
b) $210/760 = 0.2763$
c) $440/500 = 0.88$

11. a) $100\% - 30\% = 70\%$
b) Marginal.
c)

		Online Banking		
		Yes	No	
Age	Under 50	0.25	0.15	**0.40**
	50 or Older	0.05	0.55	**0.60**
		0.30	**0.70**	**1.00**

d) $0.25/0.40 = 0.625$
e) No, because the conditional probability of banking online for those under 50 is 0.625. The probability of banking online is 0.30 which is not the same.

CHAPTER EXERCISE ANSWERS

13. a) Outcomes are equally likely and independent.
b) This is likely a personal probability expressing his degree of belief that there will be a rate cut.

15. a) There is no such thing as the "law of averages." The overall probability of an airplane crash does not change due to recent crashes.
b) There is no such thing as the "law of averages." The overall probability of an airplane crash does not change due to a period in which there were no crashes.

17. a) It would be foolish to insure your neighbor's house for $300. Although you would probably simply collect $300, there is a chance you could end up paying much more than $300. That risk is not worth the $300.
b) The insurance company insures many people. The overwhelming majority of customers pay and never have a claim.

The few customers who do have a claim are offset by the many who simply send their premiums without a claim. The relative risk to the insurance company is low.

19. a) Yes.
b) Yes.
c) No, probabilities sum to more than 1.
d) Yes.
e) No, sum isn't 1 and one value is negative.

21. 0.078

23. The events are disjoint. Use the addition rule.
a) 0.72
b) 0.89
c) 0.28

25. a) 0.5184
b) 0.0784
c) 0.4816

27. a) The repair needs for the two cars must be independent of one another.
b) This may not be reasonable. An owner may treat the two cars similarly, taking good (or poor) care of both. This may decrease (or increase) the likelihood that each needs to be repaired.

29. a) 0.68
b) 0.32
c) 0.04

31. a) 0.340
b) 0.080

33. a) 0.4712
b) 0.7112
c) $1 - P(\text{interview}) = 1 - 0.2888 = 0.7112$

35. a) The events are disjoint (an M&M can't be two colors at once), so use the addition rule where applicable.
  i) 0.30
  ii) 0.30
  iii) 0.90
  iv) 0
b) The events are independent (picking out one M&M doesn't affect the outcome of the next pick), so use the multiplication rule.
  i) 0.027
  ii) 0.128
  iii) 0.512
  iv) 0.271

37. a) Disjoint.
b) Independent.
c) No. Once you know that one of a pair of disjoint events has occurred, the other one cannot occur, so its probability has become zero.

39. a) 0.125
b) 0.125
c) 0.875
d) Independence.

41. a) 0.0225
b) 0.092
c) 0.00008
d) 0.556

43. a) Your thinking is correct. There are 47 cards left in the deck, 26 black and only 21 red.
b) This is not an example of the Law of Large Numbers. The card draws are not independent.

45. a) 0.550
b) 0.792
c) 0.424
d) 0.918

47. a) 0.333
b) 0.429
c) 0.667

49. a) 0.11
b) 0.27
c) 0.407
d) 0.344

51. No. 28.8% of men with OK blood pressure have high cholesterol, but 40.7% of men with high blood pressure have high cholesterol.

53. a) 0.086
b) 0.437
c) 0.156

d) 0.174
e) 0.177
f) No.

55. a) 0.47
b) 0.266
c) Having a garage and a pool are not independent events.
d) Having a garage and a pool are not disjoint events.

57. a) 96.5%
b) The probability of U.S. adults having a landline, given that they have a cell phone, is 58.2/(58.2 + 2.8) or about 95.4%. About 96.6% of U.S. adults have a landline. It appears that having a cell phone and having a landline are independent, since the probabilities are roughly the same.

59. No. 12.5% of the cars were of European origin, but about 16.9% of the students drive European cars.

61. a) 15.4%
b) 11.4%
c) 73.9%
d) 18.5%

Random Variables and Probability Models

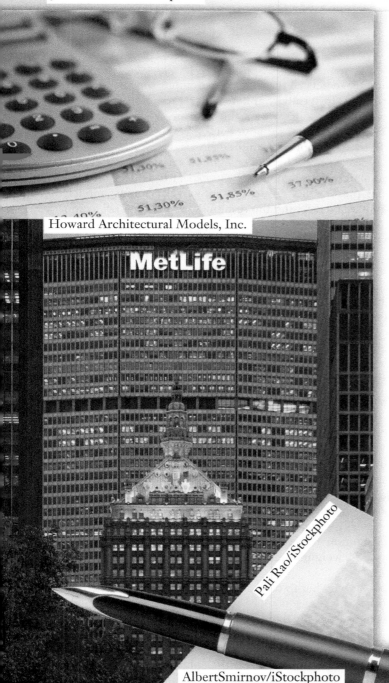

Metropolitan Life Insurance Company

In 1863, at the height of the U.S. Civil War, a group of businessmen in New York City decided to form a new company to insure Civil War soldiers against disabilities and injuries suffered from the war. After the war ended, they changed direction and decided to focus on selling life insurance. The new company was named Metropolitan Life (MetLife) because the bulk of the company's clients were in the "metropolitan" area of New York City.

Although an economic depression in the 1870s put many life insurance companies out of business, MetLife survived, modeling their business on similar successful programs in England. Taking advantage of spreading industrialism and the selling methods of British insurance agents, the company soon was enrolling as many as 700 new policies per day. By 1909, MetLife was the nation's largest life insurer in the United States.

During the Great Depression of the 1930s, MetLife expanded their public service by promoting public health campaigns, focusing on educating the urban poor in major U.S. cities about the risk of tuberculosis. Because the company invested primarily in urban and farm mortgages, as opposed to the stock market, they survived the crash of 1929 and ended up investing heavily in the post-war U.S. housing boom. They were the principal investors in both the Empire State

Building (1929) and Rockefeller Center (1931). During World War II, the company was the single largest contributor to the Allied cause, investing more than half of their total assets in war bonds.

Today, in addition to life insurance, MetLife manages pensions and investments. In 2000, the company held an initial public offering and entered the retail banking business in 2001 with the launch of MetLife Bank. The company's public face is well known because of their use of Snoopy, the dog from the cartoon strip "Peanuts."

Insurance companies make bets all the time. For example, they bet that you're going to live a long life. Ironically, you bet that you're going to die sooner. Both you and the insurance company want the company to stay in business, so it's important to find a "fair price" for your bet. Of course, the right price for *you* depends on many factors, and nobody can predict exactly how long you'll live. But when the company averages its bets over enough customers, it can make reasonably accurate estimates of the amount it can expect to collect on a policy before it has to pay out the benefit. To do that effectively, it must model the situation with a probability model. Using the resulting probabilities, the company can find the fair price of almost any situation involving risk and uncertainty.

Here's a simple example. An insurance company offers a "death and disability" policy that pays $100,000 when a client dies or $50,000 if the client is permanently disabled. It charges a premium of only $500 per year for this benefit. Is the company likely to make a profit selling such a plan? To answer this question, the company needs to know the *probability* that a client will die or become disabled in any year. From actuarial information such as this and the appropriate model, the company can calculate the expected value of this policy.

1   Expected Value of a Random Variable

To model the insurance company's risk, we need to define a few terms. The amount the company pays out on an individual policy is an example of a **random variable**, called that because its value is based on the outcome of a random event. We use a capital letter, in this case, X, to denote a random variable. We'll denote a particular *value* that it can have by the corresponding lowercase letter, in this case, x. For the insurance company, x can be $100,000 (if you die that year), $50,000 (if you are disabled), or $0 (if neither occurs). Because we can list all the outcomes, we call this random variable a **discrete random variable**. A random variable that can take on any value between two values is called a **continuous random variable**. Continuous random variables are common in business applications for modeling physical quantities like heights and weights, and monetary quantities such as profits, revenues, and spending.

Sometimes it is obvious whether to treat a random variable as discrete or continuous, but at other times the choice is more subtle. Age, for example, might be viewed as discrete if it is measured only to the nearest decade with possible values 10, 20, 30, ... In a scientific context, however, it might be measured more precisely and treated as continuous.

For both discrete and continuous variables, the collection of all the possible values and the probabilities associated with them is called the **probability model** for the random variable. For a discrete random variable, we can list the probability of all possible values in a table, or describe it by a formula. For example, to model the possible outcomes of a fair die, we can let X be the number showing on the face. The probability model for X is simply:

$$P(X = x) = \begin{cases} 1/6 & \text{if } x = 1, 2, 3, 4, 5, \text{ or } 6 \\ 0 & \text{otherwise} \end{cases}$$

Suppose in our insurance risk example that the death rate in any year is 1 out of every 1000 people and that another 2 out of 1000 suffer some kind of disability. The loss, which we'll denote as X, is a discrete random variable because it takes on only 3 possible values. We can display the probability model for X in a table, as in Table 1.

Notation Alert!

The most common letters for random variables are X, Y, and Z, but any capital letter might be used.

Policyholder Outcome	Payout *x* (cost)	Probability $P(X = x)$
Death	100,000	$\dfrac{1}{1000}$
Disability	50,000	$\dfrac{2}{1000}$
Neither	0	$\dfrac{997}{1000}$

Table 1　Probability model for an insurance policy.

Of course, we can't predict exactly what *will* happen during any given year, but we can say what we *expect* to happen—in this case, what we expect the profit of a policy will be. The expected value of a policy is a **parameter** of the probability model. In fact, it's the mean. We'll signify this with the notation $E(X)$, for expected value (or sometimes μ to indicate that it is a mean). This isn't an average of data values, so we won't estimate it. Instead, we calculate it directly from the probability model for the random variable. Because it comes from a model and not data, we use the parameter μ to denote it (and *not* $\bar{y}$ or $\bar{x}$.)

To see what the insurance company can expect, think about some convenient number of outcomes. For example, imagine that they have exactly 1000 clients and that the outcomes in one year followed the probability model exactly: 1 died, 2 were disabled, and 997 survived unscathed. Then our expected payout would be:

Notation Alert!

The expected value (or mean) of a random variable is written $E(X)$ or μ. (Be sure not to confuse the mean of a random variable, calculated from probabilities, with the mean of a collection of data values which is denoted by $\bar{y}$ or $\bar{x}$.)

$$\mu = E(X) = \frac{100,000(1) + 50,000(2) + 0(997)}{1000} = 200$$

So our expected payout comes to $200 per policy.

Instead of writing the expected value as one big fraction, we can rewrite it as separate terms, each divided by 1000.

$$\mu = E(X) = \$100,000\left(\frac{1}{1000}\right) + \$50,000\left(\frac{2}{1000}\right) + \$0\left(\frac{997}{1000}\right)$$
$$= \$200$$

Writing it this way, we can see that for each policy, there's a 1/1000 chance that we'll have to pay $100,000 for a death and a 2/1000 chance that we'll have to pay $50,000 for a disability. Of course, there's a 997/1000 chance that we won't have to pay anything.

So the **expected value** of a (discrete) random variable is found by multiplying each possible value of the random variable by the probability that it occurs and then summing all those products. This gives the general formula for the expected value of a discrete random variable:[1]

$$E(X) = \sum x\, P(x).$$

Be sure that *every* possible outcome is included in the sum. Verify that you have a valid probability model to start with—the probabilities should each be between 0 and 1 and should sum to one. (Recall the rules of probability.)

For Example   Calculating expected value of a random variable

Question: A fund-raising lottery offers 500 tickets for $3 each. If the grand prize is $250 and 4 second prizes are $50 each, what is the expected value of a single ticket? (Don't count the price of the ticket in this yet). Now, including the price, what is the expected value of the ticket? (Knowing this value, does it make any "sense" to buy a lottery ticket?) The fund-raising group has a target of $1000 to be raised by the lottery. Can they expect to make this much?

Answer: Each ticket has a 1/500 chance of winning the grand prize of $250, a 4/500 chance of winning $50 and a 495/500 chance of winning nothing. So $E(X) = (1/500) \times \$250 + (4/500) \times \$50 + (495/500) \times \$0 = \$0.50 + \$0.40 + \$0.00 = \$0.90$. Including the price the expected value is $0.90 − $3 = −$2.10. The expected value of a ticket is −$2.10. Although no single person will lose $2.10 (they either lose $3 or win $50 or $250), $2.10 is the amount, on average, that the lottery gains per ticket. Therefore, they can expect to make $500 \times \$2.10 = \$1050$.

---

2   Standard Deviation of a Random Variable

Of course, this expected value (or mean) is not what actually happens to any *particular* policyholder. No individual policy actually costs the company $200. We are dealing with random events, so some policyholders receive big payouts and others nothing. Because the insurance company must anticipate this variability, it needs to know the standard deviation of the random variable.

For data, we calculate the standard deviation by first computing the deviation of each data value from the mean and squaring it. We perform a similar calculation when we compute the **standard deviation** of a (discrete) random variable as well. First, we find the deviation of each payout from the mean (expected value). (See Table 2.)

Policyholder Outcome	Payout x (cost)	Probability $P(X = x)$	Deviation $(x - EV)$
Death	100,000	$\dfrac{1}{1000}$	$(100{,}000 - 200) = 99{,}800$
Disability	50,000	$\dfrac{2}{1000}$	$(50{,}000 - 200) = 49{,}800$
Neither	0	$\dfrac{997}{1000}$	$(0 - 200) = -200$

| Table 2   Deviations between the expected value and each payout (cost).

Next, we square each deviation. The **variance** is the expected value of those squared deviations. To find it, we multiply each by the appropriate probability and sum those products:

$$Var(X) = 99{,}800^2\left(\frac{1}{1000}\right) + 49{,}800^2\left(\frac{2}{1000}\right) + (-200)^2\left(\frac{997}{1000}\right)$$
$$= 14{,}960{,}000.$$

---

[1] The concept of expected values for continuous random variables is similar, but the calculation requires calculus and is beyond the scope of this text.

Finally, we take the square root to get the standard deviation:

$$SD(X) = \sqrt{14{,}960{,}000} \approx \$3867.82$$

The insurance company can expect an average payout of \$200 per policy, with a standard deviation of \$3867.82.

Think about that. The company charges \$500 for each policy and expects to pay out \$200 per policy. Sounds like an easy way to make \$300. (In fact, most of the time—probability 997/1000—the company pockets the entire \$500.) But would you be willing to take on this risk yourself and sell all your friends policies like this? The problem is that occasionally the company loses big. With a probability of 1/1000, it will pay out \$100,000, and with a probability of 2/1000, it will pay out \$50,000. That may be more risk than you're willing to take on. The standard deviation of \$3867.82 gives an indication of the uncertainty of the profit, and that seems like a pretty big spread (and risk) for an average profit of \$300.

Here are the formulas for these arguments. Because these are parameters of our probability model, the variance and standard deviation can also be written as σ^2 and σ, respectively (sometimes with the name of the random variable as a subscript). You should recognize both kinds of notation:

$$\sigma^2 = Var(X) = \Sigma(x - \mu)^2 P(x), \text{ and}$$
$$\sigma = SD(X) = \sqrt{Var(X)}.$$

Guided Example   Computer Inventory

iStockphoto

As the head of inventory for a computer company, you've had a challenging couple of weeks. One of your warehouses recently had a fire, and you had to flag all the computers stored there to be recycled. On the positive side, you were thrilled that you had managed to ship two computers to your biggest client last week. But then you discovered that your assistant hadn't heard about the fire and had mistakenly transported a whole truckload of computers from the damaged warehouse into the shipping center. It turns out that 30% of all the computers shipped last week were damaged. You don't know whether your biggest client received two damaged computers, two undamaged ones, or one of each. Computers were selected at random from the shipping center for delivery.

If your client received two undamaged computers, everything is fine. If the client gets one damaged computer, it will be returned at your expense—\$100—and you can replace it. However, if both computers are damaged, the client will cancel all other orders this month, and you'll lose \$10,000. What is the expected value and the standard deviation of your loss under this scenario?

PLAN	Setup State the problem.	We want to analyze the potential consequences of shipping damaged computers to a large client. We'll look at the expected value and standard deviation of the amount we'll lose.
		Let X = amount of loss. We'll denote the receipt of an undamaged computer by **U** and the receipt of a damaged computer by **D**. The three possibilities are: two undamaged computers (**U** and **U**), two damaged computers (**D** and **D**), and one of each (**UD** or **DU**). Because the computers were selected randomly and the number in the warehouse is large, we can assume independence.

(continued)

DO

Model List the possible values of the random variable, and compute all the values you'll need to determine the probability model.

Because the events are independent, we can use the multiplication rule and find:

$$P(UU) = P(U) \times P(U)$$
$$= 0.7 \times 0.7 = 0.49$$

$$P(DD) = P(D) \times P(D)$$
$$= 0.3 \times 0.3 = 0.09$$

So, $P(UD \text{ or } DU) = 1 - (0.49 + 0.09) = 0.42$

We have the following model for all possible values of X.

Outcome	x	$P(X = x)$
Two damaged	10000	$P(DD) = 0.09$
One damaged	100	$P(UD \text{ or } DU) = 0.42$
Neither damaged	0	$P(UU) = 0.49$

Mechanics Find the expected value.

$$E(X) = 0(0.49) + 100(0.42) + 10000(0.09)$$
$$= \$942.00$$

Find the variance.

$$Var(X) = (0 - 942)^2 \times (0.49)$$
$$+ (100 - 942)^2 \times (0.42)$$
$$+ (10000 - 942)^2 \times (0.09)$$
$$= 8{,}116{,}836$$

Find the standard deviation.

$$SD(X) = \sqrt{8{,}116{,}836} = \$2849.01$$

REPORT

Conclusion Interpret your results in context.

REALITY CHECK

MEMO

Re: Damaged Computers

The recent shipment of two computers to our large client may have some serious negative impact. Even though there is about a 50% chance that they will receive two perfectly good computers, there is a 9% chance that they will receive two damaged computers and will cancel the rest of their monthly order. We have analyzed the expected loss to the firm as \$942 with a standard deviation of \$2849.01. The large standard deviation reflects the fact that there is a real possibility of losing \$10,000 from the mistake.

Both numbers seem reasonable. The expected value of \$942 is between the extremes of \$0 and \$10,000, and there's great variability in the outcome values.

For Example Calculating standard deviation of a random variable

Question: In the lottery earlier in this chapter, we found the expected gain per ticket to be $2.10. What is the standard deviation? What does it say about your chances in the lottery? Comment.

Answer:

$$\sigma^2 = Var(X) = \sum (x - E(X))^2 P(X) = \sum (x - 2.10)^2 P(x)$$

$$= \sum (250 - 2.10)^2 \frac{1}{500} + (50 - 2.10)^2 \frac{4}{500} + (0 - 2.10)^2 \frac{495}{500}$$

$$= \sum 61,454.41 \times \frac{1}{500} + 2,294.41 \times \frac{4}{500} + 4.41 \times \frac{495}{500}$$

$$= 145.63$$

so $\sigma = \sqrt{145.63} = \$12.07$

That's a lot of variation for a mean of $2.10, which reflects the fact that there is a small chance that you'll win a lot but a large chance you'll win nothing.

3   Properties of Expected Values and Variances

Our example insurance company expected to pay out an average of $200 per policy, with a standard deviation of about $3868. The expected profit then was $500 − $200 = $300 per policy. Suppose that the company decides to lower the price of the premium by $50 to $450. It's pretty clear that the expected profit would drop an average of $50 per policy, to $450 − $200 = $250.

What about the standard deviation? We know that adding or subtracting a constant from data shifts the mean but doesn't change the variance or standard deviation. The same is true of random variables:[2]

$$E(X \pm c) = E(X) \pm c,$$
$$Var(X \pm c) = Var(X), \text{ and}$$
$$SD(X \pm c) = SD(X).$$

What if the company decides to *double* all the payouts—that is, pay $200,000 for death and $100,000 for disability? This would double the average payout per policy and also increase the variability in payouts. In general, multiplying each value of a random variable by a constant multiplies the mean by that constant and multiplies the variance by the *square* of the constant:

$$E(aX) = aE(X), \text{ and}$$
$$Var(aX) = a^2 Var(X).$$

Taking square roots of the last equation shows that the standard deviation is multiplied by the absolute value of the constant:

$$SD(aX) = |a|SD(X).$$

This insurance company sells policies to more than just one person. We've just seen how to compute means and variances for one person at a time. What happens to the mean and variance when we have a collection of customers? The profit on a group of customers is the *sum* of the individual profits, so we'll need to know how to find expected values and variances for sums. To start, consider a simple case with

---

[2]The rules in this section are true for both discrete *and* continuous random variables.

just two customers who we'll call Mr. Ecks and Ms. Wye. With an expected payout of $200 on each policy, we might expect a total of $200 + $200 = $400 to be paid out on the two policies—nothing surprising there. In other words, we have the **Addition Rule for Expected Values of Random Variables**: *The expected value of the sum (or difference) of random variables is the sum (or difference) of their expected values:*

$$E(X \pm Y) = E(X) \pm E(Y).$$

The variability is another matter. Is the risk of insuring two people the same as the risk of insuring one person for twice as much? We wouldn't expect both clients to die or become disabled in the same year. In fact, because we've spread the risk, the standard deviation should be smaller. Indeed, this is the fundamental principle behind insurance. By spreading the risk among many policies, a company can keep the standard deviation quite small and predict costs more accurately. It's much less risky to insure thousands of customers than one customer when the total expected payout is the same, assuming that the events are independent. Catastrophic events such as hurricanes or earthquakes that affect large numbers of customers at the same time destroy the independence assumption, and often the insurance company along with it.

But how much smaller is the standard deviation of the sum? It turns out that, if the random variables are independent, we have the **Addition Rule for Variances of (Independent) Random Variables**: *The variance of the sum or difference of two independent random variables is the sum of their individual variances:*

$$Var(X \pm Y) = Var(X) + Var(Y)$$

if X and Y are independent.

Math Box

Pythagorean Theorem of Statistics

We often use the standard deviation to measure variability, but when we add independent random variables, we use their variances. Think of the Pythagorean Theorem. In a right triangle (only), the *square* of the length of the hypotenuse is the sum of the *squares* of the lengths of the other two sides:

$$c^2 = a^2 + b^2.$$

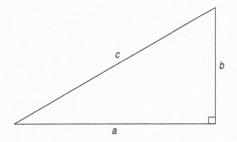

For independent random variables (only), the *square* of the standard deviation of their sum is the sum of the *squares* of their standard deviations:

$$SD^2(X + Y) = SD^2(X) + SD^2(Y).$$

It's simpler to write this with *variances:*

$$Var(X + Y) = Var(X) + Var(Y),$$

but we'll use the standard deviation formula often as well:

$$SD(X + Y) = \sqrt{Var(X) + Var(Y)}.$$

For Mr. Ecks and Ms. Wye, the insurance company can expect their outcomes to be independent, so (using X for Mr. Ecks's payout and Y for Ms. Wye's):

$$Var(X + Y) = Var(X) + Var(Y)$$
$$= 14{,}960{,}000 + 14{,}960{,}000$$
$$= 29{,}920{,}000.$$

Let's compare the variance of writing two independent policies to the variance of writing only one for twice the size. If the company had insured only Mr. Ecks for twice as much, the variance would have been

$$Var(2X) = 2^2 Var(X) = 4 \times 14{,}960{,}000 = 59{,}840{,}000, \text{ or}$$

twice as big as with two independent policies, even though the expected payout is the same.

Of course, variances are in squared units. The company would prefer to know standard deviations, which are in dollars. The standard deviation of the payout for two independent policies is $SD(X + Y) = \sqrt{Var(X + Y)} = \sqrt{29{,}920{,}000} = \$5469.92$. But the standard deviation of the payout for a single policy of twice the size is twice the standard deviation of a single policy: $SD(2X) = 2SD(X) = 2(\$3867.82) = \$7735.64$, or about 40% more than the standard deviation of the sum of the two independent policies.

If the company has two customers, then it will have an expected annual total payout (cost) of \$400 with a standard deviation of about \$5470. If they write one policy with an expected annual payout of \$400, they increase the standard deviation by about 40%. Spreading risk by insuring many independent customers is one of the fundamental principles in insurance and finance.

Let's review the rules of expected values and variances for sums and differences.

- *The expected value of the sum of two random variables is the sum of the expected values.*

- *The expected value of the difference of two random variables is the difference of the expected values:*

$$E(X \pm Y) = E(X) \pm E(Y).$$

- *If the random variables are independent, the variance of their sum or difference is always the sum of the variances:*

$$Var(X \pm Y) = Var(X) + Var(Y).$$

Do we always *add* variances? Even when we take the *difference* of two random quantities? Yes! Think about the two insurance policies. Suppose we want to know the mean and standard deviation of the *difference* in payouts to the two clients. Since each policy has an expected payout of \$200, the expected difference is \$200 − \$200 = \$0. If we computed the variance of the difference by subtracting variances, we would get \$0 for the variance. But that doesn't make sense. Their difference won't always be exactly \$0. In fact, the difference in payouts could range from \$100,000 to −\$100,000, a spread of \$200,000. The variability in differences *increases* as much as the variability in sums. If the company has two customers, the difference in payouts has a mean of \$0 and a standard deviation of about \$5470.

- **For random variables, does $X + X + X = 3X$?** Maybe, but be careful. As we've just seen, insuring one person for \$300,000 is not the same risk as insuring three people for \$100,000 each. When each instance represents a different outcome for the same random variable, though, it's easy to fall into the trap of writing all of them with the same symbol. Don't make this common mistake. Make sure you write each instance as a *different* random variable. Just because each random variable describes a similar situation doesn't mean that each random outcome will be the same. What you really mean is $X_1 + X_2 + X_3$. Written this way, it's clear that the sum shouldn't necessarily equal 3 times *anything*.

For Example   Sums of random variables

You are considering investing $1000 into one or possibly two different investment funds. Historically, each has delivered 5% a year in profit with a standard deviation of 3%. So, a $1000 investment would produce $50 with a standard deviation of $30.

Question: Assuming the two funds are independent, what are the relative advantages and disadvantages of putting $1000 into one, or splitting the $1000 and putting $500 into each? Compare the means and SDs of the profit from the two strategies.

Answer: Let X = amount gained by putting $1000 into one

$$E(X) = 0.05 \times 1000 = \$50 \text{ and } SD(X) = 0.03 \times 1000 = \$30.$$

Let W = amount gained by putting $500 into each. W_1 and W_2 are the amounts from each fund respectively. $E(W_1) = E(W_2) = 0.05 \times 500 = \$25$. So $E(W) = E(W_1) + E(W_2) = \$25 + \$25 = \$50$. The expected values of the two strategies are the same. You expect on average to earn $50 on $1000.

$$
\begin{aligned}
SD(W) &= \sqrt{SD^2(W_1) + SD^2(W_2)} \\
&= \sqrt{(0.03 \times 500)^2 + (0.03 \times 500)^2} \\
&= \sqrt{15^2 + 15^2} \\
&= \$21.213
\end{aligned}
$$

The standard deviation of the amount earned is $21.213 by splitting the investment amount compared to $30 for investing in one. The expected values are the same. Spreading the investment into more than one vehicle *reduces* the variation. On the other hand, keeping it all in one vehicle increases the chances of both extremely good and extremely bad returns. Which one is better depends on an individual's appetite for risk.[3]

Just Checking

1 Suppose that the time it takes a customer to get and pay for seats at the ticket window of a baseball park is a random variable with a mean of 100 seconds and a standard deviation of 50 seconds. When you get there, you find only two people in line in front of you.

a) How long do you expect to wait for your turn to get tickets?
b) What's the standard deviation of your wait time?
c) What assumption did you make about the two customers in finding the standard deviation?

4   Discrete Probability Distributions

We've seen how to compute means and standard deviations of random variables. But plans based just on averages are, on average, wrong. At least that's what Sam Savage, Professor at Stanford University says in his book, *The Flaw of Averages*. Unfortunately, many business owners make decisions based solely on averages—the average amount sold last year, the average number of customers seen last month, etc. Instead of relying on averages, the business decisionmaker can incorporate much more by modeling the situation with a probability model. Probability models can play an important and pivotal role in helping decisionmakers better predict both the outcome and the consequences of their decisions. In this section we'll see that some fairly simple models provide a framework for thinking about how to model a wide variety of business phenomena.

---

[3]The assumption of independence is crucial, but not always (or ever) reasonable. As a March 3, 2010, article on *CNN Money* stated:

"It's only when economic conditions start to return to normal . . . that investors, and investments, move independently again. That's when diversification reasserts its case. . . ."

http://money.cnn.com/2010/03/03/pf/funds/diversification.moneymag/index.htm

The Uniform Distribution

When we first studied probability, we saw that equally likely events were the simplest case. For example, a single die can turn up 1, 2, . . . , 6 on one toss. A probability model for the toss is Uniform because each of the outcomes has the same probability (1/6) of occurring. Similarly if X is a random variable with possible outcomes 1, 2, . . . , n and $P(X = i) = 1/n$ for each value of i, then we say X has a **discrete Uniform distribution, U[1, . . . , *n*].**

Bernoulli Trials

When Google Inc. designed their web browser *Chrome*, they worked hard to minimize the probability that their browser would have trouble displaying a website. Before releasing the product, they had to test many websites to discover those that might fail. Although web browsers are relatively new, *quality control inspection* such as this is common throughout manufacturing worldwide and has been in use in industry for nearly 100 years.

The developers of *Chrome* sampled websites, recording whether the browser displayed the website correctly or had a problem. We call the act of inspecting a website a trial. There are two possible outcomes—either the website is displayed correctly or it isn't. The developers thought that whether any particular website displayed correctly was independent from other sites. Situations like this occur often and are called **Bernoulli trials.** To summarize, trials are Bernoulli if:

- There are only two possible outcomes (called *success* and *failure*) for each **trial**.
- The probability of success, denoted p, is the same on every trial. (The probability of failure, $1 - p$ is often denoted q.)
- The trials are independent. Finding that one website does not display correctly does not change what might happen with the next website.

Common examples of Bernoulli trials include tossing a coin, collecting responses on Yes/No questions from surveys or even shooting free throws in a basketball game. Bernoulli trials are remarkably versatile and can be used to model a wide variety of real-life situations. The specific question you might ask in different situations will give rise to different random variables that, in turn, have different probability models.

Of course, the *Chrome* developers wanted to find websites that wouldn't display so they could fix any problems in the browser. So for them a "success" was finding a failed website. The labels "success" and "failure" are often applied arbitrarily, so be sure you know what they mean in any particular situation.

The Geometric Distribution

What's the probability that the first website that fails to display is the second one that we test? Let X denote the number of trials (websites) until the first such "success." For X to be 2, the first website must have displayed correctly (which has probability $1 - p$), and then the second one must have failed to display correctly—a success, with probability p. Since the trials are independent, these probabilities can be multiplied, and so $P(X = 2) = (1 - p)(p)$ or qp. Maybe you won't find a success until the fifth trial. What are the chances of that? You'd have to fail 4 times in a row and then succeed, so $P(X = 5) = (1 - p)^4(p) = q^4p$. See the Math Box for an extension and more explanation.

Whenever we want to know how long (how many trials) it will take us to achieve the first success, the model that tells us this probability is called the **geometric probability distribution.** Geometric distributions are completely specified by one parameter, p, the probability of success. We denote them Geom(p).

Daniel Bernoulli (1700–1782) was the nephew of Jakob. He was the first to work out the mathematics for what we now call Bernoulli trials.

St. Andrews University/The MacTutor History of Mathematics Archive

Random Variables and Probability Models

The geometric distribution can tell Google something important about its software. No large complex program is entirely free of bugs. So before releasing a program or upgrade, developers typically ask not whether it is free of bugs, but how long it is likely to be until the next bug is discovered. If the expected number of pages displayed until the next failure is high enough, then the program is ready to ship.

Notation Alert!

Now we have two more reserved letters. Whenever we deal with Bernoulli trials, p represents the probability of success, and q represents the probability of failure. (Of course, $q = 1 - p$.)

Geometric probability model for Bernoulli trials: Geom(p)

p = probability of success (and $q = 1 - p$ = probability of failure)
X = number of trials until the first success occurs

$$P(X = x) = q^{x-1}p$$

Expected value: $\mu = \dfrac{1}{p}$

Standard deviation: $\sigma = \sqrt{\dfrac{q}{p^2}}$

Math Box

Finding the Expected Value of a Geometric Distribution

We want to find the mean (expected value) of random variable X, using a geometric distribution with probability of success p.

First write the probabilities:

x	1	2	3	4	...
$P(X = x)$	p	qp	q^2p	q^3p	...

The expected value is: $E(X) = 1p + 2qp + 3q^2p + 4q^3p + \cdots$

Let $p = 1 - q$:
$= (1 - q) + 2q(1 - q) + 3q^2(1 - q) + 4q^3(1 - q) + \cdots$

Simplify:
$= 1 - q + 2q - 2q^2 + 3q^2 - 3q^3 + 4q^3 - 4q^4 + \cdots$

That's an infinite geometric series, with first term 1 and common ratio q:
$= 1 + q + q^2 + q^3 + \cdots$
$= \dfrac{1}{1 - q}$

So, finally $E(X) = \dfrac{1}{p}$.

Independence

One of the important requirements for Bernoulli trials is that the trials be independent. Sometimes that's a reasonable assumption. Is it true for our example? It's easy to imagine that related sites might have similar problems, but if the sites are selected at random, whether one has a problem should be independent of others.

The 10% Condition: Bernoulli trials must be independent. In theory, we need to sample from a population that's infinitely big. However, if the population is finite, it's still okay to proceed as long as the sample is smaller than 10% of the population. In Google's case, they just happened to have a directory of millions of websites, so most samples would easily satisfy the 10% condition.

The Binomial Distribution

Suppose Google tests 5 websites. What's the probability that *exactly* 2 of them have problems (2 "successes")? When we studied the geometric distribution we asked how long it would take until our first success. Now we want to find the probability of getting exactly 2 successes among the 5 trials. We are still talking about Bernoulli trials, but we're asking a different question.

This time we're interested in the *number of successes* in the 5 trials, which we'll denote by X. We want to find $P(X = 2)$. Whenever the random variable of interest is the number of successes in a series of Bernoulli trials, it's called a **Binomial random variable.** It takes two parameters to define this **Binomial probability distribution:** the number of trials, n, and the probability of success, p. We denote this distribution Binom(n, p).

Suppose that in this phase of development, 10% of the sites exhibited some sort of problem so that $p = 0.10$. (Early in the development phase of a product, it is not uncommon for the number of defects to be much higher than it is when the product is released.) Exactly 2 successes in 5 trials means 2 successes and 3 failures. It seems logical that the probability should be $(p)^2(1 - p)^3$. Unfortunately, it's not *quite* that easy. That calculation would give you the probability of finding two successes and then three failures—*in that order*. But you could find the two successes in a lot of other ways, for example in the 2nd and 4th website you test. The probability of that sequence is $(1 - p)p(1 - p)p(1 - p)$ which is also $p^2(1 - p)^3$. In fact, as long as there are two successes and three failures, the probability will always be the same, regardless of the order of the sequence of successes and failures. The probability will be $(p)^2(1 - p)^3$. To find the probability of getting 2 successes in 5 trials in any order, we just need to know how many ways that outcome can occur.

Fortunately, the possible sequences that lead to the same number of successes are *disjoint*. (For example, if your successes came on the first two trials, they couldn't come on the last two.) So once we find all the different sequences, we can add up their probabilities. And since the probabilities are all the same, we just need to find how many sequences there are and multiply $(p)^2(1 - p)^3$ by that number.

Each different order in which we can have k successes in n trials is called a "combination." The total number of ways this can happen is written $\binom{n}{k}$ or $_nC_k$ and pronounced "n choose k:"

$$\binom{n}{k} = {}_nC_k = \frac{n!}{k!(n - k)!} \text{ where } n! = n \times (n - 1) \times \cdots \times 1.$$

For 2 successes in 5 trials,

$$\binom{5}{2} = \frac{5!}{2!(5 - 2)!} = \frac{(5 \times 4 \times 3 \times 2 \times 1)}{(2 \times 1 \times 3 \times 2 \times 1)} = \frac{(5 \times 4)}{(2 \times 1)} = 10.$$

So there are 10 ways to get 2 successes in 5 websites, and the probability of each is $(p)^2(1 - p)^3$. To find probability of exactly 2 successes in 5 trials, we multiply the probability of any particular order by this number:

$P($*exactly 2 successes in 5 trials*$) = 10p^2(1 - p)^3 = 10(0.10)^2(0.90)^3 = 0.0729$

In general, we can write the probability of exactly k successes in n trials as $P(X = k) = \binom{n}{k}p^k q^{n-k}$.

If the probability that any single website has a display problem is 0.10, what's the expected number of websites with problems if we test 100 sites? You probably said 10. We suspect you didn't use the formula for expected value that involves multiplying each value times its probability and adding them up. In fact, there is an easier way to find the expected value for a Binomial random variable. You just multiply the probability of success by n. In other words, $E(X) = np$. We prove this in the next Math Box.

The standard deviation is less obvious and you can't just rely on your intuition. Fortunately, the formula for the standard deviation also boils down to something simple: $SD(X) = \sqrt{npq}$. If you're curious to know where that comes from, it's in the Math Box, too.

In our website example, with $n = 100$, $E(X) = np = 100(0.10) = 10$ so we expect to find 10 successes out of the 100 trials. The standard deviation is

$$\sqrt{100 \times 0.10 \times 0.90} = 3 \text{ websites.}$$

To summarize, a Binomial probability model describes the distribution of the number of successes in a specified number of trials.

Binomial model for Bernoulli trials: Binom(n, p)

n = number of trials
p = probability of success (and $q = 1 - p$ = probability of failure)
X = number of successes in n trials

$$P(X = x) = \binom{n}{x} p^x q^{n-x}, \text{where } \binom{n}{x} = \frac{n!}{x!(n - x)!}$$

Mean: $\mu = np$
Standard deviation: $\sigma = \sqrt{npq}$

Math Box

Mean and Standard Deviation of the Binomial Model

To derive the formulas for the mean and standard deviation of the Binomial distribution we start with the most basic situation.

Consider a single Bernoulli trial with probability of success p. Let's find the mean and variance of the number of successes.

Here's the probability model for the number of successes:

x	0	1
$P(X = x)$	q	p

Find the expected value:

$$E(X) = 0q + 1p$$
$$E(X) = p$$

Now the variance:

$$Var(X) = (0 - p)^2 q + (1 - p)^2 p$$
$$= p^2 q + q^2 p$$
$$= pq(p + q)$$
$$= pq(1)$$
$$Var(X) = pq$$

What happens when there is more than one trial? A Binomial distribution simply counts the number of successes in a series of n independent Bernoulli trials. That makes it easy to find the mean and standard deviation of a binomial random variable, Y.

$$\text{Let } Y = X_1 + X_2 + X_3 + \cdots + X_n$$
$$E(Y) = E(X_1 + X_2 + X_3 + \cdots + X_n)$$
$$= E(X_1) + E(X_2) + E(X_3) + \cdots + E(X_n)$$
$$= p + p + p + \cdots + p \,(\text{There are } n \text{ terms.})$$

So, as we thought, the mean is $E(Y) = np$.

And since the trials are independent, the variances add:

$$Var(Y) = Var(X_1 + X_2 + X_3 + \cdots + X_n)$$
$$= Var(X_1) + Var(X_2) + Var(X_3) + \cdots + Var(X_n)$$
$$= pq + pq + pq + \cdots + pq \,(\text{Again, } n \text{ terms.})$$
$$Var(Y) = npq$$

Voila! The standard deviation is $SD(Y) = \sqrt{npq}$.

Guided Example   The American Red Cross

Keith Brofsky/Getty Images

Every two seconds someone in America needs blood.

The American Red Cross is a non-profit organization that runs like a large business. It serves over 3000 hospitals around the United States, providing a wide range of high quality blood products and blood donor and patient testing services. It collects blood from over 4 million donors and provides blood to millions of patients with a dedication to meeting customer needs.[4]

The balancing of supply and demand is complicated not only by the logistics of finding donors that meet health criteria, but by the fact that the blood type of donor and patient must be matched. People with O-negative blood are called "universal donors" because O-negative blood can be given to patients with any blood type. Only about 6% of people have O-negative blood, which presents a challenge in managing and planning. This is especially true, since, unlike a manufacturer who can balance supply by planning to produce or to purchase more or less of a key item, the Red Cross gets its supply from volunteer donors who show up more-or-less at random (at least in terms of blood type). Modeling the arrival of samples with various blood types helps Red Cross managers to plan their blood allocations.

Here's a small example of the kind of planning required. Of the next 20 donors to arrive at a blood donation center, how many universal donors can be expected? Specifically, what are the mean and standard deviation of the number of universal donors? What is the probability that there are 2 or 3 universal donors?

Question 1: What are the mean and standard deviation of the number of universal donors?
Question 2: What is the probability that there are exactly 2 or 3 universal donors out of the 20 donors?

(continued)

---

[4]Source: www.redcross.org

PLAN	Setup State the question.	We want to know the mean and standard deviation of the number of universal donors among 20 people and the probability that there are 2 or 3 of them.
	Check to see that these are Bernoulli trials.	✓ There are two outcomes: success = O-negative failure = other blood types
	Variable Define the random variable.	✓ $p = 0.06$
	Model Specify the model.	✓ **10% Condition:** Fewer than 10% of all possible donors have shown up.
		Let X = number of O-negative donors among $n = 20$ people. We can model X with a Binom(20, 0.06).
DO	Mechanics Find the expected value and standard deviation. Calculate the probability of 2 or 3 successes.	$E(X) = np = 20(0.06) = 1.2$ $SD(X) = \sqrt{npq} = \sqrt{20(0.06)(0.94)} \approx 1.06$ $P(X = 2 \text{ or } 3) = P(X = 2) + P(X = 3)$ $= \binom{20}{2}(0.06)^2(0.94)^{18}$ $+ \binom{20}{3}(0.06)^3(0.94)^{17}$ $\approx 0.2246 + 0.0860$ $= 0.3106$
REPORT	Conclusion Interpret your results in context.	MEMO **Re: Blood Drive** In groups of 20 randomly selected blood donors, we'd expect to find an average of 1.2 universal donors, with a standard deviation of 1.06. About 31% of the time, we'd expect to find exactly 2 or 3 universal donors among the 20 people.

Simeon Denis Poisson was a French mathematician interested in rare events. He originally derived his model to approximate the Binomial model when the probability of a success, p, is very small and the number of trials, n, is very large. Poisson's contribution was providing a simple approximation to find that probability. When you see the formula, however, you won't necessarily see the connection to the Binomial.

The Poisson Distribution

Not all discrete events can be modeled as Bernoulli trials. Sometimes we're interested simply in the number of events that occur over a given interval of time or space. For example, we might want to model the number of customers arriving in our store in the next ten minutes, the number of visitors to our website in the next minute, or the number of defects that occur in a computer monitor of a certain size. In cases like these, the number of occurrences can be modeled by a **Poisson random variable.** The Poisson's parameter, the mean of the distribution, is usually denoted by λ.

W. S. Gosset, the quality control chemist at the Guinness brewery in the early 20th century, was one of the first to use the Poisson in industry. He used it to model and predict the number of yeast cells so he'd know how much to add to the stock. The Poisson is a good model to consider whenever your data consist of counts of occurrences. It requires only that the events be independent and that the mean number of occurrences stays constant.

Poisson probability model for occurrences: Poisson (λ)

λ = mean number of occurrences
X = number of occurrences

$$P(X = x) = \frac{e^{-\lambda}\lambda^x}{x!}$$

Expected value: $E(X) = \lambda$
Standard deviation: $SD(X) = \sqrt{\lambda}$

Where Does *e* Come From?

The constant *e* equals 2.7182818 . . . (to 7 decimal places). One of the places *e* originally turned up was in calculating how much money you'd earn if you could get interest compounded more often. If you earn 100% per year simple interest, at the end of the year, you'd have twice as much money as when you started. But if the interest were compounded and paid at the end of every month, each month you'd earn 1/12 of 100% interest. At the year's end you'd have $(1 + 1/12)^{12} = 2.613$ times as much instead of 2. If the interest were paid every day, you'd get $(1 + 1/365)^{365} = 2.714$ times as much. If the interest were paid every second, you'd get $(1 + 1/3153600)^{3153600} = 2.7182818$ times as much. This is where *e* shows up. If you could get the interest compounded continually, you'd get *e* times as much. In other words, as *n* gets large, the limit of $(1 + 1/n)^n = e$. This unexpected result was discovered by Jacob Bernoulli in 1683.

For example, data show an average of about 4 hits per minute to a small business website during the afternoon hours from 1:00 to 5:00 P.M. We can use the Poisson distribution to find the probability that any number of hits will arrive. For example, if we let X be the number of hits arriving in the next minute, then $P(X = x) = \frac{e^{-\lambda}\lambda^x}{x!} = \frac{e^{-4}4^x}{x!}$, using the given average rate of 4 per minute. So, the probability of no hits during the next minute would be $P(X = 0) = \frac{e^{-4}4^0}{0!} = e^{-4} = 0.0183$ (The constant *e* is the base of the natural logarithms and is approximately 2.71828).

One interesting and useful feature of the Poisson distribution is that it scales according to the interval size. For example, suppose we want to know the probability of no hits to our website in the next 30 seconds. Since the mean rate is 4 hits per minute, it's 2 hits per 30 seconds, so we can use the model with $\lambda = 2$ instead. If we let Y be the number of hits arriving in the next 30 seconds, then:

$$P(Y = 0) = \frac{e^{-2}2^0}{0!} = e^{-2} = 0.1353.$$

(Recall that $0! = 1$.) The Poisson distribution has been used to model phenomena such as customer arrivals, hot streaks in sports, and disease clusters.

Whenever or wherever rare events happen closely together, people want to know whether the occurrence happened by chance or whether an underlying change caused the unusual occurrence. The Poisson distribution can be used to find the probability of the occurrence and can be the basis for making the judgment.

Just Checking

Roper Worldwide reports that they are able to contact 76% of the randomly selected households drawn for a telephone survey.

2 Explain why these phone calls can be considered Bernoulli trials.

3 Which of the models of this chapter (Geometric, Binomial, or Poisson) would you use to model the number of successful contracts from a list of 1000 sampled households?

4 Roper also reports that even after they contacted a household, only 38% of the contacts agreed to he interviewed. So the probability of getting a completed interview from a randomly selected household is only 0.29. Which of the models of this chapter would you use to model the number of households Roper has to call before they get the first completed interview?

For Example   Probability models

A venture capital firm has a list of potential investors who have previously invested in new technologies. On average, these investors invest about 5% of the time. A new client of the firm is interested in finding investors for a mobile phone application that enables financial transactions, an application that is finding increasing acceptance in much of the developing world. An analyst at the firm starts calling potential investors.

Questions:

1. What is the probability that the first person she calls will want to invest?
2. What is the probability that none of the first five people she calls will be interested?
3. How many people will she have to call until the probability of finding someone interested is at least 0.50?
4. How many investors will she have to call, on average, to find someone interested?
5. If she calls 10 investors, what is the probability that exactly 2 of them will be interested?
6. What assumptions are you making to answer these questions?

Answers:

1. Each investor has a 5% or 1/20 chance of wanting to invest, so the chance that the first person she calls is interested is 1/20.
2. P(first one not interested) $= 1 - 1/20 = 19/20$. Assuming the trials are independent, P(none are interested) $= P$(1st not interested) $\times$ P(2nd not interested) $\times$ $\cdots$ $\times$ P (5th not interested) $= (19/20)^5 = 0.774$.
3. By trial and error, $(19/20)^{13} = 0.513$ and $(19/20)^{14} = 0.488$, so she would need to call 14 people to have the probability of *no one* interested drop below 0.50, therefore making the probability that someone is interested greater than 0.50.
4. This uses a geometric model. Let X = number of people she calls until 1st person is interested. $E(X) = 1/p = 1/(1/20) = 20$ people.
5. Using the Binomial model, let Y = number of people interested in 10 calls, then

$$P(Y = 2) = \binom{10}{2}p^2(1 - p)^8 = \frac{10 \times 9}{2}(1/20)^2(19/20)^8 = 0.0746$$

6. We are assuming that the trials are independent and that the probability of being interested in investing is the same for all potential investors.

What Can Go Wrong?

- **Probability distributions are still just models.** Models can be useful, but they are not reality. Think about the assumptions behind your models. Question probabilities as you would data.

- **If the model is wrong, so is everything else.** Before you try to find the mean or standard deviation of a random variable, check to make sure the probability distribution is reasonable. As a start, the probabilities should all be between 0 and 1 and they should add up to 1. If not, you may have calculated a probability incorrectly or left out a value of the random variable.

- **Watch out for variables that aren't independent.** You can add expected values of *any* two random variables, but you can only add variances of independent random variables. Suppose a survey includes questions about the number of hours of sleep people get each night and also the number of hours they are awake each day. From their answers, we find the mean and standard deviation of hours asleep and hours awake. The expected total must be 24 hours; after all, people are either asleep or awake. The means still add just fine. Since all the totals are exactly 24 hours, however, the standard deviation of the total will be 0. We can't add variances here because the number of hours you're awake depends on the number of hours you're asleep. Be sure to check for independence before adding variances.

- **Don't write independent instances of a random variable with notation that looks like they are the same variables.** Make sure you write each instance as a different random variable. Just because each random variable describes a similar situation doesn't mean that each random outcome will be the same. These are *random* variables, not the variables you saw in Algebra. Write $X_1 + X_2 + X_3$ rather than $X + X + X$.

- **Don't forget:** Variances of independent random variables add. Standard deviations don't.

- **Don't forget:** Variances of independent random variables add, even when you're looking at the difference between them.

- **Be sure you have Bernoulli trials.** Be sure to check the requirements first: two possible outcomes per trial ("success" and "failure"), a constant probability of success, and independence. Remember that the 10% Condition provides a reasonable substitute for independence.

Ethics in Action

Kurt Williams was about to open a new SEP IRA account and was interested in exploring various investment options. Although he had some ideas about how to invest his money, Kurt thought it best to seek the advice of a professional, so he made an appointment with Keith Klingman, a financial advisor at James, Morgan, and Edwards, LLC. Prior to their first meeting, Kurt told Keith that he preferred to keep his investments simple and wished to allocate his money equally among only two funds. Also, he mentioned that while he was willing to take on some risk to yield higher returns, he was concerned about taking on too much risk given the increased volatility in the markets. After their conversation, Keith began to prepare for their first meeting. Based on historical performance, the firm expected annual returns and standard deviations for the various funds it offers investors. Because Kurt was interested in investing his SEP IRA money in only two funds, Keith decided to compile figures on the expected annual return and standard deviation (a measure of risk) for potential SEP IRA account consisting of different combinations of two funds. If X and Y represent the annual returns for two different funds, Keith knew he could represent the annual return for a specific SEP IRA account as $\frac{1}{2}X + \frac{1}{2}Y$. While calculating the expected annual, $E\left(\frac{1}{2}X + \frac{1}{2}Y\right)$, was straightforward, Keith seemed to recall a more complicated formula for finding the standard deviation. He remembered that he would first need to compute the variance, and after doing some research, decided to use the expression $Var\left(\frac{1}{2}X + \frac{1}{2}Y\right) =$ $\frac{1}{2}^2 Var(X) + \frac{1}{2}^2 Var(Y)$. After completing his computations, he noticed that various combinations of two different equity funds offered some of the highest expected annual returns with relatively low standard deviations. He had anticipated lower standard deviations for accounts that involved mixed assets, such as an equity fund and a bond fund. He was pleasantly surprised with the results, since his firm made more money with investments in equity funds. Keith was confident that these figures would help Kurt realize that he would be best served by investing his SEP IRA money in equity funds only.

ETHICAL ISSUE *Keith incorrectly assumed that funds are independent. It is likely that similar funds are positively correlated (e.g., two equity funds would tend to move in the same direction) while different types of funds are likely negatively correlated (e.g., equity and bond funds tend to move in opposite directions). By not taking the covariance into account, Keith's computations for the variance (and standard deviation) are incorrect. He would have underestimated the variance (and therefore the volatility) for an account consisting of two equity funds (related to Items A and B, ASA Ethical Guidelines).*

ETHICAL SOLUTION *Keith should have recognized that these funds are not independent. His initial uncertainty about how to compute the variance should have made him cautious about his computation results; instead he let his bias toward wanting to sell equity funds affect his judgment. He should not present these figures as fact to Kurt.*

What Have We Learned?

Learning Objectives

■ Understand how probability models relate values to probabilities.
  • For discrete random variables, probability models assign a probability to each possible outcome.

■ Know how to find the mean, or expected value, of a discrete probability model from $\mu = \Sigma x P(X = x)$ and the standard deviation from $\sigma = \sqrt{\Sigma(x - \mu)^2 P(x)}$.

■ Foresee the consequences of shifting and scaling random variables, specifically

$$E(X \pm c) = E(X) \pm c \qquad E(aX) = aE(X)$$
$$Var(X \pm c) = Var(X) \qquad Var(aX) = a^2 Var(X)$$
$$SD(X \pm c) = SD(X) \qquad SD(aX) = |a| SD(X)$$

■ Understand that when adding or subtracting random variables the expected values add or subtract well: $E(X \pm y) = E(X) \pm E(Y)$. However, when adding or subtracting independent random variables, the variances *add*:

$$Var(X \pm Y) = Var(X) + Var(Y)$$

■ Be able to explain the properties and parameters of the Uniform, the Binomial, the Geometric, and the Poisson distributions.

Terms

Addition Rule for Expected Values of Random Variables

$E(X \pm Y) = E(X) \pm E(Y)$

Addition Rule for Variances of Random Variables

(Pythagorean Theorem of Statistics)

If X and Y are *independent*: $Var(X \pm Y) = Var(X) + Var(Y)$,
and $SD(X \pm Y) = \sqrt{Var(X) + Var(Y)}$.

Bernoulli trials

A sequence of trials are called Bernoulli trials if:

1. There are exactly two possible outcomes (usually denoted *success* and *failure*).

2. The probability of success is constant.

3. The trials are independent.

Binomial probability distribution

A Binomial distribution is appropriate for a random variable that counts the number of Bernoulli trials.

Changing a random variable by a constant

$$E(X \pm c) = E(X) \pm c \qquad Var(X \pm c) = Var(X) \qquad SD(X \pm c) = SD(X)$$
$$E(aX) = aE(X) \qquad Var(aX) = a^2 Var(X) \qquad SD(aX) = |a| SD(X)$$

Discrete random variable

A random variable that can take one of a finite number[5] of distinct outcomes.

Expected value

The expected value of a random variable is its theoretical long-run average value, the center of its model. Denoted μ or $E(X)$, it is found (if the random variable is discrete) by summing the products of variable values and probabilities:

$$\mu = E(X) = \Sigma x P(x)$$

Geometric probability distribution

A model appropriate for a random variable that counts the number of Bernoulli trials until the first success.

---

[5]Technically, there could be an infinite number of outcomes as long as they're *countable*. Essentially, that means we can imagine listing them all in order, like the counting numbers 1, 2, 3, 4, 5, ...

Parameter	A numerically valued attribute of a model, such as the values of μ and σ representing the mean and standard deviation.
Poisson model	A discrete model often used to model the number of arrivals of events such as customers arriving in a queue or calls arriving into a call center.
Probability density function (pdf)	A function $f(x)$ that represents the probability distribution of a continuous random variable X. The probability that X is in an interval A is the area under the curve $f(x)$ over A.
Probability model	A function that associates a probability P with each value of a discrete random variable X, denoted $P(X = x)$, or with any interval of values of a continuous random variable.
Random variable	Assumes any of several different values as a result of some random event. Random variables are denoted by a capital letter, such as X.
Standard deviation of a random variable	Describes the spread in the model and is the square root of the variance.
Uniform distribution	For a discrete uniform distribution over a set of n values, each value has probability $1/n$.
Variance	The variance of a random variable is the expected value of the squared deviations from the mean. For discrete random variables, it can be calculated as:

$$\sigma^2 = Var(X) = \Sigma(x - \mu)^2 P(x).$$

Brief CASE

Investment Options

A young entrepreneur has just raised $30,000 from investors, and she would like to invest it while she continues her fund-raising in hopes of starting her company one year from now. She wants to do due diligence and understand the risk of each of her investment options. After speaking with her colleagues in finance, she believes that she has three choices: (1) she can purchase a $30,000 certificate of deposit (CD); (2) she can invest in a mutual fund with a balanced portfolio; or (3) she can invest in a growth stock that has a greater potential payback but also has greater volatility. Each of her options will yield a different payback on her $30,000, depending on the state of the economy.

During the next year, she knows that the CD yields a constant annual percentage rate, regardless of the state of the economy. If she invests in a balanced mutual fund, she estimates that she will earn as much as 12% if the economy remains strong, but could possibly lose as much as 4% if the economy takes a downturn. Finally, if she invests all $30,000 in a growth stock, experienced investors tell her that she can earn as much as 40% in a strong economy, but may lose as much as 40% in a poor economy.

Estimating these returns, along with the likelihood of a strong economy, is challenging. Therefore, often a "sensitivity analysis" is conducted, where figures are computed using a range of values for each of the uncertain parameters in the problem. Following this advice, this investor decides to compute measures for a range of interest rates for CDs, a range of returns for the mutual fund, and a range of returns for the growth stock. In addition, the likelihood of a strong economy is unknown, so she will vary these probabilities as well.

Assume that the probability of a strong economy over the next year is 0.3, 0.5, or 0.7. To help this investor make an informed decision, evaluate the expected value and volatility of each of her investments using the following ranges of rates of growth:

CD: Look up the current annual rate for the return on a 3-year CD and use this value $\pm$ 0.5%

iStockphoto

Novic/Dreamstime

(continued)

Mutual Fund: Use values of 8%, 10%, and 12% for a strong economy and values of 0%, −2%, and −4% for a weak economy.

Growth Stock: Use values of 10%, 25%, and 40% in a strong economy and values of −10%, −25%, and −40% in a weak economy.

Discuss the expected returns and uncertainty of each of the alternative investment options for this investor in each of the scenarios you analyzed. Be sure to compare the volatility of each of her options.

Exercises

SECTION 1

1. A company's employee database includes data on whether or not the employee includes a dependent child in his or her health insurance.

a) Is this variable discrete or continuous?
b) What are the possible values it can take on?

2. The database also, of course, includes each employee's compensation.

a) Is this variable discrete or continuous?
b) What are the possible values it can take on?

3. Suppose that the probabilities of a customer purchasing 0, 1, or 2 books at a book store are 0.2, 0.4, and 0.4, respectively. What is the expected number of books a customer will purchase?

4. A day trader buys an option on a stock that will return $100 profit if the stock goes up today and lose $400 if it goes down. If the trader thinks there is a 75% chance that the stock will go up,

a) What is her expected value of the option's profit?
b) What do you think of this option?

SECTION 2

5. Find the standard deviation of the book purchases in exercise 3.

6. Find the standard deviation of the day trader's option value in exercise 4.

7. An orthodontist has three financing packages, and each has a different service charge. He estimates that 30% of patients use the first plan, which has a $10 finance charge; 50% use the second plan, which has a $20 finance charge; and 20% use the third plan, which has a $30 finance charge.

a) Find the expected value of the service charge.
b) Find the standard deviation of the service charge.

8. A marketing agency has developed three vacation packages to promote a timeshare plan at a new resort. They estimate that 20% of potential customers will choose the Day Plan, which does not include overnight accommodations; 40% will choose the Overnight Plan, which includes one night at the resort; and 40% will choose the Weekend Plan, which includes two nights.

a) Find the expected value of the number of nights potential customers will need.
b) Find the standard deviation of the number of nights potential customers will need.

SECTION 3

9. Given independent random variables, X and Y, with means and standard deviations as shown, find the mean and standard deviation of each of the variables in parts a to d.

a) $3X$
b) $Y + 6$
c) $X + Y$
d) $X - Y$

	Mean	SD
X	10	2
Y	20	5

10. Given independent random variables, X and Y, with means and standard deviations as shown, find the mean and standard deviation of each of the variables in parts a to d.

a) $X - 20$
b) $0.5Y$
c) $X + Y$
d) $X - Y$

	Mean	SD
X	80	12
Y	12	3

11. A broker has calculated the expected values of two different financial instruments X and Y. Suppose that $E(X) = \$100$, $E(Y) = \$90$, $SD(X) = \$12$ and $SD(Y) = \$8$. Find each of the following.

a) $E(X + 10)$ and $SD(X + 10)$
b) $E(5Y)$ and $SD(5Y)$
c) $E(X + Y)$ and $SD(X + Y)$
d) What assumption must you make in part c?

12. A company selling glass ornaments by mail-order expects, from previous history, that 6% of the ornaments it ships will break in shipping. You purchase two ornaments as gifts and have them shipped separately to two different addresses. What is the probability that both arrive safely? What did you assume?

SECTION 4

13. At many airports, a traveler entering the U.S. is sent randomly to one of several stations where his passport and visa are checked. If each of the 6 stations is equally likely, can the probabilities of which station a traveler will be sent be modeled with a Uniform model?

14. At the airport entry sites, a computer is used to randomly decide whether a traveler's baggage should be opened for inspection. If the chance of being selected is 12%, can you model your chance of having your baggage opened with a Bernoulli model? Check each of the conditions specifically.

15. The 2000 Census showed that 26% of all firms in the United States are owned by women. You are phoning local businesses, assuming that the national percentage is true in your area. You wonder how many calls you will have to make before you find one owned by a woman. What probability model should you use? (Specify the parameters as well.)

16. As in Exercise 15, you are phoning local businesses. You call 3 firms. What is the probability that all three are owned by women?

17. A manufacturer of clothing knows that the probability of a button flaw (broken, sewed on incorrectly, or missing) is 0.002. An inspector examines 50 shirts in an hour, each with 6 buttons. Using a Poisson probability model:

a) What is the probability that she finds no button flaws?
b) What is the probability that she finds at least one?

18. Replacing the buttons with snaps increases the probability of a flaw to 0.003, but the inspector can check 70 shirts an hour (still with 6 snaps each). Now what is the probability she finds no snap flaws?

CHAPTER EXERCISES

19. New website. You have just launched the website for your company that sells nutritional products online. Suppose X = the number of different pages that a customer hits during a visit to the website.

a) Assuming that there are n different pages in total on your website, what are the possible values that this random variable may take on?
b) Is the random variable discrete or continuous?

20. New website, part 2. For the website described in Exercise 1, let Y = the total time (in minutes) that a customer spends during a visit to the website.

a) What are the possible values of this random variable?
b) Is the random variable discrete or continuous?

21. Job interviews. Through the career services office, you have arranged preliminary interviews at four companies for summer jobs. Each company will either ask you to come to their site for a follow-up interview or not. Let X be the random variable equal to the total number of follow-up interviews that you might have.

a) List all the possible values of X.
b) Is the random variable discrete or continuous?
c) Do you think a uniform distribution might be appropriate as a model for this random variable? Explain briefly.

22. Help desk. The computer help desk is staffed by students during the 7:00 P.M. to 11:00 P.M. shift. Let Y denote the random variable that represents the number of students seeking help during the 15-minute time slot 10:00 to 10:15 P.M.

a) What are the possible values of Y?
b) Is the random variable discrete or continuous?

23. Lottery. Iowa has a lottery game called Pick 3 in which customers buy a ticket for $1 and choose three numbers, each from zero to nine. They also must select the play type, which determines what combinations are winners. In one type of play, called the "Straight/Box," they win if they match the three numbers in any order, but the payout is greater if the order is exact. For the case where all three of the numbers selected are different, the probabilities and payouts are:

	Probability	Payout
Straight/Box Exact	1 in 1000	$350
Straight/Box Any	5 in 1000	$50

a) Find the amount a Straight/Box player can expect to win.
b) Find the standard deviation of the player's winnings.
c) Tickets to play this game cost $1 each. If you subtract $1 from the result in part a, what is the expected result of playing this game?

24. Software company. A small software company will bid on a major contract. It anticipates a profit of $50,000 if it gets it, but thinks there is only a 30% chance of that happening.

a) What's the expected profit?
b) Find the standard deviation for the profit.

25. Commuting to work. A commuter must pass through five traffic lights on her way to work and will have to stop at each one that is red. After keeping record for several months, she developed the following probability model for the number of red lights she hits:

X = # of red	0	1	2	3	4	5
$P(X = x)$	0.05	0.25	0.35	0.15	0.15	0.05

a) How many red lights should she expect to hit each day?
b) What's the standard deviation?

26. Defects. A consumer organization inspecting new cars found that many had appearance defects (dents, scratches, paint chips, etc.). While none had more than three of these defects, 7% had three, 11% had two, and 21% had one defect.

a) Find the expected number of appearance defects in a new car.
b) What is the standard deviation?

27. Fishing tournament. A sporting goods manufacturer was asked to sponsor a local boy in two fishing tournaments. They claim the probability that he will win the first tournament is 0.4. If he wins the first tournament, they estimate the probability that he will also win the second is 0.2. They guess that if he loses the first tournament, the probability that he will win the second is 0.3.

a) According to their estimates, are the two tournaments independent? Explain your answer.
b) What's the probability that he loses both tournaments?
c) What's the probability he wins both tournaments?
d) Let random variable X be the number of tournaments he wins. Find the probability model for X.
e) What are the expected value and standard deviation of X?

28. Contracts. Your company bids for two contracts. You believe the probability that you get contract #1 is 0.8. If you get contract #1, the probability that you also get contract #2 will be 0.2, and if you do not get contract #1, the probability that you get contract #2 will be 0.3.

a) Are the outcomes of the two contract bids independent? Explain.
b) Find the probability you get both contracts.
c) Find the probability you get neither contract.
d) Let X be the number of contracts you get. Find the probability model for X.
e) Find the expected value and standard deviation of X.

29. Battery recall. A company has discovered that a recent batch of batteries had manufacturing flaws, and has issued a recall. You have 10 batteries covered by the recall, and 3 are dead. You choose 2 batteries at random from your package of 10.

a) Has the assumption of independence been met? Explain.
b) Create a probability model for the number of good batteries chosen.
c) What's the expected number of good batteries?
d) What's the standard deviation?

30. Grocery supplier. A grocery supplier believes that the mean number of broken eggs per dozen is 0.6, with a standard deviation of 0.5. You buy 3 dozen eggs without checking them.

a) How many broken eggs do you expect to get?
b) What's the standard deviation?
c) Is it necessary to assume the cartons of eggs are independent? Why?

31. Commuting, part 2. A commuter finds that she waits an average of 14.8 seconds at each of five stoplights, with a standard deviation of 9.2 seconds. Find the mean and the standard deviation of the total amount of time she waits at all five lights. What, if anything, did you assume?

32. Repair calls. A small engine shop receives an average of 1.7 repair calls per hour, with a standard deviation of 0.6. What is the mean and standard deviation of the number of calls they receive for an 8-hour day? What, if anything, did you assume?

33. Insurance company. An insurance company estimates that it should make an annual profit of $150 on each homeowner's policy written, with a standard deviation of $6000.

a) Why is the standard deviation so large?
b) If the company writes only two of these policies, what are the mean and standard deviation of the annual profit?
c) If the company writes 1000 of these policies, what are the mean and standard deviation of the annual profit?
d) What circumstances could violate the assumption of independence of the policies?

34. Casino. At a casino, people play the slot machines in hopes of hitting the jackpot, but most of the time, they lose their money. A certain machine pays out an average of $0.92 (for every dollar played), with a standard deviation of $120.

a) Why is the standard deviation so large?
b) If a gambler plays 5 times, what are the mean and standard deviation of the casino's profit?
c) If gamblers play this machine 1000 times in a day, what are the mean and standard deviation of the casino's profit?

35. Bike sale. A bicycle shop plans to offer 2 specially priced children's models at a sidewalk sale. The basic model will return a profit of $120 and the deluxe model $150. Past experience indicates that sales of the basic model will have a mean of 5.4 bikes with a standard deviation of 1.2, and sales of the deluxe model will have a mean of 3.2 bikes with a standard deviation of 0.8 bikes. The cost of setting up for the sidewalk sale is $200.

a) Define random variables and use them to express the bicycle shop's net profit.
b) What's the mean of the net profit?
c) What's the standard deviation of the net profit?
d) Do you need to make any assumptions in calculating the mean? How about the standard deviation?

36. Farmers' market. A farmer has 100 lbs of apples and 50 lbs of potatoes for sale. The market price for apples (per pound) each day is a random variable with a mean of 0.5 dollars and a standard deviation of 0.2 dollars. Similarly, for a pound of potatoes, the mean price is 0.3 dollars and the standard deviation is 0.1 dollars. It also costs him 2 dollars to bring all the apples and potatoes to the market. The market is busy with eager shoppers, so we can assume that he'll be able to sell all of each type of produce at that day's price.

a) Define your random variables, and use them to express the farmer's net income.
b) Find the mean of the net income.
c) Find the standard deviation of the net income.
d) Do you need to make any assumptions in calculating the mean? How about the standard deviation?

37. Movie rentals. To compete with Netflix, the owner of a movie rental shop decided to try sending DVDs through the mail. In order to determine how many copies of newly released titles he should purchase, he carefully observed turnaround times. Since nearly all of his customers were in his local community, he tested delivery times by sending DVDs to his friends. He found the mean delivery time was 1.3 days, with a standard deviation of 0.5 days. He also noted that the times were the same whether going to the customer or coming back to the shop.

a) Find the mean and standard deviation of the round-trip delivery times for a DVD (mailed to the customer and then mailed back to the shop).
b) The shop owner tries to process a DVD that is returned to him and get it back in the mail in one day, but circumstances sometimes prevent it. His mean turnaround time is 1.1 days, with a standard deviation of 0.3 days. Find the mean and standard deviation of the turnaround times combined with the round-trip times in part a.

38. Online applications. Researchers for an online marketing company suggest that new customers who have to become a member before they can check out on the website are very intolerant of long applications. One way to rate an application is by the total number of keystrokes required to fill it out.

a) One common frustration is having to enter an e-mail address twice. If the mean length of e-mail addresses is 13.3 characters, with a standard deviation of 2.8 characters, what is the mean and standard deviation of total characters typed if entered twice?
b) The company found the mean and standard deviation of the length of customers' names (including spaces) were 13.4 and 2.4 characters, respectively, and for addresses, 30.8 and 6.3 characters. What is the mean and standard deviation of the combined lengths of entering the e-mail addresses twice and then the name and the address?

39. eBay. A collector purchased a quantity of action figures and is going to sell them on eBay. He has 19 Hulk figures. In recent auctions, the mean selling price of similar figures has been $12.11, with a standard deviation of $1.38. He also has 13 Iron Man figures which have had a mean selling price of $10.19, with a standard deviation of $0.77.

His insertion fee will be $0.55 on each item, and the closing fee will be 8.75% of the selling price. He assumes all will sell without having to be relisted.

a) Define your random variables, and use them to create a random variable for the collector's net income.
b) Find the mean (expected value) of the net income.
c) Find the standard deviation of the net income.
d) Do you have to assume independence for the sales on eBay? Explain.

40. Real estate. A real estate broker purchased 3 two-bedroom houses in a depressed market for a combined cost of $71,000. He expects the cleaning and repair costs on each house to average $3700, with a standard deviation of $1450. When he sells them, after subtracting taxes and other closing costs, he expects to realize an average of $39,000 per house, with a standard deviation of $1100.

a) Define your random variables, and use them to create a random variable for the broker's net profit.
b) Find the mean (expected value) of the net profit.
c) Find the standard deviation of the net profit.
d) Do you have to assume independence for the repairs and sale prices of the houses? Explain.

41. Bernoulli. Can we use probability models based on Bernoulli trials to investigate the following situations? Explain.

a) Each week a doctor rolls a single die to determine which of his six office staff members gets the preferred parking space.
b) A medical research lab has samples of blood collected from 120 different individuals. How likely is it that the majority of them are Type A blood, given that Type A is found in 43% of the population?
c) From a workforce of 13 men and 23 women, all five promotions go to men. How likely is that, if promotions are based on qualifications rather than gender?
d) We poll 500 of the 3000 stockholders to see how likely it is that the proposed budget will pass.
e) A company realizes that about 10% of its packages are not being sealed properly. In a case of 24 packages, how likely is it that more than 3 are unsealed?

42. Bernoulli, part 2. Can we use probability models based on Bernoulli trials to investigate the following situations? Explain.

a) You are rolling 5 dice. How likely is it to get at least two 6's to win the game?
b) You survey 500 potential customers to determine their color preference.
c) A manufacturer recalls a doll because about 3% have buttons that are not properly attached. Customers return 37 of these dolls to the local toy store. How likely are they to find any buttons not properly attached?

d) A city council of 11 Republicans and 8 Democrats picks a committee of 4 at random. How likely are they to choose all Democrats?

e) An executive reads that 74% of employees in his industry are dissatisfied with their jobs. How many dissatisfied employees can he expect to find among the 481 employees in his company?

43. Closing sales. A salesman normally makes a sale (closes) on 80% of his presentations. Assuming the presentations are independent, find the probability of each of the following.

a) He fails to close for the first time on his fifth attempt.

b) He closes his first presentation on his fourth attempt.

c) The first presentation he closes will be on his second attempt.

d) The first presentation he closes will be on one of his first three attempts.

44. Computer chip manufacturer. Suppose a computer chip manufacturer rejects 2% of the chips produced because they fail presale testing. Assuming the bad chips are independent, find the probability of each of the following.

a) The fifth chip they test is the first bad one they find.

b) They find a bad one within the first 10 they examine.

c) The first bad chip they find will be the fourth one they test.

d) The first bad chip they find will be one of the first three they test.

45. Side effects. Researchers testing a new medication find that 7% of users have side effects. To how many patients would a doctor expect to prescribe the medication before finding the first one who has side effects?

46. Credit cards. College students are a major target for advertisements for credit cards. At a university, 65% of students surveyed said they had opened a new credit card account within the past year. If that percentage is accurate, how many students would you expect to survey before finding one who had not opened a new account in the past year?

47. Missing pixels. A company that manufactures large LCD screens knows that not all pixels on their screen light, even if they spend great care when making them. In a sheet 6 ft by 10 ft (72 in. by 120 in.) that will be cut into smaller screens, they find an average of 4.7 blank pixels. They believe that the occurrences of blank pixels are independent. Their warranty policy states that they will replace any screen sold that shows more than 2 blank pixels.

a) What is the mean number of blank pixels per square foot?

b) What is the standard deviation of blank pixels per square foot?

c) What is the probability that a 2 ft by 3 ft screen will have at least one defect?

d) What is the probability that a 2 ft by 3 ft screen will be replaced because it has too many defects?

48. Bean bags. Cellophane that is going to be formed into bags for items such as dried beans or bird seed is passed over a light sensor to test if the alignment is correct before it passes through the heating units that seal the edges. Small adjustments can be made by the machine automatically. But if the alignment is too bad, the process is stopped and an operator has to manually adjust it. These misalignment stops occur randomly and independently. On one line, the average number of stops is 52 per 8-hour shift.

a) What is the mean number of stops per hour?

b) What is the standard deviation of stops per hour?

49. Hurricane insurance. An insurance company needs to assess the risks associated with providing hurricane insurance. Between 1990 and 2006, Florida was hit by 22 tropical storms or hurricanes. If tropical storms and hurricanes are independent and the mean has not changed, what is the probability of having a year in Florida with each of the following. (Note that 1990 to 2006 is 17 years.)

a) No hits?

b) Exactly one hit?

c) More than three hits?

50. Hurricane insurance, part 2. Between 1965 and 2007, there were 95 major hurricanes (category 3 or more) in the Atlantic basin. Assume that hurricanes are independent and the mean has not changed.

a) What is the mean number of major hurricanes per year? (There are 43 years from 1965 to 2007.)

b) What is the standard deviation of the frequency of major hurricanes?

c) What is the probability of having a year with no major hurricanes?

d) What is the probability of going three years in a row without a major hurricane?

51. Professional tennis. Serena Williams made a successful first serve 67% of the time in a Wimbledon finals match against her sister Venus. If she continues to serve at the same rate the next time they play and serves 6 times in the first game, determine the following probabilities. (Assume that each serve is independent of the others.)

a) All 6 first serves will be in.

b) Exactly 4 first serves will be in.

c) At least 4 first serves will be in.

52. American Red Cross. Only 4% of people have Type AB blood. A bloodmobile has 12 vials of blood on a rack. If the distribution of blood types at this location is consistent with the general population, what's the probability they find AB blood in:

a) None of the 12 samples?

b) At least 2 samples?

c) 3 or 4 samples?

53. Satisfaction survey. A cable provider wants to contact customers in a particular telephone exchange to see how satisfied they are with the new digital TV service the company has provided. All numbers are in the 452 exchange, so there are 10,000 possible numbers from 452-0000 to 452-9999. If they select the numbers with equal probability:

a) What distribution would they use to model the selection?

b) What is the probability the number selected will be an even number?

c) What is the probability the number selected will end in 000?

54. Manufacturing quality. In an effort to check the quality of their cell phones, a manufacturing manager decides to take a random sample of 10 cell phones from yesterday's production run, which produced cell phones with serial numbers ranging (according to when they were produced) from 43005000 to 43005999. If each of the 1000 phones is equally likely to be selected:

a) What distribution would they use to model the selection?

b) What is the probability that a randomly selected cell phone will be one of the last 100 to be produced?

c) What is the probability that the first cell phone selected is either from the last 200 to be produced or from the first 50 to be produced?

d) What is the probability that the first two cell phones are both from the last 100 to be produced?

55. Web visitors. A website manager has noticed that during the evening hours, about 3 people per minute check out from their shopping cart and make an online purchase. She believes that each purchase is independent of the others and wants to model the number of purchases per minute.

a) What model might you suggest to model the number of purchases per minute?

b) What is the probability that in any one minute at least one purchase is made?

c) What is the probability that no one makes a purchase in the next 2 minutes?

56. Quality control. The manufacturer in Exercise 54 has noticed that the number of faulty cell phones in a production run of cell phones is usually small and that the quality of one day's run seems to have no bearing on the next day.

a) What model might you use to model the number of faulty cell phones produced in one day?

b) If the mean number of faulty cell phones is 2 per day, what is the probability that no faulty cell phones will be produced tomorrow?

c) If the mean number of faulty cell phones is 2 per day, what is the probability that 3 or more faulty cell phones were produced in today's run?

Just Checking Answers

1 a) $100 + 100 = 200$ seconds
   b) $\sqrt{50^2 + 50^2} = 70.7$ seconds
   c) The times for the two customers are independent.

2 There are two outcomes (contact, no contact), the probability of contact stays constant at 0.76, and random calls should be independent.

3 Binomial

4 Geometric

Answers

SECTION EXERCISE ANSWERS

1. a) Discrete.
    b) Yes/no.

3. 1.2

5. 0.748

7. a) $19
    b) $7

9. a) $\mu = 30; \sigma = 6$
    b) $\mu = 26; \sigma = 5$
    c) $\mu = 30; \sigma = 5.39$
    d) $\mu = -10; \sigma = 5.39$

11. a) 110 and 12.
     b) 450 and 40.

    c) 190 and 14.422.
    d) X and Y are independent for the SD calculation, but not necessarily for the sum.

13. Yes.

15. Geometric, $p = 0.26$.

17. x
     a) 0.5488
     b) 0.4512

CHAPTER EXERCISE ANSWERS

19. a) $1, 2, \ldots, n$
     b) Discrete.

21. a) 0,1,2,3,4
   b) Discrete.
   c) No, the outcomes are not equally likely.

23. a) $0.60
   b) $11.59
   c) −$0.40

25. a) 2.25 lights
   b) 1.26 lights

(continued in next column)

27. a) No, the probability he wins the second changes depending on whether he won the first.
   b) 0.42
   c) 0.08
   d)

X	0	1	2
P(X = x)	0.42	0.50	0.08

   e) $E(X) = 0.66$ tournaments; $\sigma = 0.62$ tournaments

29. a) No, the probability of one battery being dead will depend on the state of the other one since there are only 10 batteries.
   b)

Number good	0	1	2
P(number good)	$\left(\frac{3}{10}\right)\left(\frac{2}{9}\right) = \frac{6}{90}$	$\left(\frac{3}{10}\right)\left(\frac{7}{9}\right) + \left(\frac{7}{10}\right)\left(\frac{3}{9}\right) = \frac{42}{90}$	$\left(\frac{7}{10}\right)\left(\frac{6}{9}\right) = \frac{42}{90}$

   c) $\mu = 1.4$ batteries
   d) $\sigma = 0.61$ batteries

31. $\mu = E$ (total wait time) $= 74.0$ seconds
   $\sigma = SD$ (total wait time) ≈ 20.57 seconds
   (Answers to standard deviation may vary slightly due to rounding of the standard deviation of the number of red lights each day.) The standard deviation may be calculated only if the days are independent of each other. This seems reasonable.

33. a) The standard deviation is large because the profits on insurance are highly variable. Although there will be many small gains, there will occasionally be large losses when the insurance company has to pay a claim.
   b) $\mu = E$ (two policies) $= \$300$
      $\sigma = SD$(two policies) $\approx \$8,485.28$
   c) $\mu = E$(1000 policies) $= \$150,000$
      $\sigma = SD$(1000 policies) $= \$189,736.66$
   d) A natural disaster affecting many policyholders such as a large fire or hurricane.

35. a) $B =$ number basic; $D =$ number deluxe
      Net Profit $= 120B + 150D − 200$
   b) $928.00
   c) $187.45
   d) Mean—no; SD—yes (sales are independent).

37. a) $\mu = E$(time) $= 2.6$ days
      $\sigma = SD$(time) ≈ 0.707 days
   b) $\mu = E$(combined time) $= 3.7$ days
      $\sigma = SD$(combined time) ≈ 0.768 days

39. a) Let $X_i =$ price of ith Hulk figure sold; $Y_i =$ price of ith Iron Man figure sold; Insertion Fee $= \$0.55$; $T =$ Closing Fee $= 0.875(X_1 + X_2 + \cdots + X_{19} + Y_1 + \cdots + Y_{13})$
      Net Income $= (X_1 + X_2 + \cdots + X_{19} + Y_1 + \cdots + Y_{13}) − 32(0.55) − 0.0875(X_1 + X_2 + \cdots + X_{19} + Y_1 + \cdots + Y_{13})$
   b) $\mu = E$ (net income) $= \$313.24$
   c) $\sigma = SD$ (net income) $= \$6.05$
   d) Yes, to compute the standard deviation.

41. a) No, these are not Bernoulli trials. The possible outcomes are 1, 2, 3, 4, 5, and 6. There are more than two possible outcomes.

   b) Yes, these may be considered Bernoulli trials. There are only two possible outcomes: Type A and not Type A. Assuming the 120 donors are representative of the population, the probability of having Type A blood is 43%. The trials are not independent because the population is finite, but the 120 donors represent less than 10% of all possible donors.
   c) No, these are not Bernoulli trials. The probability of choosing a man changes after each promotion and the 10% condition is violated.
   d) No, these are not Bernoulli trials. We are sampling without replacement, so the trials are not independent. Samples without replacement may be considered Bernoulli trials if the sample size is less than 10% of the population, but 500 is more than 10% of 3000.
   e) Yes, these may be considered Bernoulli trials. There are only two possible outcomes: sealed properly and not sealed properly. The probability that a package is unsealed is constant at about 10%, as long as the packages checked are a representative sample of all.

43. a) 0.0819
   b) 0.0064
   c) 0.16
   d) 0.992

45. $E(X) = 14.28$, so 15 patients

47. a) 0.078 pixels
   b) 0.280 pixels
   c) 0.375
   d) 0.012

49. a) 0.274
   b) 0.355
   c) 0.043

51. a) 0.090
   b) 0.329
   c) 0.687

53. a) A uniform; all numbers should be equally likely to be selected.
   b) 0.5
   c) 0.001

55. a) The Poisson model
   b) 0.9502
   c) 0.0025

The Normal Distribution

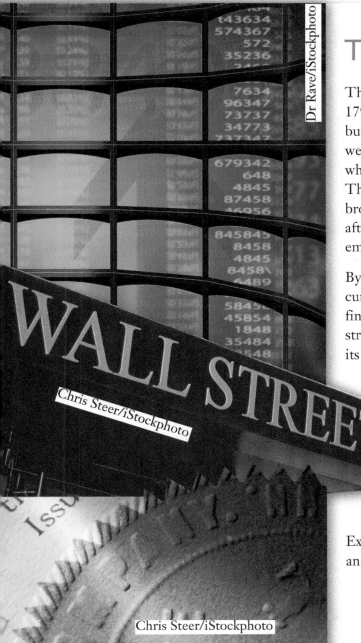

The NYSE

The New York Stock Exchange (NYSE) was founded in 1792 by 24 stockbrokers who signed an agreement under a buttonwood tree on Wall Street in New York. The first offices were in a rented room at 40 Wall Street. In the 1830s traders who were not part of the Exchange did business in the street. They were called "curbstone brokers." It was the curbstone brokers who first made markets in gold and oil stocks and, after the Civil War, in small industrial companies such as the emerging steel, textile, and chemical industries.

By 1903 the New York Stock Exchange was established at its current home at 18 Broad Street. The curbstone brokers finally moved indoors in 1921 to a building on Greenwich street in lower Manhattan. In 1953 the curb market changed its name to the American Stock Exchange. In 1993 the American Stock Exchange pioneered the market for derivatives by introducing the first exchange-traded fund, Standard & Poor's Depositary Receipts (SPDRs).

The NYSE Euronext holding company was created in 2007 as a combination of the NYSE Group, Inc., and Euronext N.V. And in 2008, NYSE Euronext merged with the American Stock Exchange. The combined exchange is the world's largest and most liquid exchange group.

1   The Standard Deviation as a Ruler

WHO	Months
WHAT	CAPE10 values for the NYSE
WHEN	1880 through mid 2010
WHY	Investment guidance

Investors have always sought ways to help them decide when to buy and when to sell. Such measures have become increasingly sophisticated. But all rely on identifying when the stock market is in an unusual state—either unusually undervalued (buy!) or unusually overvalued (sell!). One such measure is the Cyclically Adjusted Price/Earnings Ratio (CAPE10) developed by Yale professor Robert Shiller. The CAPE10 is based on the standard Price/Earnings (P/E) ratio of stocks, but designed to smooth out short-term fluctuations by "cyclically adjusting" them. The CAPE10 has been as low as 4.78, in 1920, and as high as 44.20, in late 1999. The long-term average CAPE10 (since year 1881) is 16.34.

Investors who follow the CAPE10 use the metric to signal times to buy and sell. One mutual fund strategy buys only when the CAPE10 is 33% lower than the long-term average and sells (or "goes into cash") when the CAPE10 is 50% higher than the long-term average. Between January 1, 1971, and October 23, 2009, this strategy would have outperformed such standard measures as the Wiltshire 5000 in both average return and volatility, but it is important to note that the strategy would have been completely in cash from just before the stock market crash of 1987 all the way to March of 2009! Shiller popularized the strategy in his book *Irrational Exuberance*. Figure 1 shows a time series plot of the CAPE10 values for the New York Stock Exchange from 1880 until the middle of 2010. Generally, the CAPE10 hovers around 15. But occasionally, it can take a large excursion. One such time was in 1999 and 2000, when the CAPE10 exceeded 40. But was this just a random peak or were these values really extraordinary?

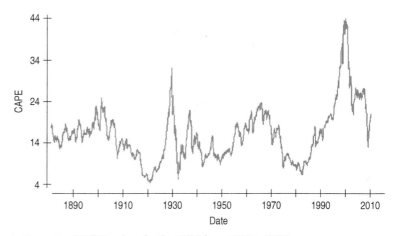

| Figure 1   CAPE10 values for the NYSE from 1880 to 2010.

We can look at the overall distribution of CAPE10 values. Figure 2 shows a histogram of the same values. Now we don't see patterns over time, but we may be able to make a better judgment of whether values are extraordinary.

Overall, the main body of the distribution looks unimodal and reasonably symmetric. But then there's a tail of values that trails off to the high end. How can we assess how extraordinary they are?

Investors follow a wide variety of measures that record various aspects of stocks, bonds, and other investments. They are usually particularly interested in identifying times when these measures are extraordinary because those often represent times of increased risk or opportunity. But these are quantitative values, not categories.

How can we characterize the usual behavior of a random variable that can take on any value in a range of values? The distributions we have already learned won't provide the tools we need, but many of the basic concepts still work. The random variables we need are *continuous*.

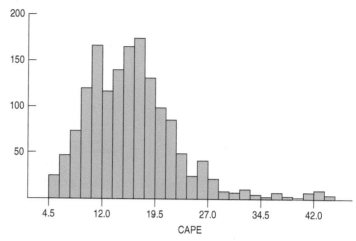

| Figure 2   The distribution of the CAPE10 values shown in Figure 1.

We saw that z-scores provide a standard way to compare values. In a sense, we use the standard deviation as a ruler, asking how many standard deviations a value is from the mean. That's what a z-score reports; the number of standard deviations away from the mean. We can convert the CAPE10 values to z-scores by subtracting their mean (16.3559) and dividing by their standard deviation (6.58). Figure 3 shows the resulting distribution.

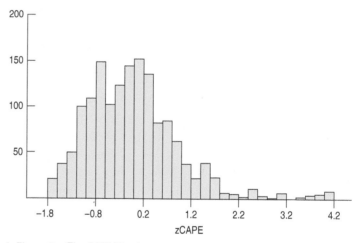

| Figure 3   The CAPE10 values as z-scores.

It's easy to see that the z-scores have the same distribution as the original values, but now we can also see that the largest of them is above 4. How extraordinary is it for a value to be four standard deviations away from the mean? Fortunately, there's a fact about unimodal, symmetric distributions that can guide us.[1]

The 68–95–99.7 Rule

In a unimodal, symmetric distribution, about 68% of the values fall within 1 standard deviation of the mean, about 95% fall within 2 standard deviations of the mean, and about 99.7%—almost all—fall within 3 standard deviations of the

---

[1]All of the CAPE10 values in the right tail occurred after 1993. Until that time the distribution of CAPE10 values was quite symmetric and clearly unimodal.

mean. Calling this rule the **68–95–99.7 Rule** provides a mnemonic for these three values.[2]

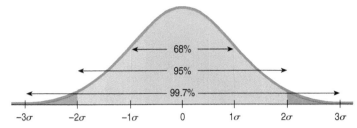

Figure 4   The 68–95–99.7 Rule tells us how much of most unimodal, symmetric models is found within one, two, or three standard deviations of the mean.

For Example   An extraordinary day for the Dow?

On May 6, 2010, the Dow Jones Industrial Average (DJIA) lost 404.7 points. Although that wasn't the most ever lost in a day, it was a large amount for that period. During the previous year, the mean change in the DJIA was −9.767 with a standard deviation of 98.325 points. A histogram of day-to-day changes in the DJIA looks like this:

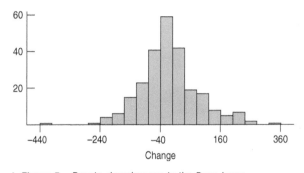

Figure 5   Day-to-day changes in the Dow Jones Industrial Average for the year ending June 2010.

Question: Use the 68–95–99.7 Rule to characterize how extraordinary the May 6 changes were. Is the rule appropriate?

Answer: The histogram is unimodal and symmetric, so the 68–95–99.7 rule is an appropriate model. The z-score corresponding to the May 6 change is

$$\frac{-404.7 - (-9.767)}{98.325} = -4.017$$

A z-score bigger than 3 in magnitude will occur with a probability of less than 0.015. A z-score of 4 is even less likely. This was a truly extraordinary event.

---

2   The Normal Distribution

The 68–95–99.7 Rule is useful in describing how unusual a z-score is. But often in business we want a more precise answer than one of these three values. To say more about how big we expect a z-score to be, we need to *model* the data's distribution.

"All models are wrong—but some are useful."

—GEORGE BOX, FAMOUS STATISTICIAN

---

[2]This rule is also called the "Empirical Rule" because it originally was observed without any proof. It was first published by Abraham de Moivre in 1733, 75 years before the underlying reason for it—which we're about to see—was known.

A model will let us say much more precisely how often we'd be likely to see z-scores of different sizes. Of course, like all models of the real world, the model will be wrong—wrong in the sense that it can't match reality exactly. But it can still be useful. Like a physical model, it's something we can look at and manipulate to learn more about the real world.

Models help our understanding in many ways. Just as a model of an airplane in a wind tunnel can give insights even though it doesn't show every rivet,[3] models of data give us summaries that we can learn from and use, even though they don't fit each data value exactly. It's important to remember that they're only *models* of reality and not reality itself. But without models, what we can learn about the world at large is limited to only what we can say about the data we have at hand.

There is no universal standard for z-scores, but there is a model that shows up over and over in Statistics. You may have heard of "bell-shaped curves." Statisticians call them Normal distributions. **Normal distributions** are appropriate models for distributions whose shapes are unimodal and roughly symmetric. There is a Normal distribution for every possible combination of mean and standard deviation. We write $N(\mu, \sigma)$ to represent a Normal distribution with a mean of μ and a standard deviation of σ. We use Greek symbols here because *this* mean and standard deviation are not numerical summaries of data. They are part of the model. They don't come from the data. Rather, they are numbers that we choose to help specify the distribution. Such numbers are called **parameters**.

If we model data with a Normal distribution and standardize them using the corresponding μ and σ, we still call the standardized values **z-scores**, and we write

$$z = \frac{y - \mu}{\sigma}.$$

If we standardize the data first (using its mean and standard deviation) it will have mean 0 and standard deviation 1. Then, to model it with a Normal, we'll need only the model $N(0,1)$. The Normal distribution with mean 0 and standard deviation 1 is called the **standard Normal distribution** (or the **standard Normal model**).

But be careful. You shouldn't use a Normal model for just any data set. Remember that standardizing won't change the shape of the distribution. If the distribution is not unimodal and symmetric to begin with, standardizing won't make it Normal.

1 Your Accounting teacher has announced that the lower of your two tests will be dropped. You got a 90 on test 1 and an 80 on test 2. You're all set to drop the 80 until she announces that she grades "on a curve." She standardized the scores in order to decide which is the lower one. If the mean on the first test was 88 with a standard deviation of 4 and the mean on the second was 75 with a standard deviation of 5,

a) Which one will be dropped?
b) Does this seem "fair"?

Finding Normal Percentiles

Finding the probability that a proportion is at least 1 SD above the mean is easy. We know that 68% of the values lie within 1 SD of the mean, so 32% lie farther away. Since the Normal distribution is symmetric, half of those 32% (or 16%) are

---

[3]In fact, the model is useful *because* it doesn't have every rivet. It is because models offer a simpler view of reality that they are so useful as we try to understand reality.

more than 1 SD above the mean. But what if we want to know the percentage of observations that fall more than 1.8 SD above the mean? We already know that no more than 16% of observations have z-scores above 1. By similar reasoning, no more than 2.5% of the observations have a z-score above 2. Can we be more precise with our answer than "between 16% and 2.5%"?

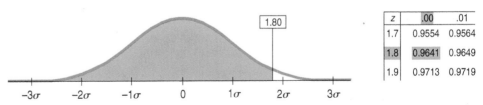

Figure 6   A table of Normal percentiles (Table Z in Appendix D) lets us find the percentage of individuals in a standard Normal distribution falling below any specified z-score value.

When the value doesn't fall exactly 0, 1, 2, or 3 standard deviations from the mean, we can look it up in a table of **Normal percentiles**.[4] Tables use the standard Normal distribution, so we'll have to convert our data to z-scores before using the table. If our data value was 1.8 standard deviations above the mean, we would standardize it to a z-score of 1.80, and then find the value associated with a z-score of 1.80. If we use a table, as shown in Figure 6, we find the z-score by looking down the left column for the first two digits (1.8) and across the top row for the third digit, 0. The table gives the percentile as 0.9641. That means that 96.4% of the z-scores are less than 1.80. Since the total area is always 1, and $1 - 0.9641 = 0.0359$ we know that only 3.6% of all observations from a Normal distribution have z-scores higher than 1.80. We can also find the probabilities associated with z-scores using technology such as calculators, statistical software, and various websites.

For Example   GMAT scores and the Normal model

The Graduate Management Admission Test (GMAT) has scores from 200 to 800. Scores are supposed to follow a distribution that is roughly unimodal and symmetric and is designed to have an overall mean of 500 and a standard deviation of 100. In any one year, the mean and standard deviation may differ from these target values by a small amount, but we can use these values as good overall approximations.

Question: Suppose you earned a 600 on your GMAT test. From that information and the 68–95–99.7 Rule, where do you stand among all students who took the GMAT?

Answer: Because we're told that the distribution is unimodal and symmetric, we can approximate the distribution with a Normal model. We are also told the scores have a mean of 500 and an SD of 100. So, we'll use a $N(500,100)$. It's good practice at this point to draw the distribution. Find the score whose percentile you want to know and locate it on the picture. When you finish the calculation, you should check to make sure that it's a reasonable percentile from the picture.

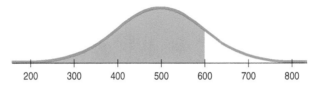

A score of 600 is 1 SD above the mean. That corresponds to one of the points in the 68–95–99.7% Rule. About 32% (100% − 68%) of those who took the test were more than one standard deviation from the mean, but only half of those were on the high side. So about 16% (half of 32%) of the test scores were better than 600.

---

[4]Many calculators and statistics computer packages do this as well.

For Example   More GMAT scores

Question: Assuming the GMAT scores are nearly Normal with $N(500,100)$, what proportion of GMAT scores falls between 450 and 600?

Answer: *The first step is to find the z-scores associated with each value.* Standardizing the scores we are given, we find that for 600, $z = (600 - 500)/100 = 1.0$ and for 450, $z = (450 - 500)/100 = -0.50$. We can label the axis below the picture either in the original values or the z-scores or even use both scales as the following picture shows.

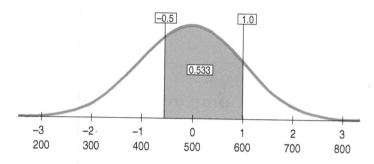

From the normal distribution table, we find the area $z \leq 1.0 = 0.8413$, which means that 84.13% of scores fall below 1.0, and the area $z \leq -0.50 = 0.3085$, which means that 30.85% of the values fall below -0.5, so the proportion of z-scores *between* them is $84.13\% - 30.85\% = 53.28\%$. So, the Normal model estimates that about 53.3% of GMAT scores fall between 450 and 600.

Finding areas from z-scores is the simplest way to work with the Normal distribution. But sometimes we start with areas and are asked to work backward to find the corresponding z-score or even the original data value. For instance, what z-score represents the first quartile, Q1, in a Normal distribution? In our first set of examples, we knew the z-score and used the table or technology to find the percentile. Now we want to find the cut point for the 25th percentile. Make a picture, shading the leftmost 25% of the area. Look in a normal distribution table for an area of 0.2500. The exact area is not there, but 0.2514 is the closest number. That shows up in the table with -0.6 in the left margin and .07 in the top margin. The z-score for Q1, then, is approximately $z = -0.67$. Computers and calculators can determine the cut point more precisely (and more easily).[5]

For Example   An exclusive MBA program

Question: Suppose an MBA program says it admits only people with GMAT scores among the top 10%. How high a GMAT score does it take to be eligible?

Answer: The program takes the top 10%, so their cutoff score is the 90th percentile. Draw an approximate picture like this one.

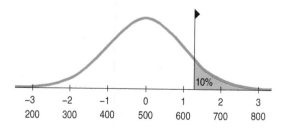

	0.07	0.08	0.09
1.0	0.8577	0.8599	0.8621
1.1	0.8790	0.8810	0.8830
1.2	0.8980	0.8997	0.9015
1.3	0.9147	0.9162	0.9177
1.4	0.9292	0.9306	0.9319

(continued)

---

[5]We'll often use those more precise values in our examples. If you're finding the values from the table you may not get *exactly* the same number to all decimal places as your classmate who's using a computer package.

From our picture we can see that the z-value is between 1 and 1.5 (if we've judged 10% of the area correctly), and so the cut-off score is between 600 and 650 or so. Using technology, you may be able to select the 10% area and find the z-value directly. Using a normal distribution table, locate 0.90 (or as close to it as you can; here 0.8997 is closer than 0.9015) in the *interior* of the table and find the corresponding z-score (see table above). Here the 1.2 is in the left margin, and the .08 is in the margin above the entry. Putting them together gives 1.28. Now, convert the z-score back to the original units. From the normal distribution table, the cut point is $z = 1.28$. A z-score of 1.28 is 1.28 standard deviations above the mean. Since the standard deviation is 100, that's 128 GMAT points. The cutoff is 128 points above the mean of 500, or 628. Because the program wants GMAT scores in the top 10%, the cutoff is 628. (Actually since GMAT scores are reported only in multiples of 10, you'd have to score at least a 630.)

Guided Example   Cereal Company

A cereal manufacturer has a machine that fills the boxes. Boxes are labeled "16 oz," so the company wants to have that much cereal in each box. But since no packaging process is perfect, there will be minor variations. If the machine is set at exactly 16 oz and the Normal distribution applies (or at least the distribution is roughly symmetric), then about half of the boxes will be underweight, making consumers unhappy and exposing the company to bad publicity and possible lawsuits. To prevent underweight boxes, the manufacturer has to set the mean a little higher than 16.0 oz. Based on their experience with the packaging machine, the company believes that the amount of cereal in the boxes fits a Normal distribution with a standard deviation of 0.2 oz. The manufacturer decides to set the machine to put an average of 16.3 oz in each box. Let's use that model to answer a series of questions about these cereal boxes.

Question 1: What fraction of the boxes will be underweight?

PLAN	**Setup** State the variable and the objective.	The variable is weight of cereal in a box. We want to determine what fraction of the boxes risk being underweight.
	Model Check to see if a Normal distribution is appropriate.	We have no data, so we cannot make a histogram. But we are told that the company believes the distribution of weights from the machine is Normal.
	Specify which Normal distribution to use.	We use an N(16.3, 0.2) model.
DO	**Mechanics** Make a graph of this Normal distribution. Locate the value you're interested in on the picture, label it, and shade the appropriate region.	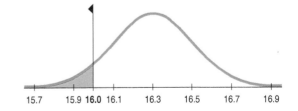

REALITY CHECK	Estimate from the picture the percentage of boxes that are underweight. (This will be useful later to check that your answer makes sense.)	(It looks like a low percentage—maybe less than 10%.) We want to know what fraction of the boxes will weigh less than 16 oz.
	Convert your cutoff value into a z-score.	$$z = \frac{y - \mu}{\sigma} = \frac{16 - 16.3}{0.2} = -1.50.$$
	Look up the area in the Normal table, or use technology.	Area $(y < 16)$ = Area $(Z < -1.50)$ = 0.0668.
REPORT	**Conclusion** State your conclusion in the context of the problem.	We estimate that approximately 6.7% of the boxes will contain less than 16 oz of cereal.

Question 2: The company's lawyers say that 6.7% is too high. They insist that no more than 4% of the boxes can be underweight. So the company needs to set the machine to put a little more cereal in each box. What mean setting do they need?

PLAN	**Setup** State the variable and the objective.	The variable is weight of cereal in a box. We want to determine a setting for the machine.
	Model Check to see if a Normal model is appropriate.	We have no data, so we cannot make a histogram. But we are told that a Normal model applies.
	Specify which Normal distribution to use. This time you are not given a value for the mean!	We don't know μ, the mean amount of cereal. The standard deviation for this machine is 0.2 oz. The model, then, is $N(\mu, 0.2)$.
REALITY CHECK	We found out earlier that setting the machine to $\mu = 16.3$ oz made 6.7% of the boxes too light. We'll need to raise the mean a bit to reduce this fraction.	We are told that no more than 4% of the boxes can be below 16 oz.
DO	**Mechanics** Make a graph of this Normal distribution. Center it at μ (since you don't know the mean) and shade the region below 16 oz.	
	Using the Normal table, a calculator, or software, find the z-score that cuts off the lowest 4%.	The z-score that has 0.04 area to the left of it is $z = -1.75$.
	Use this information to find μ. It's located 1.75 standard deviations to the right of 16.	Since 16 must be 1.75 standard deviations below the mean, we need to set the mean at $16 + 1.75 \cdot 0.2 = 16.35$.
REPORT	**Conclusion** State your conclusion in the context of the problem.	The company must set the machine to average 16.35 oz of cereal per box.

(continued)

Question 3: The company president vetoes that plan, saying the company should give away less free cereal, not more. Her goal is to set the machine no higher than 16.2 oz and still have only 4% underweight boxes. The only way to accomplish this is to reduce the standard deviation. What standard deviation must the company achieve, and what does that mean about the machine?

PLAN	Setup State the variable and the objective.	The variable is weight of cereal in a box. We want to determine the necessary standard deviation to have only 4% of boxes underweight.
	Model Check that a Normal model is appropriate.	The company believes that the weights are described by a Normal distribution.
	Specify which Normal distribution to use. This time you don't know σ.	Now we know the mean, but we don't know the standard deviation. The model is therefore $N(16.2, \sigma)$.
REALITY CHECK	We know the new standard deviation must be less than 0.2 oz.	

DO	Mechanics Make a graph of this Normal distribution. Center it at 16.2, and shade the area you're interested in. We want 4% of the area to the left of 16 oz.	
	Find the z-score that cuts off the lowest 4%.	We already know that the z-score with 4% below it is $z = -1.75$.
	Solve for σ. (Note that we need 16 to be 1.75 σ's below 16.2, so 1.75σ must be 0.2 oz. You could just start with that equation.)	$$z = \frac{y - \mu}{\sigma}$$ $$-1.75 = \frac{16 - 16.2}{\sigma}$$ $$1.75\sigma = 0.2$$ $$\sigma = 0.114.$$

REPORT	Conclusion State your conclusion in the context of the problem.	The company must get the machine to box cereal with a standard deviation of only 0.114 oz. This means the machine must be more consistent (by nearly a factor of 2) in filling the boxes.
	As we expected, the standard deviation is lower than before—actually, quite a bit lower.	

3 Normal Probability Plots

A specialized graphical display can help you to decide whether the Normal model is appropriate: the **Normal probability plot.** If the distribution of the data is roughly Normal, the plot is roughly a diagonal straight line. Deviations from a straight line indicate that the distribution is not Normal. This plot is usually able to show deviations from Normality more clearly than the corresponding histogram, but it's usually easier to understand *how* a distribution fails to be Normal by looking at its histogram. Normal probability plots are difficult to make by hand, but are provided by most statistics software.

Some data on a car's fuel efficiency provide an example of data that are nearly Normal. The overall pattern of the Normal probability plot is straight. The two trailing low values correspond to the values in the histogram that trail off the low end. They're not quite in line with the rest of the data set. The Normal probability plot shows us that they're a bit lower than we'd expect of the lowest two values in a Normal distribution.

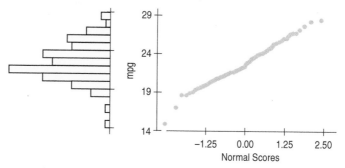

Figure 7 Histogram and Normal probability plot for gas mileage (mpg) recorded for a Nissan Maxima. The vertical axes are the same, so each dot on the probability plot would fall into the bar on the histogram immediately to its left.

By contrast, the Normal probability plot of a sample of men's *Weights* in Figure 8 from a study of lifestyle and health is far from straight. The weights are skewed to the high end, and the plot is curved. We'd conclude from these pictures that approximations using the Normal model for these data would not be very accurate.

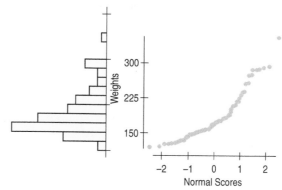

Figure 8 Histogram and Normal probability plot for men's weights. Note how a skewed distribution corresponds to a bent probability plot.

For Example   **Using a normal probability plot**

A normal probability plot of the CAPE10 prices looks like this:

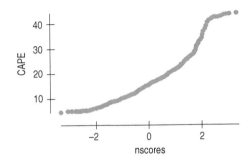

Question: What does this plot say about the distribution of the CAPE10 scores?

Answer: The bent shape of the probability plot—and in particular, the sharp bend on the right—indicates a deviation from Normality—in this case the CAPE scores in the right tail do not stretch out as far as we'd expect for a Normal model.

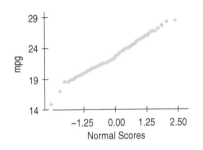

How does a normal probability plot work?

Why does the Normal probability plot work like that? We looked at 100 fuel efficiency measures for a car. The smallest of these has a z-score of -3.16. The Normal model can tell us what value to expect for the smallest z-score in a batch of 100 if a Normal model were appropriate. That turns out to be -2.58. So our first data value is smaller than we would expect from the Normal.

We can continue this and ask a similar question for each value. For example, the 14th-smallest fuel efficiency has a z-score of almost exactly -1, and that's just what we should expect (-1.1 to be exact). We can continue in this way, comparing each observed value with the value we'd expect from a Normal model. The easiest way to make the comparison, of course, is to graph it.[6] If our observed values look like a sample from a Normal model, then the probability plot stretches out in a straight line from lower left to upper right. But if our values deviate from what we'd expect, the plot will bend or have jumps in it. The values we'd expect from a Normal model are called Normal scores, or sometimes nscores. You can't easily look them up in the table, so probability plots are best made with technology and not by hand.

The best advice on using Normal probability plots is to see whether they are straight. If so, then your data look like data from a Normal model. If not, make a histogram to understand how they differ from the model.

4   The Distribution of Sums of Normals

Another reason normal models show up so often is that they have some special properties. An important one is that the sum or difference of two independent Normal random variables is also Normal.

A company manufactures small stereo systems. At the end of the production line, the stereos are packaged and prepared for shipping. Stage 1 of this process is called "packing." Workers must collect all the system components (a main unit, two speakers, a power cord, an antenna, and some wires), put each in plastic bags, and then place everything inside a protective form. The packed form then moves on to

---

[6]Sometimes the Normal probability plot switches the two axes, putting the data on the x-axis and the z-scores on the y-axis.

Stage 2, called "boxing," in which workers place the form and a packet of instructions in a cardboard box and then close, seal, and label the box for shipping.

The company says that times required for the packing stage are unimodal and symmetric and can be described by a Normal distribution with a mean of 9 minutes and standard deviation of 1.5 minutes. (See Figure 9.) The times for the boxing stage can also be modeled as Normal, with a mean of 6 minutes and standard deviation of 1 minute.

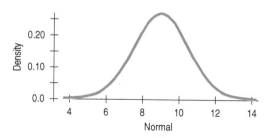

Figure 9   The Normal model for the packing stage with a mean of 9 minutes and standard deviation of 1.5 minutes.

The company is interested in the total time that it takes to get a system through both packing and boxing, so they want to model the sum of the two random variables. Fortunately, the special property that adding independent Normals yields another Normal allows us to apply our knowledge of Normal probabilities to questions about the sum or difference of independent random variables. To use this property of Normals, we'll need to check two assumptions: that the variables are Independent and that they can be modeled by the Normal distribution.

Guided Example   Packaging Stereos

Consider the company that manufactures and ships small stereo systems that we discussed previously.

If the time required to pack the stereos can be described by a Normal distribution, with a mean of 9 minutes and standard deviation of 1.5 minutes, and the times for the boxing stage can also be modeled as Normal, with a mean of 6 minutes and standard deviation of 1 minute, what is the probability that packing an order of two systems takes over 20 minutes? What percentage of the stereo systems takes longer to pack than to box?

Question 1: What is the probability that packing an order of two systems takes more than 20 minutes?

PLAN	Setup State the problem.	We want to estimate the probability that packing an order of two systems takes more than 20 minutes.
	Variables Define your random variables.	Let P_1 = time for packing the first system
		P_2 = time for packing the second system
		T = total time to pack two systems
	Write an appropriate equation for the variables you need.	$T = P_1 + P_2$

(continued)

	Think about the model assumptions.	✓ **Normal Model Assumption.** We are told that packing times are well modeled by a Normal model, and we know that the sum of two Normal random variables is also Normal.
		✓ **Independence Assumption.** There is no reason to think that the packing time for one system would affect the packing time for the next, so we can reasonably assume the two are independent.

DO

Mechanics Find the expected value. (Expected values always add.)

$$E(T) = E(P_1 + P_2)$$
$$= E(P_1) + E(P_2)$$
$$= 9 + 9 = 18 \text{ minutes}$$

Find the variance.

For sums of independent random variables, variances add. (In general, we don't need the variables to be Normal for this to be true—just independent.)

Since the times are independent,

$$Var(T) = Var(P_1 + P_2)$$
$$= Var(P_1) + Var(P_2)$$
$$= 1.5^2 + 1.5^2$$
$$Var(T) = 4.50$$
$$SD(T) = \sqrt{4.50} \approx 2.12 \text{ minutes}$$

Find the standard deviation.

Now we use the fact that both random variables follow Normal distributions to say that their sum is also Normal.

We can model the time, T, with a $N(18, 2.12)$ model.

Sketch a picture of the Normal distribution for the total time, shading the region representing over 20 minutes.

Find the z-score for 20 minutes.

$$z = \frac{20 - 18}{2.12} = 0.94$$

Use technology or a table to find the probability.

$$P(T > 20) = P(z > 0.94) = 0.1736$$

REPORT

Conclusion Interpret your result in context.

MEMO

Re: Computer Systems Packing

Using past history to build a model, we find slightly more than a 17% chance that it will take more than 20 minutes to pack an order of two stereo systems.

Question 2: What percentage of stereo systems take longer to pack than to box?

PLAN

Setup State the question.

We want to estimate the percentage of the stereo systems that takes longer to pack than to box.

Variables Define your random variables.

Let P = time for packing a system
B = time for boxing a system
D = difference in times to pack and box a system

Write an appropriate equation.

$D = P - B$

What are we trying to find? Notice that we can tell which of two quantities is greater by subtracting and asking whether the difference is positive or negative.

A system that takes longer to pack than to box will have $P > B$, and so D will be positive. We want to find $P(D > 0)$.

Remember to think about the assumptions.

✓ **Normal Model Assumption.** We are told that both random variables are well modeled by Normal distributions, and we know that the difference of two Normal random variables is also Normal.

✓ **Independence Assumption.** There is no reason to think that the packing time for a system will affect its boxing time, so we can reasonably assume the two are independent.

DO

Mechanics Find the expected value.

$$E(D) = E(P - B)$$
$$= E(P) - E(B)$$
$$= 9 - 6 = 3 \text{ minutes}$$

For the difference of independent random variables, the variance is the sum of the individual variances.

Since the times are independent,

$$Var(D) = Var(P - B)$$
$$= Var(P) + Var(B)$$
$$= 1.5^2 + 1^2$$

$$Var(D) = 3.25$$

Find the standard deviation.

$$SD(D) = \sqrt{3.25} \approx 1.80 \text{ minutes}$$

State what model you will use.

We can model D with $N(3, 1.80)$.

Sketch a picture of the Normal distribution for the difference in times and shade the region representing a difference greater than zero.

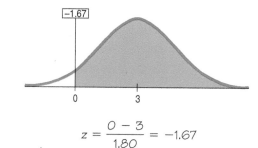

Find the z-score. Then use a table or technology to find the probability.

$$z = \frac{0 - 3}{1.80} = -1.67$$
$$P(D > 0) = P(z > -1.67) = 0.9525$$

REPORT

Conclusion Interpret your result in context.

MEMO

Re: Computer Systems Packing

In our second analysis, we found that just over 95% of all the stereo systems will require more time for packing than for boxing.

5   The Normal Approximation for the Binomial

The Normal distribution can approximate discrete events when the number of possible events is large. In particular, it is a good model for sums of independent random variables of which a Binomial random variable is a special case. Here's an example of how the Normal can be used to calculate binomial probabilities. Suppose that the Tennessee Red Cross anticipates the need for at least 1850 units of O-negative blood this year. It estimates that it will collect blood from 32,000 donors. How likely is the Tennessee Red Cross to meet its need? We could use the binomial model with $n = 32{,}000$ and $p = 0.06$. The probability of getting *exactly* 1850 units of O-negative blood from 32,000 donors is $\binom{32000}{1850} \times 0.06^{1850} \times 0.94^{30150}$. No calculator on earth can calculate 32000 choose 1850 (it has more than 100,000 digits).[7] And that's just the beginning. The problem said *at least* 1850, so we would have to calculate it again for 1851, for 1852, and all the way up to 32,000. When we're dealing with a large number of trials like this, making direct calculations of the probabilities becomes tedious (or outright impossible).

The Binomial model has mean $np = 1920$ and standard deviation $\sqrt{npq} \approx 42.48$. We can approximate its distribution with a Normal distribution using the same mean and standard deviation. Remarkably enough, that turns out to be a very good approximation. Using that mean and standard deviation, we can find the *probability:*

$$P(X \geq 1850) = P\left(z \geq \frac{1850 - 1920}{42.48}\right) \approx P(z \geq -1.65) \approx 0.95$$

There seems to be about a 95% chance that this Red Cross chapter will have enough O-negative blood.

We can't always use a Normal distribution to make estimates of Binomial probabilities. The success of the approximation depends on the sample size. Suppose we are searching for a prize in cereal boxes, where the probability of finding a prize is 20%. If we buy five boxes, the actual Binomial probabilities that we get 0, 1, 2, 3, 4, or 5 prizes are 33%, 41%, 20%, 5%, 1%, and 0.03%, respectively. The histogram just below shows that this probability model is skewed. We shouldn't try to estimate these probabilities by using a Normal model.

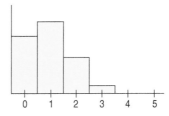

But if we open 50 boxes of this cereal and count the number of prizes we find, we'll get the histogram below. It is centered at $np = 50(0.2) = 10$ prizes, as expected, and it appears to be fairly symmetric around that center.

---

[7]If your calculator *can* find Binom(32000, 0.06), then apparently it's smart enough to use an approximation.

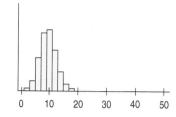

The third histogram (shown just below) shows the same distribution, still centered at the expected value of 10 prizes. It looks close to Normal for sure. With this larger sample size, it appears that a Normal distribution might be a useful approximation.

*The continuity correction

When we use a continuous model to model a set of discrete events, we may need to make an adjustment called the **continuity correction**. We approximated the Binomial distribution (50, 0.2) with a Normal distribution. But what does the Normal distribution say about the probability that $X = 10$? Every specific value in the Normal probability model has probability 0. That's not the answer we want.

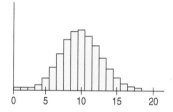

Because X is really discrete, it takes on the exact values 0, 1, 2, . . . , 50, each with positive probability. The histogram holds the secret to the correction. Look at the bin corresponding to $X = 10$ in the histogram. It goes from 9.5 to 10.5. What we really want is to find the area under the normal curve *between* 9.5 and 10.5. So when we use the Normal distribution to approximate discrete events, we go halfway to the next value on the left and/or the right. We approximate $P(X = 10)$ by finding $P(9.5 \leq X \leq 10.5)$. For a Binomial (50, 0.2), $\mu = 10$ and $\sigma = 2.83$.

$$\text{So } P(9.5 \leq X \leq 10.5) \approx P\left(\frac{9.5 - 10}{2.83} \leq z \leq \frac{10.5 - 10}{2.83}\right)$$

$$= P(-0.177 \leq z \leq 0.177)$$

$$= 0.1405$$

By comparison, the *exact* Binomial probability is 0.1398.

A Normal distribution is a close enough approximation to the Binomial only for a large enough number of trials. And what we mean by "large enough" depends on the probability of success. We'd need a larger sample if the probability of success were very low (or very high). It turns out that a Normal distribution works pretty well if we expect to see at least 10 successes and 10 failures. That is, we check the Success/Failure Condition.

Success/Failure Condition: A Binomial model is approximately Normal if we expect at least 10 successes and 10 failures:

$$np \geq 10 \text{ and } nq \geq 10.$$

Why 10? Well, actually it's 9, as revealed in the following Math Box.

> ## Math Box
>
> ### Why Check $np > 10$?
>
> It's easy to see where the magic number 10 comes from. You just need to remember how Normal models work. The problem is that a Normal model extends infinitely in both directions. But a Binomial model must have between 0 and n successes, so if we use a Normal to approximate a Binomial, we have to cut off its tails. That's not very important if the center of the Normal model is so far from 0 and n that the lost tails have only a negligible area. More than three standard deviations should do it because a Normal model has little probability past that.
>
> So the mean needs to be at least 3 standard deviations from 0 and at least 3 standard deviations from n. Let's look at the 0 end.
>
> | | |
> |---|---|
> | We require: | $\mu - 3\sigma > 0$ |
> | Or, in other words: | $\mu > 3\sigma$ |
> | For a Binomial that's: | $np > 3\sqrt{npq}$ |
> | Squaring yields: | $n^2 p^2 > 9npq$ |
> | Now simplify: | $np > 9q$ |
> | Since $q \leq 1$, we require: | $np > 9$ |
>
> For simplicity we usually demand that np (and nq for the other tail) be at least 10 to use the Normal approximation which gives the Success/Failure Condition.[8]

For Example   Using the Normal distribution

Some LCD panels have stuck or "dead" pixels that have defective transistors and are permanently unlit. If a panel has too many dead pixels, it must be rejected. A manufacturer knows that, when the production line is working correctly, the probability of rejecting a panel is .07.

Questions:

a) How many screens do they expect to reject in a day's production run of 500 screens? What is the standard deviation?

b) If they reject 40 screens today, is that a large enough number that they should be concerned that something may have gone wrong with the production line?

c) In the past week of 5 days of production, they've rejected 200 screens—an average of 40 per day. Should that raise concerns?

Answers:

a) $\mu = 0.07 \times 500 = 35$ is the expected number of rejects

$\sigma = \sqrt{npq} = \sqrt{500 \times 0.07 \times 0.93} = 5.7$

b) $P(X \geq 45) = P\left(z \geq \dfrac{40 - 35}{5.7}\right) = P(z \geq 0.877) \approx 0.29$, not an extraordinarily large number of rejects

c) Using the Normal approximation:

$\mu = 0.07 \times 2500 = 1.75$

$\sigma = \sqrt{2500 \times 0.07 \times 0.93} = 12.757$

$P(X \geq 200) = P\left(z \geq \dfrac{200 - 175}{12.757}\right) = P(z \geq 1.96) \approx 0.025$

---

[8]Looking at the final step, we see that we need $np > 9$ in the worst case, when q (or p) is near 1, making the Binomial model quite skewed. When q and p are near 0.5—for example, between 0.4 and 0.6—the Binomial model is nearly symmetric, and $np > 5$ ought to be safe enough. Although we'll always check for 10 expected successes and failures, keep in mind that for values of p near 0.5, we can be somewhat more forgiving.

6   Other Continuous Random Variables

The Normal distribution differs from the probability distributions because it doesn't specify probabilities for individual values, but rather, for intervals of values. When a random variable can take on any value in an interval, we can't model it using a discrete probability model and must use a continuous probability model instead. For any continuous random variable, the distribution of its probability can be shown with a curve. That curve is called the **probability density function (pdf),** usually denoted as $f(x)$. Technically, the curve we've been using to work with the Normal distribution is known as the Normal probability density function.

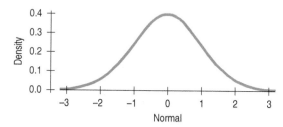

Figure 10   The standard Normal density function (a normal with mean 0 and standard deviation 1). The probability of finding a *z*-score in any interval is the area over that interval under the curve. For example, the probability that the *z*-score falls between −1 and 1 is about 68%, which can be seen approximately from the density function or found more precisely from a table or technology.

Density functions must satisfy two requirements. They must stay nonnegative for every possible value, and the total area under the curve must be exactly 1.0. This last requirement corresponds to the Probability Assignment Rule, which said that the total probability (equal to 1.0) must be assigned somewhere.

Any density function can give the probability that the random variable lies in an interval. But remember, the probability that X lies in the interval from a to b is the *area* under the density function, $f(x)$, between the values a and b and not the value $f(a)$ or $f(b)$. In general, finding that area requires calculus or numerical analysis, and is beyond the scope of this text. But for the models we'll discuss, the probabilities are found either from tables (the Normal) or simple computations (Uniform).

There are many (in fact, there are an infinite number of) possible continuous distributions, but we'll explore only three of the most commonly used to model business phenomena. In addition to the Normal distribution, we'll look at the Uniform distribution and the Exponential distribution.

How can *every* value have probability 0?

At first it may seem illogical that each value of a continuous random variable has probability 0. Let's look at the standard Normal random variable, Z. We could find (from a table, website, or computer program) that the probability that Z lies between 0 and 1 is 0.3413.

(continued)

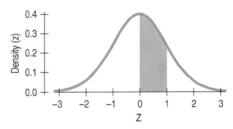

That's the area under the Normal pdf (in red) between the values 0 and 1. So, what's the probability that Z is between 0 and 1/10?

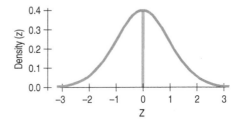

That area is only 0.0398. What is the chance then that Z will fall between 0 and 1/100? There's not much area—the probability is only 0.0040. If we kept going, the probability would keep getting smaller. The probability that Z is between 0 and 1/100,000 is less than 0.0001.

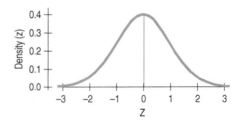

So, what's the probability that Z is *exactly* 0? Well, there's *no* area under the curve right at $x = 0$, so the probability is 0. It's only intervals that have positive probability, but that's OK. In real life we never mean exactly 0.0000000000 or any other value. If you say "exactly 164 pounds," you might really mean between 163.5 and 164.5 pounds or even between 163.99 and 164.01 pounds, but realistically not 164.000000000 . . . pounds.

The Uniform Distribution

We've already seen the discrete version of the uniform probability model. A continuous uniform shares the principle that all events should be equally likely, but with a continuous distribution we can't talk about the probability of a particular value because each value has probability zero. Instead, for a continuous random variable X, we say that the probability that X lies in any interval depends only on the length of that interval. Not surprisingly the density function of a continuous uniform random variable looks flat (see Figure 11).

The density function of a continuous uniform random variable defined on the interval a to b can be defined by the formula (see Figure 11)

$$f(x) = \begin{cases} \dfrac{1}{b-a} & if \quad a \le x \le b \\ 0 & otherwise \end{cases}$$

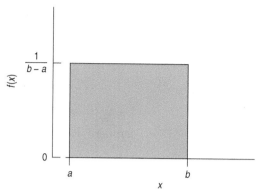

Figure 11 The density function of a continuous uniform random variable on the interval from *a* to *b*.

From Figure 11, it's easy to see that the probability that *X* lies in any interval between *a* and *b* is the same as any other interval of the same length. In fact, the probability is just the ratio of the length of the interval to the total length: $b - a$. In other words:

For values c and d (c ≤ d) both within the interval [a, b]:

$$P(c \leq X \leq d) = \frac{(d - c)}{(b - a)}$$

As an example, suppose you arrive at a bus stop and want to model how long you'll wait for the next bus. The sign says that busses arrive about every 20 minutes, but no other information is given. You might assume that the arrival is equally likely to be anywhere in the next 20 minutes, and so the density function would be

$$f(x) = \begin{cases} \dfrac{1}{20} & if \quad 0 \leq x \leq 20 \\ 0 & otherwise \end{cases}$$

and would look as shown in Figure 12.

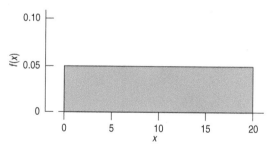

Figure 12 The density function of a continuous uniform random variable on the interval [0,20]. Notice that the mean (the balancing point) of the distribution is at 10 minutes and that the area of the box is 1.

Just as the mean of a data distribution is the balancing point of a histogram, the mean of any continuous random variable is the balancing point of the density function. Looking at Figure 12, we can see that the balancing point is halfway between the end points at 10 minutes. In general, the expected value is:

$$E(X) = \frac{a + b}{2}$$

for a uniform distribution on the interval (a, b). With $a = 0$ and $b = 20$, the expected value would be 10 minutes.

The variance and standard deviation are less intuitive:

$$Var(X) = \frac{(b - a)^2}{12}; SD(X) = \sqrt{\frac{(b - a)^2}{12}}.$$

Using these formulas, our bus wait will have an expected value of 10 minutes with a standard deviation of $\sqrt{\frac{(20 - 0)^2}{12}} = 5.77$ minutes.

Just Checking

2 As a group, the Dutch are among the tallest people in the world. The average Dutch man is 184 cm tall—just over 6 feet (and the average Dutch woman is 170.8 cm tall—just over 5′7″). If a Normal model is appropriate and the standard deviation for men is about 8 cm, what percentage of all Dutch men will be over 2 meters (6′6″) tall?

3 Suppose it takes you 20 minutes, on average, to drive to work, with a standard deviation of 2 minutes. Suppose a

Normal model is appropriate for the distributions of driving times.

a) How often will you arrive at work in less than 22 minutes?

b) How often will it take you more than 24 minutes?

c) Do you think the distribution of your driving times is unimodal and symmetric?

d) What does this say about the accuracy of your prediction? Explain.

The Exponential Model

The Poisson distribution is a good model for the arrival of, or occurrence, of events. We found, for example, the probability that x visits to our website will occur within the next minute. The exponential distribution with parameter λ can be used to model the time *between* those events. Its density function has the form:

$$f(x) = \lambda e^{-\lambda x} \ \text{for } x \geq 0 \text{ and } \lambda > 0$$

The use of the parameter λ again is not coincidental. It highlights the relationship between the exponential and the Poisson.

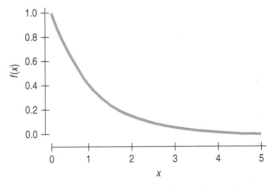

| Figure 13 The exponential density function with $\lambda = 1$.

If a discrete random variable can be modeled by a Poisson model with rate λ, then the times between events can be modeled by an exponential model with the same parameter λ. The mean of the exponential is $1/\lambda$. The inverse relationship between the two means makes intuitive sense. If λ increases and we expect *more* hits per minute, then the expected time between hits should go down. The standard deviation of an exponential random variable is $1/\lambda$.

Like any continuous random variable, probabilities of an exponential random variable can be found only through the density function. Fortunately, the area under the exponential density between any two values, s and t ($s \le t$), has a particularly easy form:

$$P(s \le X \le t) = e^{-\lambda s} - e^{-\lambda t}.$$

In particular, by setting s to be 0, we can find the probability that the waiting time will be less than t from

$$P(X \le t) = P(0 \le X \le t) = e^{-\lambda 0} - e^{-\lambda t} = 1 - e^{-\lambda t}.$$

The function $P(X \le t) = F(t)$ is called the **cumulative distribution function (cdf)** of the random variable X. If arrivals of hits to our website can be well modeled by a Poisson with $\lambda = 4$/minute, then the probability that we'll have to wait less than 20 seconds (1/3 of a minute) is $F(1/3) = P(0 \le X \le 1/3) = 1 - e^{-4/3} = 0.736$. That seems about right. Arrivals are coming about every 15 seconds on average, so we shouldn't be surprised that nearly 75% of the time we won't have to wait more than 20 seconds for the next hit.

What Can Go Wrong?

- **Probability models are still just models.** Models can be useful, but they are not reality. Think about the assumptions behind your models. Question probabilities as you would data.

- **Don't assume everything's Normal.** Just because a random variable is continuous or you happen to know a mean and standard deviation doesn't mean that a Normal model will be useful. You must think about whether the **Normality Assumption** is justified. Using a Normal model when it really does not apply will lead to wrong answers and misleading conclusions.

  A sample of CEOs has a mean total compensation of $10,307,311.87 with a standard deviation of $17,964,615.16. Using the Normal model rule, we should expect about 68% of the CEOs to have compensations between −$7,657,303.29 and $28,271,927.03. In fact, more than 90% of the CEOs have annual compensations in this range. What went wrong? The distribution is skewed, not symmetric. Using the 68–95–99.7 Rule for data like these will lead to silly results.

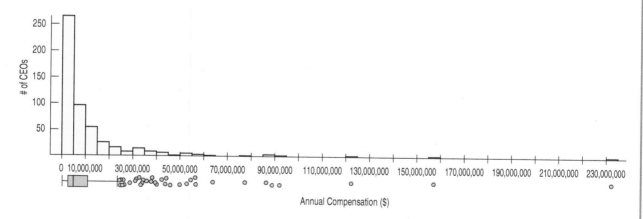

- **Don't use the Normal approximation with small *n*.** To use a Normal approximation in place of a Binomial model, there must be at least 10 expected successes and 10 expected failures.

Ethics in Action

Although e-government services are available online, many Americans, especially those who are older, prefer to deal with government agencies in person. For this reason, the U.S. Social Security Administration (SSA) has local offices distributed across the country. Pat Mennoza is the office manager for one of the larger SSA offices in Phoenix. Since the initiation of the SSA website, his staff has been severely reduced. Yet, because of the number of retirees in the area, his office is one of the busiest. Although there have been no formal complaints, Pat expects that customer waiting times have increased. He decides to keep track of customer wait times for a one-month period in the hopes of making a case for hiring additional staff. He finds that the average wait time is 5 minutes with a standard deviation of 6 minutes. He reasons that 50% of customers who visit his office wait longer than 5 minutes for service. The target wait time is 10 minutes or less. Applying the Normal probability model, Pat finds that more than 20% of customers will have to wait longer than 10 minutes! He has uncovered what he suspected. His next step is to request additional staff based on his findings.

ETHICAL ISSUE *Waiting times are generally skewed and therefore not usually modeled using the Normal distribution. Pat should have checked the data to see if a Normal model was appropriate. Using the Normal for data that are highly skewed to the right will inflate the probability a customer will have to wait longer than 10 minutes. Related to Item A, ASA Ethical Guidelines.*

ETHICAL SOLUTION *Check reasonableness of applying the Normal probability model.*

What Have We Learned?

Learning Objectives

■ Recognize normally distributed data by making a histogram and checking whether it is unimodal, symmetric, and bell-shaped, or by making a normal probability plot using technology and checking whether the plot is roughly a straight line.

• The Normal model is a distribution that will be important for much of the rest of this course.

• Before using a Normal model, we should check that our data are plausibly from a normally distributed population.

• A Normal probability plot provides evidence that the data are Normally distributed if it is linear.

■ Understand how to use the Normal model to judge whether a value is extreme.

• Standardize values to make z-scores and obtain a standard scale. Then refer to a standard Normal distribution.

• Use the 68–95–99.7 Rule as a rule-of-thumb to judge whether a value is extreme.

■ Know how to refer to tables or technology to find the probability of a value randomly selected from a Normal model falling in any interval.

• Know how to perform calculations about Normally distributed values and probabilities.

■ Recognize when independent random Normal quantities are being added or subtracted.

• The sum or difference will also follow a Normal model

• The *variance* of the sum or difference will be the sum of the individual variances.

• The mean of the sum or difference will be the sum or difference, respectively, of the means.

■ Recognize when other continuous probability distributions are appropriate models.

Terms	
68–95–99.7 Rule (or Empirical Rule)	In a Normal model, 68% of values fall within one standard deviation of the mean, 95% fall within two standard deviations of the mean, and 99.7% fall within three standard deviations of the mean. This is also approximately true for most unimodal, symmetric distributions.
Cumulative distribution function (cdf)	A function for a continuous probability model that gives the probability of all values below a given value.
Exponential Distribution	A continuous distribution appropriate for modeling the times between events whose occurrences follow a Poisson model.
Normal Distribution	A unimodal, symmetric, "bell-shaped" distribution that appears throughout Statistics.
Normal probability plot	A display to help assess whether a distribution of data is approximately Normal. If the plot is nearly straight, the data satisfy the Nearly Normal Condition.
Probability Density Function (pdf)	A function for any continuous probability model that gives the probability of a random value falling between any two values as the area under the pdf between those two values.
Standard Normal model or Standard Normal distribution	A Normal model, $N(\mu, \sigma)$ with mean $\mu = 0$ and standard deviation $\sigma = 1$.
Uniform Distribution	A continuous distribution that assigns a probability to any range of values (between 0 and 1) proportional to the difference between the values.

Brief CASE

The CAPE10 index is based on the Price/Earnings (P/E) ratios of stocks. We can examine the P/E ratios without applying the smoothing techniques used to find the CAPE10. The file **CAPE10** on www.pearsonhighered.com/sharpe holds the data, giving dates, CAPE10 values, and P/E values.

Examine the P/E values. Would you judge that a Normal model would be appropriate for those values from the 1880s through the 1980s? Explain (and show the plots you made.)

Now consider the more recent P/E values in this context. Do you think they have been extreme? Explain.

Technology Help: Making Normal Probability Plots

The best way to tell whether your data can be modeled well by a Normal model is to make a picture or two. We've already talked about making histograms. Normal probability plots are almost never made by hand because the values of the Normal scores are tricky to find. But most statistics software make Normal plots, though various packages call the same plot by different names and array the information differently.

EXCEL   *XL*STAT

Excel offers a "Normal probability plot" as part of the Regression command in the Data Analysis extension, but (as of this writing) it is not a correct Normal probability plot and should not be used.

JMP

To make a "Normal Quantile Plot" in JMP,

- Make a histogram using **Distributions** from the **Analyze** menu.
- Click on the drop-down menu next to the variable name.
- Choose **Normal Quantile Plot** from the drop-down menu.
- JMP opens the plot next to the histogram.

Comments

JMP places the ordered data on the vertical axis and the Normal scores on the horizontal axis. The vertical axis aligns with the histogram's axis, a useful feature.

MINITAB

To make a "Normal Probability Plot" in MINITAB,

- Choose **Probability Plot** from the **Graph** menu.
- Select "Single" for the type of plot. Click **OK.**
- Enter the name of the variable in the "Graph variables" box. Click **OK.**

Comments

MINITAB places the ordered data on the horizontal axis and the Normal scores on the vertical axis.

SPSS

To make a Normal "P-P plot" in SPSS,

- Choose **P-P** from the **Graphs** menu.
- Select the variable to be displayed in the source list.
- Click the arrow button to move the variable into the target list.
- Click the **OK** button.

Comments

SPSS places the ordered data on the horizontal axis and the Normal scores on the vertical axis. You may safely ignore the options in the P-P dialog.

Exercises

SECTION 1

1. An incoming MBA student took placement exams in economics and mathematics. In economics, she scored 82 and in math 86. The overall results on the economics exam had a mean of 72 and a standard deviation of 8, while the mean math score was 68, with a standard deviation of 12. On which exam did she do better compared with the other students?

2. The first Statistics exam had a mean of 65 and a standard deviation of 10 points; the second had a mean of 80 and a standard deviation of 5 points. Derrick scored an 80 on both tests. Julie scored a 70 on the first test and a 90 on the second. They both totaled 160 points on the two exams, but Julie claims that her total is better. Explain.

3. Your company's Human Resources department administers a test of "Executive Aptitude." They report test grades as z-scores, and you got a score of 2.20. What does this mean?

4. After examining a child at his 2-year checkup, the boy's pediatrician said that the z-score for his height relative to American 2-year-olds was -1.88. Write a sentence to explain to the parents what that means.

5. Your company will admit to the executive training program only people who score in the top 3% on the executive aptitude test discussed in Exercise 1.

a) With your z-score of 2.20, did you make the cut?
b) What do you need to assume about test scores to find your answer in part a?

6. The pediatrician in Exercise 4 explains to the parents that the most extreme 5% of cases often require special treatment or attention.

a) Does this child fall into that group?
b) What do you need to assume about the heights of 2-year-olds to find your answer to part a?

SECTION 2

7. The Environmental Protection Agency (EPA) fuel economy estimates for automobiles suggest a mean of 24.8 mpg and a standard deviation of 6.2 mpg for highway driving. Assume that a Normal model can be applied.

a) Draw the model for auto fuel economy. Clearly label it, showing what the 68–95–99.7 Rule predicts about miles per gallon.
b) In what interval would you expect the central 68% of autos to be found?
c) About what percent of autos should get more than 31 mpg?
d) About what percent of cars should get between 31 and 37.2 mpg?
e) Describe the gas mileage of the worst 2.5% of all cars.

8. Some IQ tests are standardized to a Normal model with a mean of 100 and a standard deviation of 16.

a) Draw the model for these IQ scores. Clearly label it, showing what the 68–95–99.7 Rule predicts about the scores.
b) In what interval would you expect the central 95% of IQ scores to be found?
c) About what percent of people should have IQ scores above 116?
d) About what percent of people should have IQ scores between 68 and 84?
e) About what percent of people should have IQ scores above 132?

9. What percent of a standard Normal model is found in each region? Be sure to draw a picture first.

a) $z > 1.5$
b) $z < 2.25$
c) $-1 < z < 1.15$
d) $|z| > 0.5$

10. What percent of a standard Normal model is found in each region? Draw a picture first.

a) $z > -2.05$
b) $z < -0.33$
c) $1.2 < z < 1.8$
d) $|z| < 1.28$

11. In a standard Normal model, what value(s) of z cut(s) off the region described? Don't forget to draw a picture.

a) the highest 20%
b) the highest 75%
c) the lowest 3%
d) the middle 90%

12. In a standard Normal model, what value(s) of z cut(s) off the region described? Remember to draw a picture first.

a) the lowest 12%
b) the highest 30%
c) the highest 7%
d) the middle 50%

SECTION 3

13. Speeds of cars were measured as they passed one point on a road to study whether traffic speed controls were needed. Here's a histogram and normal probability plot of the measured speeds. Is a Normal model appropriate for these data? Explain.

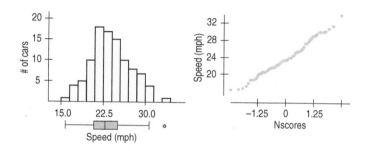

14. Has the Consumer Price Index (CPI) fluctuated around its mean according to a Normal model? Here are some displays. Is a Normal model appropriate for these data? Explain.

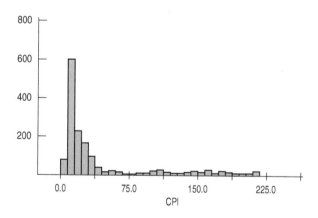

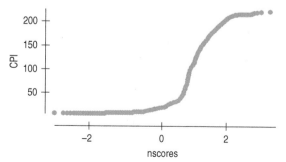

SECTION 4

15. For a new type of tire, a NASCAR team found the average distance a set of tires would run during a race is 168 miles, with a standard deviation of 14 miles. Assume that tire mileage is independent and follows a Normal model.

a) If the team plans to change tires twice during a 500-mile race, what is the expected value and standard deviation of miles remaining after two changes?

b) What is the probability they won't have to change tires a third time before the end of a 500-mile race?

16. In the 4 × 100 medley relay event, four swimmers swim 100 yards, each using a different stroke. A college team preparing for the conference championship looks at the times their swimmers have posted and creates a model based on the following assumptions:

- The swimmers' performances are independent.
- Each swimmer's times follow a Normal model.
- The means and standard deviations of the times (in seconds) are as shown here.

Swimmer	Mean	SD
1 (backstroke)	50.72	0.24
2 (breaststroke)	55.51	0.22
3 (butterfly)	49.43	0.25
4 (freestyle)	44.91	0.21

a) What are the mean and standard deviation for the relay team's total time in this event?

b) The team's best time so far this season was 3:19.48. (That's 199.48 seconds.) What is the probability that they will beat that time in the next event?

SECTION 5

17. Because many passengers who make reservations do not show up, airlines often overbook flights (sell more tickets than there are seats). A Boeing 767-400ER holds 245 passengers. If the airline believes the rate of passenger no-shows is 5% and sells 255 tickets, is it likely they will not have enough seats and someone will get bumped?

a) Use the Normal model to approximate the Binomial to determine the probability of at least 246 passengers showing up.

b) Should the airline change the number of tickets they sell for this flight? Explain.

18. Shortly after the introduction of the Belgian euro coin, newspapers around the world published articles claiming the coin is biased. The stories were based on reports that someone had spun the coin 250 times and gotten 140 heads—that's 56% heads.

a) Use the Normal model to approximate the Binomial to determine the probability of spinning a fair coin 250 times and getting at least 140 heads.

b) Do you think this is evidence that spinning a Belgian euro is unfair? Would you be willing to use it at the beginning of a sports event? Explain.

SECTION 6

19. A cable provider wants to contact customers in a particular telephone exchange to see how satisfied they are with the new digital TV service the company has provided. All numbers are in the 452 exchange, so there are 10,000 possible numbers from 452-0000 to 452-9999. If they select the numbers with equal probability:

a) What distribution would they use to model the selection?

b) The new business "incubator" was assigned the 200 numbers between 452-2500 and 452-2699, but these businesses don't subscribe to digital TV. What is the probability that the randomly selected number will be for an incubator business?

c) Numbers above 9000 were only released for domestic use last year, so they went to newly constructed residences. What is the probability that a randomly selected number will be one of these?

20. In an effort to check the quality of their cell phones, a manufacturing manager decides to take a random sample of 10 cell phones from yesterday's production run, which produced cell phones with serial numbers ranging (according to when they were produced) from 43005000 to 43005999. If each of the 1000 phones is equally likely to be selected:

a) What distribution would they use to model the selection?

b) What is the probability that a randomly selected cell phone will be one of the last 100 to be produced?

c) What is the probability that the first cell phone selected is either from the last 200 to be produced or from the first 50 to be produced?

CHAPTER EXERCISES

For Exercises 21–28, use the 68–95–99.7 Rule to approximate the probabilities rather than using technology to find the values more precisely. Answers given for probabilities or percentages from Exercise 29 and on assume that a calculator or software has been used. Answers found from using Z-tables may vary slightly.

T 21. Mutual fund returns. In the last quarter of 2007, a group of 64 mutual funds had a mean return of 2.4% with a standard deviation of 5.6%. If a Normal model can be used to model them, what percent of the funds would you expect to be in each region?

Be sure to draw a picture first.

a) Returns of 8.0% or more

b) Returns of 2.4% or less

c) Returns between −8.8% and 13.6%

d) Returns of more than 19.2%

22. Human resource testing. Although controversial and the subject of some recent law suits (e.g., *Satchell et al. vs. FedEx Express*), some human resource departments administer standard IQ tests to all employees. The Stanford-Binet test scores are well modeled by a Normal model with mean 100 and standard deviation 16. If the applicant pool is well modeled by this distribution, a randomly selected applicant would have what probability of scoring in the following regions?

a) 100 or below
b) Above 148
c) Between 84 and 116
d) Above 132

23. Mutual funds, again. From the 64 mutual funds in Exercise 21 with quarterly returns that are well modeled by a Normal model with a mean of 2.4% and a standard deviation of 5.6%, find the cutoff return value(s) that would separate the

a) highest 50%.
b) highest 16%.
c) lowest 2.5%.
d) middle 68%.

24. Human resource testing, again. For the IQ test administered by human resources and discussed in Exercise 22, what cutoff value would separate the

a) lowest 0.15% of all applicants?
b) lowest 16%?
c) middle 95%?
d) highest 2.5%?

25. Currency exchange rates. The daily exchange rates for the five-year period 2003 to 2008 between the euro (EUR) and the British pound (GBP) are well modeled by a Normal distribution with mean 1.459 euros (to pounds) and standard deviation 0.033 euros. Given this model, what is the probability that on a randomly selected day during this period, the pound was worth

a) less than 1.459 euros?
b) more than 1.492 euros?
c) less than 1.393 euros?
d) Which would be more unusual, a day on which the pound was worth less than 1.410 euros or more than 1.542 euros?

26. Stock prices. For the 900 trading days from January 2003 through July 2006, the daily closing price of IBM stock (in $) is well modeled by a Normal model with mean $85.60 and standard deviation $6.20. According to this model, what is the probability that on a randomly selected day in this period the stock price closed

a) above $91.80?
b) below $98.00?

c) between $73.20 and $98.00?
d) Which would be more unusual, a day on which the stock price closed above $93 or below $70?

27. Currency exchange rates, again. For the model of the EUR/GBP exchange rate discussed in Exercise 25, what would the cutoff rates be that would separate the

a) highest 16% of EUR/GBP rates?
b) lowest 50%?
c) middle 95%?
d) lowest 2.5%?

28. Stock prices, again. According to the model in Exercise 26, what cutoff value of price would separate the

a) lowest 16% of the days?
b) highest 0.15%?
c) middle 68%?
d) highest 50%?

29. Mutual fund probabilities. According to the Normal model $N(0.024, 0.056)$ describing mutual fund returns in the 4th quarter of 2007 in Exercise 21, what percent of this group of funds would you expect to have return

a) over 6.8%?
b) between 0% and 7.6%?
c) more than 1%?
d) less than 0%?

30. Normal IQs. Based on the Normal model $N(100, 16)$ describing IQ scores from Exercise 22, what percent of applicants would you expect to have scores

a) over 80?
b) under 90?
c) between 112 and 132?
d) over 125?

31. Mutual funds, once more. Based on the model $N(0.024, 0.056)$ for quarterly returns from Exercise 21, what are the cutoff values for the

a) highest 10% of these funds?
b) lowest 20%?
c) middle 40%?
d) highest 80%?

32. More IQs. In the Normal model $N(100, 16)$ for IQ scores from Exercise 22, what cutoff value bounds the

a) highest 5% of all IQs?
b) lowest 30% of the IQs?
c) middle 80% of the IQs?
d) lowest 90% of all IQs?

33. Mutual funds, finis. Consider the Normal model $N(0.024, 0.056)$ for returns of mutual funds in Exercise 21 one last time.

a) What value represents the 40th percentile of these returns?
b) What value represents the 99th percentile?
c) What's the IQR of the quarterly returns for this group of funds?

34. IQs, finis. Consider the IQ model $N(100, 16)$ one last time.

a) What IQ represents the 15th percentile?
b) What IQ represents the 98th percentile?
c) What's the IQR of the IQs?

35. Parameters. Every Normal model is defined by its parameters, the mean and the standard deviation. For each model described here, find the missing parameter. As always, start by drawing a picture.

a) $\mu = 20$, 45% above 30; $\sigma = ?$
b) $\mu = 88$, 2% below 50; $\sigma = ?$
c) $\sigma = 5$, 80% below 100; $\mu = ?$
d) $\sigma = 15.6$, 10% above 17.2; $\mu = ?$

36. Parameters, again. Every Normal model is defined by its parameters, the mean and the standard deviation. For each model described here, find the missing parameter. Don't forget to draw a picture.

a) $\mu = 1250$, 35% below 1200; $\sigma = ?$
b) $\mu = 0.64$, 12% above 0.70; $\sigma = ?$
c) $\sigma = 0.5$, 90% above 10.0; $\mu = ?$
d) $\sigma = 220$, 3% below 202; $\mu = ?$

37. SAT or ACT? Each year thousands of high school students take either the SAT or ACT, standardized tests used in the college admissions process. Combined SAT scores can go as high as 1600, while the maximum ACT composite score is 36. Since the two exams use very different scales, comparisons of performance are difficult. (A convenient rule of thumb is $SAT = 40 \times ACT + 150$; that is, multiply an ACT score by 40 and add 150 points to estimate the equivalent SAT score.) Assume that one year the combined SAT can be modeled by $N(1000, 200)$ and the ACT can be modeled by $N(27, 3)$. If an applicant to a university has taken the SAT and scored 1260 and another student has taken the ACT and scored 33, compare these students scores using z-values. Which one has a higher relative score? Explain.

38. Economics. Anna, a business major, took final exams in both Microeconomics and Macroeconomics and scored 83 on both. Her roommate Megan, also taking both courses, scored 77 on the Micro exam and 95 on the Macro exam. Overall, student scores on the Micro exam had a mean of 81 and a standard deviation of 5, and the Macro scores had a mean of 74 and a standard deviation of 15. Which student's overall performance was better? Explain.

39. Claims. Two companies make batteries for cell phone manufacturers. One company claims a mean life span of 2 years, while the other company claims a mean life span of 2.5 years (assuming average use of minutes/month for the cell phone).

a) Explain why you would also like to know the standard deviations of the battery life spans before deciding which brand to buy.
b) Suppose those standard deviations are 1.5 months for the first company and 9 months for the second company. Does this change your opinion of the batteries? Explain.

40. Car speeds. The police department of a major city needs to update its budget. For this purpose, they need to understand the variation in their fines collected from motorists for speeding. As a sample, they recorded the speeds of cars driving past a location with a 20 mph speed limit, a place that in the past has been known for producing fines. The mean of 100 readings was 23.84 mph, with a standard deviation of 3.56 mph. (The police actually recorded every car for a two-month period. These are 100 representative readings.)

a) How many standard deviations from the mean would a car going the speed limit be?
b) Which would be more unusual, a car traveling 34 mph or one going 10 mph?

41. CEOs. A business publication recently released a study on the total number of years of experience in industry among CEOs. The mean is provided in the article, but not the standard deviation. Is the standard deviation most likely to be 6 months, 6 years, or 16 years? Explain which standard deviation is correct and why.

42. Stocks. A newsletter for investors recently reported that the average stock price for a blue chip stock over the past 12 months was $72. No standard deviation was given. Is the standard deviation more likely to be $6, $16, or $60? Explain.

43. Web visitors. A website manager has noticed that during the evening hours, about 3 people per minute check out from their shopping cart and make an online purchase. She believes that each purchase is independent of the others.

a) What model might you suggest to model the number of purchases per minute?
b) What model would you use to model the time between events?
c) What is the mean time between purchases?
d) What is the probability that the time to the next purchase will be between 1 and 2 minutes?

44. Monitoring quality. A cell phone manufacturer samples cell phones from the assembly to test. She noticed that the number of faulty cell phones in a production run of cell phones is usually small and that the quality of one day's run seems to have no bearing on the next day.

a) What model might you use to model the number of faulty cell phones produced in one day?

She wants to model the time between the events of producing a faulty phone. The mean number of defective cell phones is 2 per day.

b) What model would you use to model the time between events?

c) What would the probability be that the time to the next failure is 1 day or less?

d) What is the mean time between failures?

45. Lefties. A lecture hall has 200 seats with folding arm tablets, 30 of which are designed for left-handers. The typical size of classes that meet there is 188, and we can assume that about 13% of students are left-handed. Use a Normal approximation to find the probability that a right-handed student in one of these classes is forced to use a lefty arm tablet.

46. Seatbelts. Police estimate that 80% of drivers wear their seatbelts. They set up a safety roadblock, stopping cars to check for seatbelt use. If they stop 120 cars, what's the probability they find at least 20 drivers not wearing their seatbelt? Use a Normal approximation.

47. Rickets. Vitamin D is essential for strong, healthy bones. Although the bone disease rickets was largely eliminated in England during the 1950s, some people there are concerned that this generation of children is at increased risk because they are more likely to watch TV or play computer games than spend time outdoors. Recent research indicated that about 20% of British children are deficient in vitamin D. A company that sells vitamin D supplements tests 320 elementary school children in one area of the country. Use a Normal approximation to find the probability that no more than 50 of them have vitamin D deficiency.

48. Tennis. A tennis player has taken a special course to improve her serving. She thinks that individual serves are independent of each other. She has been able to make a successful first serve 70% of the time. Use a Normal approximation to find the probability she'll make at least 65 of her first serves out of the 80 she serves in her next match if her success percentage has not changed.

49. Low job satisfaction. Suppose that job satisfaction scores can be modeled with $N(100, 12)$. Human resource departments of corporations are generally concerned if the job satisfaction drops below a certain score. What score would you consider to be unusually low? Explain.

50. Low return. Exercise 21 proposes modeling quarterly returns of a group of mutual funds with $N(0.024, 0.056)$. The manager of this group of funds would like to flag any fund whose return is unusually low for a quarter. What level of return would you consider to be unusually low? Explain.

51. Management survey. A survey of 200 middle managers showed a distribution of the number of hours of exercise they participated in per week with a mean of 3.66 hours and a standard deviation of 4.93 hours.

a) According to the Normal model, what percent of managers will exercise fewer than one standard deviation below the mean number of hours?

b) For these data, what does that mean? Explain.

c) Explain the problem in using the Normal model for these data.

52. Customer database. A large philanthropic organization keeps records on the people who have contributed to their cause. In addition to keeping records of past giving, the organization buys demographic data on neighborhoods from the U.S. Census Bureau. Eighteen of these variables concern the ethnicity of the neighborhood of the donor. Here is a histogram and summary statistics for the percentage of whites in the neighborhoods of 500 donors.

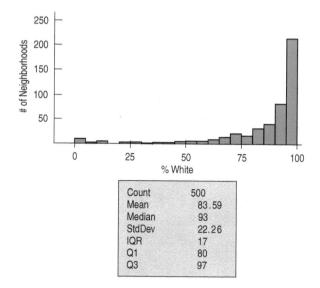

Count	500
Mean	83.59
Median	93
StdDev	22.26
IQR	17
Q1	80
Q3	97

a) Which is a better summary of the percentage of white residents in the neighborhoods, the mean or the median? Explain.

b) Which is a better summary of the spread, the IQR or the standard deviation? Explain.

c) From a Normal model, about what percentage of neighborhoods should have a percent white residents within one standard deviation of the mean?

d) What percentage of neighborhoods actually have a percent white within one standard deviation of the mean?

e) Explain the problem in using the Normal model for these data.

53. Drug company. Manufacturing and selling drugs that claim to reduce an individual's cholesterol level is big business. A company would like to market their drug to women if their cholesterol is in the top 15%. Assume the cholesterol levels of adult American women can be described by a Normal model with a mean of 188 mg/dL and a standard deviation of 24.

a) Draw and label the Normal model.
b) What percent of adult women do you expect to have cholesterol levels over 200 mg/dL?
c) What percent of adult women do you expect to have cholesterol levels between 150 and 170 mg/dL?
d) Estimate the interquartile range of the cholesterol levels.
e) Above what value are the highest 15% of women's cholesterol levels?

54. Tire company. A tire manufacturer believes that the tread life of its snow tires can be described by a Normal model with a mean of 32,000 miles and a standard deviation of 2500 miles.

a) If you buy a set of these tires, would it be reasonable for you to hope that they'll last 40,000 miles? Explain.
b) Approximately what fraction of these tires can be expected to last less than 30,000 miles?
c) Approximately what fraction of these tires can be expected to last between 30,000 and 35,000 miles?
d) Estimate the IQR for these data.
e) In planning a marketing strategy, a local tire dealer wants to offer a refund to any customer whose tires fail to last a certain number of miles. However, the dealer does not want to take too big a risk. If the dealer is willing to give refunds to no more than 1 of every 25 customers, for what mileage can he guarantee these tires to last?

Just Checking Answers

1 a) On the first test, the mean is 88 and the SD is 4, so $z = (90 - 88)/4 = 0.5$. On the second test, the mean is 75 and the SD is 5, so $z = (80 - 75)/5 = 1.0$. The first test has the lower z-score, so it is the one that will be dropped.

   b) The second test is 1 standard deviation above the mean, farther away than the first test, so it's the better score relative to the class.

2 The mean is 184 centimeters, with a standard deviation of 8 centimeters. 2 meters is 200 centimeters, which is 2 standard deviations above the mean. We expect 5% of the men to be more than 2 standard deviations below or above the mean, so half of those, 2.5%, are likely to be above 2 meters.

3 a) We know that 68% of the time we'll be within 1 standard deviation (2 min) of 20. So 32% of the time we'll arrive in less than 18 or more than 22 minutes. Half of those times (16%) will be greater than 22 minutes, so 84% will be less than 22 minutes.

   b) 24 minutes is 2 standard deviations above the mean. Because of the 95% rule, we know 2.5% of the times will be more than 24 minutes.

   c) Traffic incidents may occasionally increase the time it takes to get to school, so the driving times may be skewed to the right, and there may be outliers.

   d) If so, the Normal model would not be appropriate and the percentages we predict would not be accurate.

Answers

SECTION EXERCISE ANSWERS

1. In economics she scored 1.25 standard deviations above the mean. On the math exam she scored 1.50 standard deviations above the mean, so she did "better" on the math exam.

3. You scored 2.2 standard deviations above the mean.

5. a) According to the 68–95–99.7 Rule, only 5% of the distribution is beyond 2 standard deviations from the mean, so only 2.5% is more than 2 standard deviations above the mean. So less than 3% of the distribution is above a z-score of 2.20. You qualify.

   b) You need to assume that the distribution is unimodal and symmetric for the 68–95–99.7 Rule to apply.

7. a)

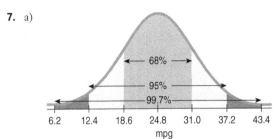

   b) 18.6 to 31.0 mpg
   c) 16%
   d) 13.5%
   e) less than 12.4 mpg

9. a) 6.68%
b) 98.78%
c) 71.63%
d) 61.71%

11. a) 0.842
b) −0.675
c) −1.881
d) −1.645 to 1.645

13. Yes. The histogram is unimodal and symmetric and the Normal probability plot is straight.

15. a) $\mu = E(\text{miles remaining}) = 164$ miles
$\sigma = SD(\text{miles remaining}) \approx 19.799$ miles
b) 0.580

17. a) 0.141 (0.175 with continuity correction)
b) Answers may vary. That's a fairly high proportion, but the decision depends on the relative costs of not selling seats and bumping passengers.

19. a) A uniform; all numbers should be equally likely to be selected.
b) 0.02
c) 0.10

CHAPTER EXERCISE ANSWERS

21. a) 16%
b) 50%
c) 95%
d) 0.15%

23. a) 2.4%
b) 8.0%
c) −8.8%
d) $(-3.2\% < x < 8.0\%)$

25. a) 50%
b) 16%
c) 2.5%
d) More than 1.542 is more unusual.

27. a) $x > 1.492$
b) $x < 1.459$
c) $(1.393 < x < 1.525)$
d) $x < 1.393$

29. a) 21.6% (using technology).
b) 48.9%
c) 59.9%
d) 33.4%

31. a) $x > 9.58\%$
b) $x < -2.31\%$
c) $(-0.54\% < x < 5.34\%)$
d) $x > -2.31\%$

33. a) 0.98%
b) 15.4%
c) 7.56%

35. a) 79.58
b) 18.50

c) 95.79
d) −2.79

37. $z_{\text{SAT}} = 1.30$; $z_{\text{ACT}} = 2$. The ACT score is the better score because it is farther above the mean in standard deviation units than the SAT score.

39. a) To know about their consistency and how long they might last. Standard deviation measures variability, which translates to consistency in everyday use. A type of battery with a small standard deviation would be more likely to have life spans close to their mean life span than a type of battery with a larger standard deviation.
b) The second company's batteries have a higher mean life span, but a larger standard deviation, so they have more variability. The decision is not clear-cut. The first company's batteries are not likely to fail in less than 21 months, but that wouldn't be surprising for the second company. But the second company's batteries could easily last longer than 39 months—a span very unlikely for the first company.

41. CEOs can have between 0 and maybe 40 (or possibly 50) year's experience. A standard deviation of 1/2 year is impossible because many CEOs would be 10 or 20 SDs away from the mean, whatever it is. An SD of 16 years would mean that 2 SDs on either side of the mean is plus or minus 32, for a range of 64 years. That's too high. So, the SD must be 6 years.

43. a) The Poisson model
b) The exponential model
c) 1/3 minutes
d) 0.0473

45. 0.053

47. 0.025

49. Any Job Satisfaction score more than 2 standard deviations below the mean or less than $100 - 2(12) = 76$ might be considered unusually low. We would expect to find someone with a Job Satisfaction score less than $100 - 3(12) = 64$ very rarely.

51. a) About 16%
b) One standard deviation below the mean is −1.27 hours, which is impossible.
c) Because the standard deviation is larger than the mean, the distribution is strongly skewed to the right, not symmetric.

53. a)

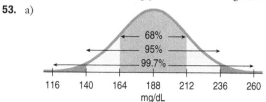

b) 30.85%
c) 17.00%
d) IQR = Q3 − Q1 = 32.38
e) Above 212.87 points.

Sampling Distributions

Marketing Credit Cards: The MBNA Story

When Delaware substantially raised its interest rate ceiling in 1981, banks and other lending institutions rushed to establish corporate headquarters there. One of these was the Maryland Bank National Association, which established a credit card branch in Delaware using the acronym MBNA. Starting in 1982 with 250 employees in a vacant supermarket in Ogletown, Delaware, MBNA grew explosively in the next two decades.

One of the reasons for this growth was MBNA's use of affinity groups—issuing cards endorsed by alumni associations, sports teams, interest groups, and labor unions, among others. MBNA sold the idea to these groups by letting them share a small percentage of the profit. By 2006, MBNA had become Delaware's largest private employer. At its peak, MBNA had more than 50 million cardholders and had outstanding credit card loans of $82.1 billion, making MBNA the third-largest U.S. credit card bank.

From Chapter 10 of *Business Statistics*, Second Edition, Norean R. Sharpe, Richard D. De Veaux, Paul F. Velleman.

"In American corporate history, I doubt there are many companies that burned as brightly, for such a short period of time, as MBNA," said Rep. Mike Castle, R-Del.[1] MBNA was bought by Bank of America in 2005 for $35 billion. Bank of America kept the brand briefly before issuing all cards under its own name in 2007.

Unlike the early days of the credit card industry when MBNA established itself, the environment today is intensely competitive, with companies constantly looking for ways to attract new customers and to maximize the profitability of the customers they already have. Many of the large companies have millions of customers, so instead of trying out a new idea with all their customers, they almost always conduct a pilot study or trial first, conducting a survey or an experiment on a sample of their customers.

Credit card companies make money on their cards in three ways: they earn a percentage of every transaction, they charge interest on balances that are not paid in full, and they collect fees (yearly fees, late fees, etc.). To generate all three types of revenue, the marketing departments of credit card banks constantly seek ways to encourage customers to increase the use of their cards.

A marketing specialist at one company had an idea of offering double air miles to their customers with an airline-affiliated card if they increased their spending by at least $800 in the month following the offer. To forecast the cost and revenue of the offer, the finance department needed to know what percent of customers would actually qualify for the double miles. The marketer decided to send the offer to a random sample of 1000 customers to find out. In that sample, she found that 211 (21.1%) of the cardholders increased their spending by more than the required $800. But, another analyst drew a different sample of 1000 customers of whom 202 (20.2%) of the cardholders exceeded $800.

The two samples don't agree. We know that observations vary, but how much variability among samples should we expect to see?

Why do sample proportions vary at all? How can two samples of the same population measuring the same quantity get different results? The answer is fundamental to statistical inference. Each proportion is based on a *different* sample of cardholders. The proportions vary from sample to sample because the samples are comprised of different people.

WHO	Cardholders of a bank's credit card
WHAT	Whether cardholders increased their spending by at least $800 in the subsequent month
WHEN	February 2008
WHERE	United States
WHY	To predict costs and benefits of a program offer

1 The Distribution of Sample Proportions

We'd like to know how much proportions can vary from sample to sample. We've talked about *Plan*, *Do*, and *Report*, but to learn more about the variability, we have to add *Imagine*. When we sample, we see only the results from the actual sample that we draw, but we can *imagine* what we might have seen had we drawn *all* other possible random samples. What would the histogram of all those sample proportions look like?

If we could take many random samples of 1000 cardholders, we would find the proportion of each sample who spent more than $800 and collect all of those proportions into a histogram. Where would you expect the center of that histogram to be? Of course, we don't *know* the answer, but it is reasonable to think that it will be at the true proportion in the population. We probably will never know the value of the true proportion. But it is important to us, so we'll give it a label, *p* for "true proportion."

Imagine

We see only the sample we actually drew, but if we *imagine* the results of all the other possible samples we could have drawn (by modeling or simulating them), we can learn more.

---

[1]Delaware *News Online*, January 1, 2006.

In fact, we can do better than just imagining. We can *simulate*. We can't really take all those different random samples of size 1000, but we can use a computer to pretend to draw random samples of 1000 individuals from some population of values over and over. In this way, we can study the process of drawing many samples from a real population. A *simulation* can help us understand how sample proportions vary due to random sampling.

When we have only two possible outcomes for an event, the convention in Statistics is to arbitrarily label one of them "success" and the other "failure." Here, a "success" would be that a customer increases card charges by at least $800, and a "failure" would be that the customer didn't. In the simulation, we'll set the true proportion of successes to a known value, draw random samples, and then record the sample proportion of successes, which we'll denote by $\hat{p}$, for each sample.

The proportion of successes in each of our simulated samples will vary from one sample to the next, but the *way* in which the proportions vary shows us how the proportions of real samples would vary. Because we can specify the true proportion of successes, we can see how close each sample comes to estimating that true value. Here's a histogram of the proportions of cardholders who increased spending by at least $800 in 2000 independent samples of 1000 cardholders, when the true proportion is $p = 0.21$. (We know this is the true value of p because in a simulation we can control it.)

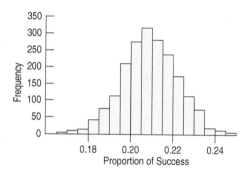

Figure 1 The distribution of 2000 sample values of $\hat{p}$, from simulated samples of size 1000 drawn from a population in which the true p is 0.21.

It should be no surprise that we don't get the same proportion for each sample we draw, even though the underlying true value, p, stays the same at $p = 0.21$. Since each $\hat{p}$ comes from a random sample, we don't expect them to all be equal to p. And since each comes from a *different* independent random sample, we don't expect them to be equal to each other, either. The remarkable thing is that even though the $\hat{p}$'s vary from sample to sample, they do so in a way that we can model and understand.

For Example   The distribution of a sample proportion

A supermarket has installed "self-checkout" stations that allow customers to scan and bag their own groceries. These are popular, but because customers occasionally encounter a problem, a staff member must be available to help out. The manager wants to estimate what proportion of customers need help so that he can optimize the number of self-check stations per staff monitor. He collects data from the stations for 30 days, recording the proportion of customers on each day that need help and makes a histogram of the observed proportions.

Questions:

1. If the proportion needing help is independent from day to day, what shape would you expect his histogram to follow?

2. Is the assumption of independence reasonable?

Answers:

1. Normal, centered at the true proportion.

2. Possibly not. For example, shoppers on weekends might be less experienced than regular weekday shoppers and would then need more help.

2 Sampling Distribution for Proportions

The collection of $\hat{p}$'s may be better behaved than you expected. The histogram in Figure 1 is unimodal and symmetric. It is also bell-shaped—and that means that the Normal may be an appropriate model. It is one of the early discoveries and successes of statistics that this distribution of sample proportions can be modeled by the Normal.

The distribution that we displayed in Figure 1 is just one simulation. The more proportions we simulate, the more the distribution settles down to a smooth bell shape. The distribution of proportions over all possible independent samples from the same population is called the **sampling distribution** of the proportions.

In fact, we can use the Normal model to describe the behavior of proportions. With the Normal model, we can find the percentage of values falling between any two values. But to make that work, we need to know the mean and standard deviation.

We know already that a sampling distribution of a sample proportion is centered around the true proportion, p. An amazing fact about proportions gives us the appropriate standard deviation to use as well. It turns out that once we know the mean, p, and the sample size, n, we also know the standard deviation of the sampling distribution as you can see from its formula:

$$SD(\hat{p}) = \sqrt{\frac{p(1-p)}{n}} = \sqrt{\frac{pq}{n}}.$$

If the true proportion of credit cardholders who increased their spending by more than \$800 is 0.21, then for samples of size 1000, we expect the distribution of sample proportions to have a standard deviation of:

$$SD(\hat{p}) = \sqrt{\frac{p(1-p)}{n}} = \sqrt{\frac{0.21(1-0.21)}{1000}} = 0.0129, \text{ or about } 1.3\%.$$

Remember that the two samples of size 1000 had proportions of 21.1% and 20.2%. Since the standard deviation of proportions is 1.3%, these two proportions are not even a full standard deviation apart. In other words, the two samples don't really disagree. Proportions of 21.1% and 20.2% from samples of 1000 are both *consistent* with a true proportion of 21%. This difference between sample proportions is referred to as **sampling error**. But it's not really an *error*. It's just the *variability* you'd expect to see from one sample to another. A better term might be *sampling variability*.

Look back at Figure 1 to see how well the model worked in our simulation. If $p = 0.21$, we now know that the standard deviation should be about 0.013. The 68–95–99.7 Rule from the Normal model says that 68% of the samples will have proportions within 1 SD of the mean of 0.21. How closely does our simulation match the predictions? The actual standard deviation of our 2000 *sample* proportions is 0.0129 or 1.29%. And, of the 2000 simulated samples, 1346 of them had proportions between 0.197 and .223 (one standard deviation on either side of 0.21). The 68–95–99.7 Rule predicts 68%—the actual number is 1346/2000 or 67.3%.

Now we know everything we need to know to model the sampling distribution. We know the mean and standard deviation of the sampling distribution of proportions: they're p, the true population proportion, and $\sqrt{\frac{pq}{n}}$. So the particular Normal model, $N\left(p, \sqrt{\frac{pq}{n}}\right)$, is a **sampling distribution model for the sample proportion**.

We saw this worked well in a simulation, but can we rely on it in all situations? It turns out that this model can be justified theoretically with just a little mathematics.

Notation Alert!

We use p for the proportion in the population and $\hat{p}$ for the observed proportion in a sample. We'll also use q for the proportion of failures ($q = 1 - p$), and $\hat{q}$ for its observed value, just to simplify some formulas.

We have now answered the question raised at the start of the chapter. To discover how variable a sample proportion is, we need to know the proportion and the size of the sample. That's all.

Effect of Sample Size

Because n is in the denominator of $SD(\hat{p})$, the larger the sample, the smaller the standard deviation. We need a small standard deviation to make sound business decisions, but larger samples cost more. That tension is a fundamental issue in statistics.

It won't work for *all* situations, but it works for most situations that you'll encounter in practice. We'll provide conditions to check so you'll know when the model is useful.

> ## The sampling distribution model for a proportion
>
> Provided that the sampled values are independent and the sample size is large enough, the sampling distribution of $\hat{p}$ is modeled by a Normal model with mean $\mu(\hat{p}) = p$ and standard deviation $SD(\hat{p}) = \sqrt{\dfrac{pq}{n}}$.

Just Checking

1 You want to poll a random sample of 100 shopping mall customers about whether they like the proposed location for the new coffee shop on the third floor, with a panoramic view of the food court. Of course, you'll get just one number, your sample proportion, $\hat{p}$. But if you imagined all the possible samples of 100 customers you could draw and imagined the histogram of all the sample proportions from these samples, what shape would it have?

2 Where would the center of that histogram be?

3 If you think that about half the customers are in favor of the plan, what would the standard deviation of the sample proportions be?

The sampling distribution model for $\hat{p}$ is valuable for a number of reasons. First, because it is known from mathematics to be a good model (and one that gets better and better as the sample size gets larger), we don't need to actually draw many samples and accumulate all those sample proportions, or even to simulate them. The Normal sampling distribution model tells us what the distribution of sample proportions would look like. Second, because the Normal model is a mathematical model, we can calculate what fraction of the distribution will be found in any region. You can find the fraction of the distribution in *any* interval of values using a table or with technology.

How Good Is the Normal Model?

We've seen that the simulated proportions follow the 68–95–99.7 Rule well. But do all sample proportions really work like this? Stop and think for a minute about what we're claiming. We've said that if we draw repeated random samples of the same size, n, from some population and measure the proportion, $\hat{p}$, we get for each sample, then the collection of these proportions will pile up around the underlying population proportion, p, in such a way that a histogram of the sample proportions can be modeled well by a Normal model.

There must be a catch. Suppose the samples were of size 2, for example. Then the only possible numbers of successes could be 0, 1, or 2, and the proportion values would be 0, 0.5, and 1. There's no way the histogram could ever look like a Normal model with only three possible values for the variable (Figure 2).

Well, there *is* a catch. The claim is only approximately true. (But, that's fine. Models are *supposed* to be only approximately true.) And the model becomes a better and better representation of the distribution of the sample proportions as the sample size gets bigger.[2] Samples of size 1 or 2 just aren't going to work very well, but the distributions of proportions of many larger samples do have histograms that are remarkably close to a Normal model.

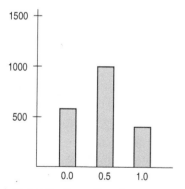

Figure 2 Proportions from samples of size 2 can take on only three possible values. A Normal model does not work well here.

---

[2] Formally, we say the claim is true in the limit as the sample size (n) grows.

For Example — Sampling distribution for proportions

Time-Warner provides cable, phone, and Internet services to customers, some of whom subscribe to "packages" including several services. Nationwide, suppose that 30% of their customers are "package subscribers" and subscribe to all three types of service. A local representative in Phoenix, Arizona, wonders if the proportion in his region is the same as the national proportion.

Questions: If the same proportion holds in his region and he takes a survey of 100 customers at random from his subscriber list:

1. What proportion of customers would you expect to be package subscribers?

2. What is the standard deviation of the sample proportion?

3. What shape would you expect the sampling distribution of the proportion to have?

4. Would you be surprised to find out that in a sample of 100, 49 of the customers are package subscribers? Explain. What might account for this high percentage?

Answers:

1. Because 30% of customers nationwide are package subscribers, we would expect the same for the sample proportion.

2. The standard deviation is $SD(\hat{p}) = \sqrt{\dfrac{pq}{n}} = \sqrt{\dfrac{(0.3)(0.7)}{100}} = 0.046$.

3. Normal.

4. 49 customers results in a sample proportion of 0.49. The mean is 0.30 with a standard deviation of 0.046. This sample proportion is more than 4 standard deviations higher than the mean: $\dfrac{(0.49 - 0.30)}{0.046} = 4.13$. It would be very unusual to find such a large proportion in a random sample. Either it is a very unusual sample, or the proportion in his region is not the same as the national average.

Assumptions and Conditions

Most models are useful only when specific assumptions are true. In the case of the model for the distribution of sample proportions, there are two assumptions:

> **Independence Assumption:** The sampled values must be *independent* of each other.
>
> **Sample Size Assumption:** The sample size, n, must be *large* enough.

Of course, the best we can do with assumptions is to think about whether they are likely to be true, and we should do so. However, we often can check corresponding *conditions* that provide information about the assumptions as well. Think about the Independence Assumption and check the following corresponding conditions before using the Normal model to model the distribution of sample proportions:

> **Randomization Condition:** If your data come from an experiment, subjects should have been randomly assigned to treatments. If you have a survey, your sample should be a simple random sample of the population. If some other sampling design was used, be sure the sampling method was not biased and that the data are representative of the population.
>
> **10% Condition:** If sampling has not been made with replacement (that is, returning each sampled individual to the population before drawing the next individual), then the sample size, n, must be no larger than 10% of the population. If it is, you must adjust the size of the confidence interval with methods more advanced than those found in this text.
>
> **Success/Failure Condition:** The Success/Failure condition says that the sample size must be big enough so that both the number of "successes," np, and the number of "failures," nq, are expected to be at least 10.[3] Expressed

---

[3] We saw where the 10 came from in the Math Box earlier in this chapter.

without the symbols, this condition just says that we need to expect at least 10 successes and at least 10 failures to have enough data for sound conclusions. For the bank's credit card promotion example, we labeled as a "success" a cardholder who increases monthly spending by at least $800 during the trial. The bank observed 211 successes and 789 failures. Both are at least 10, so there are certainly enough successes and enough failures for the condition to be satisfied.[4]

These two conditions seem to contradict each other. The Success/Failure condition wants a big sample size. How big depends on p. If p is near 0.5, we need a sample of only 20 or so. If p is only 0.01, however, we'd need 1000. But the 10% condition says that the sample size can't be too large a fraction of the population. Fortunately, the tension between them isn't usually a problem in practice. Often, as in polls that sample from all U.S. adults, or industrial samples from a day's production, the populations are much larger than 10 times the sample size.

For Example   Assumptions and conditions for sample proportions

The analyst conducting the Time-Warner survey says that, unfortunately, only 20 of the customers he tried to contact actually responded, but that of those 20, 8 are package subscribers.

Questions:

1. If the proportion of package subscribers in his region is 0.30, how many package subscribers, on average, would you expect in a sample of 20?

2. Would you expect the shape of the sampling distribution of the proportion to be Normal? Explain.

Answers:

1. You would expect $0.30 \cdot 20 = 6$ package subscribers.

2. No. Because 6 is less than 10, we should be cautious in using the Normal as a model for the sampling distribution of proportions. (The number of *observed* successes, 8, is also less than 10.)

Guided Example   Foreclosures

Galina Barksaya/
Shutterstock

An analyst at a home loan lender was looking at a package of 90 mortgages that the company had recently purchased in central California. The analyst was aware that in that region about 13% of the homeowners with current mortgages will default on their loans in the next year and the house will go into foreclosure. In deciding to buy the collection of mortgages, the finance department assumed that no more than 15 of the mortgages would go into default. Any amount above that will result in losses for the company. In the package of 90 mortgages, what's the probability that there will be more than 15 foreclosures?

PLAN	Setup State the objective of the study.	We want to find the probability that in a group of 90 mortgages, more than 15 will default. Since 15 out of 90 is 16.7%, we need the probability of finding more than 16.7% defaults out of a sample of 90, if the proportion of defaults is 13%.

(continued)

---

[4]The Success/Failure condition is about the number of successes and failures we *expect*, but if the number of successes and failures that *occurred* is ≥ 10, then you can use that.

Model Check the conditions.

✓ **Independence Assumption** If the mortgages come from a wide geographical area, one homeowner defaulting should not affect the probability that another does. However, if the mortgages come from the same neighborhood(s), the independence assumption may fail and our estimates of the default probabilities may be wrong.

✓ **Randomization Condition.** The 90 mortgages in the package can be considered as a random sample of mortgages in the region.

✓ **10% Condition.** The 90 mortgages are less than 10% of the population.

✓ **Success/Failure Condition**

$$np = 90(0.13) = 11.7 \geq 10$$
$$nq = 90(0.87) = 78.3 \geq 10$$

State the parameters and the sampling distribution model.

The population proportion is $p = 0.13$. The conditions are satisfied, so we'll model the sampling distribution of $\hat{p}$ with a Normal model, with mean 0.13 and standard deviation

$$SD(\hat{p}) = \sqrt{\frac{pq}{n}} = \sqrt{\frac{(0.13)(0.87)}{90}} \approx 0.035.$$

Our model for $\hat{p}$ is $N(0.13, 0.035)$. We want to find $P(\hat{p} > 0.167)$.

Plot Make a picture. Sketch the model and shade the area we're interested in, in this case the area to the right of 16.7%.

0.025	0.06	0.095	0.130	0.165	0.2	0.235
-3σ	-2σ	-1σ	p	1σ	2σ	3σ

DO

Mechanics Use the standard deviation as a ruler to find the *z*-score of the cutoff proportion. Find the resulting probability from a table, a computer program, or a calculator.

$$z = \frac{\hat{p} - p}{SD(\hat{p})} = \frac{0.167 - 0.13}{0.035} = 1.06$$

$$P(\hat{p} > 0.167) = P(z > 1.06) = 0.1446$$

REPORT

Conclusion Interpret the probability in the context of the question.

MEMO

Re: Mortgage Defaults

Assuming that the 90 mortgages we recently purchased are a random sample of mortgages in this region, there is about a 14.5% chance that we will exceed the 15 foreclosures that Finance has determined as the break-even point.

3 The Central Limit Theorem

Proportions summarize categorical variables. When we sample at random, the results we get will vary from sample to sample. The Normal model seems an incredibly simple way to summarize all that variation. Could something that simple work for means? We won't keep you in suspense. It turns out that means also have a sampling distribution that we can model with a Normal model. And it turns out that there's a theoretical result that proves it to be so. As we did with proportions, we can get some insight from a simulation.

Simulating the Sampling Distribution of a Mean

Here's a simple simulation with a quantitative variable. Let's start with one fair die. If we toss this die 10,000 times, what should the histogram of the numbers on the face of the die look like? Here are the results of a simulated 10,000 tosses:

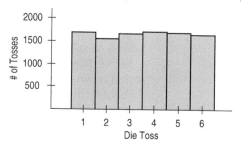

That's called the *uniform distribution*, and it's certainly not Normal. Now let's toss a *pair* of dice and record the average of the two. If we repeat this (or at least simulate repeating it) 10,000 times, recording the average of each pair, what will the histogram of these 10,000 averages look like? Before you look, think a minute. Is getting an average of 1 on *two* dice as likely as getting an average of 3 or 3.5? Let's see:

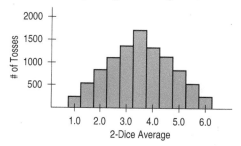

We're much more likely to get an average near 3.5 than we are to get one near 1 or 6. Without calculating those probabilities exactly, it's fairly easy to see that the *only* way to get an average of 1 is to get two 1s. To get a total of 7 (for an average of 3.5), though, there are many more possibilities. This distribution even has a name—the *triangular distribution*.

What if we average three dice? We'll simulate 10,000 tosses of three dice and take their average.

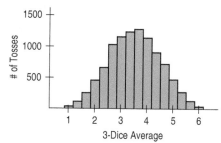

What's happening? First notice that it's getting harder to have averages near the ends. Getting an average of 1 or 6 with three dice requires all three to come up 1 or 6, respectively. That's less likely than for two dice to come up both 1 or both 6. The distribution is being pushed toward the middle. But what's happening to the shape?

Let's continue this simulation to see what happens with larger samples. Here's a histogram of the averages for 10,000 tosses of five dice.

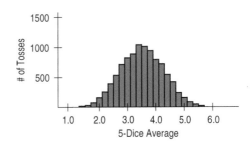

The pattern is becoming clearer. Two things are happening. The first fact we knew already from the Law of Large Numbers. It says that as the sample size (number of dice) gets larger, each sample average tends to become closer to the population mean. So we see the shape continuing to tighten around 3.5. But the shape of the distribution is the surprising part. It's becoming bell-shaped. In fact, it's approaching the Normal model.

Are you convinced? Let's skip ahead and try 20 dice. The histogram of averages for throws 10,000 of 20 dice looks like this.

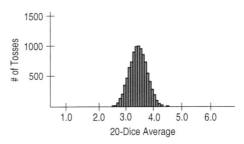

Now we see the Normal shape again (and notice how much smaller the spread is). But can we count on this happening for situations other than dice throws? What kinds of sample means have sampling distributions that we can model with a Normal model? It turns out that Normal models work well amazingly often.

The Central Limit Theorem

The dice simulation may look like a special situation. But it turns out that what we saw with dice is true for means of repeated samples for almost every situation. When we looked at the sampling distribution of a proportion, we had to check only a few conditions. For means, the result is even more remarkable. There are almost no conditions at all.

Let's say that again: The sampling distribution of *any* mean becomes Normal as the sample size grows. All we need is for the observations to be independent and collected with randomization. We don't even care about the shape of the population distribution![5] This surprising fact was proved in a fairly general form in 1810 by Pierre-Simon Laplace, and caused quite a stir (at least in mathematics circles)

| Pierre-Simon Laplace, 1749–1827.

"The theory of probabilities is at bottom nothing but common sense reduced to calculus."

—LAPLACE, IN *THÉORIE ANALYTIQUE DES PROBABILITIÉS*, 1812

---

[5]Technically, the data must come from a population with a finite variance.

because it is so unintuitive. Laplace's result is called the **Central Limit Theorem**[6] (CLT).

Not only does the distribution of means of many random samples get closer and closer to a Normal model as the sample size grows, but *this is true regardless of the shape of the population distribution!* Even if we sample from a skewed or bimodal population, the Central Limit Theorem tells us that means of repeated random samples will tend to follow a Normal model as the sample size grows. Of course, you won't be surprised to learn that it works better and faster the closer the population distribution is to a Normal model. And it works better for larger samples. If the data come from a population that's exactly Normal to start with, then the observations themselves are Normal. If we take samples of size 1, their "means" are just the observations—so, of course, they have a Normal sampling distribution. But now suppose the population distribution is very skewed. The CLT works, although it may take a sample size of dozens or even hundreds of observations for the Normal model to work well.

For example, think about a real bimodal population, one that consists of only 0s and 1s. The CLT says that even means of samples from this population will follow a Normal sampling distribution model. But wait. Suppose we have a categorical variable and we assign a 1 to each individual in the category and a 0 to each individual not in the category. Then we find the mean of these 0s and 1s. That's the same as counting the number of individuals who are in the category and dividing by *n*. That mean will be the *sample proportion*, $\hat{p}$, of individuals who are in the category (a "success"). So maybe it wasn't so surprising after all that proportions, like means, have Normal sampling distribution models; proportions are actually just a special case of Laplace's remarkable theorem. Of course, for such an extremely bimodal population, we need a reasonably large sample size—and that's where the Success/Failure condition for proportions comes in.

> ### The Central Limit Theorem (CLT)
> The mean of a random sample has a sampling distribution whose shape can be approximated by a Normal model. The larger the sample, the better the approximation will be.

Pierre-Simon Laplace
Laplace was one of the greatest scientists and mathematicians of his time. In addition to his contributions to probability and statistics, he published many new results in mathematics, physics, and astronomy (where his nebular theory was one of the first to describe the formation of the solar system in much the way it is understood today). He also played a leading role in establishing the metric system of measurement.

His brilliance, though, sometimes got him into trouble. A visitor to the Académie des Sciences in Paris reported that Laplace let it be known widely that he considered himself the best mathematician in France. The effect of this on his colleagues was not eased by the fact that Laplace was right.

Be careful. We have been slipping smoothly between the real world, in which we draw random samples of data, and a magical mathematical-model world, in which we describe how the sample means and proportions we observe in the real world might behave if we could see the results from every random sample that we might have drawn. Now we have *two* distributions to deal with. The first is the real-world distribution of the sample, which we might display with a histogram (for quantitative data) or with a bar chart or table (for categorical data). The second is the math-world *sampling distribution* of the statistic, which we model with a Normal model based on the Central Limit Theorem. Don't confuse the two.

For example, don't mistakenly think the CLT says that the *data* are Normally distributed as long as the sample is large enough. In fact, as samples get larger, we expect the distribution of the data to look more and more like the distribution of the population from which it is drawn—skewed, bimodal, whatever—but not necessarily Normal. You can collect a sample of CEO salaries for the next 1000 years, but the histogram will never look Normal. It will be skewed to the right.

---

[6]The word "central" in the name of the theorem means "fundamental." It doesn't refer to the center of a distribution.

The Central Limit Theorem doesn't talk about the distribution of the data from the sample. It talks about the sample *means* and sample *proportions* of many different random samples drawn from the same population. Of course, we never actually draw all those samples, so the CLT is talking about an imaginary distribution—the sampling distribution model.

The CLT does require that the sample be big enough when the population shape is not unimodal and symmetric. But it is still a very surprising and powerful result.

For Example   **The Central Limit Theorem**

The supermarket manager in the example earlier in this chapter also examines the amount spent by customers using the self-checkout stations. He finds that the distribution of these amounts is unimodal but skewed to the high end because some customers make unusually expensive purchases. He finds the mean spent on each of the 30 days studied and makes a histogram of those values.

Questions:

1. What shape would you expect for this histogram?

2. If, instead of averaging all customers on each day, he selects the first 10 for each day and just averages those, how would you expect his histogram of the means to differ from the one in (1)?

Answers:

1. Normal. It doesn't matter that the sample is drawn from a skewed distribution; the CLT tells us that the means will follow a Normal model.

2. The CLT requires large samples. Samples of 10 are not large enough.

---

4   The Sampling Distribution of the Mean

The CLT says that the sampling distribution of any mean or proportion is approximately Normal. But which Normal? We know that any Normal model is specified by its mean and standard deviation. For proportions, the sampling distribution is centered at the population proportion. For means, it's centered at the population mean. What else would we expect?

What about the standard deviations? We noticed in our dice simulation that the histograms got narrower as the number of dice we averaged increased. This shouldn't be surprising. Means vary less than the individual observations. Think about it for a minute. Which would be more surprising, having *one* person in your Statistics class who is over 6′9″ tall or having the *mean* of 100 students taking the course be over 6′9″? The first event is fairly rare.[7] You may have seen somebody this tall in one of your classes sometime. But finding a class of 100 whose mean height is over 6′9″ tall just won't happen. Why? *Means have smaller standard deviations than individuals.*

"The n's justify the means."

—APOCRYPHAL STATISTICAL SAYING

That is, the Normal model for the sampling distribution of the mean has a standard deviation equal to $SD(\bar{y}) = \dfrac{\sigma}{\sqrt{n}}$ where σ is the standard deviation of the population. To emphasize that this is a standard deviation *parameter* of the sampling distribution model for the sample mean, $\bar{y}$, we write $SD(\bar{y})$ or $\sigma(\bar{y})$.

---

[7]If students are a random sample of adults, fewer than 1 out of 10,000 should be taller than 6′9″. Why might college students not really be a random sample with respect to height? Even if they're not a perfectly random sample, a college student over 6′9″ tall is still rare.

> ### The sampling distribution model for a mean
>
> When a random sample is drawn from any population with mean μ and standard deviation σ, its sample mean, $\bar{y}$, has a sampling distribution with the same mean μ but whose standard deviation is $\dfrac{\sigma}{\sqrt{n}}$, and we write $\sigma(\bar{y}) = SD(\bar{y}) = \dfrac{\sigma}{\sqrt{n}}$. No matter what population the random sample comes from, the shape of the sampling distribution is approximately Normal as long as the sample size is large enough. The larger the sample used, the more closely the Normal approximates the sampling distribution model for the mean.

We now have two closely related sampling distribution models. Which one we use depends on which kind of data we have.

- When we have categorical data, we calculate a sample proportion, $\hat{p}$. Its sampling distribution follows a Normal model with a mean at the population proportion, p, and a standard deviation $SD(\hat{p}) = \sqrt{\dfrac{pq}{n}} = \dfrac{\sqrt{pq}}{\sqrt{n}}$.

- When we have quantitative data, we calculate a sample mean, $\bar{y}$. Its sampling distribution has a Normal model with a mean at the population mean, μ, and a standard deviation $SD(\bar{y}) = \dfrac{\sigma}{\sqrt{n}}$.

The means of these models are easy to remember, so all you need to be careful about is the standard deviations. Remember that these are standard deviations of the *statistics* $\hat{p}$ and $\bar{y}$. They both have a square root of n in the denominator. That tells us that the larger the sample, the less either statistic will vary. The only difference is in the numerator. If you just start by writing $SD(\bar{y})$ for quantitative data and $SD(\hat{p})$ for categorical data, you'll be able to remember which formula to use.

Assumptions and Conditions for the Sampling Distribution of the Mean

The CLT requires essentially the same assumptions as we saw for modeling proportions:

Independence Assumption: The sampled values must be independent of each other.

Randomization Condition: The data values must be sampled randomly, or the concept of a sampling distribution makes no sense.

Sample Size Assumption: The sample size must be sufficiently large. We can't check these directly, but we can think about whether the Independence Assumption is plausible. We can also check some related conditions:

10% Condition: When the sample is drawn without replacement (as is usually the case), the sample size, n, should be no more than 10% of the population.

Large Enough Sample Condition: The CLT doesn't tell us how large a sample we need. The truth is, it depends; there's no one-size-fits-all rule. If the population is unimodal and symmetric, even a fairly small sample is okay. You may hear that 30 or 50 observations is always enough to guarantee Normality, but in truth, it depends on the shape of the original data distribution. For highly skewed distributions, it may require samples of several hundred for the sampling distribution of means to be approximately Normal. Always plot the data to check.

Sample Size—Diminishing Returns

The standard deviation of the sampling distribution declines only with the square root of the sample size. The mean of a random sample of 4 has half $\left(\dfrac{1}{\sqrt{4}} = \dfrac{1}{2}\right)$ the standard deviation of an individual data value. To cut it in half again, we'd need a sample of 16, and a sample of 64 to halve it once more. In practice, random sampling works well, and means have smaller standard deviations than the individual data values that were averaged. This is the power of averaging.

If only we could afford a much larger sample, we could get the standard deviation of the sampling distribution *really* under control so that the sample mean could tell us still more about the unknown population mean. As we shall see, that square root limits how much we can make a sample tell about the population. This is an example of something that's known as the **Law of Diminishing Returns**.

For Example   Working with the sampling distribution of the mean

Suppose that the weights of boxes shipped by a company follow a unimodal, symmetric distribution with a mean of 12 lbs and a standard deviation of 4 lbs. Boxes are shipped in palettes of 10 boxes. The shipper has a limit of 150 lbs for such shipments.

Question: What's the probability that a palette will exceed that limit?

Answer: Asking the probability that the total weight of a sample of 10 boxes exceeds 150 lbs is the same as asking the probability that the *mean* weight exceeds 15 lbs. First we'll check the conditions. We will assume that the 10 boxes on the palette are a random sample from the population of boxes and that their weights are mutually independent. We are told that the underlying distribution of weights is unimodal and symmetric, so a sample of 10 boxes should be large enough. And 10 boxes is surely less than 10% of the population of boxes shipped by the company.

Under these conditions, the CLT says that the sampling distribution of $\bar{y}$ has a Normal model with mean 12 and standard deviation

$$SD(\bar{y}) = \frac{\sigma}{\sqrt{n}} = \frac{4}{\sqrt{10}} = 1.26 \text{ and } z = \frac{\bar{y} - \mu}{SD(\bar{y})} = \frac{15 - 12}{1.26} = 2.38$$

$$P(\bar{y} > 150) = P(z > 2.38) = 0.0087$$

So the chance that the shipper will reject a palette is only .0087—less than 1%.

---

5   How Sampling Distribution Models Work

Both of the sampling distributions we've looked at are Normal. We know for proportions, $SD(\hat{p}) = \sqrt{\dfrac{pq}{n}}$, and for means, $SD(\bar{y}) = \dfrac{\sigma}{\sqrt{n}}$. These are great if we know, or can pretend that we know, p or σ, and sometimes we'll do that.

Often we know only the observed proportion, $\hat{p}$, or the sample standard deviation, s. So of course we just use what we know, and we estimate. That may not seem like a big deal, but it gets a special name. Whenever we estimate the standard deviation of a sampling distribution, we call it a **standard error (SE)**.

For a sample proportion, $\hat{p}$, the standard error is:

$$SE(\hat{p}) = \sqrt{\frac{\hat{p}\hat{q}}{n}}.$$

For the sample mean, $\bar{y}$, the standard error is:

$$SE(\bar{y}) = \frac{s}{\sqrt{n}}.$$

You may see a "standard error" reported by a computer program in a summary or offered by a calculator. It's safe to assume that if no statistic is specified, what was meant is $SE(\bar{y})$, the standard error of the mean.

Just Checking

4 The entrance exam for business schools, the GMAT, given to 100 students had a mean of 520 and a standard deviation of 120. What was the standard error for the mean of this sample of students?

5 As the sample size increases, what happens to the standard error, assuming the standard deviation remains constant?

6 If the sample size is doubled, what is the impact on the standard error?

To keep track of how the concepts we've seen combine, we can draw a diagram relating them. At the heart is the idea that *the statistic itself (the proportion or the mean) is a random quantity.* We can't know what our statistic will be because it comes from a random sample. A different random sample would have given a different result. This sample-to-sample variability is what generates the sampling distribution, the distribution of all the possible values that the statistic could have had.

We could simulate that distribution by pretending to take lots of samples. Fortunately, for the mean and the proportion, the CLT tells us that we can model their sampling distribution directly with a Normal model.

The two basic truths about sampling distributions are:

1. Sampling distributions arise because samples vary. Each random sample will contain different cases and, so, a different value of the statistic.

2. Although we can always simulate a sampling distribution, the Central Limit Theorem saves us the trouble for means and proportions.

When we don't know σ, we estimate it with the standard deviation of the one real sample. That gives us the standard error, $SE(\bar{y}) = \dfrac{s}{\sqrt{n}}$.

Figure 3 diagrams the process.

Figure 3 We start with a population model, which can have any shape. It can even be bimodal or skewed (as this one is). We label the mean of this model μ and its standard deviation, σ.

We draw one real sample (solid line) of size n and show its histogram and summary statistics. We *imagine* (or simulate) drawing many other samples (dotted lines), which have their own histograms and summary statistics.

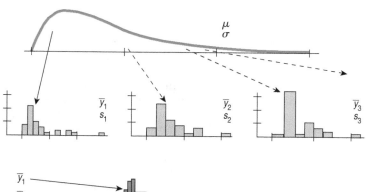

We (imagine) gathering all the means into a histogram.

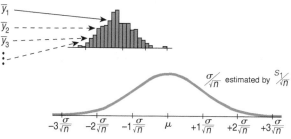

The CLT tells us we can model the shape of this histogram with a Normal model. The mean of this Normal is μ, and the standard deviation is $SD(\bar{y}) = \dfrac{\sigma}{\sqrt{n}}$.

What Can Go Wrong?

- **Don't confuse the sampling distribution with the distribution of the sample.** When you take a sample, you always look at the distribution of the values, usually with a histogram, and you may calculate summary statistics. Examining the distribution of the sample like this is wise. But that's not the sampling distribution. The sampling distribution is an imaginary collection of the values that a statistic might have taken for all the random samples—the one you got and the ones that you didn't get. Use the sampling distribution model to make statements about how the statistic varies.

- **Beware of observations that are not independent.** The CLT depends crucially on the assumption of independence. Unfortunately, this isn't something you can check in your data. You have to think about how the data were gathered. Good sampling practice and well-designed randomized experiments ensure independence.

- **Watch out for small samples from skewed populations.** The CLT assures us that the sampling distribution model is Normal if n is large enough. If the population is nearly Normal, even small samples may work. If the population is very skewed, then n will have to be large before the Normal model will work well. If we sampled 15 or even 20 CEOs and used $\bar{y}$ to make a statement about the mean of all CEOs' compensation, we'd likely get into trouble because the underlying data distribution is so skewed. Unfortunately, there's no good rule to handle this.[8] It just depends on how skewed the data distribution is. Always plot the data to check.

Ethics in Action

Home Illusions, a national retailer of contemporary furniture and home décor has recently experienced customer complaints about the delivery of its products. This retailer uses different carriers depending on the order destination. Its policy with regard to most items it sells and ships is to simply deliver to the customer's doorstep. However, its policy with regard to furniture is to "deliver, unpack, and place furniture in the intended area of the home." Most of their recent complaints have been from customers in the northeastern region of the United States who were dissatisfied because their furniture deliveries were not unpacked and placed in their homes. Since the retailer uses different carriers, it is important for them to label their packages correctly so the delivery company can distinguish between furniture and nonfurniture deliveries. Home Illusions sets as a target "1% or less" for incorrect labeling of packages. Joe Zangard, V.P. Logistics, was asked to look into the problem. The retailer's largest warehouse in the northeast prepares about 1000 items per week for shipping. Joe's initial attention was directed at this facility, not only because of its large volume, but also because he had some reservations about the newly hired warehouse manager, Brent Mossir. Packages at the warehouse were randomly selected and examined over a period of several weeks. Out of 1000 packages, 13 were labeled incorrectly. Since Joe had expected the count to be 10 or fewer, he was confident that he had now pinpointed the problem. His next step was to set up a meeting with Brent in order to discuss the ways in which he can improve the labeling process at his warehouse.

ETHICAL ISSUE *Joe is treating the sample proportion as if it were the true fixed value. By not recognizing that this sample proportion varies from sample to sample, he has unfairly judged the labeling process at Brent's warehouse. This is consistent with his initial misgivings about Brent being hired as warehouse manager (related to Item A, ASA Ethical Guidelines).*

ETHICAL SOLUTION *Joe Zangard needs to use the normal distribution to model the sampling distribution for the sample proportion. In this way, he would realize that the sample proportion observed is less than one standard deviation away from 1% (the upper limit of the target) and thus not conclusively larger than the limit.*

---

[8]For proportions, there is a rule: the Success/Failure condition. That works for proportions because the standard deviation of a proportion is linked to its mean. You may hear that 30 or 50 observations is enough to guarantee Normality, but it really depends on the skewness of the original data distribution.

What Have We Learned?

Learning Objectives

- Model the variation in statistics from sample to sample with a sampling distribution.
  - The Central Limit Theorem tells us that the sampling distribution of both the sample proportion and the sample mean are Normal.

- Understand that, usually, the mean of a sampling distribution is the value of the parameter estimated.
  - For the sampling distribution of $\hat{p}$, the mean is p.
  - For the sampling distribution of $\bar{y}$ the mean is μ.

- Interpret the standard deviation of a sampling distribution.
  - The standard deviation of a sampling model is the most important information about it.
  - The standard deviation of the sampling distribution of a proportion is $\sqrt{\dfrac{pq}{n}}$, where $q = 1 - p$.
  - The standard deviation of the sampling distribution of a mean is $\dfrac{\sigma}{\sqrt{n}}$, where σ is the population standard deviation.

- Understand that the Central Limit Theorem is a *limit* theorem.
  - The sampling distribution of the mean is Normal, *no matter what the underlying distribution of the data is.*
  - The CLT says that this happens in the limit, as the sample size grows. The Normal model applies sooner when sampling from a unimodal, symmetric population and more gradually when the population is very non-Normal.

Terms

Central Limit Theorem
: The Central Limit Theorem (CLT) states that the sampling distribution model of the sample mean (and proportion) is approximately Normal for large n, regardless of the distribution of the population, as long as the observations are independent.

Sampling distribution
: The distribution of a statistic over many independent samples of the same size from the same population.

Sampling distribution model for a mean
: If the independence assumption and randomization condition are met and the sample size is large enough, the sampling distribution of the sample mean is well modeled by a Normal model with a mean equal to the population mean, μ, and a standard deviation equal to $\dfrac{\sigma}{\sqrt{n}}$.

Sampling distribution model for a proportion
: If the independence assumption and randomization condition are met and we expect at least 10 successes and 10 failures, then the sampling distribution of a proportion is well modeled by a Normal model with a mean equal to the true proportion value, p, and a standard deviation equal to $\sqrt{\dfrac{pq}{n}}$.

Sampling error
: The variability we expect to see from sample to sample is often called the sampling error, although sampling variability is a better term.

Standard error
: When the standard deviation of the sampling distribution of a statistic is estimated from the data, the resulting statistic is called a standard error (SE).

Brief CASE

M. Eric Honeycutt/
iStockphoto

iStockphoto

Real Estate Simulation

Many variables important to the real estate market are skewed, limited to only a few values or considered as categorical variables. Yet, marketing and business decisions are often made based on means and proportions calculated over many homes. One reason these statistics are useful is the Central Limit Theorem.

Data on 1063 houses sold recently in the Saratoga, New York area, are in the file **Saratoga_Real_Estate** on the website www.pearsonhighered.com/sharpe. Let's investigate how the CLT guarantees that the sampling distribution of proportions approaches the Normal and that the same is true for means of a quantitative variable even when samples are drawn from populations that are far from Normal.

Part 1: Proportions

The variable *Fireplace* is a dichotomous variable where 1 = *has a fireplace* and 0 = *does not have a fireplace*.

- Calculate the proportion of homes that have fireplaces for all 1063 homes. Using this value, calculate what the standard error of the sample proportion would be for a sample of size 50.
- Using the software of your choice, draw 100 samples of size 50 from this population of homes, find the proportion of homes with fireplaces in each of these samples, and make a histogram of these proportions.
- Compare the mean and standard deviation of this (sampling) distribution to what you previously calculated.

Part 2: Means

- Select one of the quantitative variables and make a histogram of the entire population of 1063 homes. Describe the distribution (including its mean and SD).
- Using the software of your choice, draw 100 samples of size 50 from this population of homes, find the means of these samples, and make a histogram of these means.
- Compare the (sampling) distribution of the means to the distribution of the population.
- Repeat the exercise with samples of sizes 10 and of 30. What do you notice about the effect of the sample size?

Some statistics packages make it easier than others to draw many samples and find means. Your instructor can provide advice on the path to follow for your package.

An alternative approach is to have each member of the class draw one sample to find the proportion and mean and then combine the statistics for the entire class.

Exercises

SECTION 1

1. An investment website can tell what devices are used to access the site. The site managers wonder whether they should enhance the facilities for trading via "smart phones" so they want to estimate the proportion of users who access the site that way (even if they also use their computers sometimes). They draw a random sample of 200 investors from their customers. Suppose that the true proportion of smart phone users is 36%.

a) What would you expect the shape of the sampling distribution for the sample proportion to be?
b) What would be the mean of this sampling distribution?
c) If the sample size were increased to 500, would your answers change? Explain.

2. The proportion of adult women in the United States is approximately 51%. A marketing survey telephones 400 people at random.

a) What proportion of women in the sample of 400 would you expect to see?
b) How many women, on average, would you expect to find in a sample of that size? (*Hint:* Multiply the expected proportion by the sample size.)

SECTION 2

3. The investment website of Exercise 1 draws a random sample of 200 investors from their customers. Suppose that the true proportion of smart phone users is 36%.

a) What would the standard deviation of the sampling distribution of the proportion of smart phone users be?
b) What is the probability that the sample proportion of smart phone users is greater than 0.36?
c) What is the probability that the sample proportion is between 0.30 and 0.40?
d) What is the probability that the sample proportion is less than 0.28?
e) What is the probability that the sample proportion is greater than 0.42?

4. The proportion of adult women in the United States is approximately 51%. A marketing survey telephones 400 people at random.

a) What is the sampling distribution of the observed proportion that are women?
b) What is the standard deviation of that proportion?
c) Would you be surprised to find 53% women in a sample of size 400? Explain.
d) Would you be surprised to find 41% women in a sample of size 400? Explain.
e) Would you be surprised to find that there were fewer than 160 women in the sample? Explain.

5. A real estate agent wants to know how many owners of homes worth over $1,000,000 might be considering putting their home on the market in the next 12 months. He surveys 40 of them and finds that 10 of them are considering such a move. Are all the assumptions and conditions for finding the sampling distribution of the proportion satisfied? Explain briefly.

6. A tourist agency wants to know what proportion of vistors to the Eiffel Tower are from the Far East. To find out they survey 100 people in the line to purchase tickets to the top of the tower one Sunday afternoon in May. Are all the assumptions and conditions for finding the sampling distribution of the proportion satisfied? Explain briefly.

SECTION 3

7. A sample of 40 games sold for the iPad has prices that have a distribution that is skewed to the high end with a mean of $3.48 and a standard deviation of $2.23. Teens who own iPads typically own about 20 games. Using the 68–95–99.7 Rule, draw and label an appropriate sampling model for the average amount a teen would spend per game if they had 20 games, assuming those games were a representative sample of available games.

8. Statistics for the closing price of the USAA Aggressive Growth Fund for the year 2009 indicate that the average closing price was $23.90, with a standard deviation of $3.00. Using the 68–95–99.7 Rule, draw and label an appropriate sampling model for the mean closing price of 36 days' closing prices selected at random. What (if anything) do you need to assume about the distribution of prices? Are those assumptions reasonable?

SECTION 4

9. According to the Gallup poll, 27% of U.S. adults have high levels of cholesterol. They report that such elevated levels "could be financially devastating to the U.S. health-care system" and are a major concern to health insurance providers. According to recent studies, cholesterol levels in healthy U.S. adults average about 215 mg/dL with a standard deviation of about 30 mg/dL and are roughly Normally distributed. If the cholesterol levels of a sample of 42 healthy U.S. adults is taken,

a) What shape should the sampling distribution of the mean have?
b) What would the mean of the sampling distribution be?
c) What would its standard deviation be?
d) If the sample size were increased to 100, how would your answers to parts a–c change?

10. As in Exercise 9, cholesterol levels in healthy U.S. adults average about 215 mg/dL with a standard deviation of about 30 mg/dL and are roughly Normally distributed. If the cholesterol levels of a sample of 42 healthy US adults is taken, what is the probability that the mean cholesterol level of the sample

a) Will be no more than 215?
b) Will be between 205 and 225?
c) Will be less than 200?
d) Will be greater than 220?

SECTION 5

11. A marketing researcher for a phone company surveys 100 people and finds that that proportion of clients who are likely to switch providers when their contract expires is 0.15.

a) What is the standard deviation of the sampling distribution of the proportion?
b) If she wants to reduce the standard deviation by half, how large a sample would she need?

12. A market researcher for a provider of iPod accessories wants to know the proportion of customers who own cars to assess the market for a new iPod car charger. A survey of 500 customers indicates that 76% own cars.

a) What is the standard deviation of the sampling distribution of the proportion?
b) How large would the standard deviation have been if he had surveyed only 125 customers (assuming the proportion is about the same)?

13. Organizers of a fishing tournament believe that the lake holds a sizable population of largemouth bass. They assume that the weights of these fish have a model that is skewed to the right with a mean of 3.5 pounds and a standard deviation of 2.32 pounds.

a) Explain why a skewed model makes sense here.
b) Explain why you cannot determine the probability that a largemouth bass randomly selected ("caught") from the lake weighs over 3 pounds.
c) Each contestant catches 5 fish each day. Can you determine the probability that someone's catch averages over 3 pounds? Explain.
d) The 12 contestants competing each caught the limit of 5 fish. What's the standard deviation of the mean weight of the 60 fish caught?
e) Would you be surprised if the mean weight of the 60 fish caught in the competition was more than 4.5 pounds? Use the 68–95–99.7 Rule.

14. In 2008 and 2009, Systemax bought two failing electronics stores, Circuit City and CompUSA. They have kept both the names active and customers can purchase products from either website. If they take a random sample of a mixture of recent purchases from the two websites, the distribution of the amounts purchased will be bimodal.

a) As their sample size increases, what's the expected shape of the distribution of amounts purchased in the sample?
b) As the sample size increases, what's the expected shape of the sampling model for the mean amount purchased of the sample?

CHAPTER EXERCISES

15. Send money. When they send out their fundraising letter, a philanthropic organization typically gets a return from about 5% of the people on their mailing list. To see what the response rate might be for future appeals, they did a simulation using samples of size 20, 50, 100, and 200. For each sample size, they simulated 1000 mailings with success rate $p = 0.05$ and constructed the histogram of the 1000 sample proportions, shown below. Explain how these histograms demonstrate what the Central Limit Theorem says about the sampling distribution model for sample proportions. Be sure to talk about shape, center, and spread.

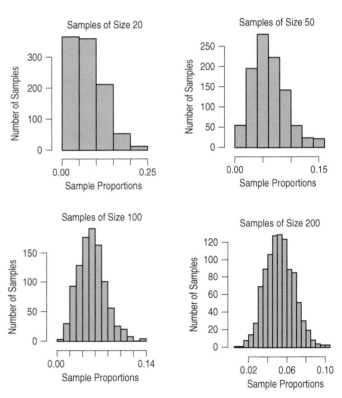

16. Character recognition. An automatic character recognition device can successfully read about 85% of handwritten credit card applications. To estimate what might happen when this device reads a stack of applications, the company did a simulation using samples of size 20, 50, 75, and 100. For each sample size, they simulated 1000 samples with success rate $p = 0.85$ and constructed the histogram of the 1000 sample proportions, shown here. Explain how these histograms demonstrate what the Central Limit Theorem says about the sampling distribution model for sample proportions. Be sure to talk about shape, center, and spread.

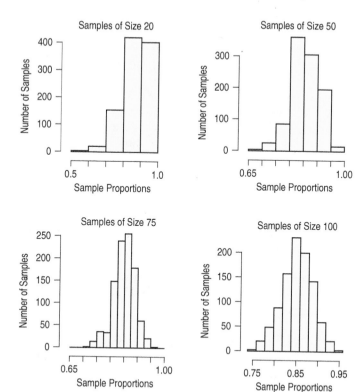

Samples of Size 20 / Samples of Size 50 / Samples of Size 75 / Samples of Size 100

17. Send money, again. The philanthropic organization in Exercise 15 expects about a 5% success rate when they send fundraising letters to the people on their mailing list. In Exercise 15 you looked at the histograms showing distributions of sample proportions from 1000 simulated mailings for samples of size 20, 50, 100, and 200. The sample statistics from each simulation were as follows:

n	mean	st. dev.
20	0.0497	0.0479
50	0.0516	0.0309
100	0.0497	0.0215
200	0.0501	0.0152

a) According to the Central Limit Theorem, what should the theoretical mean and standard deviations be for these sample sizes?
b) How close are those theoretical values to what was observed in these simulations?
c) Looking at the histograms in Exercise 15, at what sample size would you be comfortable using the Normal model as an approximation for the sampling distribution?
d) What does the Success/Failure Condition say about the choice you made in part c?

18. Character recognition, again. The automatic character recognition device discussed in Exercise 16 successfully reads about 85% of handwritten credit card applications. In Exercise 16 you looked at the histograms showing distributions of sample proportions from 1000 simulated samples of size 20, 50, 75, and 100. The sample statistics from each simulation were as follows:

n	mean	st. dev.
20	0.8481	0.0803
50	0.8507	0.0509
75	0.8481	0.0406
100	0.8488	0.0354

a) According to the Central Limit Theorem, what should the theoretical mean and standard deviations be for these sample sizes?
b) How close are those theoretical values to what was observed in these simulations?
c) Looking at the histograms in Exercise 16, at what sample size would you be comfortable using the Normal model as an approximation for the sampling distribution?
d) What does the Success/Failure Condition say about the choice you made in part c?

19. Stock picking. In a large Business Statistics class, the professor has each person select stocks by throwing 16 darts at pages of the *Wall Street Journal*. They then check to see whether their stock picks rose or fell the next day and report their proportion of "successes." As a lesson, the professor has selected pages of the *Journal* for which exactly half the publicly traded stocks went up and half went down. The professor then makes a histogram of the reported proportions.

a) What shape would you expect this histogram to be? Why?
b) Where do you expect the histogram to be centered?
c) How much variability would you expect among these proportions?
d) Explain why a Normal model should not be used here.

20. Quality management. Manufacturing companies strive to maintain production consistency, but it is often difficult for outsiders to tell whether they have succeeded. Sometimes, however, we can find a simple example. The candy company that makes M&M's candies claims that 10% of the candies it produces are green and that bags are packed randomly. We can check on their production controls by sampling bags of candies. Suppose we open bags containing about 50 M&M's and record the proportion of green candies.

a) If we plot a histogram showing the proportions of green candies in the various bags, what shape would you expect it to have?
b) Can that histogram be approximated by a Normal model? Explain.

c) Where should the center of the histogram be?

d) What should the standard deviation of the proportion be?

21. Bigger portfolio. The class in Exercise 19 expands its stock-picking experiment.

a) The students use computer-generated random numbers to choose 25 stocks each. Use the 68–95–99.7 Rule to describe the sampling distribution model.

b) Confirm that you can use a Normal model here.

c) They increase the number of stocks picked to 64 each. Draw and label the appropriate sampling distribution model. Check the appropriate conditions to justify your model.

d) Explain how the sampling distribution model changes as the number of stocks picked increases.

22. More quality. Would a bigger sample help us to assess manufacturing consistency? Suppose instead of the 50-candy bags of Exercise 20, we work with bags that contain 200 M&M's each. Again we calculate the proportion of green candies found.

a) Explain why it's appropriate to use a Normal model to describe the distribution of the proportion of green M&M's they might expect.

b) Use the 68–95–99.7 Rule to describe how this proportion might vary from bag to bag.

c) How would this model change if the bags contained even more candies?

23. A winning investment strategy? One student in the class of Exercise 19 claims to have found a winning strategy. He watches a cable news show about investing and *during the show* throws his darts at the pages of the *Journal*. He claims that of 200 stocks picked in this manner, 58% were winners.

a) What do you think of his claim? Explain.

b) If there are 100 students in the class, are you surprised that one was this successful? Explain.

24. Even more quality. In a really large bag of M&M's, we found 12% of 500 candies were green. Is this evidence that the manufacturing process is out of control and has made too many greens? Explain.

25. Speeding. State police believe that 70% of the drivers traveling on a major interstate highway exceed the speed limit. They plan to set up a radar trap and check the speeds of 80 cars.

a) Using the 68–95–99.7 Rule, draw and label the distribution of the proportion of these cars the police will observe speeding.

b) Do you think the appropriate conditions necessary for your analysis are met? Explain.

26. Smoking, 2008. Public health statistics indicate that 20.6% of American adults smoke cigarettes. Using the 68–95–99.7 Rule, describe the sampling distribution model for the proportion of smokers among a randomly selected group of 50 adults. Be sure to discuss your assumptions and conditions.

27. Vision. It is generally believed that nearsightedness affects about 12% of all children. A school district has registered 170 incoming kindergarten children.

a) Can you apply the Central Limit Theorem to describe the sampling distribution model for the sample proportion of children who are nearsighted? Check the conditions and discuss any assumptions you need to make.

b) Sketch and clearly label the sampling model, based on the 68–95–99.7 Rule.

c) How many of the incoming students might the school expect to be nearsighted? Explain.

28. Mortgages. In early 2007 the Mortgage Lenders Association reported that homeowners, hit hard by rising interest rates on adjustable-rate mortgages, were defaulting in record numbers. The foreclosure rate of 1.6% meant that millions of families were in jeopardy of losing their homes. Suppose a large bank holds 1731 adjustable-rate mortgages.

a) Can you use the Normal model to describe the sampling distribution model for the sample proportion of foreclosures? Check the conditions and discuss any assumptions you need to make.

b) Sketch and clearly label the sampling model, based on the 68–95–99.7 Rule.

c) How many of these homeowners might the bank expect will default on their mortgages? Explain.

29. Loans. Based on past experience, a bank believes that 7% of the people who receive loans will not make payments on time. The bank has recently approved 200 loans.

a) What are the mean and standard deviation of the proportion of clients in this group who may not make timely payments?

b) What assumptions underlie your model? Are the conditions met? Explain.

c) What's the probability that over 10% of these clients will not make timely payments?

30. Contacts. The campus representative for Lens.com wants to know what percentage of students at a university currently wear contact lens. Suppose the true proportion is 30%.

a) We randomly pick 100 students. Let $\hat{p}$ represent the proportion of students in this sample who wear contacts. What's the appropriate model for the distribution of $\hat{p}$? Specify the name of the distribution, the mean, and the standard deviation. Be sure to verify that the conditions are met.

b) What's the approximate probability that more than one third of this sample wear contacts?

31. Back to school? Best known for its testing program, ACT, Inc., also compiles data on a variety of issues in education. In 2004 the company reported that the national college freshman-to-sophomore retention rate held steady at 74% over the previous four years. Consider colleges with freshman classes of 400 students. Use the 68–95–99.7 Rule to describe the sampling distribution model for the percentage of those students we expect to return to that school for their sophomore years. Do you think the appropriate conditions are met?

32. Binge drinking. A national study found that 44% of college students engage in binge drinking (5 drinks at a sitting for men, 4 for women). Use the 68–95–99.7 Rule to describe the sampling distribution model for the proportion of students in a randomly selected group of 200 college students who engage in binge drinking. Do you think the appropriate conditions are met?

33. Back to school, again. Based on the 74% national retention rate described in Exercise 31, does a college where 522 of the 603 freshman returned the next year as sophomores have a right to brag that it has an unusually high retention rate? Explain.

34. Binge sample. After hearing of the national result that 44% of students engage in binge drinking (5 drinks at a sitting for men, 4 for women), a professor surveyed a random sample of 244 students at his college and found that 96 of them admitted to binge drinking in the past week. Should he be surprised at this result? Explain.

35. Polling. Just before a referendum on a school budget, a local newspaper polls 400 voters in an attempt to predict whether the budget will pass. Suppose that the budget actually has the support of 52% of the voters. What's the probability the newspaper's sample will lead them to predict defeat? Be sure to verify that the assumptions and conditions necessary for your analysis are met.

36. Seeds. Information on a packet of seeds claims that the germination rate is 92%. What's the probability that more than 95% of the 160 seeds in the packet will germinate? Be sure to discuss your assumptions and check the conditions that support your model.

37. Apples. When a truckload of apples arrives at a packing plant, a random sample of 150 is selected and examined for bruises, discoloration, and other defects. The whole truckload will be rejected if more than 5% of the sample is unsatisfactory. Suppose that in fact 8% of the apples on the truck do not meet the desired standard. What's the probability that the shipment will be accepted anyway?

38. Genetic defect. It's believed that 4% of children have a gene that may be linked to juvenile diabetes. Researchers hoping to track 20 of these children for several years test

732 newborns for the presence of this gene. What's the probability that they find enough subjects for their study?

39. Nonsmokers. While some nonsmokers do not mind being seated in a smoking section of a restaurant, about 60% of the customers demand a smoke-free area. A new restaurant with 120 seats is being planned. How many seats should be in the nonsmoking area in order to be very sure of having enough seating there? Comment on the assumptions and conditions that support your model, and explain what "very sure" means to you.

40. Meals. A restaurateur anticipates serving about 180 people on a Friday evening, and believes that about 20% of the patrons will order the chef's steak special. How many of those meals should he plan on serving in order to be pretty sure of having enough steaks on hand to meet customer demand? Justify your answer, including an explanation of what "pretty sure" means to you.

41. Sampling. A sample is chosen randomly from a population that can be described by a Normal model.
a) What's the sampling distribution model for the sample mean? Describe shape, center, and spread.
b) If we choose a larger sample, what's the effect on this sampling distribution model?

42. Sampling, part II. A sample is chosen randomly from a population that was strongly skewed to the left.
a) Describe the sampling distribution model for the sample mean if the sample size is small.
b) If we make the sample larger, what happens to the sampling distribution model's shape, center, and spread?
c) As we make the sample larger, what happens to the expected distribution of the data in the sample?

43. Waist size. A study commissioned by a clothing manufacturer measured the *Waist Size* of 250 men, finding a mean of 36.33 inches and a standard deviation of 4.02 inches. Here is a histogram of these measurements:

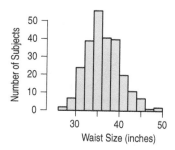

a) Describe the histogram of *Waist Size.*
b) To explore how the mean might vary from sample to sample, they simulated by drawing many samples of size 2, 5, 10, and 20, with replacement, from the 250 measurements.

Here are histograms of the sample means for each simulation. Explain how these histograms demonstrate what the Central Limit Theorem says about the sampling distribution model for sample means.

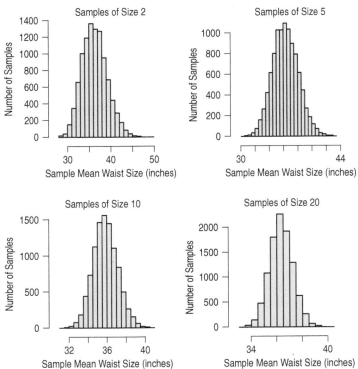

44. CEO compensation. The average total annual compensation for CEOs of the 800 largest U.S. companies (in $1000) is 10,307.31 and the standard deviation is 17964.62. Here is a histogram of their annual compensations (in $1000):

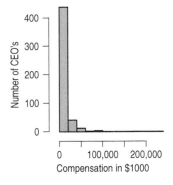

a) Describe the histogram of *Total Compensation*. A research organization simulated sample means by drawing samples of 30, 50, 100, and 200, with replacement, from the 800 CEOs. The histograms show the distributions of means for many samples of each size.
b) Explain how these histograms demonstrate what the Central Limit Theorem says about the sampling distribution model for sample means. Be sure to talk about shape, center, and spread.

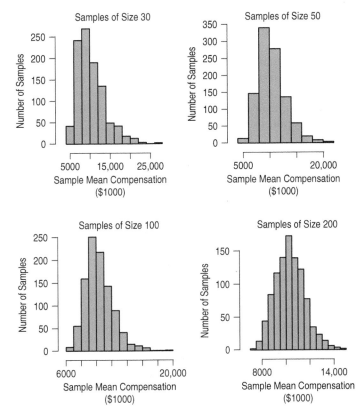

c) Comment on the "rule of thumb" that "With a sample size of at least 30, the sampling distribution of the mean is Normal."

45. Waist size revisited. A study commissioned by a clothing manufacturer measured the *Waist Sizes* of a random sample of 250 men. The mean and standard deviation of the *Waist Sizes* for all 250 men are 36.33 in and 4.019 inches, respectively. In Exercise 43 you looked at the histograms of simulations that drew samples of sizes 2, 5, 10, and 20 (with replacement). The summary statistics for these simulations were as follows:

n	mean	st. dev.
2	36.314	2.855
5	36.314	1.805
10	36.341	1.276
20	36.339	0.895

a) According to the Central Limit Theorem, what should the theoretical mean and standard deviation be for each of these sample sizes?
b) How close are the theoretical values to what was observed in the simulation?
c) Looking at the histograms in Exercise 43, at what sample size would you be comfortable using the Normal model as an approximation for the sampling distribution?
d) What about the shape of the distribution of *Waist Size* explains your choice of sample size in part c?

46. CEOs revisited. In Exercise 44 you looked at the annual compensation for 800 CEOs, for which the true mean and standard deviation were (in thousands of dollars) 10,307.31 and 17,964.62, respectively. A simulation drew samples of sizes 30, 50, 100, and 200 (with replacement) from the total annual compensations of the Fortune 800 CEOs. The summary statistics for these simulations were as follows:

n	mean	st. dev.
30	10,251.73	3359.64
50	10,343.93	2483.84
100	10,329.94	1779.18
200	10,340.37	1230.79

a) According to the Central Limit Theorem, what should the theoretical mean and standard deviation be for each of these sample sizes?
b) How close are the theoretical values to what was observed from the simulation?
c) Looking at the histograms in Exercise 44, at what sample size would you be comfortable using the Normal model as an approximation for the sampling distribution?
d) What about the shape of the distribution of *Total Compensation* explains your answer in part c?

47. GPAs. A college's data about the incoming freshmen indicates that the mean of their high school GPAs was 3.4, with a standard deviation of 0.35; the distribution was roughly mound-shaped and only slightly skewed. The students are randomly assigned to freshman writing seminars in groups of 25. What might the mean GPA of one of these seminar groups be? Describe the appropriate sampling distribution model—shape, center, and spread—with attention to assumptions and conditions. Make a sketch using the 68–95–99.7 Rule.

48. Home values. Assessment records indicate that the value of homes in a small city is skewed right, with a mean of $140,000 and standard deviation of $60,000. To check the accuracy of the assessment data, officials plan to conduct a detailed appraisal of 100 homes selected at random. Using the 68–95–99.7 Rule, draw and label an appropriate sampling model for the mean value of the homes selected.

49. The trial of the pyx. In 1150, it was recognized in England that coins should have a standard weight of precious metal as the basis for their value. A guinea, for example, was supposed to contain 128 grains of gold. (There are 360 grains in an ounce.) In the "trial of the pyx," coins minted under contract to the crown were weighed and compared to standard coins (which were kept in a wooden box called the pyx). Coins were allowed to deviate by no more than 0.28 grains—roughly equivalent to specifying that the standard deviation should be no greater than 0.09 grains (although they didn't know what a standard deviation was in 1150). In fact, the trial was performed by weighing 100 coins at a time and requiring the *sum* to deviate by no more than $100 \times 0.28 = 28$ or 28 grains—equivalent to the sum having a standard deviation of about 9 grains.

a) In effect, the trial of the pyx required that the mean weight of the sample of 100 coins have a standard deviation of 0.09 grains. Explain what was wrong with performing the trial in this manner.
b) What should the limit have been on the standard deviation of the mean?

Note: Because of this error, the crown was exposed to being cheated by private mints that could mint coins with greater variation and then, after their coins passed the trial, select out the heaviest ones and recast them at the proper weight, retaining the excess gold for themselves. The error persisted for over 600 years, until sampling distributions became better understood.

50. Safe cities. Allstate Insurance Company identified the 10 safest and 10 least-safe U.S. cities from among the 200 largest cities in the United States, based on the mean number of years drivers went between automobile accidents. The cities on both lists were all smaller than the 10 largest cities. Using facts about the sampling distribution model of the mean, explain why this is not surprising.

Just Checking Answers

1. A Normal model (approximately).
2. At the actual proportion of all customers who like the new location.
3. $SD(\hat{p}) = \sqrt{\dfrac{(0.5)(0.5)}{100}} = 0.05$
4. $SE(\bar{y}) = 120/\sqrt{100} = 12$
5. Decreases.
6. The standard error decreases by $1/\sqrt{2}$.

Answers

SECTION EXERCISE ANSWERS

1. a) Normal.
b) 0.36
c) They wouldn't change. The shape is still approximately Normal and the mean is still the true proportion.

3. a) 0.0339
b) 0.5
c) 0.842 (0.843 using a rounded answer from part a)
d) 0.01
e) 0.039

5. Yes. Assuming the survey is random, they should be independent. We don't know the true proportion, so we can't check np and nq, but we have observed 10 successes, which is sufficient.

7.

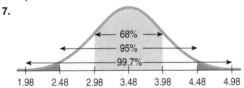

9. a) Normal.
b) 215 mg/dl
c) 4.63 mg/dl
d) Only c would change, to 3.0 mg/dl.

11. a) 0.0357
b) 400

13. a) One would expect many small fish and a few large ones.
b) We don't know the exact distribution, but we know it isn't Normal, so we don't have a model we can use to determine a probability.
c) Probably not. With a skewed distribution, a sample of size 5 is not large enough to use the Central Limit Theorem.
d) With a sample of 60, we can use the CLT even for a skewed population. The standard deviation is 0.30.
e) Yes, 4.5 pounds is more than 2 standard deviations above the mean, so by the 68–95–99.7 rule, it would happen less than 2.5% of the time.

CHAPTER EXERCISE ANSWERS

15. All the histograms are centered near 0.05. As n gets larger, the histograms approach the Normal shape, and the variability in the sample proportions decreases.

17. a)

n	Observed mean	Theoretical mean	Observed st. dev.	Theoretical st. dev.
20	0.0497	0.05	0.0479	0.0487
50	0.0516	0.05	0.0309	0.0308
100	0.0497	0.05	0.0215	0.0218
200	0.0501	0.05	0.0152	0.0154

b) They are all quite close to what we expect from the theory.
c) The histogram is unimodal and symmetric for $n = 200$.
d) The success/failure condition says that np and nq should both be at least 10, which is not satisfied until $n = 200$ for $p = 0.05$. The theory predicted my choice.

19. a) Symmetric, because probabilities of success and failure are equal.
b) 0.5
c) 0.125
d) $np = 8 < 10$

21. a) About 68% should have proportions between 0.4 and 0.6, about 95% between 0.3 and 0.7, and about 99.7% between 0.2 and 0.8.
b) $np = 12.5, nq = 12.5$; both are ≥ 10.
c)

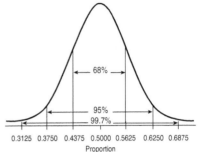

$np = nq = 32$; both are ≥ 10.
d) Becomes narrower (less spread around 0.5).

23. This is a fairly unusual result: about 2.26 SDs above the mean. The probability of that is about 0.012. So, in a class of 100 this is certainly a reasonable possibility.

25. a)

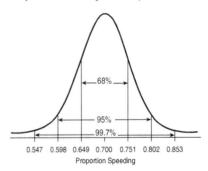

b) Both $np = 56$ and $nq = 24 \geq 10$. Drivers *may* be independent of each other, but if flow of traffic is very fast, they may not be. Or weather conditions may affect all drivers. In these cases they may get more or fewer speeders than they expect.

27. a) Assume that these children are typical of the population. They represent fewer than 10% of all children. We expect 20.4 nearsighted and 149.6 not; both are at least 10.
b)

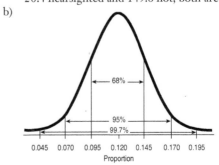

c) Probably between 12 and 29.

29. a) $\mu = 7\%, \sigma = 1.8\%$

b) Assume that clients pay independently of each other, that we have a random sample of all possible clients, and that these represent less than 10% of all possible clients. $np = 14$ and $nq = 186$ are both at least 10.

c) 0.048

31.

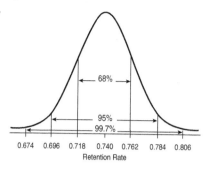

These are not random samples, and not all colleges may be typical (representative). $np = 296$, $nq = 104$ are large enough.

33. Yes; if their students were typical, a retention rate of $522/603 = 86.6\%$ would be over 7 standard deviations above the expected rate of 74%.

35. 0.212. Reasonable that those polled are independent of each other and represent less than 10% of all potential voters. We assume the sample was selected at random. Success/Failure Condition met: $np = 208$, $nq = 192$. Both ≥ 10.

37. 0.088 using $N(0.08, 0.022)$ model.

39. Answers will vary. Using $\mu + 3\sigma$ for "very sure," the restaurant should have 89 nonsmoking seats. Assumes customers at any time are independent of each other, a random sample, and represent less than 10% of all potential customers. $np = 72$, $nq = 48$, so Normal model is reasonable ($\mu = 0.60$, $\sigma = 0.045$).

41.
a) Normal, center at μ, standard deviation $\sigma/\sqrt{n}$.
b) Standard deviation will be smaller. Center will remain the same.

43.
a) The histogram is unimodal and slightly skewed to the right, centered at 36 inches with a standard deviation near 4 inches.
b) All the histograms are centered near 36 inches. As n gets larger, the histograms approach the Normal shape and the

variability in the sample means decreases. The histograms are fairly normal by the time the sample reaches size 5.

45. a)

n	Observed mean	Theoretical mean	Observed st. dev.	Theoretical st. dev.
2	36.314	36.33	2.855	2.842
5	36.314	36.33	1.805	1.797
10	36.341	36.33	1.276	1.271
20	36.339	36.33	0.895	0.899

b) They are all very close to what we would expect.
c) For samples as small as 5, the sampling distribution of sample means is unimodal and very symmetric.
d) The distribution of the original data is nearly unimodal and symmetric, so it doesn't take a very large sample size for the distribution of sample means to be approximately Normal.

47.

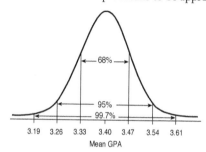

Normal, $\mu = 3.4$, $\sigma = 0.07$. We assume that the students are randomly assigned to the seminars and represent less than 10% of all possible students, and that individual's GPAs are independent of one another.

49.
a) The mean of 100 coins varies less from sample to sample than the individual coins.
b) $SD(\bar{y}) = \dfrac{\sigma}{\sqrt{n}} = \dfrac{0.09}{\sqrt{100}} = 0.009$

Confidence Intervals
for Proportions

José Luis Gutiérrez/
iStockphoto

The Gallup Organization

Dr. George Gallup was working as a market research director at an advertising agency in the 1930s when he founded the Gallup Organization to measure and track the public's attitudes toward political, social, and economic issues. He gained notoriety a few years later when he defied common wisdom and predicted that Franklin Roosevelt would win the U.S. presidential election in 1936. Today, the Gallup Poll is a household name. During the late 1930s, he founded the Gallup International Research Institute to conduct polls across the globe. International businesses use the Gallup polls to track how consumers think and feel about such issues as corporate behavior, government policies, and executive compensation.

During the late twentieth century, the Gallup Organization partnered with CNN and *USA Today* to conduct and publish public opinion polls. As Gallup once said, "If politicians and special interests have polls to guide them in pursuing their interests, the voters should have polls as well."[1]

National Archives/Getty Images

---

[1]Source: The Gallup Organization, Princeton, NJ, www.gallup.com.

Gallup's Web-based data storage system now holds data from polls taken over the last 65 years on a variety of topics, including consumer confidence, household savings, stock market investment, and unemployment.

WHO	U.S. adults
WHAT	Proportion who think economy is getting better
WHEN	March 2010
WHY	To measure expectations about the economy

To plan their inventory and production needs, businesses use a variety of forecasts about the economy. One important attribute is consumer confidence in the overall economy. Tracking changes in consumer confidence over time can help businesses gauge whether the demand for their products is on an upswing or about to experience a downturn. The Gallup Poll periodically asks a random sample of U.S. adults whether they think economic conditions are getting better, getting worse, or staying about the same. When they polled 2976 respondents in March 2010, only 1012 thought economic conditions in the United States were getting better—a sample proportion of $\hat{p} = 1012/2976 = 34.0\%$.[2] We (and Gallup) hope that this observed proportion is close to the population proportion, p, but we know that a second sample of 2976 adults wouldn't have a sample proportion of exactly 34.0%. In fact, Gallup did sample another group of adults just a few days later and found a sample proportion of 38.0%.

We know it isn't surprising that two random samples give slightly different results. We'd like to say something, not about different random *samples*, but about the proportion of *all* adults who thought that economic conditions in the United States were getting better in March 2010. The sampling distribution will be the key to our ability to generalize from our sample to the population.

1 A Confidence Interval

What do we know about our sampling distribution model? We know that it's centered at the true proportion, p, of all U.S. adults who think the economy is improving. But we don't know p. It isn't 34.0%. That's the $\hat{p}$ from our sample. What we do know is that the sampling distribution model of $\hat{p}$ is centered at p, and we know that the standard deviation of the sampling distribution is $\sqrt{\dfrac{pq}{n}}$. We also know, from the Central Limit Theorem, that the shape of the sampling distribution is approximately Normal, when the sample is large enough.

We don't know p, so we can't find the true standard deviation of the sampling distribution model. But we'll use $\hat{p}$ and find the standard error:

$$SE(\hat{p}) = \sqrt{\frac{\hat{p}\hat{q}}{n}} = \sqrt{\frac{(0.34)(1 - 0.34)}{2976}} = 0.009$$

Because the Gallup sample of 2976 is large, we know that the sampling distribution model for $\hat{p}$ should look approximately like the one shown in Figure 1.

Notation Alert! ———————

Remember that $\hat{p}$ is our sample estimate of the true proportion p. Recall also that q is just shorthand for $1 - p$, and $\hat{q} = 1 - \hat{p}$.

---

[2]A proportion is a *number* between 0 and 1. In business it's usually reported as a percentage. You may see it written either way.

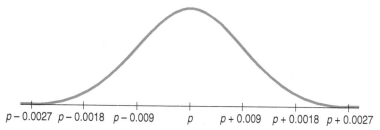

$p-0.0027$ $p-0.0018$ $p-0.009$ p $p+0.009$ $p+0.0018$ $p+0.0027$

Figure 1 The sampling distribution of sample proportions is centered at the true proportion, p, with a standard deviation of 0.009.

The sampling distribution model for $\hat{p}$ is Normal with a mean of p and a standard deviation we estimate to be $\sqrt{\dfrac{\hat{p}\hat{q}}{n}}$. Because the distribution is Normal, we'd expect that about 68% of all samples of 2976 U.S. adults taken in March 2010 would have had sample proportions within 1 standard deviation of p. And about 95% of all these samples will have proportions within $p \pm 2$ SEs. But where is *our* sample proportion in this picture? And what value does p have? We still don't know!

We do know that for 95% of random samples, $\hat{p}$ will be no more than 2 SEs away from p. So let's reverse it and look at it from $\hat{p}$'s point of view. If I'm $\hat{p}$, there's a 95% chance that p is no more than 2 SEs away from me. If I reach out 2 SEs, or 2×0.009, away from me on both sides, I'm 95% sure that p will be within my grasp. Of course, I won't know, and even if my interval does catch p, I still don't know its true value. The best I can do is state a probability that I've covered the true value in the interval.

ACME p-trap: Guaranteed*
to capture p.

*with 95% confidence

$\hat{p}-2$ SE $\qquad$ $\hat{p}$ $\qquad$ $\hat{p}+2$ SE

Figure 2 Reaching out 2 *SEs* on either side of $\hat{p}$ makes us 95% confident we'll trap the true proportion, p.

What Can We Say about a Proportion?

So what can we really say about p? Here's a list of things we'd like to be able to say and the reasons we can't say most of them:

1. **"34.0% of *all* U.S. adults thought the economy was improving."** It would be nice to be able to make absolute statements about population values with certainty, but we just don't have enough information to do that. There's no way to be sure that the population proportion is the same as the sample proportion; in fact, it almost certainly isn't. Observations vary. Another sample would yield a different sample proportion.

2. **"It is *probably* true that 34.0% of all U.S. adults thought the economy was improving."** No. In fact, we can be pretty sure that whatever the true proportion is, it's not exactly 34.0%, so the statement is not true.

3. **"We don't know exactly what proportion of U.S. adults thought the economy was improving, but we know that it's within the interval 34.0% ± 2 × 0.9%. That is, it's between 32.2% and 35.8%."** This is getting closer, but we still can't be certain. We can't know for sure that the true proportion is in this interval—or in any particular range.

4. **"We don't know exactly what proportion of U.S. adults thought the economy was improving, but the interval from 32.2% to 35.8%** *probably* **contains the true proportion."** We've now fudged twice—first by giving an interval and second by admitting that we only think the interval "probably" contains the true value.

That last statement is true, but it's a bit wishy-washy. We can tighten it up by quantifying what we mean by "probably." We saw that 95% of the time when we reach out 2 SEs from $\hat{p}$, we capture p, *so we can be 95% confident that this is one of those times*. After putting a number on the probability that this interval covers the true proportion, we've given our best guess of where the parameter is and how certain we are that it's within some range.

5. **"We are 95% confident that between 32.2% and 35.8% of U.S. adults thought the economy was improving."** This is now an appropriate interpretation of our confidence intervals. It's not perfect, but it's about the best we can do.

Each confidence interval discussed in the text has a name. You'll see many different kinds of confidence intervals. Some will be about more than *one* sample, some will be about statistics other than *proportions*, and some will use models other than the Normal. The interval calculated and interpreted here is an example of a **one-proportion z-interval**.[3] We'll lay out the formal definition in the next few pages.

What Does "95% Confidence" Really Mean?

What do we mean when we say we have 95% confidence that our interval contains the true proportion? Formally, what we mean is that "95% of samples of this size will produce confidence intervals that capture the true proportion." This is correct but a little long-winded, so we sometimes say "we are 95% confident that the true proportion lies in our interval." Our uncertainty is about whether the particular sample we have at hand is one of the successful ones or one of the 5% that fail to produce an interval that captures the true value. We have seen how proportions vary from sample to sample. If other pollsters had selected their own samples of adults, they would have found some who thought the economy was getting better, but each sample proportion would almost certainly differ from ours. When they each tried to estimate the true proportion, they'd center their confidence intervals at the proportions they observed in their own samples. Each would have ended up with a different interval.

Figure 3 shows the confidence intervals produced by simulating 20 samples. The purple dots are the simulated proportions of adults in each sample who thought the economy was improving, and the orange segments show the confidence intervals found for each simulated sample. The green line represents the true percentage of adults who thought the economy was improving. You can see that most of the simulated confidence intervals include the true value—but one missed. (Note that it is the *intervals* that vary from sample to sample; the green line doesn't move.)

---

[3]In fact, this confidence interval is so standard for a single proportion that you may see it simply called a "confidence interval for the proportion."

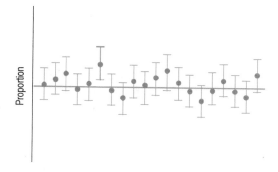

Figure 3   The horizontal green line shows the true proportion of people in March 2010 who thought the economy was improving. Most of the 20 simulated samples shown here produced 95% confidence intervals that captured the true value, but one missed.

Of course, a huge number of possible samples *could* be drawn, each with its own sample proportion. This simulation approximates just some of them. Each sample can be used to make a confidence interval. That's a large pile of possible confidence intervals, and ours is just one of those in the pile. Did *our* confidence interval "work"? We can never be sure because we'll never know the true proportion of all U.S. adults who thought in March 2010 that the economy was improving. However, the Central Limit Theorem assures us that 95% of the intervals in the pile are winners, covering the true value, and only 5%, on average, miss the target. That's why we're 95% *confident* that our interval is a winner.

For Example   **Finding a 95% confidence interval for a proportion**

The Chamber of Commerce of a mid-sized city has supported a proposal to change the zoning laws for a new part of town. The new regulations would allow for mixed commercial and residential development. The vote on the measure is scheduled for three weeks from today, and the president of the Chamber of Commerce is concerned that they may not have the majority of votes that they will need to pass the measure. She commissions a survey that asks likely voters if they plan to vote for the measure. Of the 516 people selected at random from likely voters, 289 said they would likely vote for the measure.

Questions:

a. Find a 95% confidence interval for the true proportion of voters who will vote for the measure. (Use the 68–95–99.7% Rule.)

b. What would you report to the president of the Chamber of Commerce?

Answer:

a. $\hat{p} = \dfrac{289}{516} = 0.56$ So, $SE(\hat{p}) = \sqrt{\dfrac{\hat{p}\hat{q}}{n}} = \sqrt{\dfrac{(0.56)(0.44)}{516}} = 0.022$

A 95% confidence interval for p can be found from $\hat{p} \pm 2\,SE(\hat{p}) = 0.56 \pm 2(0.022) = (0.516, 0.604)$ or 51.6% to 60.4%.

b. We are 95% confident that the true proportion of voters who plan to vote for the measure is between 51.6% and 60.4%. This assumes that the sample we have is representative of all likely voters.

---

2   Margin of Error: Certainty vs. Precision

We've just claimed that at a certain confidence level we've captured the true proportion of all U.S. adults who thought the economy was improving in March 2010. Our confidence interval stretched out the same distance on either side of the estimated proportion with the form:

$$\hat{p} \pm 2\,SE(\hat{p}).$$

The *extent* of that interval on either side of $\hat{p}$ is called the **margin of error (ME)**. In general, confidence intervals look like this:

$$estimate \pm ME.$$

The margin of error for our 95% confidence interval was 2 SEs. What if we wanted to be more confident? To be more confident, we'd need to capture p more often, and to do that, we'd need to make the interval wider. For example, if we want to be 99.7% confident, the margin of error will have to be 3 SEs.

$\hat{p} - 3\ SE$ $\hat{p}$ $\hat{p} + 3\ SE$

Figure 4 Reaching out 3 SEs on either side of $\hat{p}$ makes us 99.7% confident we'll trap the true proportion p. Compare the width of this interval with the interval in Figure 2.

The more confident we want to be, the larger the margin of error must be. We can be 100% confident that any proportion is between 0% and 100%, but that's not very useful. Or we could give a narrow confidence interval, say, from 33.98% to 34.02%. But we couldn't be very confident about a statement this precise. Every confidence interval is a balance between certainty and precision.

The tension between certainty and precision is always there. There is no simple answer to the conflict. Fortunately, in most cases we can be both sufficiently certain and sufficiently precise to make useful statements. The choice of confidence level is somewhat arbitrary, but you must choose the level yourself. The data can't do it for you. The most commonly chosen confidence levels are 90%, 95%, and 99%, but any percentage can be used. (In practice, though, using something like 92.9% or 97.2% might be viewed with suspicion.)

Critical Values

In our opening example, our margin of error was 2 SEs, which produced a 95% confidence interval. To change the confidence level, we'll need to change the *number* of SEs to correspond to the new level. A wider confidence interval means more confidence. For any confidence level the number of SEs we must stretch out on either side of $\hat{p}$ is called the **critical value**. Because it is based on the Normal

Notation Alert! ─────

We put an asterisk on a letter to indicate a critical value. We usually use "*z*" when we talk about Normal models, so z^* is always a critical value from a Normal model.

Some common confidence levels and their associated critical values:	
CI	**z^***
90%	1.645
95%	1.960
99%	2.576

model, we denote it z^*. For any confidence level, we can find the corresponding critical value from a computer, a calculator, or a Normal probability table.

For a 95% confidence interval, the precise critical value is $z^* = 1.96$. That is, 95% of a Normal model is found within ±1.96 standard deviations of the mean. We've been using $z^* = 2$ from the 68–95–99.7 Rule because 2 is very close to 1.96 and is easier to remember. Usually, the difference is negligible, but if you want to be precise, use 1.96.[4]

Suppose we could be satisfied with 90% confidence. What critical value would we need? We can use a smaller margin of error. Our greater precision is offset by our acceptance of being wrong more often (that is, having a confidence interval that misses the true value). Specifically, for a 90% confidence interval, the critical value is only 1.645 because for a Normal model, 90% of the values are within 1.645 standard deviations from the mean. By contrast, suppose your boss demands more confidence. If she wants an interval in which she can have 99% confidence, she'll need to include values within 2.576 standard deviations, creating a wider confidence interval.

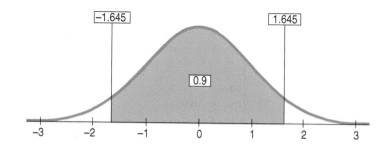

Figure 5 For a 90% confidence interval, the critical value is 1.645 because for a Normal model, 90% of the values fall within 1.645 standard deviations of the mean.

For Example — Finding confidence intervals for proportions with different levels of confidence

The president of the Chamber of Commerce is worried that 95% confidence is too low and wants a 99% confidence interval.

Question: Find a 99% confidence interval. Would you reassure her that the measure will pass? Explain.

Answer: In the example earlier in this chapter, we used 2 as the value of z^* for 95% confidence. A more precise value would be 1.96 for 95% confidence. For 99% confidence, the critical z-value is 2.756. So, a 99% confidence interval for the true proportion is

$$\hat{p} \pm 2.576 \, SE(\hat{p}) = 0.56 \pm 2.576(0.022) = (0.503, 0.617)$$

The confidence interval is now wider: 50.3% to 61.7%.

The Chamber of Commerce needs at least 50% for the vote to pass. At a 99% confidence level, it looks now as if the measure will pass. However, we must assume that the sample is representative of the voters in the actual election and that people vote in the election as they said they will when they took the survey.

---

3 Assumptions and Conditions

The statements we made about what all U.S. adults thought about the economy were possible because we used a Normal model for the sampling distribution. But is that model appropriate?

As we've seen, all statistical models make assumptions. If those assumptions are not true, the model might be inappropriate, and our conclusions based on it may be

---

[4]It's been suggested that since 1.96 is both an unusual value and so important in Statistics, you can recognize someone who's had a Statistics course by just saying "1.96" and seeing whether they react.

wrong. Because the confidence interval is built on the Normal model for the sampling distribution, the assumptions and conditions are the same as those we discussed previously. But, because they are so important, we'll go over them again.

You can never be certain that an assumption is true, but you can decide intelligently whether it is reasonable. When you have data, you can often decide whether an assumption is plausible by checking a related condition in the data. However, you'll want to make a statement about the world at large, not just about the data. So the assumptions you make are not just about how the data look, but about how representative they are.

Here are the assumptions and the corresponding conditions to check before creating (or believing) a confidence interval about a proportion.

Independence Assumption

You first need to think about whether the independence assumption is plausible. You can look for reasons to suspect that it fails. You might wonder whether there is any reason to believe that the data values somehow affect each other. (For example, might any of the adults in the sample be related?) This condition depends on your knowledge of the situation. It's not one you can check by looking at the data. However, now that you have data, there are two conditions that you can check:

- **Randomization Condition:** Were the data sampled at random or generated from a properly randomized experiment? Proper randomization can help ensure independence.

- **10% Condition:** Samples are almost always drawn without replacement. Usually, you'd like to have as large a sample as you can. But if you sample from a small population, the probability of success may be different for the last few individuals you draw than it was for the first few. For example, if most of the women have already been sampled, the chance of drawing a woman from the remaining population is lower. If the sample exceeds 10% of the population, the probability of a success changes so much during the sampling that a Normal model may no longer be appropriate. But if less than 10% of the population is sampled, it is safe to assume to have independence.

Sample Size Assumption

The model we use for inference is based on the Central Limit Theorem. So, the sample must be large enough for the Normal sampling model to be appropriate. It turns out that we need more data when the proportion is close to either extreme (0 or 1). This requirement is easy to check with the following condition:

- **Success/Failure Condition:** We must expect our sample to contain at least 10 "successes" and at least 10 "failures." Recall that by tradition we arbitrarily label one alternative (usually the outcome being counted) as a "success" even if it's something bad. The other alternative is then a "failure." So we check that both $n\hat{p} \geq 10$ and $n\hat{q} \geq 10$.

One-proportion z-interval

When the conditions are met, we are ready to find the confidence interval for the population proportion, p. The confidence interval is $\hat{p} \pm z^* \times SE(\hat{p})$, where the standard deviation of the proportion is estimated by $SE(\hat{p}) = \sqrt{\dfrac{\hat{p}\hat{q}}{n}}$.

For Example | Assumptions and conditions for a confidence interval for proportions

We previously reported a confidence interval to the president of the Chamber of Commerce.

Question: Were the assumptions and conditions for making this interval satisfied?

Answer: Because the sample was randomized, we assume that the responses of the people surveyed were independent so the randomization condition is met. We assume that 516 people represent fewer than 10% of the likely voters in the town so the 10% condition is met. Because 289 people said they were likely to vote for the measure and thus 227 said they were not, both are much larger than 10 so the Success/Failure condition is also met.

All the conditions to make a confidence interval for the proportion appear to have been satisfied.

Guided Example | Public Opinion

Sipa/Newscom

In the film *Up in the Air*, George Clooney portrays a man whose job it is to tell workers that they have been fired. The reactions to such news took a somewhat odd turn in France in the spring of 2009 when workers at Sony France took the boss hostage for a night and barricaded their factory entrance with a tree trunk. He was freed only after he agreed to reopen talks on their severance packages. Similar incidents occurred at 3M and Caterpillar plants in France. A poll taken by *Le Parisien* in April 2009 found 45% of the French "supportive" of such action. A similar poll taken by *Paris Match*, April 2–3, 2009, found 30% "approving" and 63% were "understanding" or "sympathetic" of the action. Only 7% condemned the practice of "bossnapping."

The *Paris Match* poll was based on a random representative sample of 1010 adults. What can we conclude about the proportion of all French adults who sympathize with (without supporting outright) the practice of bossnapping?

To answer this question, we'll build a confidence interval for the proportion of all French adults who sympathize with the practice of bossnapping. As with other procedures, there are three steps to building and summarizing a confidence interval for proportions: Plan, Do, and Report.

WHO	Adults in France
WHAT	Proportion who sympathize with the practice of bossnapping
WHEN	April 2–3, 2009
WHERE	France
HOW	1010 adults were randomly sampled by the French Institute of Public Opinion (l'Ifop) for the magazine *Paris Match*
WHY	To investigate public opinion of bossnapping

PLAN

Setup State the context of the question.

Identify the *parameter* you wish to estimate. Identify the *population* about which you wish to make statements.

Choose and state a confidence level.

Model Think about the assumptions and check the conditions to decide whether we can use the Normal model.

We want to find an interval that is likely with 95% confidence to contain the true proportion, *p*, of French adults who sympathize with the practice of bossnapping. We have a random sample of 1010 French adults, with a sample proportion of 63%.

✓ **Independence Assumption:** A French polling agency, l'Ifop, phoned a random sample of French adults. It is unlikely that any respondent influenced another.

✓ **Randomization Condition:** l'Ifop drew a random sample from all French adults. We don't have details of their randomization but assume that we can trust it.

✓ **10% Condition:** Although sampling was necessarily without replacement, there are many more French adults than were sampled. The sample is certainly less than 10% of the population.

(continued)

✓ **Success/Failure Condition:**
$n\hat{p} = 1010 \times 0.63 = 636 \geq 10$ and
$n\hat{q} = 1010 \times 0.37 = 374 \geq 10$,
so the sample is large enough.

State the sampling distribution model for the statistic. Choose your method.

The conditions are satisfied, so I can use a Normal model to find a one-proportion z-interval.

DO

Mechanics Construct the confidence interval. First, find the standard error. (Remember: It's called the "standard error" because we don't know p and have to use $\hat{p}$ instead.)

$n = 1010, \hat{p} = 0.63,$ so
$$SE(\hat{p}) = \sqrt{\frac{0.63 \times 0.37}{1010}} = 0.015$$

Next, find the margin of error. We could informally use 2 for our critical value, but 1.96 is more accurate.[5]

Because the sampling model is Normal, for a 95% confidence interval, the critical value $z^* = 1.96$. The margin of error is:
$$ME = z^* \times SE(\hat{p}) = 1.96 \times 0.015 = 0.029$$
So the 95% confidence interval is:
$$0.63 \pm 0.029 \text{ or } (0.601, 0.659).$$

Write the confidence interval.

REALITY CHECK

Check that the interval is plausible. We may not have a strong expectation for the center, but the width of the interval depends primarily on the sample size—especially when the estimated proportion is near 0.5.

The confidence interval covers a range of about plus or minus 3%. That's about the width we might expect for a sample size of about 1000 (when $\hat{p}$ is reasonably close to 0.5).

REPORT

Conclusion Interpret the confidence interval in the proper context. We're 95% confident that our interval captured the true proportion.

MEMO

Re: Bossnapping Survey

The polling agency l'Ifop surveyed 1010 French adults and asked whether they approved, were sympathetic to or disapproved of recent bossnapping actions. Although we can't know the true proportion of French adults who were sympathetic (without supporting outright), based on this survey we can be 95% confident that between 60.1% and 65.9% of all French adults were. Because this is an ongoing concern for public safety, we may want to repeat the survey to obtain more current data. We may also want to keep these results in mind for future corporate public relations.

Just Checking

Think some more about the 95% confidence interval we just created for the proportion of French adults who were sympathetic to bossnapping.

1   If we wanted to be 98% confident, would our confidence interval need to be wider or narrower?

2   Our margin of error was about If we wanted to reduce it to without increasing the sample size, would our level of confidence be higher or lower?

3   If the organization had polled more people, would the interval's margin of error have likely been larger or smaller?

---

[5]If you are following along on your calculator and not rounding off (as we have done for this example), you'll get $SE = 0.0151918$ and a ME of 0.029776.

4 Choosing the Sample Size

Every confidence interval must balance precision—the width of the interval—against confidence. Although it is good to be precise and comforting to be confident, there is a trade-off between the two. A confidence interval that says that the percentage is between 10% and 90% wouldn't be of much use, although you could be quite confident that it covered the true proportion. An interval from 43% to 44% is reassuringly precise, but not if it carries a confidence level of 35%. It's a rare study that reports confidence levels lower than 80%. Levels of 95% or 99% are more common.

The time to decide whether the margin of error is small enough to be useful is when you design your study. Don't wait until you compute your confidence interval. To get a narrower interval without giving up confidence, you need to have less variability in your sample proportion. How can you do that? Choose a larger sample.

Consider a company planning to offer a new service to their customers. Product managers want to estimate the proportion of customers who are likely to purchase this new service to within 3% with 95% confidence. How large a sample do they need?

Let's look at the margin of error:

$$ME = z^*\sqrt{\frac{\hat{p}\hat{q}}{n}}$$

$$0.03 = 1.96\sqrt{\frac{\hat{p}\hat{q}}{n}}.$$

They want to find n, the sample size. To find n, they need a value for $\hat{p}$. They don't know $\hat{p}$ because they don't have a sample yet, but they can probably guess a value. The worst case—the value that makes the SD (and therefore n) largest—is 0.50, so if they use that value for $\hat{p}$, they'll certainly be safe.

The company's equation, then, is:

$$0.03 = 1.96\sqrt{\frac{(0.5)(0.5)}{n}}.$$

To solve for n, just multiply both sides of the equation by $\sqrt{n}$ and divide by 0.03:

$$0.03\sqrt{n} = 1.96\sqrt{(0.5)(0.5)}$$

$$\sqrt{n} = \frac{1.96\sqrt{(0.5)(0.5)}}{0.03} \approx 32.67$$

Then square the result to find n:

$$n \approx (32.67)^2 \approx 1067.1$$

That method will probably give a value with a fraction. To be safe, always round up. The company will need at least 1068 respondents to keep the margin of error as small as 3% with a confidence level of 95%.

Unfortunately, bigger samples cost more money and require more effort. Because the standard error declines only with the *square root* of the sample size, to cut the standard error (and thus the ME) in half, you must *quadruple* the sample size.

Generally a margin of error of 5% or less is acceptable, but different circumstances call for different standards. The size of the margin of error may be a marketing decision or one determined by the amount of financial risk you (or the company) are willing to accept. Drawing a large sample to get a smaller ME,

What $\hat{p}$ Should We Use?

Often you'll have an estimate of the population proportion based on experience or perhaps on a previous study. If so, use that value as $\hat{p}$ in calculating what size sample you need. If not, the cautious approach is to use $\hat{p} = 0.5$. That will determine the largest sample necessary regardless of the true proportion. It's the *worst case* scenario.

however, can run into trouble. It takes time to survey 2400 people, and a survey that extends over a week or more may be trying to hit a target that moves during the time of the survey. A news event or new product announcement can change opinions in the middle of the survey process.

Keep in mind that the sample size for a survey is the number of respondents, not the number of people to whom questionnaires were sent or whose phone numbers were dialed. Also keep in mind that a low response rate turns any study essentially into a voluntary response study, which is of little value for inferring population values. It's almost always better to spend resources on increasing the response rate than on surveying a larger group. A complete or nearly complete response by a modest-size sample can yield useful results.

Surveys are not the only place where proportions pop up. Credit card banks sample huge mailing lists to estimate what proportion of people will accept a credit card offer. Even pilot studies may be mailed to 50,000 customers or more. Most of these customers don't respond. But in this case, that doesn't make the sample smaller. In fact, they did respond in a way—they just said "No thanks." To the bank, the response rate[6] is $\hat{p}$. With a typical success rate below 1%, the bank needs a very small margin of error—often as low as 0.1%—to make a sound business decision. That calls for a large sample, and the bank should take care when estimating the size needed. For our election poll example, we used $p = 0.5$, both because it's safe and because we honestly believed p to be near 0.5. If the bank used 0.5, they'd get an absurd answer. Instead they base their calculation on a value of p that they expect to find from their experience.

> **Why 1000?**
>
> Public opinion polls often use a sample size of 1000, which gives an ME of about 3% (at 95% confidence) when p is near 0.5. But businesses and nonprofit organizations often use much larger samples to estimate the response to a direct mail campaign. Why? Because the proportion of people who respond to these mailings is very low, often 5% or even less. An ME of 3% may not be precise enough if the response rate is that low. Instead, an ME like 0.1% would be more useful, and that requires a very large sample size.

Photodisc

> ## How much of a difference can it make?
>
> A credit card company is about to send out a mailing to test the market for a new credit card. From that sample, they want to estimate the true proportion of people who will sign up for the card nationwide. To be within a tenth of a percentage point, or 0.001 of the true acquisition rate with 95% confidence, how big does the test mailing have to be? Similar mailings in the past lead them to expect that about 0.5% of the people receiving the offer will accept it. Using those values, they find:
>
> $$ME = 0.001 = z^* \sqrt{\frac{pq}{n}} = 1.96 \sqrt{\frac{(0.005)(0.995)}{n}}$$
>
> $$(0.001)^2 = 1.96^2 \frac{(0.005)(0.995)}{n} \Rightarrow n = \frac{1.96^2(0.005)(0.995)}{(0.001)^2}$$
>
> $$= 19{,}111.96 \ or \ 19{,}112$$
>
> That's a perfectly reasonable size for a trial mailing. But if they had used 0.50 for their estimate of p they would have found:
>
> $$ME = 0.001 = z^* \sqrt{\frac{pq}{n}} = 1.96 \sqrt{\frac{(0.5)(0.5)}{n}}$$
>
> $$(0.001)^2 = 1.96^2 \frac{(0.5)(0.5)}{n} \Rightarrow n = \frac{1.96^2(0.5)(0.5)}{(0.001)^2} = 960{,}400.$$
>
> Quite a different result!

---

[6]Be careful. In marketing studies like this *every* mailing yields a response—"yes" or "no"—and response rate means the success rate, the proportion of customers who accept the offer. That's a different use of the term response rate from the one used in survey response.

For Example — Sample size calculations for a confidence interval for a proportion

The President of the Chamber of Commerce in the previous examples is worried that the 99% confidence interval is too wide. Recall that it was (0.503, 0.617), which has a width of 0.114.

Question: How large a sample would she need to take to have a 99% interval half as wide? One quarter as wide? What if she wanted a 95% confidence interval that was plus or minus 3 percentage points? How large a sample would she need?

Answer: Because the formula for the confidence interval is dependent on the inverse of the square root of the sample size:

$$\hat{p} \pm z^* \sqrt{\frac{\hat{p}\hat{q}}{n}},$$

a sample size four times as large will produce a confidence interval *half* as wide. The original 99% confidence interval had a sample size of 516. If she wants it half as wide, she will need about $4 \times 516 = 2064$ respondents. To get it a quarter as wide she'd need $4^2 \times 516 = 8192$ respondents!

If she wants a 99% confidence interval that's plus or minus 3 percentage points, she must calculate

$$\hat{p} \pm z^* \sqrt{\frac{\hat{p}\hat{y}}{n}} = \hat{p} \pm 0.03$$

so

$$2.576 \sqrt{\frac{(0.5)(0.5)}{n}} = 0.03$$

which means that

$$n \approx \left(\frac{2.576}{0.03}\right)^2 (0.5)(0.5) = 1843.27$$

Rounding up, she'd need 1844 respondents. We used 0.5 because we didn't have any information about the election before taking the survey. Using $p = 0.56$ instead would give $n = 1817$.

*5 A Confidence Interval for Small Samples

When the Success/Failure condition fails, all is not lost. A simple adjustment to the calculation lets us make a confidence interval anyway. All we do is add four *synthetic* observations, two to the successes and two to the failures. So instead of the proportion $\hat{p} = \frac{y}{n}$, we use the adjusted proportion $\widetilde{p} = \frac{y + 2}{n + 4}$, and for convenience, we write $\widetilde{n} = n + 4$. We modify the interval by using these adjusted values for both the center of the interval *and* the margin of error. Now the adjusted interval is:

$$\widetilde{p} \pm z^* \sqrt{\frac{\widetilde{p}(1 - \widetilde{p})}{\widetilde{n}}}.$$

This adjusted form gives better performance overall[7] and works much better for proportions near 0 or 1. It has the additional advantage that we don't need to check the Success/Failure condition that $n\hat{p}$ and $n\hat{q}$ are greater than 10.

Suppose a student in an advertising class is studying the impact of ads placed during the Super Bowl, and wants to know what proportion of students

---

[7] By "better performance" we mean that the 95% confidence interval's actual chance of covering the true population proportion is closer to 95%. Simulation studies have shown that our original, simpler confidence interval covers the true population proportion less than 95% of the time when the sample size is small or the proportion is very close to 0 or 1. The original idea was E. B. Wilson's, but the simplified approach we suggest here appeared in A. Agresti and B. A. Coull, "Approximate Is Better Than 'Exact' for Interval Estimation of Binomial Proportions," *The American Statistician*, 52 (1998): 119–126.

on campus watched it. She takes a random sample of 25 students and find that all 25 watched the Super Bowl for a $\hat{p}$ of 100%. A 95% confidence interval is $\hat{p} \pm 1.96\sqrt{\dfrac{\hat{p}\hat{q}}{n}} = 1.0 \pm 1.96\sqrt{\dfrac{1.0(0.0)}{25}} = (1.0, 1.0)$. Does she really believe that *every* one of the 30,000 students on her campus watched the Super Bowl? Probably not. And she realizes that the Success/Failure condition is severely violated because there are *no* failures.

Using the pseudo observation method described above, she adds two successes and two failures to the sample to get 27/29 successes, for $\tilde{p} = \dfrac{27}{29} = 0.931$. The standard error is no longer 0, but $SE(\tilde{p}) = \sqrt{\dfrac{\tilde{p}\tilde{q}}{\tilde{n}}} = \sqrt{\dfrac{(0.931)(0.069)}{29}} = 0.047$.

Now, a 95% confidence interval is $0.931 \pm 1.96(0.047) = (0.839, 1.023)$. In other words, she's 95% confident that between 83.9% and 102.3% of all students on campus watched the Super Bowl. Because any number greater than 100% makes no sense, she will report simply that with 95% confidence the proportion is at least 83.9%.

What Can Go Wrong?

Confidence intervals are powerful tools. Not only do they tell us what is known about the parameter value, but—more important—they also tell us what we *don't* know. In order to use confidence intervals effectively, you must be clear about what you say about them.

- **Be sure to use the right language to describe your confidence intervals.** Technically, you should say "I am 95% confident that the interval from 32.2% to 35.8% captures the true proportion of U.S. adults who thought the economy was improving in March 2010." That formal phrasing emphasizes that *your confidence (and your uncertainty) is about the interval, not the true proportion.* But you may choose a more casual phrasing like "I am 95% confident that between 32.2% and 35.8% of U.S. adults thought the economy was improving in March 2010." Because you've made it clear that the uncertainty is yours and you didn't suggest that the randomness is in the true proportion, this is OK. Keep in mind that it's the interval that's random. It's the focus of both our confidence and our doubt.

- **Don't suggest that the parameter varies.** A statement like "there is a 95% chance that the true proportion is between 32.2% and 35.8%" sounds as though you think the population proportion wanders around and sometimes happens to fall between 32.2% and 35.8%. When you interpret a confidence interval, make it clear that *you* know that the population parameter is fixed and that it is the interval that varies from sample to sample.

- **Don't claim that other samples will agree with yours.** Keep in mind that the confidence interval makes a statement about the true population proportion. An interpretation such as "in 95% of samples of U.S. adults the proportion who thought the economy was improving in March 2010 will be between 32.2% and 35.8%" is just wrong. The interval isn't about sample proportions but about the population proportion. There is nothing special about the sample we happen to have; it doesn't establish a standard for other samples.

- **Don't be certain about the parameter.** Saying "between 32.2% and 35.8% of U.S. adults thought the economy was improving in March 2010" asserts that the population proportion cannot be outside that interval. Of course, you can't be absolutely certain of that (just pretty sure).

- **Don't forget: It's about the parameter.** Don't say "I'm 95% confident that $\hat{p}$ is between 32.2% and 35.8%." Of course, you are—in fact, we calculated that our sample proportion was 34.0%. So we already *know* the sample proportion. The confidence interval is about the (unknown) population parameter, p.

- **Don't claim to know too much.** Don't say "I'm 95% confident that between 32.2% and 35.8% of all U.S. adults think the economy is improving." Gallup sampled adults during March 2010, and public opinion shifts over time.

- **Do take responsibility.** Confidence intervals are about *un*certainty. *You* are the one who is uncertain, not the parameter. You have to accept the responsibility and consequences of the fact that not all the intervals you compute will capture the true value. In fact, about 5% of the 95% confidence intervals you find will fail to capture the true value of the parameter. You *can* say "I am 95% confident that between 32.2% and 35.8% of U.S. adults thought the economy was improving in March 2010."

Confidence intervals and margins of error depend crucially on the assumption and conditions. When they're not true the results may be invalid. For your own surveys, follow the survey designs outlined previously. For surveys you read about, so be sure to:

- **Watch out for biased sampling.** Just because we have more statistical machinery now doesn't mean we can forget what we've already learned. A questionnaire that finds that 85% of people enjoy filling out surveys still suffers from nonresponse bias even though now we're able to put confidence intervals around this (biased) estimate.

- **Think about independence.** The assumption that the values in a sample are mutually independent is one that you usually cannot check. It always pays to think about it, though.

- **Be careful of sample size.** The validity of the confidence interval for proportions may be affected by sample size. Avoid using the confidence interval on "small" samples.

Ethics in Action

One of Tim Solsby's major responsibilities at MassEast Federal Credit Union is managing online services and website content. In an effort to better serve MassEast members, Tim routinely visits the sites of other financial institutions to get ideas on how he can improve MassEast's online presence. One of the features that caught his attention was a "teen network" that focused on educating teenagers about personal finances. He thought that this was a novel idea and one that could help build a stronger online community among MassEast's members. The executive board of MassEast was meeting next month to consider proposals for improving credit union services, and Tim was eager to present his idea for adding an online teen network. To strengthen his proposal, he decided to poll current credit union members. On the MassEast Federal Credit Union website, he posted an online survey. Among the questions he asked are "Do you have teenage children in your household?" and "Would you encourage your teenage children to learn more about managing personal finances?" Based on 850 responses, Tim constructed a 95% confidence interval and was able to estimate (with 95% confidence) that between 69% and 75% of MassEast members had teenage children at home and that between 62% and 68% would encourage their teenagers to learn more about managing personal finances. Tim believed these results would help convince the executive board that MassEast should add this feature to its website.

ETHICAL ISSUE *The sampling method introduces bias because it is a voluntary response sample and not a random sample. Customers who do have teenagers are more likely to respond than those that do not (related to Item A, ASA Ethical Guidelines).*

ETHICAL SOLUTION *Tim should revise his sampling methods. He might draw a simple random sample of credit union customers and try and contact them by mail or telephone. Whatever method he uses, Tim needs to disclose the sampling procedure to the Board and discuss possible sources of bias.*

What Have We Learned?

Learning Objectives

■ Construct a confidence interval for a proportion, *p*, as the statistic, $\hat{p}$, plus and minus a **margin of error**.

  • The margin of error consists of a **critical value** based on the sampling model times a **standard error** based on the sample.

  • The critical value is found from the Normal model.

  • The standard error of a sample proportion is calculated as $\sqrt{\dfrac{\hat{p}\hat{q}}{n}}$.

■ Interpret a confidence interval correctly.

  • You can claim to have the specified level of confidence that the interval you have computed actually covers the true value.

■ Understand the importance of the sample size, *n*, in improving both the certainty (confidence level) and precision (margin of error).

  • For the same sample size and proportion, more certainty requires less precision and more precision requires less certainty.

■ Know and check the assumptions and conditions for finding and interpreting confidence intervals.

  • Independence Assumption or Randomization Condition

  • 10% Condition

  • Success/Failure Condition

■ Be able to invert the calculation of the margin of error to find the sample size required, given a proportion, a confidence level, and a desired margin of error.

Terms

Confidence interval

An interval of values usually of the form

$$estimate \pm margin\ of\ error$$

found from data in such a way that a percentage of all random samples can be expected to yield intervals that capture the true parameter value.

Critical value

The number of standard errors to move away from the mean of the sampling distribution to correspond to the specified level of confidence. The critical value, denoted z^*, is usually found from a table or with technology.

Margin of error (ME)

In a confidence interval, the extent of the interval on either side of the observed statistic value. A margin of error is typically the product of a critical value from the sampling distribution and a standard error from the data. A small margin of error corresponds to a confidence interval that pins down the parameter precisely. A large margin of error corresponds to a confidence interval that gives relatively little information about the estimated parameter.

One-proportion *z*-interval

A confidence interval for the true value of a proportion. The confidence interval is

$$\hat{p} \pm z^*SE(\hat{p})$$

where z^* is a critical value from the Standard Normal model corresponding to the specified confidence level.

Technology Help: Confidence Intervals for Proportions

Confidence intervals for proportions are so easy and natural that many statistics packages don't offer special commands for them. Most statistics programs want the "raw data" for computations. For proportions, the raw data are the "success" and "failure" status for each case. Usually, these are given as 1 or 0, but they might be category names like "yes" and "no." Often we just know the proportion of successes, $\hat{p}$, and the total count, n. Computer packages don't usually deal with summary data like this easily, but the statistics routines found on many graphing calculators allow you to create confidence intervals from summaries of the data—usually all you need to enter are the number of successes and the sample size.

In some programs you can reconstruct variables of 0's and 1's with the given proportions. But even when you have (or can reconstruct) the raw data values, you may not get *exactly* the same margin of error from a computer package as you would find working by hand. The reason is that some packages make approximations or use other methods. The result is very close but not exactly the same. Fortunately, Statistics means never having to say you're certain, so the approximate result is good enough.

EXCEL   XLSTAT

Inference methods for proportions are not part of the standard Excel tool set, but you can compute a confidence interval using Excel's equations:

For example, suppose you have 100 observations in cells A1:A100 and each cell is "yes" or "no."

- In cell B2, enter =countif(A1:A100,"yes")/100 to compute the proportion of "yes" responses. (The 100 is because you have 100 observations. Replace it with the number of observations you actually have.)
- In cell B3, enter =sqrt(B2*(1-B2)/100) to compute the standard error.
- In cell B4, enter =normsinv(.975) for a 95% confidence interval.
- In cell B5, enter =B2-B4*B3 as the lower end of the CI.
- In cell B6, enter =B2+B4*B3 as the upper end of the CI.

Comments

For summarized data, compute the proportion in cell B2 according to whether your summaries are counts, percentages, or already

proportions, and continue with the example, using total count in place of the "100" in the second step.

JMP

For a **categorical** variable that holds category labels, the **Distribution** platform includes tests and intervals for proportions. For summarized data,

- Put the category names in one variable and the frequencies in an adjacent variable.
- Designate the frequency column to have the role of frequency.
- Then use the Distribution platform.

Comments

JMP uses slightly different methods for proportion inferences than those discussed in this text. Your answers are likely to be slightly different, especially for small samples.

MINITAB

Choose **Basic Statistics** from the **Stat** menu.

- Choose **1Proportion** from the Basic Statistics submenu.
- If the data are category names in a variable, assign the variable from the variable list box to the **Samples in columns** box. If you have summarized data, click the **Summarized Data** button and fill in the number of trials and the number of successes.
- Click the **Options** button and specify the remaining details.
- If you have a large sample, check **Use test and interval based on normal distribution.** Click the **OK** button.

Comments

When working from a variable that names categories, MINITAB treats the last category as the "success" category. You can specify how the categories should be ordered.

SPSS

SPSS does not find confidence intervals for proportions.

Brief CASE

iStockphoto

Clint Hild/iStockphoto

Investment

During the period from June 27–29, 2003, the Gallup Organization asked stock market investors questions about the amount and type of their investments. The questions asked the investors were:

1. Is the total amount of your investments right now $10,000 or more, or is it less than $10,000?

2. If you had $1000 to invest, would you be more likely to invest it in stocks or bonds?

In response to the first question, 65% of the 692 investors reported that they currently have at least $10,000 invested in the stock market. In response to the second question, 48% of the 692 investors reported that they would be more likely to invest in stocks (over bonds). Compute the standard error for each sample proportion. Compute and describe the 95% confidence intervals in the context of the question. What would the size of the sample need to be for the margin of error to be 3%?

Find a recent survey about investment practices or opinions and write up a short report on your findings.

Forecasting Demand

Utilities must forecast the demand for energy use far into the future because it takes decades to plan and build new power plants. Ron Bears, who worked for a northeast utility company, had the job of predicting the proportion of homes that would choose to use electricity to heat their homes. Although he was prepared to report a confidence interval for the true proportion, after seeing his preliminary report, his management demanded a single number as his prediction.

Help Ron explain to his management why a confidence interval for the desired proportion would be more useful for planning purposes. Explain how the precision of the interval and the confidence we can have in it are related to each other. Discuss the business consequences of an interval that is too narrow and the consequences of an interval with too low a confidence level.

Exercises

SECTION 1

1. For each situation below identify the population and the sample and identify p and $\hat{p}$ if appropriate and what the value of $\hat{p}$ is. Would you trust a confidence interval for the true proportion based on these data? Explain briefly why or why not.

a) As concertgoers enter a stadium, a security guard randomly inspects their backpacks for alcoholic beverages. Of the 130 backpacks checked so far, 17 contained alcoholic beverages of some kind. The guards want to estimate the percentage of all backpacks of concertgoers at this concert that contain alcoholic beverages.

b) The website of the English newspaper *The Guardian* asked visitors to the site to say whether they approved of recent "bossnapping" actions by British workers who were outraged over being fired. Of those who responded, 49.2% said "Yes. Desperate times, desperate measures."

c) An airline wants to know the weight of carry-on baggage that customers take on their international routes, so they take a random sample of 50 bags and find that the average weight is 17.3 pounds.

2. For each situation below identify the population and the sample and explain what p and $\hat{p}$ represent and what the value of $\hat{p}$ is. Would you trust a confidence interval for the true proportion based on these data? Explain briefly why or why not.

a) A marketing analyst conducts a large survey of her customers to find out how much money they plan to spend at the company website in the next 6 months. The average amount reported from the 534 respondents is $145.34.

b) A campus survey on a large campus (40,000 students) is trying to find out whether students approve of a new parking policy allowing students to park in previously inaccessible parking lots, but for a small fee. Surveys are sent out by mail and e-mail. Of the 243 surveys returned, 134 are in favor of the change.

c) The human resources department of a large Fortune 100 company wants to find out how many employees would take advantage of an on-site day care facility. They send out an e-mail to 500 employees and receive responses from 450 of them. Of those responding, 75 say that they would take advantage of such a facility.

3. A survey of 200 students is selected randomly on a large university campus. They are asked if they use a laptop in class to take notes. Suppose that based on the survey, 70 of the 200 students responded "yes."

a) What is the value of the sample proportion $\hat{p}$?
b) What is the standard error of the sample proportion?
c) Construct an approximate 95% confidence interval for the true proportion p by taking ± 2 SEs from the sample proportion.

4. From a survey of 250 coworkers you find that 155 would like the company to provide on-site day care.

a) What is the value of the sample proportion $\hat{p}$?
b) What is the standard error of the sample proportion?
c) Construct an approximate 95% confidence interval for the true proportion p by taking ± 2 SEs from the sample proportion.

SECTION 2

5. From a survey of coworkers you find that 48% of 200 have already received this year's flu vaccine. An approximate 95% confidence interval is (0.409, 0.551). Which of the following are true? If not, explain briefly.

a) 95% of the coworkers fall in the interval (0.409, 0.551).
b) We are 95% confident that the proportion of coworkers who have received this year's flu vaccine is between 40.9% and 55.1%.
c) There is a 95% chance that a random selected coworker has received the vaccine.
d) There is a 48% chance that a random selected coworker has received the vaccine.
e) We are 95% confident that between 40.9% and 55.1% of the samples will have a proportion near 48%.

6. As in Exercise 5, from a survey of coworkers you find that 48% of 200 have already received this year's flu

vaccine. An approximate 95% confidence interval is (0.409, 0.551).

a) How would the confidence interval change if the sample size had been 800 instead of 200?
b) How would the confidence interval change if the confidence level had been 90% instead of 95%?
c) How would the confidence interval change if the confidence level had been 99% instead of 95%?

SECTION 3

7. Consider each situation described. Identify the population and the sample, explain what p and $\hat{p}$ represent, and tell whether the methods of this chapter can be used to create a confidence interval.

a) A consumer group hoping to assess customer experiences with auto dealers surveys 167 people who recently bought new cars; 3% of them expressed dissatisfaction with the salesperson.

b) A cell phone service provider wants to know what percent of U.S. college students have cell phones. A total of 2883 students were asked as they entered a football stadium, and 2243 indicated they had phones with them.

8. Consider each situation described. Identify the population and the sample, explain what p and $\hat{p}$ represent, and tell whether the methods of this chapter can be used to create a confidence interval.

a) A total of 240 potato plants in a field in Maine are randomly checked, and only 7 show signs of blight. How severe is the blight problem for the U.S. potato industry?

b) Concerned about workers' compensation costs, a small company decided to investigate on-the-job injuries. The company reported that 12 of their 309 employees suffered an injury on the job last year. What can the company expect in future years?

SECTION 4

9. Suppose you want to estimate the proportion of traditional college students on your campus who own their own car. You have no preconceived idea of what that proportion might be.

a) What sample size is needed if you wish to be 95% confident that your estimate is within 0.02 of the true proportion?
b) What sample size is needed if you wish to be 99% confident that your estimate is within 0.02 of the true proportion?
c) What sample size is needed if you wish to be 95% confident that your estimate is within 0.05 of the true proportion?

10. As in Exercise 9, you want to estimate the proportion of traditional college students on your campus who own their own car. However, from some research on other college campuses, you believe the proportion will be near 20%.

a) What sample size is needed if you wish to be 95% confident that your estimate is within 0.02 of the true proportion?
b) What sample size is needed if you wish to be 99% confident that your estimate is within 0.02 of the true proportion?
c) What sample size is needed if you wish to be 95% confident that your estimate is within 0.05 of the true proportion?

11. It's believed that as many as 25% of adults over age 50 never graduated from high school. We wish to see if this percentage is the same among the 25 to 30 age group.

a) How many of this younger age group must we survey in order to estimate the proportion of nongrads to within 6% with 90% confidence?
b) Suppose we want to cut the margin of error to 4%. What's the necessary sample size?
c) What sample size would produce a margin of error of 3%?

12. In preparing a report on the economy, we need to estimate the percentage of businesses that plan to hire additional employees in the next 60 days.

a) How many randomly selected employers must we contact in order to create an estimate in which we are 98% confident with a margin of error of 5%?
b) Suppose we want to reduce the margin of error to 3%. What sample size will suffice?
c) Why might it not be worth the effort to try to get an interval with a margin of error of 1%?

CHAPTER EXERCISES

13. Margin of error. A corporate executive reports the results of an employee satisfaction survey, stating that 52% of employees say they are either "satisfied" or "extremely satisfied" with their jobs, and then says "the margin of error is plus or minus 4%." Explain carefully what that means.

14. Margin of error. A market researcher estimates the percentage of adults between the ages of 21 and 39 who will see their television ad is 15%, adding that he believes his estimate has a margin of error of about 3%. Explain what the margin of error means.

15. Conditions. Consider each situation described below. Identify the population and the sample, explain what p and $\hat{p}$ represent, and tell whether the methods of this chapter can be used to create a confidence interval.

a) Police set up an auto checkpoint at which drivers are stopped and their cars inspected for safety problems. They find that 14 of the 134 cars stopped have at least one safety violation. They want to estimate the proportion of all cars in this area that may be unsafe.
b) A CNN show asks viewers to register their opinions on corporate corruption by logging onto a website. Of the 602 people who voted, 488 thought corporate corruption was "worse" this year than last year. The show wants to estimate the level of support among the general public.

16. More conditions. Consider each situation described below. Identify the population and the sample, explain what p and $\hat{p}$ represent, and tell whether the methods of this chapter can be used to create a confidence interval.

a) A large company with 10,000 employees at their main research site is considering moving its day care center off-site to save money. Human resources gathers employees' opinions by sending a questionnaire home with all employees; 380 surveys are returned, with 228 employees in favor of the change.
b) A company sold 1632 MP3 players last month, and within a week, 1388 of the customers had registered their products online at the company website. The company wants to estimate the percentage of all their customers who enroll their products.

17. Catalog sales. A catalog sales company promises to deliver orders placed on the Internet within 3 days. Follow-up calls to a few randomly selected customers show that a 95% confidence interval for the proportion of all orders that arrive on time is 88% ± 6%. What does this mean? Are the conclusions in parts a–e correct? Explain.

a) Between 82% and 94% of all orders arrive on time.
b) 95% of all random samples of customers will show that 88% of orders arrive on time.
c) 95% of all random samples of customers will show that 82% to 94% of orders arrive on time.
d) The company is 95% sure that between 82% and 94% of the orders placed by the customers in this sample arrived on time.
e) On 95% of the days, between 82% and 94% of the orders will arrive on time.

18. Belgian euro. Recently, two students made worldwide headlines by spinning a Belgian euro 250 times and getting 140 heads—that's 56%. That makes the 90% confidence interval (51%, 61%). What does this mean? Are the conclusions in parts a–e correct? Explain your answers.

a) Between 51% and 61% of all euros are unfair.
b) We are 90% sure that in this experiment this euro landed heads between 51% and 61% of the spins.
c) We are 90% sure that spun euros will land heads between 51% and 61% of the time.
d) If you spin a euro many times, you can be 90% sure of getting between 51% and 61% heads.
e) 90% of all spun euros will land heads between 51% and 61% of the time.

19. Confidence intervals. Several factors are involved in the creation of a confidence interval. Among them are the sample size, the level of confidence, and the margin of error. Which statements are true?

a) For a given sample size, higher confidence means a smaller margin of error.
b) For a specified confidence level, larger samples provide smaller margins of error.

c) For a fixed margin of error, larger samples provide greater confidence.

d) For a given confidence level, halving the margin of error requires a sample twice as large.

20. Confidence intervals, again. Several factors are involved in the creation of a confidence interval. Among them are the sample size, the level of confidence, and the margin of error. Which statements are true?

a) For a given sample size, reducing the margin of error will mean lower confidence.

b) For a certain confidence level, you can get a smaller margin of error by selecting a bigger sample.

c) For a fixed margin of error, smaller samples will mean lower confidence.

d) For a given confidence level, a sample 9 times as large will make a margin of error one third as big.

21. Cars. A student is considering publishing a new magazine aimed directly at owners of Japanese automobiles. He wanted to estimate the fraction of cars in the United States that are made in Japan. The computer output summarizes the results of a random sample of 50 autos. Explain carefully what it tells you.

```
z-interval for proportion
With 90.00% confidence
0.29938661 < p(japan) < 0.46984416
```

22. Quality control. For quality control purposes, 900 ceramic tiles were inspected to determine the proportion of defective (e.g., cracked, uneven finish, etc.) tiles. Assuming that these tiles are representative of all tiles manufactured by an Italian tile company, what can you conclude based on the computer output?

```
z-interval for proportion
With 95.00% confidence
0.025 < p(defective) < 0.035
```

23. E-mail. A small company involved in e-commerce is interested in statistics concerning the use of e-mail. A poll found that 38% of a random sample of 1012 adults, who use a computer at their home, work, or school, said that they do not send or receive e-mail.

a) Find the margin of error for this poll if we want 90% confidence in our estimate of the percent of American adults who do not use e-mail.

b) Explain what that margin of error means.

c) If we want to be 99% confident, will the margin of error be larger or smaller? Explain.

d) Find that margin of error.

e) In general, if all other aspects of the situation remain the same, will smaller margins of error involve greater or less confidence in the interval?

24. Biotechnology. A biotechnology firm in Boston is planning its investment strategy for future products and research labs. A poll found that only 8% of a random sample of 1012 U.S. adults approved of attempts to clone a human.

a) Find the margin of error for this poll if we want 95% confidence in our estimate of the percent of American adults who approve of cloning humans.

b) Explain what that margin of error means.

c) If we only need to be 90% confident, will the margin of error be larger or smaller? Explain.

d) Find that margin of error.

e) In general, if all other aspects of the situation remain the same, would smaller samples produce smaller or larger margins of error?

25. Teenage drivers. An insurance company checks police records on 582 accidents selected at random and notes that teenagers were at the wheel in 91 of them.

a) Create a 95% confidence interval for the percentage of all auto accidents that involve teenage drivers.

b) Explain what your interval means.

c) Explain what "95% confidence" means.

d) A politician urging tighter restrictions on drivers' licenses issued to teens says, "In one of every five auto accidents, a teenager is behind the wheel." Does your confidence interval support or contradict this statement? Explain.

26. Advertisers. Direct mail advertisers send solicitations ("junk mail") to thousands of potential customers in the hope that some will buy the company's product. The response rate is usually quite low. Suppose a company wants to test the response to a new flyer and sends it to 1000 people randomly selected from their mailing list of over 200,000 people. They get orders from 123 of the recipients.

a) Create a 90% confidence interval for the percentage of people the company contacts who may buy something.

b) Explain what this interval means.

c) Explain what "90% confidence" means.

d) The company must decide whether to now do a mass mailing. The mailing won't be cost-effective unless it produces at least a 5% return. What does your confidence interval suggest? Explain.

27. Retailers. Some food retailers propose subjecting food to a low level of radiation in order to improve safety, but sale of such "irradiated" food is opposed by many people. Suppose a grocer wants to find out what his customers think. He has cashiers distribute surveys at checkout and ask customers to fill them out and drop them in a box near the front door. He gets responses from 122 customers, of whom 78 oppose the radiation treatments. What can the grocer conclude about the opinions of all his customers?

28. Local news. The mayor of a small city has suggested that the state locate a new prison there, arguing that the construction project and resulting jobs will be good for the local economy. A total of 183 residents show up for a public hearing on the proposal, and a show of hands finds 31 in favor of the prison project. What can the city council conclude about public support for the mayor's initiative?

29. Internet music. In a survey on downloading music, the Gallup Poll asked 703 Internet users if they "ever downloaded music from an Internet site that was not authorized by a record company, or not," and 18% responded "yes." Construct a 95% confidence interval for the true proportion of Internet users who have downloaded music from an Internet site that was not authorized.

30. Economy worries. In 2008, a Gallup Poll asked 2335 U.S. adults, aged 18 or over, how they rated economic conditions. In a poll conducted from January 27–February 1, 2008, only 24% rated the economy as Excellent/Good. Construct a 95% confidence interval for the true proportion of Americans who rated the U.S. economy as Excellent/Good.

31. International business. In Canada, the vast majority (90%) of companies in the chemical industry are ISO 14001 certified. The ISO 14001 is an international standard for environmental management systems. An environmental group wished to estimate the percentage of U.S. chemical companies that are ISO 14001 certified. Of the 550 chemical companies sampled, 385 are certified.
a) What proportion of the sample reported being certified?
b) Create a 95% confidence interval for the proportion of U.S. chemical companies with ISO 14001 certification. (Be sure to check conditions.) Compare to the Canadian proportion.

32. Worldwide survey. We learned that GfK Roper surveyed people worldwide asking them "how important is acquiring wealth to you." Of 1535 respondents in India, 1168 said that it was of more than average importance. In the United States of 1317 respondents, 596 said it was of more than average importance.
a) What proportion thought acquiring wealth was of more than average importance in each country's sample?
b) Create a 95% confidence interval for the proportion who thought it was of more than average importance in India. (Be sure to test conditions.) Compare that to a confidence interval for the U.S. population.

33. Business ethics. In a survey on corporate ethics, a poll split a sample at random, asking 538 faculty and corporate recruiters the question: "Generally speaking, do you believe that MBAs are more or less aware of ethical issues in business today than five years ago?" The other half were asked: "Generally speaking, do you believe that MBAs are less or more aware of ethical issues in business today than five years ago?" These may seem like the same questions, but sometimes the order of the choices matters. In response to the first question, 53% thought MBA graduates were more aware of

ethical issues, but when the question was phrased differently, this proportion dropped to 44%.
a) What kind of bias may be present here?
b) Each group consisted of 538 respondents. If we combine them, considering the overall group to be one larger random sample, what is a 95% confidence interval for the proportion of the faculty and corporate recruiters that believe MBAs are more aware of ethical issues today?
c) How does the margin of error based on this pooled sample compare with the margins of error from the separate groups? Why?

34. Media survey. In 2007, a Gallup Poll conducted face-to-face interviews with 1006 adults in Saudi Arabia, aged 15 and older, asking them questions about how they get information. Among them was the question: "Is international television very important in keeping you well-informed about events in your country?" Gallup reported that 82% answered "yes" and noted that at 95% confidence there was a 3% margin of error and that "in addition to sampling error, question wording and practical difficulties in conducting surveys can introduce error or bias into the findings of public opinion polls."
a) What kinds of bias might they be referring to?
b) Do you agree with their margin of error? Explain.

35. Gambling. A city ballot includes a local initiative that would legalize gambling. The issue is hotly contested, and two groups decide to conduct polls to predict the outcome. The local newspaper finds that 53% of 1200 randomly selected voters plan to vote "yes," while a college Statistics class finds 54% of 450 randomly selected voters in support. Both groups will create 95% confidence intervals.
a) Without finding the confidence intervals, explain which one will have the larger margin of error.
b) Find both confidence intervals.
c) Which group concludes that the outcome is too close to call? Why?

36. Casinos. Governor Deval Patrick of Massachusetts proposed legalizing casinos in Massachusetts although they are not currently legal, and he included the revenue from them in his latest state budget. The website www.boston.com conducted an Internet poll on the question: "Do you agree with the casino plan the governor is expected to unveil?" As of the end of 2007, there were 8663 votes cast, of which 63.5% of respondents said: "No. Raising revenues by allowing gambling is shortsighted."
a) Find a 95% confidence interval for the proportion of voters in Massachusetts who would respond this way.
b) Are the assumptions and conditions satisfied? Explain.

37. Pharmaceutical company. A pharmaceutical company is considering investing in a "new and improved" vitamin D supplement for children. Vitamin D, whether ingested as a dietary supplement or produced naturally when sunlight falls upon the skin, is essential for strong, healthy bones. The bone disease rickets was largely eliminated in England during the 1950s, but now there is concern that a generation of children more likely to watch TV or play computer games than spend time outdoors is at increased risk. A recent study of 2700 children randomly selected from all parts of England found 20% of them deficient in vitamin D.

a) Find a 98% confidence interval for the proportion of children in England who are deficient in vitamin D.
b) Explain carefully what your interval means.
c) Explain what "98% confidence" means.
d) Does the study show that computer games are a likely cause of rickets? Explain.

38. Wireless access. The Pew Internet and American Life Project polled 798 Internet users in December 2006, asking whether they have logged on to the Internet using a wireless device or not and 243 responded "Yes."

a) Find a 98% confidence interval for the proportion of all U.S. Internet users who have logged in using a wireless device.
b) Explain carefully what your interval means.
c) Explain what "98% confidence" means.

*39. Funding. In 2005, a survey developed by Babson College and the Association of Women's Business Centers (WBCs) was distributed to WBCs in the United States. Of a representative sample of 20 WBCs, 40% reported that they had received funding from the national Small Business Association (SBA).

a) Check the assumptions and conditions for inference on proportions.
b) If it's appropriate, find a 90% confidence interval for the proportion of WBCs that receive SBA funding. If it's not appropriate, explain and/or recommend an alternative action.

*40. Real estate survey. A real estate agent looks over the 15 listings she has in a particular zip code in California and finds that 80% of them have swimming pools.

a) Check the assumptions and conditions for inference on proportions.
b) If it's appropriate, find a 90% confidence interval for the proportion of houses in this zip code that have swimming pools. If it's not appropriate, explain and/or recommend an alternative action.

*41. Benefits survey. A paralegal at the Vermont State Attorney General's office wants to know how many companies in Vermont provide health insurance benefits to all employees. She chooses 12 companies at random and finds that all 12 offer benefits.

a) Check the assumptions and conditions for inference on proportions.
b) Find a 95% confidence interval for the true proportion of companies that provide health insurance benefits to all their employees.

*42. Awareness survey. A telemarketer at a credit card company is instructed to ask the next 18 customers that call into the 800 number whether they are aware of the new Platinum card that the company is offering. Of the 18, 17 said they were aware of the program.

a) Check the assumptions and conditions for inference on proportions.
b) Find a 95% confidence interval for the true proportion of customers who are aware of the new card.

43. IRS. In a random survey of 226 self-employed individuals, 20 reported having had their tax returns audited by the IRS in the past year. Estimate the proportion of self-employed individuals nationwide who've been audited by the IRS in the past year.

a) Check the assumptions and conditions (to the extent you can) for constructing a confidence interval.
b) Construct a 95% confidence interval.
c) Interpret your interval.
d) Explain what "95% confidence" means in this context.

44. ACT, Inc. In 2004, ACT, Inc. reported that 74% of 1644 randomly selected college freshmen returned to college the next year. Estimate the national freshman-to-sophomore retention rate.

a) Check that the assumptions and conditions are met for inference on proportions.
b) Construct a 98% confidence interval.
c) Interpret your interval.
d) Explain what "98% confidence" means in this context.

45. Internet music, again. A Gallup Poll (Exercise 29) asked Americans if the fact that they can make copies of songs on the Internet for free made them more likely—or less likely—to buy a performer's CD. Only 13% responded that it made them "less likely." The poll was based on a random sample of 703 Internet users.

a) Check that the assumptions and conditions are met for inference on proportions.
b) Find the 95% confidence interval for the true proportion of all U.S. Internet users who are "less likely" to buy CDs.

46. ACT, Inc., again. The ACT, Inc. study described in Exercise 44 was actually stratified by type of college—public or private. The retention rates were 71.9% among 505 students enrolled in public colleges and 74.9% among 1139 students enrolled in private colleges.

a) Will the 95% confidence interval for the true national retention rate in private colleges be wider or narrower than the 95% confidence interval for the retention rate in public colleges? Explain.
b) Find the 95% confidence interval for the public college retention rate.
c) Should a public college whose retention rate is 75% proclaim that they do a better job than other public colleges of keeping freshmen in school? Explain.

47. Politics. A poll of 1005 U.S. adults split the sample into four age groups: ages 18–29, 30–49, 50–64, and 65+. In the youngest age group, 62% said that they thought the U.S. was ready for a woman president, as opposed to 35% who said "no, the country was not ready" (3% were undecided). The sample included 250 18- to 29-year-olds.

a) Do you expect the 95% confidence interval for the true proportion of all 18- to 29-year-olds who think the U.S. is ready for a woman president to be wider or narrower than the 95% confidence interval for the true proportion of all U.S. adults? Explain.

b) Find the 95% confidence interval for the true proportion of all 18- to 29-year-olds who believe the U.S. is ready for a woman president.

48. Wireless access, again. The survey in Exercise 38 asking about wireless Internet access also classified the 798 respondents by income.

	A	B	C	D
1		Wireless Users	Other Internet Users	Total
2	Under $30K	34	128	162
3	$30K--$50K	31	133	164
4	$50K--$75K	44	72	116
5	Over $75K	83	111	194
6	Don't know/refused	51	111	162
7	Total	243	555	798

a) Do you expect the 95% confidence interval for the true proportion of all those making more than $75K who are wireless users to be wider or narrower than the 95% confidence interval for the true proportion among those who make between $50K and $75K? Explain briefly.

b) Find the 95% confidence interval for the true proportion of those making more than $75K who are wireless users.

49. More Internet music. A random sample of 168 students was asked how many songs were in their digital music library and what fraction of them was legally purchased. Overall, they reported having a total of 117,079 songs, of which 23.1% were legal. The music industry would like a good estimate of the proportion of songs in students' digital music libraries that are legal.

a) Think carefully. What is the parameter being estimated? What is the population? What is the sample size?

b) Check the conditions for making a confidence interval.

c) Construct a 95% confidence interval for the fraction of legal digital music.

d) Explain what this interval means. Do you believe that you can be this confident about your result? Why or why not?

50. Trade agreement. Results from a January 2008 telephone survey conducted by Gallup showed that 57% of urban Colombian adults support a free trade agreement (FTA) with the United States. Gallup used a sample of 1000 urban Colombians aged 15 and older.

a) What is the parameter being estimated? What is the population? What is the sample size?

b) Check the conditions for making a confidence interval.

c) Construct a 95% confidence interval for the fraction of Colombians in agreement with the FTA.

d) Explain what this interval means. Do you believe that you can be this confident about your result? Why or why not?

51. CDs. A company manufacturing CDs is working on a new technology. A random sample of 703 Internet users were asked: "As you may know, some CDs are being manufactured so that you can only make one copy of the CD after you purchase it. Would you buy a CD with this technology, or would you refuse to buy it even if it was one you would normally buy?" Of these users, 64% responded that they would buy the CD.

a) Create a 90% confidence interval for this percentage.

b) If the company wants to cut the margin of error in half, how many users must they survey?

52. Internet music, last time. The research group that conducted the survey in Exercise 49 wants to provide the music industry with definitive information, but they believe that they could use a smaller sample next time. If the group is willing to have twice as big a margin of error, how many songs must be included?

53. Graduation. As in Exercise 11, we hope to estimate the percentage of adults aged 25 to 30 who never graduated from high school. What sample size would allow us to increase our confidence level to 95% while reducing the margin of error to only 2%?

54. Better hiring info. Editors of the business report in Exercise 12 are willing to accept a margin of error of 4% but want 99% confidence. How many randomly selected employers will they need to contact?

55. Pilot study. A state's environmental agency worries that a large percentage of cars may be violating clean air emissions standards. The agency hopes to check a sample of vehicles in order to estimate that percentage with a margin of error of 3% and 90% confidence. To gauge the size of the problem, the agency first picks 60 cars and finds 9 with faulty emissions systems. How many should be sampled for a full investigation?

56. Another pilot study. During routine conversations, the CEO of a new start-up reports that 22% of adults between the ages of 21 and 39 will purchase her new product. Hearing this, some investors decide to conduct a large-scale study, hoping to estimate the proportion to within 4% with 98% confidence. How many randomly selected adults between the ages of 21 and 39 must they survey?

57. Approval rating. A newspaper reports that the governor's approval rating stands at 65%. The article adds that the poll is based on a random sample of 972 adults and has a margin of error of 2.5%. What level of confidence did the pollsters use?

58. Amendment. The Board of Directors of a publicly traded company says that a proposed amendment to their bylaws is likely to win approval in the upcoming election because a poll of 1505 stock owners indicated that 52% would vote in favor. The Board goes on to say that the margin of error for this poll was 3%.

a) Explain why the poll is actually inconclusive.
b) What confidence level did the pollsters use?

T 59. Customer spending. The data set provided contains last month's credit card purchases of 500 customers randomly chosen from a segment of a major credit card issuer. The marketing department is considering a special offer for customers who spend more than $1000 per month on their card. From these data construct a 95% confidence interval for the proportion of customers in this segment who will qualify.

T 60. Advertising. A philanthropic organization knows that its donors have an average age near 60 and is considering taking out an ad in the *American Association of Retired People (AARP)* magazine. An analyst wonders what proportion of their donors are actually 50 years old or older. He takes a

random sample of the records of 500 donors. From the data provided, construct a 95% confidence interval for the proportion of donors who are 50 years old or older.

61. Health insurance. Based on a 2007 survey of U.S. households (see www.census.gov), 87% (out of 3060) of males in Massachusetts (MA) have health insurance.

a) Examine the conditions for constructing a confidence interval for the proportion males in MA who had health insurance.
b) Find the 95% confidence interval for the percent of males who have health insurance.
c) Interpret your confidence interval.

62. Health insurance, part 2. Using the same survey and data as in Exercise 61, we find that 84% of those respondents in Massachusetts who identified themselves as Black/African-Americans (out of 440) had health insurance.

a) Examine the conditions for constructing a confidence interval for the proportion of Black/African-Americans in MA who had health insurance.
b) Find the 95% confidence interval.
c) Interpret your confidence interval.

Just Checking Answers

1 Wider
2 Lower
3 Smaller

Answers

SECTION EXERCISE ANSWERS

1. a) p is the proportion of all backpacks entering the stadium which contain alcoholic beverages; $\hat{p}$ is the proportion in the sample $\hat{p} = 17/130 = 13.08\%$. Yes. This seems to be a random sample.
  b) p is the proportion of all visitors to the website who approve of recent bossnapping. $\hat{p}$ is the proportion in the sample $\hat{p} = 49.2\%$. No. This is a volunteer sample and may be biased.
  c) This question is about the mean weight, not a proportion. The methods of this chapter are not appropriate.

3. a) 0.35
  b) 0.034
  c) (0.282, 0.418) or without rounding (0.283, 0.417)

5. a) False. Doesn't make sense. Workers are not proportions.
  b) True.
  c) False. Our best guess is 0.48 not 0.95.
  d) False. Our best guess is 0.48, but we're not sure that's correct.
  e) False. The statement should be about the true proportion, not future samples.

7. a) *Population*—all customers who recently bought new cars; *sample*—167 people surveyed about their experience; p—proportion of all new car buyers who are dissatisfied with the salesperson; $\hat{p}$—proportion of new car buyers surveyed who are dissatisfied with the salesperson (3%); we can't use the methods of this chapter because only 5 people were dissatisfied. Also, sample may not be representative.
  b) *Population*—all college students; *sample*—2883 who were asked about their cell phones at the football stadium; p—proportion of all college students with cell phones; $\hat{p}$—proportion of college students at the football stadium with cell phones (77.8%); we should be cautious—students entering the football stadium may not represent all students. Sample may be biased.

9. a) About 2401 (using 1.96 standard errors).
  b) About 4148 (using 2.576 standard errors).
  c) About 385 (using 1.96 standard errors).

11. a) 141
  b) 318
  c) 564

CHAPTER EXERCISE ANSWERS

13. He believes the true proportion is within 4% of his estimate, with some (probably 95%) degree of confidence.

15. a) *Population*—all cars in the local area; *sample*—134 cars actually stopped at the checkpoint; *p*—population proportion of all cars with safety problems; $\hat{p}$—proportion of cars in the sample that actually have safety problems (10.4%); if sample (a cluster sample) is representative, then the methods of this chapter will apply.

b) *Population*—general public; *sample*—602 viewers that logged on to the website; *p*—population proportion of the general public that think corporate corruption is "worse"; $\hat{p}$—proportion that logged onto the website and voted that corporate corruption is "worse" (81.1%); can't use the methods of this chapter—sample is biased and nonrandom.

17. a) Not correct. This implies certainty.

b) Not correct. Different samples will give different results. Most likely, none of the samples will have *exactly* 88% on-time orders.

c) Not correct. A confidence interval says something about the unknown population proportion, not the sample proportion in different samples.

d) Not correct. In this sample, we *know* that 88% arrived on time.

e) Not correct. The interval is about the parameter, not about the days.

19. a) False.

b) True.

c) True.

d) False.

21. We are 90% confident that between 29.9% and 47.0% of U.S. cars are made in Japan.

23. a) 0.025 or 2.5%

b) The pollsters are 90% confident that the true proportion of adults who do not use e-mail is within 2.5% of the estimated 38%.

c) A 99% confidence interval requires a larger margin of error. In order to increase confidence, the interval must be wider.

d) 0.039 or 3.9%.

e) Smaller margins of error will give us less confidence in the interval.

25. a) (12.7%, 18.6%)

b) We are 95% confident that between 12.7% and 18.6% of all accidents involve teenage drivers.

c) About 95% of all random samples of size 582 will produce intervals that contain the true proportion of accidents involving teenage drivers.

d) Contradicts—the interval is completely below 20%.

27. Probably nothing. Those who bothered to fill out the survey are a voluntary response sample, which may be biased.

29. This was a random sample of less than 10% of all Internet users; there were $703 \times 0.18 = 127$ successes and 576 failures, both at least 10. We are 95% confident that between 15.2% and 20.8% of Internet users have downloaded music from a site that was not authorized. (Answer could be 15.2% to 20.9% if $n = 127$ is used instead of 0.18).

31. a) $385/550 = 0.70$; 70% of U.S. chemical companies in the sample are certified.

b) This was a random sample, but we don't know if it is less than 10% of all U.S. chemical companies; there were $550(0.70) = 385$ successes and 165 failures, both at least 10. We are 95% confident that between 66.2% and 73.8% of the chemical companies in the United States are certified.

It appears that the proportion of companies certified in the United States is less than in Canada.

33. a) There may be response bias based on the wording of the question.

b) (45.5%, 51.5%)

c) The margin of error based on the pooled sample is smaller, since the sample size is larger.

35. a) The interval based on the survey conducted by the college Statistics class will have the larger margin of error, since the sample size is smaller.

b) Both samples are random and are probably less than 10% of the city's voters (provided the city has more than 12,000 voters); there were 636 successes and 564 failures for the newspaper, both at least 10; there were 243 successes and 207 failures for the Statistics class, both at least 10; Newspaper poll: (50.2%, 55.8%); Statistics class: (49.4%, 58.6%).

c) The Statistics class should conclude that the outcome is too close to call because 50% is in their interval.

37. a) This was a random sample of less than 10% of all English children; there were $2700(0.20) = 540$ successes and 2160 failures, both at least 10; (18.2%, 21.8%).

b) We are 98% confident that between 18.2% and 21.8% of English children are deficient in vitamin D.

c) About 98% of random samples of size 2700 will produce confidence intervals that contain the true proportion of English children that are deficient in vitamin D.

d) No. The interval says nothing about causation.

39. a) This is not a random sample; even though it's representative we are not sure if we have less than 10% of all WBCs; there are 8 successes which is not greater than 10, so the sample is not large enough.

b) Since the conditions are not met but the sample is representative, we could perform a pseudo observation confidence interval adding two successes and two failures to the data. Then a 90% CI would be (0.251, 0.582).

41. a) This was a random sample of less than 10% of all companies in Vermont; there were 12 successes and 0 failures, which is not greater than 10, so the sample is not large enough.

b) Using the pseudo observation confidence interval, $\tilde{p} = \frac{14}{16} = 0.875$; (0.713, 1.037); so we can say that with 95% confidence the true proportion is at least 71.3%.

43. a) This was a random sample of less than 10% of all self-employed taxpayers; there were 20 successes and 206 failures, both at least 10.

b) (5.1%, 12.6%)

c) We are 95% confident that between 5.1% and 12.6% of all self-employed individuals had their tax returns audited in the past year.

d) If we were to select repeated samples of 226 individuals, we'd expect about 95% of the confidence intervals we created to contain the true proportion of all self-employed individuals who were audited.

45. a) This was a random sample of less than 10% of all U.S. adults; there were $703 \times 0.13 = 91$ successes and 612 failures, both at least 10.

b) (10.5%, 15.5%)

47. a) The 95% confidence interval for the true proportion of all 18- to 29-year-olds who believe the U.S. is ready for a woman president will be about twice as wide as the confidence interval for the true proportion of all U.S. adults, since it is based on a sample about one-fourth as large. (Assuming approximately equal proportions)

b) This was a random sample of less than 10% of all U.S. 15- to 29-year-old-adults; there were $250 \times 0.62 = 155$ successes and 95 failures, both at least 10. We are 95% confident that between 56.0% and 68.0% of 18- to 29-year-olds believe the U.S. is ready for a woman president.

49. a) The parameter is the proportion of digital songs in student libraries that are legal. The population is all songs held in digital libraries. The sample size is 117,079 songs, not 168 students.

b) This was a cluster sample (168 clusters of songs in the digital libraries); 117,079 is less than 10% of all digital songs; the number of legal songs and illegal songs in the sample are both much greater than 10.

c) We are 95% confident that between 22.9% and 23.3% of digital songs were legally purchased.

d) The very large sample size has made the confidence interval unreasonably narrow. It is hard to believe that such a narrow interval really captures the parameter of interest. Additionally, these data were collected in a cluster sample of only 168 students. This gives us less certainty about our ability to capture the true parameter.

51. a) This was a random sample of less than 10% of all Internet users; there were $703(0.64) = 450$ successes and 253 failures, both at least 10. We are 90% confident that between 61.0% and 67.0% of Internet users would still buy a CD.

b) In order to cut the margin of error in half, they must sample 4 times as many users; $4 \times 703 = 2812$ users.

53. 1801

55. 384 total, using $p = 0.15$

57. Since $z^* \approx 1.634$, which is close to 1.645, the pollsters were probably using 90% confidence.

59. This was a random sample of less than 10% of all customers; there were 67 successes and 433 failures, both at least 10. From the data set, $\hat{p} = 67/500 = 0.134$. We are 95% confident that the true proportion of customers who spend \$1000 per month or more is between 10.4% and 16.4%.

61. a) This was a random sample of less than 10% of all MA males; there were 2662 successes and 398 failures, both at least 10.

b) $(0.858, 0.882)$

c) We are 95% confident that between 85.8% and 88.2% of MA males have health insurance.

Confidence Intervals for Means

public domain

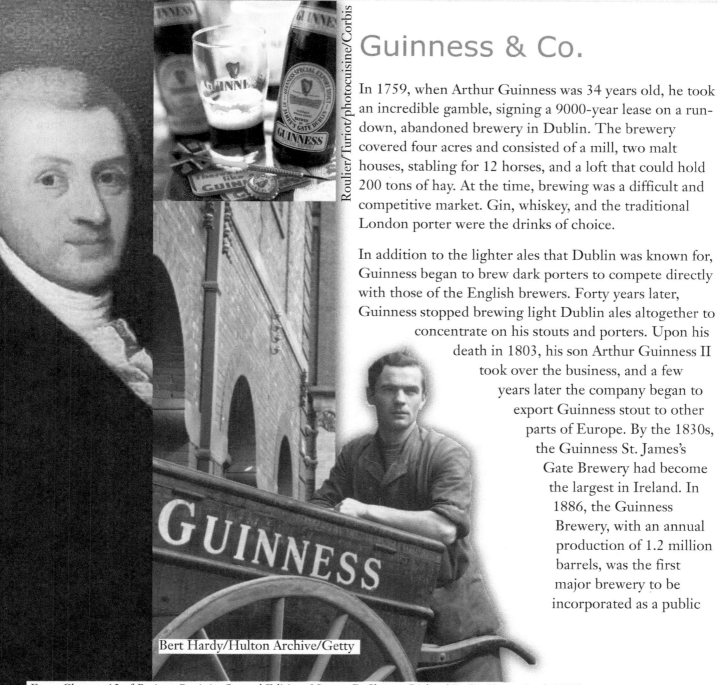

Guinness & Co.

In 1759, when Arthur Guinness was 34 years old, he took an incredible gamble, signing a 9000-year lease on a run-down, abandoned brewery in Dublin. The brewery covered four acres and consisted of a mill, two malt houses, stabling for 12 horses, and a loft that could hold 200 tons of hay. At the time, brewing was a difficult and competitive market. Gin, whiskey, and the traditional London porter were the drinks of choice.

In addition to the lighter ales that Dublin was known for, Guinness began to brew dark porters to compete directly with those of the English brewers. Forty years later, Guinness stopped brewing light Dublin ales altogether to concentrate on his stouts and porters. Upon his death in 1803, his son Arthur Guinness II took over the business, and a few years later the company began to export Guinness stout to other parts of Europe. By the 1830s, the Guinness St. James's Gate Brewery had become the largest in Ireland. In 1886, the Guinness Brewery, with an annual production of 1.2 million barrels, was the first major brewery to be incorporated as a public

Roulier/Turiot/photocuisine/Corbis

Bert Hardy/Hulton Archive/Getty

From Chapter 12 of *Business Statistics*, Second Edition, Norean R. Sharpe, Richard D. De Veaux, Paul F. Velleman.

company on the London Stock Exchange. During the 1890s, the company began to employ scientists. One of those, William S. Gosset, was hired as a chemist to test the quality of the brewing process. Gosset was not only an early pioneer of quality control methods in industry but a statistician whose work made modern statistical inference possible.[1]

As a chemist at the Guinness Brewery in Dublin, William S. Gosset was in charge of quality control. His job was to make sure that the stout (a thick, dark beer) leaving the brewery was of high enough quality to meet the standards of the brewery's many discerning customers. It's easy to imagine, when testing stout, why testing a large amount of stout might be undesirable, not to mention dangerous to one's health. So to test for quality Gosset often used a sample of only 3 or 4 observations per batch. But he noticed that with samples of this size, his tests for quality weren't quite right. He knew this because when the batches that he rejected were sent back to the laboratory for more extensive testing, too often the test results turned out to be wrong. As a practicing statistician, Gosset knew he had to be wrong *some* of the time, but he hated being wrong more often than the theory predicted. One result of Gosset's frustrations was the development of a test to handle small samples, the main subject of this chapter.

1   The Sampling Distribution for the Mean

You've learned how to create confidence intervals for proportions. Now we want to do the same thing for means. For proportions we found the confidence interval as

$$\hat{p} \pm ME.$$

The *ME* was equal to a critical value, z^*, times $SE(\hat{p})$. Our confidence interval for means will look very similar:

$$\bar{y} \pm ME.$$

And our *ME* will be a critical value times $SE(\bar{y})$. So let's put the pieces together. What the Central Limit Theorem told us is exactly what we need.

The Central Limit Theorem

When a random sample is drawn from *any* population with mean μ and standard deviation σ, its sample mean, $\bar{y}$, has a sampling distribution whose *shape* is approximately Normal as long as the sample size is large enough. The larger the sample used, the more closely the Normal approximates the sampling distribution for the mean. The mean of the sampling distribution is μ, and its standard deviation is $SD(\bar{y}) = \dfrac{\sigma}{\sqrt{n}}$.

---

[1]Source: Guinness & Co., www.guinness.com/global/story/history.

This gives us a sampling distribution and a standard deviation for the mean. All we need is a random sample of quantitative data and the true value of the population standard deviation σ.

But wait. That could be a problem. To compute $\sigma/\sqrt{n}$ we need to know σ. How are we supposed to know σ? Suppose we told you that for 25 young executives the mean value of their stock portfolios is $125,672. Would that tell you the value of σ? No, the standard deviation depends on how similarly the executives invest, not on how well they invested (the mean tells us that). But we need σ because it's the numerator of the standard deviation of the sample mean: $SD(\bar{y}) = \dfrac{\sigma}{\sqrt{n}}$. So what can we do? The obvious answer is to use the sample standard deviation, s, from the data instead of σ. The result is the standard error: $SE(\bar{y}) = \dfrac{s}{\sqrt{n}}$.

A century ago, people just plugged the standard error into the Normal model, assuming it would work. And for large sample sizes it *did* work pretty well. But they began to notice problems with smaller samples. The extra variation in the standard error was wreaking havoc with the margins of error.

Gosset was the first to investigate this phenomenon. He realized that not only do we need to allow for the extra variation with larger margins of error, but we also need a new sampling distribution model. In fact, we need a whole *family* of models, depending on the sample size, n. These models are unimodal, symmetric, and bell-shaped, but the smaller our sample, the more we must stretch out the tails. Gosset's work transformed Statistics, but most people who use his work don't even know his name.

University of York Department of Mathematics

To find the sampling distribution of $\dfrac{\bar{y}}{s/\sqrt{n}}$, Gosset simulated it *by hand*.

He drew paper slips of small samples from a hat *hundreds of times* and computed the means and standard deviations with a mechanically cranked calculator. Today you could repeat in seconds on a computer the experiment that took him over a year. Gosset's work was so meticulous that not only did he get the shape of the new histogram approximately right, but he even figured out the exact *formula* for it from his sample. The formula was not confirmed mathematically until years later by Sir Ronald Aylmer Fisher.

Gosset's *t*

Gosset made decisions about the stout's quality by using statistical inference. He knew that if he used a 95% confidence interval, he would fail to capture the true quality of the batch about 5% of the time. However, the lab told him that he was in fact rejecting about 15% of the good batches. Gosset knew something was wrong, and it bugged him.

Gosset took time off from his job to study the problem and earn a graduate degree in the emerging field of Statistics. He figured out that when he used the standard error $\dfrac{s}{\sqrt{n}}$, the shape of the sampling model was no longer Normal. He even figured out what the new model was and called it a *t*-distribution.

The Guinness Company didn't give Gosset a lot of support for his work. In fact, it had a policy against publishing results. Gosset had to convince the company that he was not publishing an industrial secret and (as part of getting permission to publish) had to use a pseudonym. The pseudonym he chose was "Student," and ever since, the model he found has been known as **Student's *t***.

Gosset's model is always bell-shaped, but the details change with the sample sizes (Figure 1). So the Student's *t*-models form a family of related distributions that depend on a parameter known as **degrees of freedom**. We often denote degrees of freedom as df and the model as t_{df}, with the numerical value of the degrees of freedom as a subscript.

Student's *t*-models are unimodal, symmetric, and bell-shaped, just like the Normal model. But *t*-models with only a few degrees of freedom have a narrower peak than the Normal model and have much fatter tails. (That's what makes the margin of error bigger.) As the degrees of freedom increase, the *t*-models look more and more like the Normal model. In fact, the *t*-model with infinite degrees of freedom is exactly Normal.[2] This is great news if you happen to have an infinite

---

[2]Formally, in the limit as the number of degrees of freedom goes to infinity.

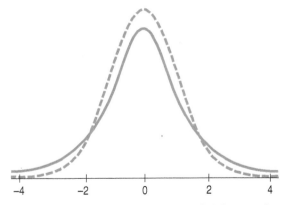

Figure 1 The *t*-model (solid curve) with 2 degrees of freedom has fatter tails than the Normal model (dashed curve). So the 68–95–99.7 Rule doesn't work for *t*-models with only a few degrees of freedom.

number of data values. Unfortunately, that's not practical. Fortunately, above a few hundred degrees of freedom it's very hard to tell the difference. Of course, in the rare situation that we *know* σ, it would be foolish not to use that information. If we don't have to estimate σ, we can use the Normal model. Typically that value of σ would be based on (lots of) experience, or on a theoretical model. Usually, however, we estimate σ by s from the data and use the *t*-model.

> ### *z* or *t*?
>
> If you know σ, use *z*. (That's rare!) Whenever you use s to estimate σ, use *t*.

> ### Using a known standard deviation
>
> Variation is inherent in manufacturing, even under the most tightly controlled processes. To ensure that parts do not vary too much, however, quality professionals monitor the processes by selecting samples at regular intervals. The mean performance of these samples is measured, and if it lies too far from the desired target mean, the process may be stopped until the underlying cause of the problem can be determined. In silicon wafer manufacturing, the thickness of the film is a crucial measurement. To assess a sample of wafers, quality engineers compare the mean thickness of the sample to the target mean. But, they don't estimate the standard deviation of the mean by using the standard error derived from the same sample. Instead they base the standard deviation of the mean on the historical process standard deviation, estimated from a vast collection of similar parts. In this case, the standard deviation can be treated as "known" and the normal model can be used for the sampling distribution instead of the *t* distribution.

2   A Confidence Interval for Means

> ### Notation Alert!
>
> Ever since Gosset, the letter *t* has been reserved in Statistics for his distribution.

To make confidence intervals, we need to use Gosset's model. Which one? Well, for means, it turns out the right value for degrees of freedom is df $= n - 1$.

> ### Practical sampling distribution model for means
>
> When certain conditions are met, the standardized sample mean,
>
> $$t = \frac{\bar{y} - \mu}{SE(\bar{y})}$$
>
> follows a Student's *t*-model with $n - 1$ degrees of freedom. We find the standard error from:
>
> $$SE(\bar{y}) = \frac{s}{\sqrt{n}}.$$

When Gosset corrected the Normal model for the extra uncertainty, the margin of error got bigger, as you might have guessed. When you use Gosset's model instead of the Normal model, your confidence intervals will be just a bit wider. That's just the correction you need. By using the *t*-model, you've compensated for the extra variability in precisely the right way.

One-sample *t*-interval

When the assumptions and conditions are met, we are ready to find the **confidence interval for the population mean**, μ. The confidence interval is:

$$\bar{y} \pm t^*_{n-1} \times SE(\bar{y})$$

where the standard error of the mean is:

$$SE(\bar{y}) = \frac{s}{\sqrt{n}}.$$

The critical value t^*_{n-1} depends on the particular confidence level, C, that you specify and on the number of degrees of freedom, $n - 1$, which we get from the sample size.

Finding t^*-Values

The Student's *t*-model is different for each value of degrees of freedom. We might print a table for each degrees of freedom value, but that's a lot of pages and not likely to be a bestseller. One way to shorten the book is to limit ourselves to 80%, 90%, 95% and 99% confidence levels. So Statistics books usually have one table of *t*-model critical values for a selected set of confidence levels.

The *t*-tables run down the page for as many degrees of freedom as can fit, and, as you can see from Figure 2, they are much easier to use than the Normal tables. Then they get to the bottom of the page and run out of room. Of course, for *enough* degrees of freedom, the *t*-model gets closer and closer to the Normal, so the tables give a final row with the critical values from the Normal model and label it "∞ df."

Two tail probability		0.20	0.10	0.05
One tail probability		0.10	0.05	0.025
Table T	**df**			
Values of t_a	*1*	3.078	6.314	12.706
	2	1.886	2.920	4.303
	3	1.638	2.353	3.182
	4	1.533	2.132	2.776
	5	1.476	2.015	2.571
	6	1.440	1.943	2.447
	7	1.415	1.895	2.365
	8	1.397	1.860	2.306
	9	1.383	1.833	2.262
	10	1.372	1.812	2.228
	11	1.363	1.796	2.201
	12	1.356	1.782	2.179
	13	1.350	1.771	2.160
	14	1.345	1.761	2.145
	15	1.341	1.753	2.131
	16	1.337	1.746	2.120
	17	1.333	1.740	2.110
	18	1.330	1.734	2.101
	19	1.328	1.729	2.093
	⋮	⋮	⋮	⋮
	∞	1.282	1.645	1.960
Confidence levels		80%	90%	95%

| Figure 2

For Example   Finding a confidence interval for the mean

According to the Environmental Defense Fund, "Americans are eating more and more salmon, drawn to its rich taste and health benefits. Increasingly they are choosing *farmed* salmon because of its wide availability and low price. But in the last few years, farmed salmon has been surrounded by controversy over its health risks and the ecological impacts of salmon aquaculture operations. Studies have shown that some farmed salmon is relatively higher in contaminants like PCBs than wild salmon, and there is mounting concern over the industry's impact on wild salmon populations."

In a widely cited study of contaminants in farmed salmon, fish from many sources were analyzed for 14 organic contaminants.[3] One of those was the insecticide mirex, which has been shown to be carcinogenic and is suspected of being toxic to the liver, kidneys, and endocrine system. Summaries for 150 mirex concentrations (in parts per million) from a variety of farmed salmon sources were reported as:

$$n = 150; \quad \bar{y} = 0.0913 \text{ ppm}; \quad s = 0.0495 \text{ ppm}$$

Question: The Environmental Protection Agency (EPA) recommends to recreational fishers as a "screening value" that mirex concentrations be no larger than 0.08 ppm. What does the 95% confidence interval say about that value?

Answer: Because $n = 150$, there are 149 df. From Table T in Appendix: Tables and Selected Formulas, we find $t^*_{140, 0.025} = 1.977$ (from technology, $t^*_{149, 0.025} = 1.976$), so a 95% confidence interval can be found from:

$$\bar{y} \pm t^* \times SE(\bar{y}) = \bar{y} \pm 1.977 \times \frac{s}{\sqrt{n}} = 0.0913 \pm 1.977 \frac{0.0495}{\sqrt{150}} = (0.0833, 0.0993)$$

If this sample is representative (as the authors claim it is), we can be 95% confident that it contains the true value of the mean mirex concentration. Because the interval from 0.0834 to 0.0992 ppm is entirely above the recommended value set by the EPA, we have reason to believe that the true mirex concentration exceeds the EPA guidelines.

3   Assumptions and Conditions

Gosset found the *t*-model by simulation. Years later, when Fisher showed mathematically that Gosset was right, he needed to make some assumptions to make the proof work. These are the assumptions we need in order to use the Student's *t*-models.

Independence Assumption

Independence Assumption: The data values should be independent. There's really no way to check independence of the data by looking at the sample, but we should think about whether the assumption is reasonable.

Randomization Condition: The data arise from a random sample or suitably randomized experiment. Randomly sampled data—and especially data from a Simple Random Sample (SRS)—are ideal.

When a sample is drawn without replacement, technically we ought to confirm that we haven't sampled a large fraction of the population, which would threaten the independence of our selections.

10% Condition: The sample size should be no more than 10% of the population. In practice, though, we often don't mention the 10% Condition when estimating means. Why not? When we made inferences about proportions, this condition was crucial because we usually had large samples. But for means our samples are

> ### We Don't *Want* to Stop
>
> We check conditions hoping that we can make a meaningful analysis of our data. The conditions serve as *disqualifiers*—we keep going unless there's a serious problem. If we find minor issues, we note them and express caution about our results. If the sample is not an SRS, but we believe it's representative of some populations, we limit our conclusions accordingly. If there are outliers, rather than stop, we perform the analysis both with and without them. If the sample looks bimodal, we try to analyze subgroups separately. Only when there's major trouble—like a strongly skewed small sample or an obviously non-representative sample—are we unable to proceed at all.

---

[3]Ronald A. Hites, Jeffery A. Foran, David O. Carpenter, M. Coreen Hamilton, Barbara A. Knuth, and Steven J. Schwager, "Global Assessment of Organic Contaminants in Farmed Salmon," *Science* 9 January 2004: Vol. 303, no. 5655, pp. 226–229.

generally smaller, so this problem arises only if we're sampling from a small population (and then there's a correction formula we could use).

Normal Population Assumption

Student's *t*-models won't work for data that are badly skewed. How skewed is too skewed? Well, formally, we assume that the data are from a population that follows a Normal model. Practically speaking, there's no way to be certain this is true.

And it's almost certainly *not* true. Models are idealized; real data are, well, real. The good news, however, is that even for small samples, it's sufficient to check a condition.

Nearly Normal Condition. The data come from a distribution that is unimodal and symmetric. This is a much more practical condition and one we can check by making a histogram.[4] For small samples, it can be hard to see any distribution shape in the histogram. Unfortunately, the condition matters most when it's hardest to check.

For very small samples ($n < 15$ or so), the data should follow a Normal model pretty closely. Of course, with so little data, it's rather hard to tell. But if you do find outliers or strong skewness, don't use these methods.

For moderate sample sizes (n between 15 and 40 or so), the *t* methods will work well as long as the data are unimodal and reasonably symmetric. Make a histogram to check.

When the sample size is larger than 40 or 50, the *t* methods are safe to use unless the data are extremely skewed. Make a histogram anyway. If you find outliers in the data and they aren't errors that are easy to fix, it's always a good idea to perform the analysis twice, once with and once without the outliers, even for large samples. The outliers may well hold additional information about the data, so they deserve special attention. If you find multiple modes, you may well have different groups that should be analyzed and understood separately.

If the data are extremely skewed, the mean may not be the most appropriate summary. But when our data consist of a collection of instances whose *total* is the business consequence—as when we add up the profits (or losses) from many transactions or the costs of many supplies—then the mean is just that total divided by *n*. And that's the value with a business consequence. Fortunately, in this instance, the Central Limit Theorem comes to our rescue. Even when we must sample from a very skewed distribution, the sampling distribution of our sample mean will be close to Normal, so we can use Student's *t* methods without much worry as long as the sample size is *large enough*.

How large is large enough? Here's the histogram of CEO compensations ($000) for Fortune 500 companies.

Notation Alert! ⎯⎯⎯⎯

When we found critical values from a Normal model, we called them z^*. When we use a Student's *t*-model, we denote the critical values t^*.

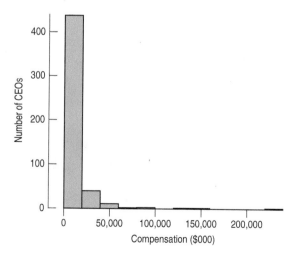

Figure 3 It's hard to imagine a distribution more skewed than these annual compensations from the Fortune 500 CEOs.

---

[4]Or we could check a normal probability plot.

Although this distribution is very skewed, the Central Limit Theorem will make the sampling distribution of the means of samples from this distribution more and more Normal as the sample size grows. Here's a histogram of the means of many samples of 100 CEOs:

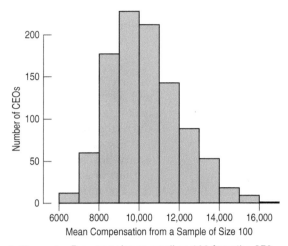

Figure 4 Even samples as small as 100 from the CEO data set produce means whose sampling distribution is nearly normal. Larger samples will have sampling distributions even more Normal.

Often, in modern business applications, we have samples of many hundreds, or thousands. We should still be on guard for outliers and multiple modes and we should be sure that the observations are independent. But if the mean is of interest, the Central Limit Theorem works quite well in ensuring that the sampling distribution of the mean will be close to the Normal for samples of this size.

For Example   Checking the assumptions and conditions for a confidence interval for means

Researchers purchased whole farmed salmon from 51 farms in eight regions in six countries. The histogram shows the concentrations of the insecticide mirex in the 150 samples of farmed salmon we examined in the previous example.

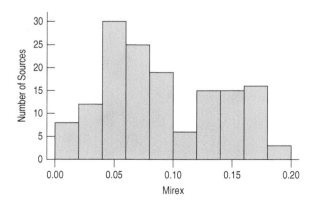

Question: Are the assumptions and conditions for making a confidence interval for the mean mirex concentration satisfied?

Answer:

✓ **Independence Assumption:** The fish were raised in many different places, and samples were purchased independently from several sources.

✓ **Randomization Condition:** The fish were selected randomly from those available for sale.

✓ **10% Condition:** There are lots of fish in the sea (and at the fish farms); 150 is certainly far fewer than 10% of the population.

✓ **Nearly Normal Condition:** The histogram of the data looks bimodal. While it might be interesting to learn the reason for that and possibly identify the subsets, we can proceed because the sample size is large.

It's okay to use these data about farm-raised salmon to make a confidence interval for the mean.

Just Checking

Shutterstock

Every 10 years, the United States takes a census that tries to count every resident. In addition, the census collects information on a variety of economic and social questions. Businesses of all types use the census data to plan sales and marketing strategies and to understand the underlying demographics of the areas that they serve.

There are two census forms: the "short form," answered by most people, and the "long form," sent only to about one in six or seven households chosen at random. According to the Census Bureau (factfinder.census.gov), "... each estimate based on the long form responses has an associated confidence interval."

1 Why does the Census Bureau need a confidence interval for long-form information, but not for the questions that appear on both the long and short forms?

2 Why must the Census Bureau base these confidence intervals on *t*-models?

The Census Bureau goes on to say, "These confidence intervals are wider ... for geographic areas with smaller populations and for characteristics that occur less frequently in the area being examined (such as the proportion of people in poverty in a middle-income neighborhood)."

3 Why is this so? For example, why should a confidence interval for the mean amount families spend monthly on housing be wider for a sparsely populated area of farms in the Midwest than for a densely populated area of an urban center? How does the formula for the one-sample *t*-interval show this will happen?

To deal with this problem, the Census Bureau reports long-form data only for "... geographic areas from which about two hundred or more long forms were completed—which are large enough to produce good quality estimates. If smaller weighting areas had been used, the confidence intervals around the estimates would have been significantly wider, rendering many estimates less useful."

4 Suppose the Census Bureau decided to report on areas from which only 50 long forms were completed. What effect would that have on a 95% confidence interval for, say, the mean cost of housing? Specifically, which values used in the formula for the margin of error would change? Which values would change a lot, and which values would change only slightly? Approximately how much wider would that confidence interval based on 50 forms be than the one based on 200 forms?

Guided Example   Insurance Profits

Shutterstock

Insurance companies take risks. When they insure a property or a life, they must price the policy in such a way that their expected profit enables them to survive. They can base their projections on actuarial tables, but the reality of the insurance business often demands that they discount policies to a variety of customers and situations. Managing this risk is made even more difficult by the fact that until the policy expires, the company won't know if they've made a profit, no matter what premium they charge.

A manager wanted to see how well one of her sales representatives was doing, so she selected 30 matured policies that had been sold by the sales

rep and computed the (net) profit (premium charged minus paid claims), for each of the 30 policies.

The manager would like you, as a consultant, to construct a 95% confidence interval for the mean profit of the policies sold by this sales rep.

Profit (in $) from 30 policies		
222.80	463.35	2089.40
1756.23	−66.20	2692.75
1100.85	57.90	2495.70
3340.66	833.95	2172.70
1006.50	1390.70	3249.65
445.50	2447.50	−397.10
3255.60	1847.50	−397.31
3701.85	865.40	186.25
−803.35	1415.65	590.85
3865.90	2756.94	578.95

PLAN

Setup State what we want to know. Identify the variables and their context.

We wish to find a 95% confidence interval for the mean profit of policies sold by this sales rep. We have data for 30 matured policies.

Make a picture. Check the distribution shape and look for skewness, multiple modes, and outliers.

Here's a boxplot and histogram of these values.

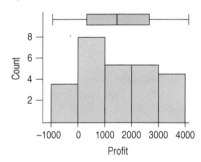

The sample appears to be unimodal and fairly symmetric with profit values between −$1000 and $4000 and no outliers.

Model Think about the assumptions and check the conditions.

✓ **Independence Assumption**

This is a random sample so observations should be independent.

✓ **Randomization Condition**

This sample was selected randomly from the matured policies sold by the sales representative of the company.

		✓ **Nearly Normal Condition**
		The distribution of profits is unimodal and fairly symmetric without strong skewness.
	State the sampling distribution model for the statistic.	We will use a Student's *t*-model with $n - 1 = 30 - 1 = 29$ degrees of freedom and find a one-sample *t*-interval for the mean.

DO

Mechanics Compute basic statistics and construct the confidence interval.

Using software, we obtain the following basic statistics:

$$n = 30$$
$$\bar{y} = \$1438.90$$
$$s = \$1329.60$$

Remember that the standard error of the mean is equal to the standard deviation divided by the square root of *n*.

The standard error of the mean is:

$$SE(\bar{y}) = \frac{s}{\sqrt{n}} = \frac{1329.60}{\sqrt{30}} = \$242.75$$

The critical value we need to make a 95% confidence interval comes from a Student's *t* table, a computer program, or a calculator. We have $30 - 1 = 29$ degrees of freedom. The selected confidence level says that we want 95% of the probability to be caught in the middle, so we exclude 2.5% in *each* tail, for a total of 5%. The degrees of freedom and 2.5% tail probability are all we need to know to find the critical value. Here it's 2.045.

There are $30 - 1 = 29$ degrees of freedom. The manager has specified a 95% level of confidence, so the critical value (from table T) is 2.045.

The margin of error is:

$$ME = 2.045 \times SE(\bar{y})$$
$$= 2.045 \times 242.75$$
$$= \$496.42$$

The 95% confidence interval for the mean profit is:

$$\$1438.90 \pm \$496.42$$
$$= (\$942.48, \$1935.32)$$

REPORT

Conclusion Interpret the confidence interval in the proper context.

MEMO

Re: Profit from Policies

From our analysis of the selected policies, we are 95% confident that the true mean profit of policies sold by this sales rep is contained in the interval from \$942.48 to \$1935.32.

When we construct confidence intervals in this way, we expect 95% of them to cover the true mean and 5% to miss the true value. That's what "95% confident" means.

Caveat: Insurance losses are notoriously subject to outliers. One very large loss could influence the average profit substantially. However, there were no such cases in this data set.

Finding Student's *t* Critical Values

The critical value in the Guided Example was found in the Student's *t* Table in Appendix: Tables and Selected Formulas. To find the critical value, locate the row of the table corresponding to the degrees of freedom and the column corresponding to the probability you want. Since a 95% confidence interval leaves 2.5% of the values on either side, we look for 0.025 at the top of the column or look for 95% confidence directly in the bottom row of the table. The value in the table at that intersection is the critical value we need. In the Guided Example, the number of degrees of freedom was $30 - 1 = 29$, so we located the value of 2.045.

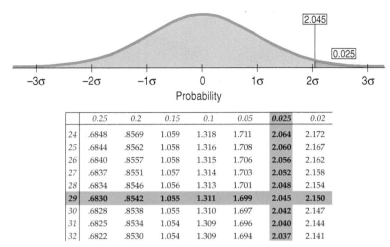

	0.25	0.2	0.15	0.1	0.05	**0.025**	0.02
24	.6848	.8569	1.059	1.318	1.711	**2.064**	2.172
25	.6844	.8562	1.058	1.316	1.708	**2.060**	2.167
26	.6840	.8557	1.058	1.315	1.706	**2.056**	2.162
27	.6837	.8551	1.057	1.314	1.703	**2.052**	2.158
28	.6834	.8546	1.056	1.313	1.701	**2.048**	2.154
29	**.6830**	**.8542**	**1.055**	**1.311**	**1.699**	**2.045**	**2.150**
30	.6828	.8538	1.055	1.310	1.697	**2.042**	2.147
31	.6825	.8534	1.054	1.309	1.696	**2.040**	2.144
32	.6822	.8530	1.054	1.309	1.694	**2.037**	2.141

Figure 5 Using Table T to look up the critical value *t** for a 95% confidence level with 29 degrees of freedom.

4 Cautions about Interpreting Confidence Intervals

Confidence intervals for means offer new, tempting, wrong interpretations. Here are some ways to keep from going astray:

- **Don't say,** "*95% of all the policies* sold by this sales rep have profits between $942.48 and $1935.32." The confidence interval is about the *mean*, not about the measurements of individual policies.

- **Don't say,** "We are 95% confident that *a randomly selected policy* will have a net profit between $942.48 and $1935.32." This false interpretation is also about individual policies rather than about the *mean* of the policies. We are 95% confident that the *mean* profit of all (similar) policies sold by this sales rep is between $942.48 and $1935.32.

- **Don't say,** "The mean profit is $1438.90 95% *of the time*." That's about means, but still wrong. It implies that the true mean varies, when in fact it is the confidence interval that would have been different had we gotten a different sample.

- Finally, **don't say,** "95% *of all samples* will have mean profits between $942.48 and $1935.32." That statement suggests that *this* interval somehow sets a standard for every other interval. In fact, this interval is no more (or less) likely to be correct than any other. You could say that 95% of all possible samples would produce intervals that contain the true mean profit. (The problem is that because we'll never know what the true mean profit is, we can't know if our sample was one of those 95%.)

Just Checking

In discussing estimates based on the long-form samples, the Census Bureau notes, "The disadvantage . . . is that . . . estimates of characteristics that are also reported on the short form will not match the [long-form estimates]."

The short-form estimates are values from a complete census, so they are the "true" values—something we don't usually have when we do inference.

5 Suppose we use long-form data to make 100 95% confidence intervals for the mean age of residents, one for each of 100 of the census-defined areas. How many of these 100 intervals should we expect will *fail* to include the true mean age (as determined from the complete short-form census data)?

5   Sample Size

How large a sample do we need? The simple answer is always "larger." But more data cost money, effort, and time. So how much is enough? Suppose your computer took an hour to download a movie you wanted to watch. You wouldn't be happy. Then you hear about a program that claims to download movies in under a half hour. You're interested enough to spend $29.95 for it, but only if it really delivers. So you get the free evaluation copy and test it by downloading a movie 10 times. Of course, the mean download time is not exactly 30 minutes as claimed. Observations vary. If the margin of error were 8 minutes, though, you'd probably be able to decide whether the software was worth the money. Doubling the sample size would require another 5 or so hours of testing and would reduce your margin of error to a bit under 6 minutes. You'd need to decide whether that's worth the effort.

As we make plans to collect data, we should have some idea of how small a margin of error is required to be able to draw a conclusion or detect a difference we want to see. If the size of the effect we're studying is large, then we may be able to tolerate a larger ME. If we need great precision, however, we'll want a smaller ME, and, of course, that means a larger sample size.

Armed with the ME and confidence level, we can find the sample size we'll need. Almost.

We know that for a mean, $ME = t^*_{n-1} \times SE(\bar{y})$ and that $SE(\bar{y}) = \dfrac{s}{\sqrt{n}}$, so we can determine the sample size by solving this equation for n:

$$ME = t^*_{n-1} \times \frac{s}{\sqrt{n}}.$$

The good news is that we have an equation; the bad news is that we won't know most of the values we need to compute it. When we thought about sample size for proportions, we ran into a similar problem. There we had to guess a working value for p to compute a sample size. Here, we need to know s. We don't know s until we get some data, but we want to calculate the sample size *before* collecting the data. We might be able to make a good guess, and that is often good enough for this purpose. If we have no idea what the standard deviation might be or if the sample size really matters (for example, because each additional individual is very expensive to sample or experiment on), it might be a good idea to run a small *pilot study* to get some feeling for the size of the standard deviation.

That's not all. Without knowing n, we don't know the degrees of freedom, and we can't find the critical value, t^*_{n-1}. One common approach is to use the corresponding z^* value from the Normal model. If you've chosen a 95% confidence level, then just use 2, following the 68–95–99.7 Rule, or 1.96 to be more precise. If your estimated sample size is 60 or more, it's probably okay—z^* was a good guess. If it's smaller than that, you may want to add a step, using z^* at first, finding n, and then replacing z^* with the corresponding t^*_{n-1} and calculating the sample size once more.

Sample size calculations are *never* exact. The margin of error you find *after* collecting the data won't match exactly the one you used to find n. The sample size formula depends on quantities that you won't have until you collect the data, but using it is an important first step. Before you collect data, it's always a good idea to know whether the sample size is large enough to give you a good chance of being able to tell you what you want to know.

By Hand

Sample size calculations

Let's give the sample size formula a spin. Suppose we want an ME of 8 minutes and we think the standard deviation of download times is about 10 minutes. Using a 95% confidence interval and $z^* = 1.96$, we solve for n:

$$8 = 1.96 \frac{10}{\sqrt{n}}$$

$$\sqrt{n} = \frac{1.96 \times 10}{8} = 2.45$$

$$n = (2.45)^2 = 6.0025$$

That's a small sample size, so we use $(6 - 1) = 5$ degrees of freedom to substitute an appropriate t^* value. At 95%, $t_5^* = 2.571$. Now we can solve the equation one more time:

$$8 = 2.571 \frac{10}{\sqrt{n}}$$

$$\sqrt{n} = \frac{2.571 \times 10}{8} \approx 3.214$$

$$n = (3.214)^2 \approx 10.33$$

To make sure the ME is no larger than you want, you should always round *up*, which gives $n = 11$ runs. So, to get an ME of 8 minutes, we should find the downloading times for $n = 11$ movies.

For Example   Finding the sample size for a confidence interval for means

In the 150 samples of farmed salmon, the mean concentration of mirex was 0.0913 ppm with a standard deviation of 0.0495 ppm. A 95% confidence interval for the mean mirex concentration was found to be: (0.0833, 0.0993).

Question: How large a sample would be needed to produce a 95% confidence interval with a margin of error of 0.004?

Answer: We will assume that the standard deviation is 0.0495 ppm. The margin of error is equal to the critical value times the standard error. Using z^*, we find:

$$0.004 = 1.96 \times \frac{0.0495}{\sqrt{n}}$$

Solving for n, we find:

$$\sqrt{n} = 1.96 \times \frac{0.0495}{0.004}$$

or

$$n = \left(1.96 \times \frac{0.0495}{0.004} \right)^2 = 588.3$$

The t^* critical value with 400 df is 1.966 instead of 1.960. Using that value, the margin of error is:

$$1.966 \times \frac{0.0495}{\sqrt{589}} = 0.00401$$

You could go back and use 1.966 instead of 1.960 in the equation for n, above, and you would find that n should be 592. That will give a margin of error of 0.004, but the uncertainty in the standard deviation is likely to make such differences unimportant.

6   Degrees of Freedom—Why $n - 1$?

The number of degrees of freedom $(n - 1)$ might have reminded you of the value we divide by to find the standard deviation of the data (since, after all, it's the same number). We promised back when we introduced that formula to say a bit more about why we divide by $n - 1$ rather than by n. The reason is closely tied to the reasoning of the *t*-distribution.

If only we knew the true population mean, μ, we would find the sample standard deviation using n instead of $n - 1$ as:

$$s = \sqrt{\frac{\sum (y - \mu)^2}{n}} \text{ and we'd call it } s.$$

We have to use $\bar{y}$ instead of μ, though, and that causes a problem. For any sample, $\bar{y}$ is as close to the data values as possible. Generally the population mean, μ, will be farther away. Think about it. GMAT scores have a population mean of 525. If you took a random sample of 5 students who took the test, their sample mean wouldn't be 525. The five data values will be closer to their own $\bar{y}$ than to 525. So if we use $\sum (y - \bar{y})^2$ instead of $\sum (y - \mu)^2$ in the equation to calculate s, our standard deviation estimate will be too small. The amazing mathematical fact is that we can compensate for the fact that $\sum (y - \bar{y})^2$ is too small just by dividing by $n - 1$ instead of by n. So that's all the $n - 1$ is doing in the denominator of s. We call $n - 1$ the degrees of freedom.

What Can Go Wrong?

First, you must decide when to use Student's *t* methods.

- **Don't confuse proportions and means.** When you treat your data as categorical, counting successes and summarizing with a sample proportion, make inferences using the Normal model methods. When you treat your data as quantitative, summarizing with a sample mean, make your inferences using Student's *t* methods.

Student's *t* methods work only when the Normal Population Assumption is true. Naturally, many of the ways things can go wrong turn out to be ways that the Normal Population Assumption can fail. It's always a good idea to look for the most common kinds of failure. It turns out that you can even fix some of them.

- **Beware of multimodality.** The Nearly Normal Condition clearly fails if a histogram of the data has two or more modes. When you see this, look for the possibility that your data come from two groups. If so, your best bet is to try to separate the data into groups. (Use the variables to help distinguish the modes, if possible. For example, if the modes seem to be composed mostly of men in one and women in the other, split the data according to the person's sex.) Then you can analyze each group separately.

- **Beware of skewed data.** Make a histogram of the data. If the data are severely skewed, you might try re-expressing the variable. Re-expressing may yield a distribution that is unimodal and symmetric, making it more appropriate for the inference methods for means. Re-expression cannot help if the sample distribution is not unimodal.

(continued)

- **Investigate outliers.** The Nearly Normal Condition also fails if the data have outliers. If you find outliers in the data, you need to investigate them. Sometimes, it's obvious that a data value is wrong and the justification for removing or correcting it is clear. When there's no clear justification for removing an outlier, you might want to run the analysis both with and without the outlier and note any differences in your conclusions. Any time data values are set aside, you *must* report on them individually. Often they will turn out to be the most informative part of your report on the data.[5]

Of course, Normality issues aren't the only risks you face when doing inferences about means.

- **Watch out for bias.** Measurements of all kinds can be biased. If your observations differ from the true mean in a systematic way, your confidence interval may not capture the true mean. And there is no sample size that will save you. A bathroom scale that's 5 pounds off will be 5 pounds off even if you weigh yourself 100 times and take the average. We've seen several sources of bias in surveys, but measurements can be biased, too. Be sure to think about possible sources of bias in your measurements.

- **Make sure data are independent.** Student's *t* methods also require the sampled values to be mutually independent. We check for random sampling and the 10% Condition. You should also think hard about whether there are likely violations of independence in the data collection method. If there are, be very cautious about using these methods.

Ethics in Action

Recent reports have indicated that waiting times in hospital emergency rooms (ERs) across the United States are getting longer, with the average reported as 30 minutes in January 2008 (WashingtonPost.com). Several reasons have been cited for this rise in average ER waiting time including the closing of hospital emergency rooms in urban areas and problems with managing hospital flow. Tyler Hospital, located in rural Ohio, joined the Joint Commission's Continuous Service Readiness program and consequently agreed to monitor its ER waiting times. After collecting data for a random sample of 30 ER patients arriving at Tyler's ER during the last month, they found an average waiting time of 26 minutes with a standard deviation of 8.25 minutes. Further statistical analysis yielded a 95% confidence interval of 22.92 to 29.08 minutes, clear indication that Tyler's ER patients wait less than 30 minutes to see a doctor.

Tyler's administration was not only pleased with the findings, but also sure that the Joint Commission would also be impressed. Their next step was to consider ways of including this message, "95% of Tyler's ER patients can expect to wait less than the national average to see a doctor," in their advertising and promotional materials.

ETHICAL ISSUE *Interpretation of the confidence interval is incorrect and misleading (related to Item C, ASA Ethical Guidelines). The confidence interval does not provide results for individual patients. So, it is incorrect to state that 95% of individual ER patients wait less (or can expect to wait less) than 30 minutes to see a doctor.*

ETHICAL SOLUTION *Interpret the results of the confidence interval correctly, in terms of the mean waiting time and not individual patients.*

---

[5]This suggestion may be controversial in some disciplines. Setting aside outliers is seen by some as unethical because the result is likely to be a narrower confidence interval or a smaller P-value. But an analysis of data with outliers left in place is *always* wrong. The outliers violate the Nearly Normal Condition and also the implicit assumption of a homogeneous population, so they invalidate inference procedures. An analysis of the nonoutlying points, along with a separate discussion of the outliers, is often much more informative, and can reveal important aspects of the data.

What Have We Learned?

Learning Objectives

■ Know the sampling distribution of the mean.

- To apply the Central Limit Theorem for the mean in practical applications, we must estimate the standard deviation. This *standard error* is

$$SE(\bar{y}) = \frac{s}{\sqrt{n}}$$

- When we use the SE, the sampling distribution that allows for the additional uncertainty is Student's *t*.

■ Construct confidence intervals for the true mean, μ.

- A confidence interval for the mean has the form $\bar{y} \pm ME$.
- The Margin of Error is $ME = t^*_{df} SE(\bar{y})$.

■ Find *t** values by technology or from tables.

- When constructing confidence intervals for means, the correct degrees of freedom is $n - 1$.

■ Check the Assumptions and Conditions before using any sampling distribution for inference.

■ Write clear summaries to interpret a confidence interval.

Terms

Degrees of freedom (df) A parameter of the Student's *t*-distribution that depends upon the sample size. Typically, more degrees of freedom reflects increasing information from the sample.

One-sample *t*-interval for the mean A one-sample *t*-interval for the population mean is:

$$\bar{y} \pm t^*_{n-1} \times SE(\bar{y}) \text{ where } SE(\bar{y}) = \frac{s}{\sqrt{n}}.$$

The critical value t^*_{n-1} depends on the particular confidence level, C, that you specify and on the number of degrees of freedom, $n - 1$.

Student's *t* A family of distributions indexed by its degrees of freedom. The *t*-models are unimodal, symmetric, and bell-shaped, but generally have fatter tails and a narrower center than the Normal model. As the degrees of freedom increase, *t*-distributions approach the Normal model.

Technology Help: Inference for Means

Statistics packages offer convenient ways to make histograms of the data. That means you have no excuse for skipping the check that the data are nearly Normal.

Any standard statistics package can compute a confidence interval.

Inference results are sometimes reported in a table. You may have to read carefully to find the values you need. Often, confidence interval bounds are given together with related results for hypothesis tests. Here is an example of that kind of output (although no package we know gives results in exactly this form).

The commands to do inference for means on common statistics programs and calculators are not always obvious. (By contrast, the resulting output is usually clearly labeled and easy to read.) The guides for each program can help you start navigating.

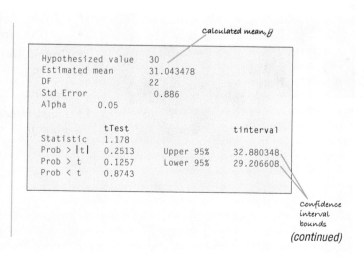

(continued)

To find a confidence interval for a mean in Excel, you can set up the calculations using Excel's functions. For example, suppose you have 100 observations in cells A1:A100.

- In cell B2, enter "=AVERAGE(A1:A100)" to compute the sample mean.
- In cell B3, enter "=STDEV(A1:A11)/SQRT(100)" to compute the standard error of the mean.
- In cell B4, enter "=TINV(.05,99)" to compute t*.
- In cell B5, enter "=B2-B4*B3" as the lower end of the CI.
- In cell B6, enter "=B2+B4*B3" as the upper end of the CI.

JMP

- From the **Analyze** menu, select **Distribution**.
- For a confidence interval, scroll down to the "Moments" section to find the interval limits. (Be sure that your variables are "Continuous" type so that this section will be available.)

Comments

"Moment" is a fancy statistical term for means, standard deviations, and other related statistics.

MINITAB

- From the **Stat** menu, choose the **Basic Statistics** submenu.
- From that menu, choose 1-sample t . . . .
- Then fill in the dialog.

Comments

The dialog offers a clear choice between confidence interval and hypothesis test.

SPSS

- From the **Analyze** menu, choose the **Compare Means** submenu.
- From that, choose **One-Sample t-test** command.

Comments

The commands suggest neither a single mean nor an interval. But the results provide both.

Brief CASE

Scott Leigh/
iStockphoto
Andy Dean/iStockphoto

Real Estate

A real estate agent is trying to understand the pricing of homes in her area, a region comprised of small to midsize towns and a small city. For each of 1200 homes recently sold in the region, the file **Real_Estate_sample1200** on the website www.pearsonhighered.com/sharpe holds the following variables:

- *Sale Price* (in $)
- *Lot size* (size of the lot in acres)
- *Waterfront* (Yes, No)
- *Age* (in years)
- *Central Air* (Yes, No)
- *Fuel Type* (Wood, Oil, Gas, Electric, Propane, Solar, Other)
- *Condition* (1 to 5, 1 = Poor, 5 = Excellent)
- *Living Area* (living area in square feet)
- *Pct College* (% in zip code who attend a four-year college)

- *Full Baths* (number of full bathrooms)
- *Half Baths* (number of half bathrooms)
- *Bedrooms* (number of bedrooms)
- *Fireplaces* (number of fireplaces)

The agent has a family interested in a four bedroom house. Using confidence intervals, how should she advise the family on what the average price of a four bedroom house might be in this area? Compare that to a confidence interval for two bedroom homes. How does the presence of central air conditioning affect the mean price of houses in this area? Use confidence intervals and graphics to help answer that question.

Explore other questions that might be useful for the real estate agent in knowing how different categorical factors affect the sale price and write up a short report on your findings.

Donor Profiles

A philanthropic organization collects and buys data on their donor base. The full database contains about 4.5 million donors and over 400 variables collected on each, but the data set **Donor_Profiles** on the website is a sample of 916 donors and includes the variables:

- *Age* (in years)
- *Homeowner* (H = Yes, U = Unknown)
- *Gender* (F = Female, M = Male, U = Unknown)
- *Wealth* (Ordered categories of total household wealth from 1 = Lowest to 9 = Highest)
- *Children* (Number of children)
- *Donated Last* (0 = Did not donate to last campaign, 1 = Did donate to last campaign)
- *Amt Donated Last* ($ amount of contribution to last campaign)

The analysts at the organization want to know how much people donate on average to campaigns, and what factors might influence that amount. Compare the confidence intervals for the mean *Amt Donated Last* by those known to own their homes with those whose homeowner status is unknown. Perform similar comparisons for *Gender* and two of the *Wealth* categories. Write up a short report using graphics and confidence intervals for what you have found. (Be careful not to make inferences directly about the differences between groups. Your inference should be about single groups.)

(The distribution of *Amt Donated Last* is highly skewed to the right, and so the median might be thought to be the appropriate summary. But the median is $0.00 so the analysts must use the mean. From simulations, they have ascertained that the sampling distribution for the mean is unimodal and symmetric for samples larger than 250 or so. Note that small differences in the mean could result in millions of dollars of added revenue nationwide. The average cost of their solicitation is $0.67 per person to produce and mail.)

Exercises

SECTION 1

1. A survey of 25 randomly selected customers found the following ages (in years):

20	32	34	29	30
30	30	14	29	11
38	22	44	48	26
25	22	32	35	32
35	42	44	44	48

Recall that the mean was 31.84 years and the standard deviation was 9.84 years.

a) What is the standard error of the mean?
b) How would the standard error change if the same size had been 100 instead of 25? (Assume that the sample standard deviation didn't change.)

2. A random sample of 20 purchases showed the following amounts (in $):

39.05	2.73	32.92	47.51
37.91	34.35	64.48	51.96
56.95	81.58	47.80	11.72
21.57	40.83	38.24	32.98
75.16	74.30	47.54	65.62

Recall that the mean was $45.26 and the standard deviation was $20.67.

a) What is the standard error of the mean?
b) How would the standard error change if the same size had been 5 instead of 20? (Assume that the sample standard deviation didn't change.)

3. For the data in Exercise 1:

a) How many degrees of freedom does the *t*-statistic have?
b) How many degrees of freedom would the *t*-statistic have if the sample size had been 100?

4. For the data in Exercise 2:

a) How many degrees of freedom does the *t*-statistic have?
b) How many degrees of freedom would the *t*-statistic have if the sample size had been 5?

SECTION 2

5. Find the critical value t^* for:

a) a 95% confidence interval based on 24 df.
b) a 95% confidence interval based on 99 df.

6. Find the critical value t^* for:

a) a 90% confidence interval based on 19 df.
b) a 90% confidence interval based on 4 df.

7. For the ages in Exercise 1:

a) Construct a 95% confidence interval for the mean age of all customers, assuming that the assumptions and conditions for the confidence interval have been met.
b) How large is the margin of error?
c) How would the confidence interval change if you had assumed that the standard deviation was known to be 10.0 years?

8. For the purchase amounts in Exercise 2:

a) Construct a 90% confidence interval for the mean purchases of all customers, assuming that the assumptions and conditions for the confidence interval have been met.
b) How large is the margin of error?
c) How would the confidence interval change if you had assumed that the standard deviation was known to be $20?

SECTION 3

9. For the confidence intervals of Exercise 7, a histogram of the data looks like this:

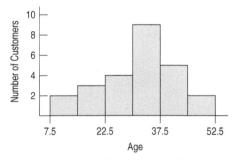

Check the assumptions and conditions for your inference.

10. For confidence intervals of Exercise 8, a histogram of the data looks like this:

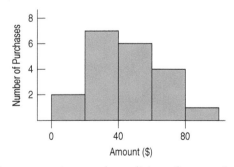

Check the assumptions and conditions for your inference.

SECTION 5

11. For the confidence interval in Exercise 7:

a) How large would the sample size have to be to cut the margin of error in half?
b) About how large would the sample size have to be to cut the margin of error by a factor of 10?

12. For the confidence interval in Exercise 8:

a) To reduce the margin of error to about $4, how large would the sample size have to be?

b) How large would the sample size have to be to reduce the margin of error to $0.80?

CHAPTER EXERCISES

13. *t*-models. Using the *t* tables, software, or a calculator, estimate:

a) the critical value of *t* for a 90% confidence interval with df = 17.

b) the critical value of *t* for a 98% confidence interval with df = 88.

14. *t*-models, part 2. Using the *t* tables, software, or a calculator, estimate:

a) the critical value of *t* for a 95% confidence interval with df = 7.

b) the critical value of *t* for a 99% confidence interval with df = 102.

15. Confidence intervals. Describe how the width of a 95% confidence interval for a mean changes as the standard deviation (*s*) of a sample increases, assuming sample size remains the same.

16. Confidence intervals, part 2. Describe how the width of a 95% confidence interval for a mean changes as the sample size (*n*) increases, assuming the standard deviation remains the same.

17. Confidence intervals and sample size. A confidence interval for the price of gasoline from a random sample of 30 gas stations in a region gives the following statistics:

$$\bar{y} = \$4.49 \quad s = \$0.29$$

a) Find a 95% confidence interval for the mean price of regular gasoline in that region.

b) Find the 90% confidence interval for the mean.

c) If we had the same statistics from a sample of 60 stations, what would the 95% confidence interval be now?

18. Confidence intervals and sample size, part 2. A confidence interval for the price of gasoline from a random sample of 30 gas stations in a region gives the following statistics:

$$\bar{y} = \$4.49 \quad SE(\bar{y}) = \$0.06$$

a) Find a 95% confidence interval for the mean price of regular gasoline in that region.

b) Find the 90% confidence interval for the mean.

c) If we had the same statistics from a sample of 60 stations, what would the 95% confidence interval be now?

19. Marketing livestock feed. A feed supply company has developed a special feed supplement to see if it will promote weight gain in livestock. Their researchers report that the 77 cows studied gained an average of 56 pounds and that a 95% confidence interval for the mean weight gain this supplement produces has a margin of error of ±11 pounds. Staff in their marketing department wrote the following conclusions. Did anyone interpret the interval correctly? Explain any misinterpretations.

a) 95% of the cows studied gained between 45 and 67 pounds.

b) We're 95% sure that a cow fed this supplement will gain between 45 and 67 pounds.

c) We're 95% sure that the average weight gain among the cows in this study was between 45 and 67 pounds.

d) The average weight gain of cows fed this supplement is between 45 and 67 pounds 95% of the time.

e) If this supplement is tested on another sample of cows, there is a 95% chance that their average weight gain will be between 45 and 67 pounds.

20. Meal costs. A company is interested in estimating the costs of lunch in their cafeteria. After surveying employees, the staff calculated that a 95% confidence interval for the mean amount of money spent for lunch over a period of six months is ($780, $920). Now the organization is trying to write its report and considering the following interpretations. Comment on each.

a) 95% of all employees pay between $780 and $920 for lunch.

b) 95% of the sampled employees paid between $780 and $920 for lunch.

c) We're 95% sure that employees in this sample averaged between $780 and $920 for lunch.

d) 95% of all samples of employees will have average lunch costs between $780 and $920.

e) We're 95% sure that the average amount all employees pay for lunch is between $780 and $920.

21. CEO compensation. A sample of 20 CEOs from the Forbes 500 shows total annual compensations ranging from a minimum of $0.1 to $62.24 million. The average for these 20 CEOs is $7.946 million. The histogram and boxplot are as follows:

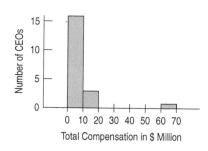

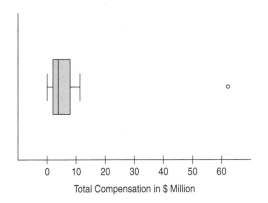

Based on these data, a computer program found that a confidence interval for the mean annual compensation of all Forbes 500 CEOs is (1.69, 14.20) $M. Why should you be hesitant to trust this confidence interval?

22. Credit card charges. A credit card company takes a random sample of 100 cardholders to see how much they charged on their card last month. A histogram and boxplot are as follows:

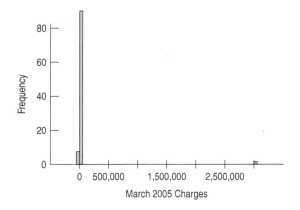

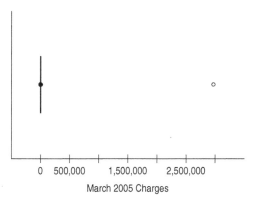

A computer program found that the 95% confidence interval for the mean amount spent in March 2005 is (−$28,366.84, $90,691.49). Explain why the analysts didn't find the confidence interval useful, and explain what went wrong.

23. Parking. Hoping to lure more shoppers downtown, a city builds a new public parking garage in the central

business district. The city plans to pay for the structure through parking fees. For a random sample of 44 weekdays, daily fees collected averaged $126, with a standard deviation of $15.

a) What assumptions must you make in order to use these statistics for inference?
b) Find a 90% confidence interval for the mean daily income this parking garage will generate.
c) Explain in context what this confidence interval means.
d) Explain what 90% confidence means in this context.
e) The consultant who advised the city on this project predicted that parking revenues would average $128 per day. Based on your confidence interval, what do you think of the consultant's prediction? Why?

24. Housing 2008 was a difficult year for the economy. There were a large number of foreclosures of family homes. In one large community, realtors randomly sampled 36 bids from potential buyers to determine the average loss in home value. The sample showed the average loss was $11,560 with a standard deviation of $1500.

a) What assumptions and conditions must be checked before finding a confidence interval? How would you check them?
b) Find a 95% confidence interval for the mean loss in value per home.
c) Interpret this interval and explain what 95% confidence means.
d) Suppose nationally, the average loss in home values at this time was $10,000. Do you think the loss in the sampled community differs significantly from the national average? Explain.

25. Parking, part 2. Suppose that for budget planning purposes the city in Exercise 23 needs a better estimate of the mean daily income from parking fees.

a) Someone suggests that the city use its data to create a 95% confidence interval instead of the 90% interval first created. How would this interval be better for the city? (You need not actually create the new interval.)
b) How would the 95% confidence interval be worse for the planners?
c) How could they achieve a confidence interval estimate that would better serve their planning needs?

26. Housing, part 2. In Exercise 24, we found a 95% confidence interval to estimate the loss in home values.

a) Suppose the standard deviation of the losses was $3000 instead of the $1500 used for that interval. What would the larger standard deviation do to the width of the confidence interval (assuming the same level of confidence)?
b) Your classmate suggests that the margin of error in the interval could be reduced if the confidence level were changed to 90% instead of 95%. Do you agree with this statement? Why or why not?
c) Instead of changing the level of confidence, would it be more statistically appropriate to draw a bigger sample?

27. State budgets. States that rely on sales tax for revenue to fund education, public safety, and other programs often end up with budget surpluses during economic growth periods (when people spend more on consumer goods) and budget deficits during recessions (when people spend less on consumer goods). Fifty-one small retailers in a state with a growing economy were recently sampled. The sample showed a mean increase of $2350 in additional sales tax revenue collected per retailer compared to the previous quarter. The sample standard deviation = $425.

a) Find a 95% confidence interval for the mean increase in sales tax revenue.
b) What assumptions have you made in this inference? Do you think the appropriate conditions have been satisfied?
c) Explain what your interval means and provide an example of what it does not mean.

28. State budgets, part 2. Suppose the state in Exercise 27 sampled 16 small retailers instead of 51, and for the sample of 16, the sample mean increase again equaled $2350 in additional sales tax revenue collected per retailer compared to the previous quarter. Also assume the sample standard deviation = $425.

a) What is the standard error of the mean increase in sales tax revenue collected?
b) What happens to the accuracy of the estimate when the interval is constructed using the smaller sample size?
c) Find and interpret a 95% confidence interval.
d) How does the margin of error for the interval constructed in Exercise 27 compare with the margin of error constructed in this exercise? Explain statistically how sample size changes the accuracy of the constructed interval. Which sample would you prefer if you were a state budget planner? Why?

29. Departures. What are the chances your flight will leave on time? The U.S. Bureau of Transportation Statistics of the Department of Transportation publishes information about airline performance. Here are a histogram and summary statistics for the percentage of flights departing on time each month from 1995 through 2006.

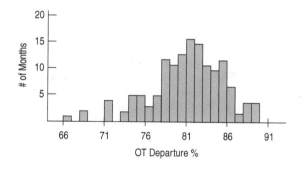

n	144
ȳ	81.1838
s	4.47094

There is no evidence of a trend over time. (The correlation of On Time Departure% with time is $r = -0.016$.)

a) Check the assumptions and conditions for inference.
b) Find a 90% confidence interval for the true percentage of flights that depart on time.
c) Interpret this interval for a traveler planning to fly.

30. Late arrivals. Will your flight get you to your destination on time? The U.S. Bureau of Transportation Statistics reported the percentage of flights that were late each month from 1995 through 2006. Here's a histogram, along with some summary statistics:

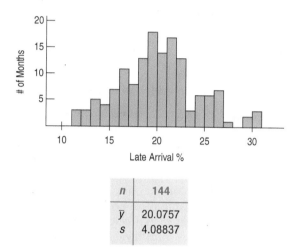

n	144
ȳ	20.0757
s	4.08837

We can consider these data to be a representative sample of all months. There is no evidence of a time trend.

a) Check the assumptions and conditions for inference about the mean.
b) Find a 99% confidence interval for the true percentage of flights that arrive late.
c) Interpret this interval for a traveler planning to fly.

31. Computer lab fees. The technology committee has stated that the average time spent by students per lab visit has increased, and the increase supports the need for increased lab fees. To substantiate this claim, the committee randomly samples 12 student lab visits and notes the amount of time spent using the computer. The times in minutes are as follows:

Time	Time
52	74
57	53
54	136
76	73
62	8
52	62

a) Plot the data. Are any of the observations outliers? Explain.

b) The previous mean amount of time spent using the lab computer was 55 minutes. Find a 95% confidence interval for the true mean. What do you conclude about the claim? If there are outliers, find intervals with and without the outliers present.

32. Cell phone batteries. A company that produces cell phones claims its standard phone battery lasts longer on average than other batteries in the market. To support this claim, the company publishes an ad reporting the results of a recent experiment showing that under normal usage, their batteries last at least 35 hours. To investigate this claim, a consumer advocacy group asked the company for the raw data. The company sends the group the following results:

35, 34, 32, 31, 34, 34, 32, 33, 35, 55, 32, 31

Find a 95% confidence interval and state your conclusion. Explain how you dealt with the outlier, and why.

33. Growth and air pollution. Government officials have difficulty attracting new business to communities with troubled reputations. Nevada has been one of the fastest growing states in the country for a number of years. Accompanying the rapid growth are massive new construction projects. Since Nevada has a dry climate, the construction creates visible dust pollution. High pollution levels may paint a less than attractive picture of the area, and can also result in fines levied by the federal government. As required by government regulation, researchers continually monitor pollution levels. In the most recent test of pollution levels, 121 air samples were collected. The dust particulate levels must be reported to the federal regulatory agencies. In the report sent to the federal agency, it was noted that the mean particulate level = 57.6 micrograms/cubic liter of air, and the 95% confidence interval estimate is (52.06 mg to 63.07 mg). A graph of the distribution of the particulate amounts was also included and is shown below.

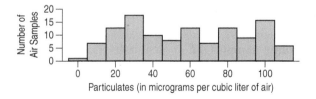

a) Discuss the assumptions and conditions for using Student's *t* inference methods with these data.

b) Do you think the confidence interval noted in the report is valid? Briefly explain why or why not.

34. Convention revenues. At one time, Nevada was the only U.S. state that allowed gambling. Although gambling continues to be one of the major industries in Nevada, the proliferation of legalized gambling in other areas of the country has required state and local governments to look at other growth possibilities. The convention and visitor's authorities in many Nevada cities actively recruit national conventions that bring thousands of visitors to the state. Various demographic and economic data are collected from surveys given to convention attendees. One statistic of interest is the amount visitors spend on slot machine gambling. Nevada often reports the slot machine expenditure as amount spent per hotel guest room. A recent survey of 500 visitors asked how much they spent on gambling. The average expenditure per room was $180.

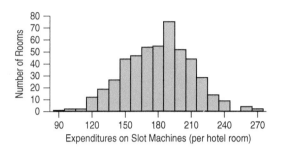

Casinos will use the information reported in the survey to estimate slot machine expenditure per hotel room. Do you think the estimates produced by the survey will accurately represent expenditures? Explain using the statistics reported and graph shown.

35. Traffic speed. Police departments often try to control traffic speed by placing speed-measuring machines on roads that tell motorists how fast they are driving. Traffic safety experts must determine where machines should be placed. In one recent test, police recorded the average speed clocked by cars driving on one busy street close to an elementary school. For a sample of 25 speeds, it was determined that the average amount over the speed limit for the 25 clocked speeds was 11.6 mph with a standard deviation of 8 mph. The 95% confidence interval estimate for this sample is 8.30 mph to 14.90 mph.

a) What is the margin of error for this problem?

b) The researchers commented that the interval was too wide. Explain specifically what should be done to reduce the margin of error to no more than ±2 mph.

36. Traffic speed, part 2. The speed-measuring machines must measure accurately to maximize effectiveness in slowing traffic. The accuracy of the machines will be tested before placement on city streets. To ensure that error rates are estimated accurately, the researchers want to take a large enough sample to ensure usable and accurate interval estimates of how much the machines may be off in measuring actual speeds. Specially, the researchers want the margin of error for a single speed measurement to be no more than ±1.5 mph.

a) Discuss how the researchers may obtain a reasonable estimate of the standard deviation of error in the measured speeds.

b) Suppose the standard deviation for the error in the measured speeds equals 4 mph. At 95% confidence, what sample size should be taken to ensure that the margin of error is no larger than ±1.0 mph?

37. Tax audits. Certified public accountants are often required to appear with clients if the IRS audits the client's tax return. Some accounting firms give the client an option to pay a fee when the tax return is completed that guarantees tax advice and support from the accountant if the client were audited. The fee is charged up front like an insurance premium and is less than the amount that would be charged if the client were later audited and then decided to ask the firm for assistance during the audit. A large accounting firm is trying to determine what fee to charge for next year's returns. In previous years, the actual mean cost to the firm for attending a client audit session was $650. To determine if this cost has changed, the firm randomly samples 32 client audit fees. The sample mean audit cost was $680 with a standard deviation of $75.

a) Develop a 95% confidence interval estimate for the mean audit cost.

b) Based on your confidence interval, what do you think of the claim that the mean cost has changed?

38. Tax audits, part 2. While reviewing the sample of audit fees, a senior accountant for the firm notes that the fee charged by the firm's accountants depends on the complexity of the return. A comparison of actual charges therefore might not provide the information needed to set next year's fees. To better understand the fee structure, the senior accountant requests a new sample that measures the time the accountants spent on the audit. Last year, the average hours charged per client audit was 3.25 hours. A new sample of 10 audit times shows the following times in hours:

4.2, 3.7, 4.8, 2.9, 3.1, 4.5, 4.2, 4.1, 5.0, 3.4

a) Assume the conditions necessary for inference are met. Find a 90% confidence interval estimate for the mean audit time.

b) Based on your answer to part a, comment on the claim that the mean fees have increased.

39. Wind power. Should you generate electricity with your own personal wind turbine? That depends on whether you have enough wind on your site. To produce enough energy, your site should have an annual average wind speed of at least 8 miles per hour, according to the Wind Energy Association. One candidate site was monitored for a year, with wind speeds recorded every 6 hours. A total of 1114 readings of wind speed averaged 8.019 mph with a standard deviation of 3.813 mph. You've been asked to make a statistical report to help the landowner decide whether to place a wind turbine at this site.

a) Discuss the assumptions and conditions for using Student's *t* inference methods with these data. Here are some plots that may help you decide whether the methods can be used:

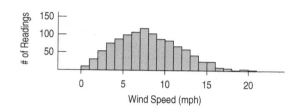

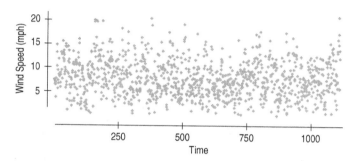

b) What would you tell the landowner about whether this site is suitable for a small wind turbine? Explain

40. Real estate crash? After the sub-prime crisis of late 2007, real estate prices fell almost everywhere in the U.S. In 2006–2007 before the crisis, the average selling price of homes in a region in upstate New York was $191,300. A real estate agency wants to know how much the prices have fallen since then. They collect a sample of 1231 homes in the region and find the average asking price to be $178,613.50 with a standard deviation of $92,701.56. You have been retained by the real estate agency to report on the current situation.

a) Discuss the assumptions and conditions for using *t*-methods for inference with these data. Here are some plots that may help you decide what to do.

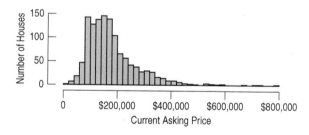

b) What would you report to the real estate agency about the current situation?

Just Checking Answers

1 Questions on the short form are answered by everyone in the population. This is a census, so means or proportions *are* the true population values. The long forms are just given to a sample of the population. When we estimate parameters from a sample, we use a confidence interval to take sample-to-sample variability into account.

2 They don't know the population standard deviation, so they must use the sample SD as an estimate. The additional uncertainty is taken into account by *t*-models.

3 The margin of error for a confidence interval for a mean depends, in part, on the standard error:

$$SE(\bar{y}) = \frac{s}{\sqrt{n}}$$

Since *n* is in the denominator, smaller sample sizes generally lead to larger SEs and correspondingly wider intervals. Because long forms are sampled at the same rate of one in every six or seven households throughout the country, samples will be smaller in less populous areas and result in wider confidence intervals.

4 The critical values for *t* with fewer degrees of freedom would be slightly larger. The $\sqrt{n}$ part of the standard error changes a lot, making the SE much larger. Both would increase the margin of error. The smaller sample is one fourth as large, so the confidence interval would be roughly twice as wide.

5 We expect 95% of such intervals to cover the true value, so 5 of the 100 intervals might be expected to miss.

Answers

SECTION EXERCISE ANSWERS

1. a) 1.968 years
   b) 0.984 years (half as large)

3. a) 24
   b) 99

5. a) 2.064
   b) 1.984

7. a) (27.78, 35.90) years
   b) 4.06 years
   c) (27.92, 35.76) years. Slightly narrower.

9. Independence: The data were from a random survey and should be independent.

   Randomization: the data were selected randomly.

   10% Condition: These customers are fewer than 10% of the customer population.

   Nearly Normal: The histogram is unimodal and symmetric, which is sufficient.

11. a) Four times as big, or *n* = 100.
   b) 100 times a big, or *n* = 2500.

CHAPTER EXERCISE ANSWERS

13. a) 1.74
   b) 2.37

15. As the variability of a sample increases, the width of a 95% confidence interval increases, assuming that sample size remains the same.

17. a) ($4.382, $4.598)
   b) ($4.400, $4.580)
   c) ($4.415, $4.565)

19. a) Not correct. A confidence interval is for the mean weight gain of the population of all cows. It says nothing about individual cows.
   b) Not correct. A confidence interval is for the mean weight gain of the population of all cows, not individual cows.

c) Not correct. We don't need a confidence interval about the average weight gain for cows in this study. We are certain that the mean weight gain of the cows in this study is 56 pounds.

d) Not correct. This statement implies that the average weight gain varies. It doesn't.

e) Not correct. This statement implies that there is something special about our interval, when this interval is actually one of many that could have been generated, depending on the cows that were chosen for the sample.

21. The assumptions and conditions for a *t*-interval are not met. With a sample size of only 20, the distribution is too skewed. There is also a large outlier that is pulling the mean higher.

23. a) The data are a random sample of all days; the distribution is unimodal and symmetric with no outliers.

b) ($122.20, $129.80)

c) We are 90% confident that the interval $122.20 to $129.80 contains the true mean daily income of the parking garage.

d) 90% of all random samples of size 44 will produce intervals that contain the true mean daily income of the parking garage.

e) $128 is a plausible value.

25. a) We can be more confident that our interval contains the mean parking revenue.

b) Wider (and less precise) interval

c) By collecting a larger sample, they could create a more precise interval without sacrificing confidence.

27. a) $2350 \pm 2.009 (59.51)$ Interval: (2230.4, 2469.6)

b) The assumptions and conditions that must be satisfied are:
1) Independence: probably OK.
2) Nearly Normal condition: can't tell.
3) Sample size of 51 is large enough.

c) We are 95% confident the interval $2230.4 to $2469.6 contains the true mean increase in sales tax revenue.
Examples of what the interval *does not* mean: The mean increase in sales tax revenue is $2350 95% of the time. 95% of all increases in sales tax revenue increases will be between $2230.4 and $2469.6. There's 95% confidence the next small retailer will have an increase in sales tax revenue between $2230.4 and $2469.6.

29. a) Given no time trend, the monthly on-time departure rates should be independent. Though not a random sample, these months should be representative, and they're fewer than 10% of all months. The histogram looks unimodal, but slightly left-skewed; not a concern with this large sample.

b) (80.57%, 81.80%)

c) We can be 90% confident that the interval from 80.57% to 81.80% holds the true mean monthly percentage of on-time flight departures.

31. a) The histogram of the lab fees shows 2 extreme outliers, so with the outliers included, the conditions for inference are violated.

b) With the outliers left in, the 95% confidence interval is (44.9, 81.6) minutes. If we remove the two extreme outliers, it is (54.6, 68.4).

In either case, we would be reluctant to conclude that the mean is above 55 minutes. The sample size is small and the presence of two large outliers advises us to be cautious about conclusions from this sample.

33. a) The assumptions and conditions that must be satisfied are: The data come from a nearly normal distribution.
The air samples were selected randomly, and there is no bias present in the sample.

b) The histogram of air samples is not nearly normal, but the sample size is large, so inference is OK.

35. a) $14.90 - 11.6$ or ± 3.3 miles per hour

b) The sample size for ME = 2 should be increased to $1.96 \times 8/2 = 7.84$.
$(7.84)^2 = 61.466 = 62$

37. a) Interval: $653 to $707

b) The confidence interval suggests the mean audit cost is higher than $650.

39. a) The timeplot shows no pattern, so it seems that the measurements are independent. Although this is not a random sample, an entire year is measured, so it is likely that we have representative values. We certainly have fewer than 10% of all possible wind readings. The histogram appears nearly normal.

b) A 95% confidence interval for the true mean speed is (7.795, 8.243) mph. Because there are many plausible values below 8 mph, we can not be confident that the true mean is at least 8 mph. We would not recommend that the turbine be placed here.

Testing Hypotheses

Mike Bentley/iStockphoto

Dow Jones Industrial Average

More than a hundred years ago Charles Dow changed the way people look at the stock market. Surprisingly, he wasn't an investment wizard or a venture capitalist. He was a journalist who wanted to make investing understandable to ordinary people. Although he died at the relatively young age of 51 in 1902, his impact on how we track the stock market has been both long-lasting and far-reaching.

In the late 1800s, when Charles Dow reported on Wall Street, investors preferred bonds, not stocks. Bonds were reliable, backed by the real machinery and other hard assets the company owned. What's more, bonds were predictable; the bond owner knew when the bond would mature and so, knew when and how much the bond would pay. Stocks simply represented "shares" of ownership, which were risky and erratic. In May 1896, Dow and Edward Jones, whom he had known since their days as reporters for the *Providence Evening Press*, launched the now-famous Dow Jones Industrial Average (DJIA) to help the public understand stock market trends.

Alan Crosthwaite/iStockphoto

Mario Tama/Staff/Getty Images

From Chapter 13 of *Business Statistics*, Second Edition, Norean R. Sharpe, Richard D. De Veaux, Paul F. Velleman.

The original DJIA averaged 11 stock prices. Of those original industrial stocks, only General Electric is still in the DJIA.

Since then, the DJIA has become synonymous with overall market performance and is often referred to simply as the Dow. The index was expanded to 20 stocks in 1916 and to 30 in 1928 at the height of the roaring 20's bull market. That bull market peaked on September 3, 1929, when the Dow reached 381.17. On October 28 and 29, 1929, the Dow lost nearly 25% of its value. Then things got worse. Within four years, on July 8, 1932, the 30 industrials reached an all-time low of 40.65. The highs of September 1929 were not reached again until 1954.

Today the Dow is a weighted average of 30 industrial stocks, with weights used to account for splits and other adjustments. The "Industrial" part of the name is largely historic. Today's DJIA includes the service industry and financial companies and is much broader than just heavy industry. And it is still one of the most watched indicators of the state of the U.S. stock market and the global economy.

WHO	Days on which the stock market was open ("trading days")
WHAT	Closing price of the Dow Jones Industrial Average (*Close*)
UNITS	Points
WHEN	August 1982 to December 1986
WHY	To test theory of stock market behavior

How does the stock market move? Here are the DJIA closing prices for the bull market that ran from mid 1982 to the end of 1986.

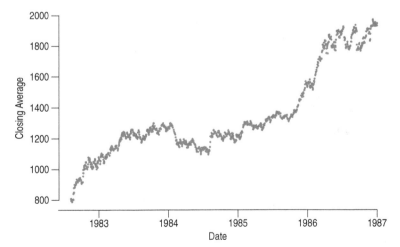

Figure 1   Daily closing prices of the Dow Jones Industrials from mid 1982 to the end of 1986.

The DJIA clearly increased during this famous bull market, more than doubling in value in less than five years. One common theory of market behavior says that on a given day, the market is just as likely to move up as down. Another way of phrasing this is that the daily behavior of the stock market is random. Can that be true during such periods of obvious increase? Let's investigate if the Dow is just as likely to move higher or lower on any given day. Out of the 1112 trading days in that period, the average increased on 573 days, a sample proportion of 0.5153 or 51.53%. That *is* more "up" days than "down" days, but is it far enough from 50% to cast doubt on the assumption of equally likely up or down movement?

1   Hypotheses

> **Hypothesis** n.;
>
> pl. Hypotheses.
>
> A supposition; a proposition or principle which is supposed or taken for granted, in order to draw a conclusion or inference for proof of the point in question; something not proved, but assumed for the purpose of argument.
>
> —*Webster's Unabridged Dictionary, 1913*

We've learned how to create confidence intervals for both means and proportions, but now we are not estimating values. We have a specific value in mind and a question to go with it. We wonder whether the market moves randomly up and down with equal probability regardless of its long-term trend. A confidence interval provides plausible values for the parameter, but now we seek a more direct test. Tests like this are useful, for example, if we want to know whether our customers are really more satisfied since the launch of our new website, whether the mean income of our preferred customers is higher than those of our regular customers, or whether our recent ad campaign really reached our target of 20% of adults in our region.

A confidence interval starts with the sample statistic (mean or proportion) and builds an interval around it. A hypothesis test turns that idea on its head. How can we state and test a hypothesis about daily changes in the DJIA? Hypotheses are working models that we adopt temporarily. To test whether the daily fluctuations are equally likely to be up as down, we assume that they are, and that any apparent difference from 50% is just random fluctuation. So, our starting hypothesis, called the null hypothesis, is that the proportion of days on which the DJIA increases is 50%. The **null hypothesis**, which we denote H_0, specifies a population model parameter and proposes a value for that parameter. We usually write down a null hypothesis about a proportion in the form $H_0: p = p_0$. (For a mean, we would write $H_0: \mu = \mu_0$.) This is a concise way to specify the two things we need most: the identity of the parameter we hope to learn about (the true proportion) and a specific hypothesized value for that parameter (in this case, 50%). We need a hypothesized value so we can compare our observed statistic to it. Which value to use for the hypothesis is not a statistical question. It may be obvious from the context of the data, but sometimes it takes a bit of thinking to translate the question we hope to answer into a hypothesis about a parameter. For our hypothesis about whether the DJIA moves up or down with equal likelihood, it's pretty clear that we need to test $H_0: p = 0.5$.

The **alternative hypothesis**, which we denote H_A, contains the values of the parameter that we consider plausible if we reject the null hypothesis. In our example, our null hypothesis is that the proportion, p, of "up" days is 0.5. What's the alternative? During a bull market, you might expect more up days than down, but for now we'll assume that we're interested in a deviation in either direction from the null hypothesis, so our alternative is $H_A: p \neq 0.5$.

What would convince you that the proportion of up days was not 50%? If on 95% of the days, the DJIA closed up, you'd probably be convinced that up and down days were not equally likely. But if the sample proportion of up days were only slightly higher than 50%, you might not be sure. After all, observations do vary, so you wouldn't be surprised to see some difference. How different from 50% must the sample proportion be before you would be convinced that the true proportion wasn't 50%? Whenever we ask about the size of a statistical difference, we naturally think of the standard deviation. So let's start by finding the standard deviation of the sample proportion of days on which the DJIA increased.

Notation Alert! ——————

Capital H is the standard letter for hypotheses. H_0 labels the null hypothesis, and H_A labels the alternative.

We've seen 51.53% up days out of 1112 trading days. Is 51.53% far enough from 50% to be convincing evidence that the true proportion of up days is greater than 50? To be formal, we'll need a probability. And to find a probability we'd like to model the behavior of the sample proportion with the Normal model, so we'll check the assumptions and conditions. The sample size of 1112 is certainly big enough to satisfy the Success/Failure condition. (We expect $0.50 \times 1112 = 556$ daily increases.) It is reasonable to assume that the daily price changes are random and independent. And we know what hypothesis we are testing. To test a hypothesis we (temporarily) *assume* that it is true so we can see whether that description of the world is plausible. If we assume that the Dow increases or decreases with equal likelihood, we'll need to center our Normal sampling model at a mean of 0.5. Then, we can find the standard deviation of the sampling model as

$$SD(\hat{p}) = \sqrt{\frac{pq}{n}} = \sqrt{\frac{(0.5)(1 - 0.5)}{1112}} = 0.015$$

> ## Why is this a standard deviation and not a standard error?
>
> This is a standard deviation because we are using the model (hypothesized) value for p and *not* the estimated value, $\hat{p}$. Once we assume that the null hypothesis is true, it gives us a value for the model parameter p. With proportions, if we know p then we also automatically know its standard deviation. Because we find the standard deviation from the model parameter, this is a standard deviation and not a standard error. When we found a confidence interval for p, we could not assume that we knew its value, so we estimated the standard deviation from the sample value, $\hat{p}$.

> To remind us that the parameter value comes from the null hypothesis, it is sometimes written as p_0 and the standard deviation as
> $$SD(\hat{p}) = \sqrt{\frac{p_0 q_0}{n}}.$$

Now we know both parameters of the Normal sampling distribution model for our null hypothesis. For the mean of the Normal we use $p = 0.50$, and for the standard deviation we use the standard deviation of the sample proportions found using the null hypothesis value, $SD(\hat{p}) = 0.015$. We want to know how likely it would be to see the observed value $\hat{p}$ as far away from 50% as the value of 51.53% that we actually have observed. Looking first at a picture (Figure 2), we can see that 51.53% doesn't look very surprising. The more exact answer (from a calculator, computer program, or the Normal table) is that the probability is about 0.308. This is the probability of observing more than 51.53% up days or more than 51.53% down days if the null model were true. In other words, if the chance of an up day for the Dow is 50%, we'd expect to see stretches of 1112 trading days with as many as 51.53% up days about 15.4% of the time and with as many as 51.53% down days about 15.4% of the time. That's not terribly unusual, so there's really no convincing evidence that the market did not act randomly.

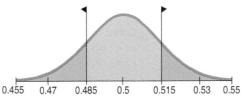

Figure 2 How likely is a proportion of more than 51.5% or less than 48.5% when the true mean is 50%? This is what it looks like. Each red area is 0.154 of the total area under the curve.

It may surprise you that even during a bull market, the direction of daily movements is random. But, the probability that any given day will end up or down appears to be about 0.5 regardless of the longer-term trends. It may be that when the stock market has a long run up (or possibly down, although we haven't checked that), it does so not by having more days of increasing or decreasing value, but by the actual amounts of the increases or decreases being unequal.

For Example | Framing hypotheses

Summit Projects is a full-service interactive agency, based in Hood River, OR, that offers companies a variety of website services. One of Summit's clients is SmartWool®, which produces and sells wool apparel including the famous SmartWool socks. Summit recently re-designed SmartWool's apparel website, and analysts at SmartWool wondered whether traffic has changed since the new website went live. In particular, an analyst might want to know if the proportion of visits resulting in a sale has changed since the new site went online. She might also wonder if the average sale amount has changed.

Questions: If the old site's proportion was 20%, frame appropriate null and alternative hypotheses for the proportion. If last year's average sale was $24.85, frame appropriate null and alternative hypotheses for the mean.[1]

Answers: For the proportion, let p = proportion of visits that result in a sale.

$$H_0: p = 0.2 \ vs. \ H_A: p \neq 0.2$$

For the average amount purchased, let μ = mean amount purchased per visit. Then

$$H_0: \mu = \$24.85 \ vs. \ H_A: \mu \neq \$24.85$$

2   A Trial as a Hypothesis Test

Alamy

We started by assuming that the probability of an up day was 50%. Then we looked at the data and concluded that we couldn't say otherwise because the proportion that we actually observed wasn't far enough from 50%. Does this reasoning of hypothesis tests seem backwards? That could be because we usually prefer to think about getting things right rather than getting them wrong. But, you've seen this reasoning before in a different context. This is the logic of jury trials.

Let's suppose a defendant has been accused of robbery. In British common law and those systems derived from it (including U.S. law), the null hypothesis is that the defendant is innocent. Instructions to juries are quite explicit about this.

The evidence takes the form of facts that seem to contradict the presumption of innocence. For us, this means collecting data. In the trial, the prosecutor presents evidence. ("If the defendant were innocent, wouldn't it be remarkable that the police found him at the scene of the crime with a bag full of money in his hand, a mask on his face, and a getaway car parked outside?") The next step is to judge the evidence. Evaluating the evidence is the responsibility of the jury in a trial, but it falls on your shoulders in hypothesis testing. The jury considers the evidence in light of the *presumption* of innocence and judges whether the evidence against the defendant would be plausible *if the defendant were in fact innocent.*

Like the jury, we ask: "Could these data plausibly have happened by chance if the null hypothesis were true?" If they are very unlikely to have occurred, then the evidence raises a reasonable doubt about the null hypothesis. Ultimately, *you* must make a decision. The standard of "beyond a reasonable doubt" is purposefully ambiguous because it leaves the jury to decide the degree to which the evidence contradicts the hypothesis of innocence. Juries don't explicitly use probability to help them decide whether to reject that hypothesis. But when you ask the same question of your null hypothesis, you have the advantage of being able to quantify exactly how surprising the evidence would be if the null hypothesis were true.

How unlikely is unlikely? Some people set rigid standards. Levels like 1 time out of 20 (0.05) or 1 time out of 100 (0.01) are common. But if *you* have to make the decision, you must judge for yourself in each situation whether the probability of observing your data is small enough to constitute "reasonable doubt."

---

[1]These numbers are hypothetical, but typical of the values that might have occurred.

3 P-Values

The fundamental step in our reasoning is the question: "Are the data surprising, given the null hypothesis?" And the key calculation is to determine exactly how likely the data we observed would be if the null hypothesis were the true model of the world. So we need a *probability*. Specifically, we want to find the probability of seeing data like these (or something even less likely) *given* the null hypothesis. This probability is the value on which we base our decision, so statisticians give this probability a special name. It's called the **P-value**.

A low enough P-value says that the data we have observed would be very unlikely if our null hypothesis were true. We started with a model, and now that same model tells us that the data we have are unlikely to have happened. That's surprising. In this case, the model and data are at odds with each other, so we have to make a choice. Either the null hypothesis is correct and we've just seen something remarkable, or the null hypothesis is wrong, (and, in fact, we were wrong to use it as the basis for computing our P-value). When you see a low P-value, you should reject the null hypothesis. There is no hard and fast rule about how low the P-value has to be. In fact, that decision is the subject of much of the rest of this chapter. Almost everyone would agree, however, that a P-value less than 0.001 indicates very strong evidence *against* the null hypothesis but a P-value greater than 0.05 provides very weak evidence.

When the P-value is *high* (or just not low *enough*), what do we conclude? In that case, we haven't seen anything unlikely or surprising at all. The data are consistent with the model from the null hypothesis, and we have no reason to reject the null hypothesis. Events that have a high probability of happening happen all the time. So, when the P-value is high does that mean we've proved the null hypothesis is true? No! We realize that many other similar hypotheses could also account for the data we've seen. The most we can say is that it doesn't appear to be false. Formally, we say that we "fail to reject" the null hypothesis. That may seem to be a pretty weak conclusion, but it's all we can say when the P-value is not low enough. All that means is that the data are consistent with the model that we started with.

What to Do with an "Innocent" Defendant

Let's see what that last statement means in a jury trial. If the evidence is not strong enough to reject the defendant's presumption of innocence, what verdict does the jury return? They do not say that the defendant is innocent. They say "not guilty." All they are saying is that they have not seen sufficient evidence to reject innocence and convict the defendant. The defendant may, in fact, be innocent, but the jury has no way to be sure.

Said statistically, the jury's null hypothesis is: innocent defendant. If the evidence is too unlikely (the P-value is low) then, given the assumption of innocence, the jury rejects the null hypothesis and finds the defendant guilty. But—and this is an important distinction—if there is *insufficient evidence* to convict the defendant (if the P-value is *not* low), the jury does not conclude that the null hypothesis is true and declare that the defendant is innocent. Juries can only *fail to reject* the null hypothesis and declare the defendant "not guilty."

In the same way, if the data are not particularly unlikely under the assumption that the null hypothesis is true, then the most we can do is to "fail to reject" our null hypothesis. We never declare the null hypothesis to be true. In fact, we simply do not know whether it's true or not. (After all, more evidence may come along later.)

Imagine a test of whether a company's new website design encourages a higher percentage of visitors to make a purchase (as compared to the site they've used for years). The null hypothesis is that the new site is no more effective at stimulating purchases than the old one. The test sends visitors randomly to one version of the

---

Beyond a Reasonable Doubt

We ask whether the data were unlikely beyond a reasonable doubt. We've just calculated how unlikely the data are if the null hypothesis is true. The probability that the observed statistic value (or an even more extreme value) could occur if the null model is true—in this case, 0.308—is the P-value That probability is certainly not *beyond a reasonable doubt*, so we fail to reject the null hypothesis here.

Don't We Want to Reject the Null?

Often, people who collect data or perform an experiment hope to reject the null. They hope the new ad campaign is *better* than the old one, or they hope their candidate is *ahead* of the opponent. But, when we test a hypothesis, we must stay neutral. We can't let our hope bias our decision. As in a jury trial, we must stay with the null hypothesis until we are convinced otherwise. The burden of proof rests with the alternative hypothesis—innocent until proven guilty. When you test a hypothesis, you must act as judge and jury, but not as prosecutor.

Conclusion

If the P-value is "low," reject H_0 and conclude H_A.

If the P-value is not "low enough," then fail to reject H_0 and the test is inconclusive.

website or the other. Of course, some will make a purchase, and others won't. If we compare the two websites on only 10 customers each, the results are likely *not to be clear*, and we'll be unable to reject the hypothesis. Does this mean the new design is a complete bust? Not necessarily. It simply means that we don't have enough evidence to reject our null hypothesis. That's why we don't start by assuming that the new design is *more* effective. If we were to do that, then we could test just a few customers, find that the results aren't clear, and claim that since we've been unable to reject our original assumption the redesign must be effective. The Board of Directors is unlikely to be impressed by that argument.

For Example   Conclusions from P-values

Question: The SmartWool analyst collects a representative sample of visits since the new website has gone online and finds that the P-value for the test of proportion is 0.0015 and the P-value for the test of the mean is 0.3740. What conclusions can she draw?

Answer: The proportion of visits that resulted in a sale since the new website went online is very unlikely to still be 0.20. There is strong evidence to suggest that the proportion has changed. She should reject the null hypothesis. However, the mean amount spent is consistent with the null hypothesis and therefore she is unable to reject the null hypothesis that the mean is still $24.85 against the alternative that it increased.

Just Checking

1 A pharmaceutical firm wants to know whether aspirin helps to thin blood. The null hypothesis says that it doesn't. The firm's researchers test 12 patients, observe the proportion with thinner blood, and get a P-value of 0.32. They proclaim that aspirin doesn't work. What would you say?

2 An allergy drug has been tested and found to give relief to 75% of the patients in a large clinical trial. Now the scientists want to see whether a new, "improved" version works even better. What would the null hypothesis be?

3 The new allergy drug is tested, and the P-value is 0.0001. What would you conclude about the new drug?

4   The Reasoning of Hypothesis Testing

Hypothesis tests follow a carefully structured path. To avoid getting lost, it helps to divide that path into four distinct sections: hypothesis, model, mechanics, and conclusion.

Hypotheses

"The null hypothesis is never proved or established, but is possibly disproved, in the course of experimentation. Every experiment may be said to exist only in order to give the facts a chance of disproving the null hypothesis."

—SIR RONALD FISHER, *THE DESIGN OF EXPERIMENTS, 1931*

First, state the null hypothesis. That's usually the skeptical claim that nothing's different. The null hypothesis assumes the default (often the status quo) is true (the defendant is innocent, the new method is no better than the old, customer preferences haven't changed since last year, etc.).

In statistical hypothesis testing, hypotheses are almost always about model parameters. To assess how unlikely our data may be, we need a null model. The null hypothesis specifies a particular parameter value to use in our model. In the usual notation, we write H_0: *parameter = hypothesized value*. The alternative hypothesis, H_A, contains the values of the parameter we consider plausible when we reject the null.

Model

To plan a statistical hypothesis test, specify the *model* for the sampling distribution of the statistic you will use to test the null hypothesis and the parameter of interest. For proportions, we use the Normal model for the sampling distribution. Of course, all models require assumptions, so you will need to state them and check any corresponding conditions. For a test of a proportion, the assumptions and conditions are the same as for a one-proportion z-interval.

Your model step should end with a statement such as: *Because the conditions are satisfied, we can model the sampling distribution of the proportion with a Normal model.* Watch out, though. Your Model step could end with: *Because the conditions are not satisfied, we can't proceed with the test.* (If that's the case, stop and reconsider.)

Each test we discuss has a name that you should include in your report. Some tests will be about more than one sample, some will involve statistics other than proportions, and some will use models other than the Normal (and so will not use z-scores). The test about proportions is called a **one-proportion z-test**.[2]

One-proportion z-test

The conditions for the one-proportion z-test are the same as for the one-proportion z-interval (except that we use the hypothesized values, p_0 and q_0, to check the Success/Failure condition). We test the hypothesis H_0: $p = p_0$ using the statistic

$$z = \frac{(\hat{p} - p_0)}{SD(\hat{p})}.$$

We also use p_0 to find the standard deviation: $SD(\hat{p}) = \sqrt{\frac{p_0 q_0}{n}}$. When the conditions are met and the null hypothesis is true, this statistic follows the standard Normal model, so we can use that model to obtain a P-value.

Mechanics

Under "Mechanics" we perform the actual calculation of our test statistic from the data. Different tests we encounter will have different formulas and different test statistics. Usually, the mechanics are handled by a statistics program or calculator. The ultimate goal of the calculation is to obtain a P-value—the probability that the observed statistic value (or an even more extreme value) could occur if the null model were correct. If the P-value is small enough, we'll reject the null hypothesis.

Conclusions and Decisions

The primary conclusion in a formal hypothesis test is only a statement about the null hypothesis. It simply states whether we reject or fail to reject that hypothesis. As always, the conclusion should be stated in context, but your conclusion about the null hypothesis should never be the end of the process. You can't make a decision based solely on a P-value. Business decisions have consequences, with actions to take or policies to change. The conclusions of a hypothesis test can help *inform* your decision, but they shouldn't be the only basis for it.

Business decisions should always take into consideration three things: the statistical significance of the test, the *cost* of the proposed action, and the **effect size** (the difference between the hypothesized and observed value) of the statistic. For

---

[2]It's also called the "one-sample test for a proportion."

Digital Vision

example, a cellular telephone provider finds that 30% of their customers switch providers (or *churn*) when their two-year subscription contract expires. They try a small experiment and offer a random sample of customers a free $350 top-of-the-line phone if they renew their contracts for another two years. Not surprisingly, they find that the new switching rate is lower by a statistically significant amount. Should they offer these free phones to all their customers? Obviously, the answer depends on more than the P-value of the hypothesis test. Even if the P-value is statistically significant, the correct business decision also depends on the cost of the free phones and by how much the churn rate is lowered (the effect size). It's rare that a hypothesis test alone is enough to make a sound business decision.

For Example   The reasoning of hypothesis tests

Question: The analyst at SmartWool selects 200 recent weblogs at random and finds that 58 of them have resulted in a sale. The null hypothesis is that $p = 0.20$. Would this be a surprising proportion of sales if the true proportion of sales were 20%?

Answer: To judge whether 58 is a surprising number of sales given the null hypothesis, we use the Normal model based on the null hypothesis. That is, use 0.20 as the mean and $\sqrt{\dfrac{p_0 q_0}{n}} = \sqrt{\dfrac{(0.2)(0.8)}{200}} = 0.02828$ as the standard deviation.

58 sales is a sample proportion of $\hat{p} = \dfrac{58}{200} = 0.29$ or 29%.

The z-value for 0.29 is then $z = \dfrac{\hat{p} - p_0}{SD(\hat{p})} = \dfrac{0.29 - 0.20}{0.02828} = 3.182$.

In other words, given that the null hypothesis is true, our sample proportion is 3.182 standard deviations higher than the mean. That seems like a surprisingly large value since the probability of being farther than 3 standard deviations from the mean is (from the 68–95–99.7 Rule) only 0.3%.

5   Alternative Hypotheses

"They make things admirably plain,
But one hard question will remain:
If one hypothesis you lose,
Another in its place you choose . . ."

—JAMES RUSSELL LOWELL,
CREDIDIMUS JOVEM REGNARE

In our example about the DJIA, we were equally interested in proportions that deviate from 50% in *either* direction. So we wrote our alternative hypothesis as H_A: $p \neq 0.5$. Such an alternative hypothesis is known as a **two-sided alternative** because we are equally interested in deviations on either side of the null hypothesis value. For two-sided alternatives, the P-value is the probability of deviating in *either* direction from the null hypothesis value.

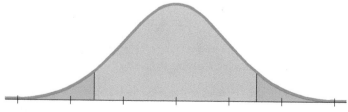

Figure 3   The P-value for a two-sided alternative adds the probabilities in both tails of the sampling distribution model outside the value that corresponds to the test statistic.

Suppose we want to test whether the proportion of customers returning merchandise has decreased under our new quality monitoring program. We know the quality has improved, so we can be pretty sure things haven't gotten worse.

Alternative Hypotheses

Proportions:

Two-sided

$H_0: p = p_0$

$H_A: p \neq p_0$

One-sided

$H_0: p = p_0$

$H_A: p < p_0 \text{ or } p > p_0$

Means:

Two-sided

$H_0: \mu = \mu_0$

$H_A: \mu \neq \mu_0$

One-sided

$H_0: \mu = \mu_0$

$H_A: \mu < \mu_0 \text{ or } \mu > \mu_0$

But have the customers noticed? We would only be interested in a sample proportion *smaller* than the null hypothesis value. We'd write our alternative hypothesis as $H_A: p < p_0$. An alternative hypothesis that focuses on deviations from the null hypothesis value in only one direction is called a **one-sided alternative**.

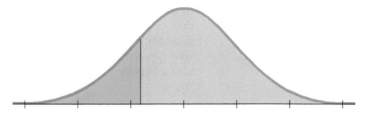

Figure 4 The P-value for a one-sided alternative considers only the probability of values beyond the test statistic value in the specified direction.

For a hypothesis test with a one-sided alternative, the P-value is the probability of deviating *only in the direction of the alternative* away from the null hypothesis value.

Guided Example Home Field Advantage

Major league sports are big business. And the fans are more likely to come out to root for the team if the home team has a good chance of winning. Anyone who follows or plays sports has heard of the "home field advantage." It is said that teams are more likely to win when they play at home. That *would* be good for encouraging the fans to come to the games. But is it true?

In the 2009 Major League Baseball (MLB) season, there were 2430 regular season games. (Tied at the end of the season the Colorado Rockies and San Diego Padres played an extra game to determine who won the Wild Card playoff spot.) It turns out that the home team won 1332 of the 2430 games, or 54.81% of the time. If there were no home field advantage, the home teams would win about half of all games played. Could this deviation from 50% be explained just from natural sampling variability, or does this evidence suggest that there really is a home field advantage, at least in professional baseball?

To test the hypothesis, we will ask whether the observed rate of home team victories, 54.81%, is so much greater than 50% that we cannot explain it away as just chance variation.

Remember the four main steps to performing a hypothesis test—hypotheses, model, mechanics, and conclusion? Let's put them to work and see what this will tell us about the home team's chances of winning a baseball game.

PLAN

Setup State what we want to know.

Define the variables and discuss their context.

We want to know whether the home team in professional baseball is more likely to win. The data are all 2430 games from the 2009 Major League Baseball season. The variable is whether or not the home team won. The parameter of interest is the proportion of home team wins. If there is an advantage, we'd expect that proportion to be greater than 0.50. The observed statistic value is $\hat{p} = 0.5481$.

Hypotheses The null hypothesis makes the claim of no home field advantage.

$H_O: p = 0.50$

We are interested only in a home field *advantage*, so the alternative hypothesis is one-sided.

$H_A: p > 0.50$

Model Think about the assumptions and check the appropriate conditions.

✓ **Independence Assumption.** Generally, the outcome of one game has no effect on the outcome of another game. But this may not always be strictly true. For example, if a key player is injured, the probability that the team will win in the next couple of games may decrease slightly, but independence is still roughly true.

Consider the time frame carefully.

✓ **Randomization Condition.** We have results for all 2430 games of the 2009 season. But we're not just interested in 2009. While these games were not randomly selected, they may be reasonably representative of all recent professional baseball games.

✓ **10% Condition.** This is not a random sample, but these 2430 games are fewer than 10% of all games played over the years.

✓ **Success/Failure Condition.** Both
$np_O = 2430(0.50) = 1215$ and
$nq_O = 2430(0.50) = 1215$ are at least 10.

Specify the sampling distribution model.

Tell what test you plan to use.

Because the conditions are satisfied, we'll use a Normal model for the sampling distribution of the proportion and do a one-proportion z-test.

DO

Mechanics The null model gives us the mean, and (because we are working with proportions) the mean gives us the standard deviation.

The null model is a Normal distribution with a mean of 0.50 and a standard deviation of:

$$SD(\hat{p}) = \sqrt{\frac{p_O q_O}{n}} = \sqrt{\frac{(0.5)(1 - 0.5)}{2430}} = 0.01014$$

The observed proportion $\hat{p}$ is 0.5481.

$$z = \frac{(\hat{p} - p_O)}{SD(\hat{p})}$$

$$= \frac{0.0481}{0.01014} = 4.74.$$

The observed proportion is 4.74 standard deviations above the hypothesized proportion.

From technology, we can find the P-value, which tells us the probability of observing a value that extreme (or more).

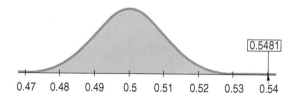

The probability of observing a $\hat{p}$ of 0.5481 or more in our Normal model can be found by computer, calculator, or table to be <0.001.

The corresponding P-value is <0.001.

(continued)

Conclusion State your conclusion about
the parameter—in context.

MEMO

Re: Home field advantage

Our analysis of outcomes during the 2009 Major League Baseball season showed a statistically significant advantage to the home team ($P < 0.001$). We can be quite confident that playing at home gives a baseball team an advantage.

For Example Finding P-values for a test of proportion

Question: From the fact that of 200 randomly selected access logs, 58 resulted in sales, find the P-value for testing the hypothesis that $p = 0.20$.

Answer: The alternative is *two-sided*, and the z-value is 3.182. So, we find the probability that z is greater than 3.182 or less than -3.182. Because the Normal is symmetric, that's the same as $2 \times P(z > 3.182) = 2 \times .00073 = 0.00146$. This is strong evidence against the null hypothesis so we *reject* it and conclude that the proportion of sales is no longer 0.20.

6 Testing Hypothesis about Means— the One-Sample *t*-Test

When we made confidence intervals about proportions, we could base the interval on the z statistic because proportions have a natural link between their value ($\hat{p}$) and the standard error ($\sqrt{(\hat{p} \times \hat{q}/n)}$). For testing a hypothesis about a proportion, we used z as the reference for the same reason. But, for means, we saw that sample means have no link between their value (μ) and the value of the standard error ($s/\sqrt{(n)}$). That seemingly small extra variation due to estimating the standard error rocked Gosset's world in 1906 and led to the discovery of the *t*-distribution. It should come as no surprise then, that for testing a hypothesis about a mean, we base the test on the *t* distribution. In fact, other than that, the test looks just like the test for a proportion.

Previously, we built a confidence interval for the mean profit of policies sold by an insurance agent whose average profit from a sample of 30 policies was $1438.90. Now the manager has a more specific concern. Company policy states that if a sales rep's mean profit is below $1500, the sales rep has been discounting too much and will have to adjust his pricing strategy. Is there evidence from this sample that the mean is really less than $1500? This question calls for a hypothesis test called the **one-sample *t*-test for the mean**.

When testing a hypothesis, it's natural to compare the difference between the observed statistic and a hypothesized value to the standard error. For means that looks like: $\dfrac{\bar{y} - \mu_0}{SE(\bar{y})}$. We already know that the appropriate probability model to use is Student's *t* with $n - 1$ degrees of freedom.

> ## One-sample *t*-test for the mean
>
> The conditions for the one-sample *t*-test for the mean are the same as for the one-sample *t*-interval. We test the hypothesis $H_0: \mu = \mu_0$ using the statistic
>
> $$t_{n-1} = \frac{\bar{y} - \mu_0}{SE(\bar{y})},$$
>
> where the standard error of $\bar{y}$ is: $SE(\bar{y}) = \frac{s}{\sqrt{n}}$.
>
> When the conditions are met and the null hypothesis is true, this statistic follows a Student's *t*-model with $n - 1$ degrees of freedom. We use that model to obtain a P-value.

Guided Example Insurance Profits Revisited

Shutterstock

Let's apply the one-sample *t*-test to the 30 mature policies sampled by the manager. From these 30 policies, the management would like to know if there's evidence that the mean profit of policies sold by this sales rep is less than $1500.

PLAN

Setup State what we want to know. Make clear what the population and parameter are.

Identify the variables and context.

> We want to test whether the mean profit of the sales rep's policies is less than $1500. We have a random sample of 30 mature policies from which to judge.

Hypotheses We give benefit of the doubt to the sales rep. The null hypothesis is that the true mean profit is equal to $1500. Because we're interested in whether the profit is less, the alternative is one-sided.

> $$H_0: \mu = \$1500$$
> $$H_A: \mu < \$1500$$

Make a graph. Check the distribution for skewness, multiple modes, and outliers.

> We checked the histogram of these data in a previous Guided Example and saw that it had a unimodal, symmetric distribution.

Model Check the conditions.

> We checked the Randomization and Nearly Normal Conditions in the previous Guided Example.

State the sampling distribution model.

Choose your method.

> The conditions are satisfied, so we'll use a Student's *t*-model with $n - 1 = 29$ degrees of freedom and a one-sample *t*-test for the mean.

DO

Mechanics Compute the sample statistics. Be sure to include the units when you write down what you know from the data.

> Using software, we obtain the following basic statistics:
>
> ```
> n = 30
> Mean = $1438.90
> StDev = $1329.60
> ```

(continued)

The *t*-statistic calculation is just a standardized value. We subtract the hypothesized mean and divide by the standard error.

We assume the null model is true to find the P-value. Make a picture of the *t*-model, centered at μ_0. Since this is a lower-tail test, shade the region to the left of the observed average profit.

The P-value is the probability of observing a sample mean as small as $1438.90 (or smaller) *if* the true mean were $1500, as the null hypothesis states. We can find this P-value from a table, calculator, or computer program.

$$t = \frac{1438.90 - 1500}{1329.60/\sqrt{30}} = -0.2517$$

(The observed mean is less than one standard error below the hypothesized value.)

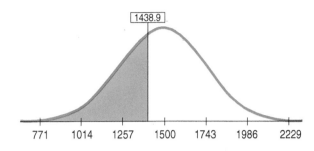

$$\text{P-value} = P(t_{29} < -0.2517) = 0.4015 \text{ (or from a table } 0.1 < P < 0.5)$$

REPORT

Conclusion Link the P-value to your decision about H_0, and state your conclusion in context.

MEMO

Re: Sales Performance

The mean profit on 30 sampled contracts closed by the sales rep in question has fallen below our standard of $1500, but there is not enough evidence in this sample of policies to indicate that the true mean is below $1500. If the mean were $1500, we would expect a sample of size 30 to have a mean this low about 40.15% of the time.

Notice that the way this hypothesis was set up, the sales rep's mean profit would have to be well below $1500 to reject the null hypothesis. Because the null hypothesis was that the mean was $1500 and the alternative was that it was less, this setup gave some benefit of the doubt to the sales rep. There's nothing intrinsically wrong with that, but keep in mind that it's always a good idea to make sure that the hypotheses are stated in ways that will guide you to make the right business decision.

For Example   Testing a mean

Question: From the 58 sales recorded in the sample of 200 access logs, the analyst finds that the mean amount spent is $26.05 with a standard deviation of $10.20. Test the hypothesis that the mean is still $24.85 against the alternative that it has increased.

Answer: We can write: $H_0: \mu = \$24.85$ *vs.* $H_A: \mu > \$24.85$.

Then $t = \dfrac{(26.05 - 24.85)}{10.2/\sqrt{58}} = 0.896.$

Because the alternative is *one-sided*, we find $P(t > 0.896)$ with 57 degrees of freedom. From technology, $P(t > 0.896) = 0.1870$, a large P-value. This is not a surprising value given the hypothesized mean of $24.85. Therefore we *fail to reject* the null hypothesis and conclude that there is not sufficient evidence to suggest that the mean has increased from 24.85. Had we used a two-sided alternative, the P-value would have been twice 0.1870 or 0.3740.

7 Alpha Levels and Significance

Sometimes we need to make a firm decision about whether or not to reject the null hypothesis. A jury must *decide* whether the evidence reaches the level of "beyond a reasonable doubt." A business must *select* a Web design. You need to decide which section of a Statistics course to enroll in.

When the P-value is small, it tells us that our data are rare *given the null hypothesis*. As humans, we are suspicious of rare events. If the data are "rare enough," we just don't think that could have happened due to chance. Since the data *did* happen, something must be wrong. All we can do now is to reject the null hypothesis.

But how rare is "rare"? How low does the P-value have to be?

We can define "rare event" arbitrarily by setting a threshold for our P-value. If our P-value falls below that point, we'll reject the null hypothesis. We call such results *statistically significant*. The threshold is called an **alpha level**. Not surprisingly, it's labeled with the Greek letter α. Common α-levels are 0.10, 0.05, 0.01, and 0.001. You have the option—almost the *obligation*—to consider your alpha level carefully and choose an appropriate one for the situation. If you're assessing the safety of air bags, you'll want a low alpha level; even 0.01 might not be low enough. If you're just wondering whether folks prefer their pizza with or without pepperoni, you might be happy with $\alpha = 0.10$. It can be hard to justify your choice of α, though, so often we arbitrarily choose 0.05.

Sir Ronald Fisher (1890–1962) was one of the founders of modern Statistics.

Notation Alert!

The first Greek letter, α, is used in Statistics for the threshold value of a hypothesis test. You'll hear it referred to as the alpha level. Common values are 0.10, 0.05, 0.01, and 0.001.

Where did the value 0.05 come from?

In 1931, in a famous book called *The Design of Experiments*, Sir Ronald Fisher discussed the amount of evidence needed to reject a null hypothesis. He said that it was *situation dependent*, but remarked, somewhat casually, that for many scientific applications, 1 out of 20 *might be* a reasonable value, especially in a *first* experiment—one that will be followed by confirmation. Since then, some people—indeed some entire disciplines—have acted as if the number 0.05 were sacrosanct.

The alpha level is also called the **significance level**. When we reject the null hypothesis, we say that the test is "significant at that level." For example, we might say that we reject the null hypothesis "at the 5% level of significance." You must select the alpha level *before* you look at the data. Otherwise you can be accused of finagling the conclusions by tuning the alpha level to the results after you've seen the data.

What can you say if the P-value does not fall below α? When you have not found sufficient evidence to reject the null according to the standard you have established, you should say: "The data have failed to provide sufficient evidence to reject the null hypothesis." Don't say: "We accept the null hypothesis." You certainly haven't proven or established the null hypothesis; it was assumed to begin with. You *could* say that you have *retained* the null hypothesis, but it's better to say that you've failed to reject it.

It could happen to you!

Of course, if the null hypothesis *is* true, no matter what alpha level you choose, you still have a probability α of rejecting the null hypothesis by mistake. When we do reject the null hypothesis, no one ever thinks that *this* is one of those rare times. As statistician Stu Hunter notes, "The statistician says 'rare events do happen—but not to me!' "

Look again at the home field advantage example. The P-value was <0.001. This is so much smaller than any reasonable alpha level that we can reject H_0. We concluded: "We reject the null hypothesis. There is sufficient evidence to conclude that there is a home field advantage over and above what we expect with random variation." On the other hand, when testing the mean in the insurance example, the

P-value was 0.4015, a very high P-value. In this case we can say only that we have failed to reject the null hypothesis that $\mu = \$1500$. We certainly can't say that we've proved it, or even that we've accepted it.

The automatic nature of the reject/fail-to-reject decision when we use an alpha level may make you uncomfortable. If your P-value falls just slightly above your alpha level, you're not allowed to reject the null. Yet a P-value just barely below the alpha level leads to rejection. If this bothers you, you're in good company. Many statisticians think it better to report the P-value than to choose an alpha level and carry the decision through to a final reject/fail-to-reject verdict. So when you declare your decision, it's always a good idea to report the P-value as an indication of the strength of the evidence.

> **It's in the stars**
>
> Some disciplines carry the idea further and code P-values by their size. In this scheme, a P-value between 0.05 and 0.01 gets highlighted by a single asterisk (*). A P-value between 0.01 and 0.001 gets two asterisks (**), and a P-value less than 0.001 gets three (***). This can be a convenient summary of the weight of evidence against the null hypothesis, but it isn't wise to take the distinctions too seriously and make black-and-white decisions near the boundaries. The boundaries are a matter of tradition, not science; there is nothing special about 0.05. A P-value of 0.051 should be looked at seriously and not casually thrown away just because it's larger than 0.05, and one that's 0.009 is not very different from one that's 0.011.

Sometimes it's best to report that the conclusion is not yet clear and to suggest that more data be gathered. (In a trial, a jury may "hang" and be unable to return a verdict.) In such cases, it's an especially good idea to report the P-value, since it's the best summary we have of what the data say or fail to say about the null hypothesis.

What do we mean when we say that a test is statistically significant? All we mean is that the test statistic had a P-value lower than our alpha level. Don't be lulled into thinking that "statistical significance" necessarily carries with it any practical importance or impact.

For large samples, even small, unimportant ("insignificant") deviations from the null hypothesis can be statistically significant. On the other hand, if the sample is not large enough, even large, financially or scientifically important differences may not be statistically significant.

When you report your decision about the null hypothesis, it's good practice to report the effect size (the magnitude of the difference between the observed statistic value and the null hypothesis value in the data units) along with the P-value.

For Example   Setting the α level

Question: The manager of the analyst at SmartWool wants her to use an α level of 0.05 for all her hypothesis tests. Would her conclusions for the two hypothesis tests have changed if she used an α level of 0.05?

Answer: Using $\alpha = 0.05$, we reject the null hypothesis when the P-value is less than 0.05 and fail to reject when the P-value is greater than or equal to 0.05. For the test of proportion, $P = 0.00146$, which is much less than 0.05 and so we reject. For the test of means, the P-value was 0.1870, which is greater than 0.05, so we fail to reject. Our conclusions are the same as before using this α level.

8   Critical Values

When building a confidence interval, we calculated the margin of error as the product of an estimated standard error for the statistic and a critical value. For proportions, we found a **critical value**, z^*, to correspond to our selected confidence level. For means, we found the critical value t^* based on both the confidence level and the degrees of freedom. Critical values can also be used as a shortcut for hypothesis tests. Before computers and calculators were common, P-values were hard to find. It was easier to select a few common alpha levels (0.05, 0.01, 0.001, for example) and learn the corresponding critical values for the Normal model (that is, the critical values corresponding to confidence levels 0.95, 0.99, and 0.999, respectively). Rather than find the probability that corresponded to your observed statistic, you'd just calculate how many standard deviations it was away from the hypothesized value and compare that value directly against these z^* values. (Remember that whenever we measure the distance of a value from the mean in standard deviations, we are finding a z-score.) Any z-score larger in magnitude (that is, more extreme) than a particular critical value has to be less likely, so it will have a P-value smaller than the corresponding alpha.

If we were willing to settle for a flat reject/fail-to-reject decision, comparing an observed z-score with the critical value for a specified alpha level would give a shortcut path to that decision. For the home field advantage example, if we choose $\alpha = 0.05$, then in order to reject H_0, our z-score has to be larger than the one-sided critical value of 1.645. The observed proportion was 4.74 standard deviations above 0.5, so we clearly reject the null hypothesis. This is perfectly correct and does give us a yes/no decision, but it gives us less information about the hypothesis because we don't have the P-value to think about. With technology, P-values are easy to find. And since they give more information about the strength of the evidence, you should report them.

Here are the traditional z^* critical values from the Normal model[3]:

α	1-sided	2-sided
0.05	1.645	1.96
0.01	2.33	2.576
0.001	3.09	3.29

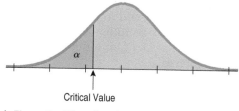
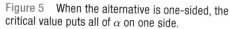
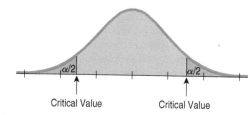

Figure 5 When the alternative is one-sided, the critical value puts all of α on one side.

Figure 6 When the alternative is two-sided, the critical value splits α equally into two tails.

When testing means, you'll need to know both the α level and the degrees of freedom to find the t^* critical value. With large n, the t^* critical values will be close to the z^* critical values (above) that you use for testing proportions.

For Example   Testing using critical values

Question: Find the critical z and t values for the SmartWool hypotheses using $\alpha = 0.05$ and show that the same decisions would have been made using critical values.

Answer: For the two-sided test of proportions, the critical z values at $\alpha = 0.05$ are ± 1.96. Because the z value was 3.182, much larger than 1.96, we reject the null hypothesis.

For the one-sided test of means, with $n = 58$, the critical t value at $\alpha = 0.05$ is 1.676 (using df = 50 from a table) or 1.672 (using df = 57 from technology). In either case, the t value of 0.896 is smaller than the critical value, so we fail to reject the null hypothesis.

---

[3]In a sense, these are the flip side of the 68–95–99.7 Rule. There we chose simple statistical distances from the mean and recalled the areas of the tails. Here we select convenient tail areas (0.05, 0.01, and 0.001, either on one side or adding both together), and record the corresponding statistical distances.

9 Confidence Intervals and Hypothesis Tests

A Technical Note

For means, you can test a hypothesis by seeing if the null value falls in the appropriate confidence interval. However, for proportions, this isn't *exactly* true. For a confidence interval, we estimate the standard deviation of $\hat{p}$ from $\hat{p}$ itself, making it a *standard error*. For the corresponding hypothesis test, we use the model's *standard deviation* for $\hat{p}$ based on the null hypothesis value p_0. When $\hat{p}$ and p_0 are close, these calculations give similar results. When they differ, you're likely to reject H₀ (because the observed proportion is far from your hypothesized value). In that case, you're better off building your confidence interval with a standard error estimated from the data rather than rely on the model you just rejected.

"Extraordinary claims require extraordinary proof."

—Carl Sagan

Confidence intervals and hypothesis tests are built from the same calculations. They have the same assumptions and conditions. As we have just seen, you can approximate a hypothesis test by examining the confidence interval. Just ask whether the null hypothesis value is consistent with a confidence interval for the parameter at the corresponding confidence level. Because confidence intervals are naturally two-sided, they correspond to two-sided tests. For example, a 95% confidence interval corresponds to a two-sided hypothesis test at $\alpha = 5\%$. In general, a confidence interval with a confidence level of $C\%$ corresponds to a two-sided hypothesis test with an α level of $100 - C\%$.

The relationship between confidence intervals and one-sided hypothesis tests gives us a choice. For a one-sided test with $\alpha = 5\%$, you could construct a one-sided confidence level of 95%, leaving 5% in one tail.

A one-sided confidence interval leaves one side unbounded. For example, in the home field example, we wondered whether the home field gave the home team an *advantage*, so our test was naturally one-sided. A 95% one-sided confidence interval for a proportion would be constructed from one side of the associated two-sided confidence interval:

$$0.5481 - 1.645 \times 0.01014 = 0.531.$$

In order to leave 5% on one side, we used the z^* value 1.645 that leaves 5% in one tail. Writing the one-sided interval as $(0.531, \infty)$ allows us to say with 95% confidence that we know the home team will win, on average, at least 53.1% of the time. To test the hypothesis H₀: $p = 0.50$ we note that the value 0.50 is not in this interval. The lower bound of 0.531 is clearly above 0.50, showing the connection between hypothesis testing and confidence intervals.

For convenience, and to provide more information, however, we sometimes report a two-sided confidence interval even though we are interested in a one-sided test. For the home field example, we could report a 90% two-sided confidence interval:

$$0.5481 \pm 1.645 \times 0.01014 = (0.531, 0.565).$$

Notice that we *matched* the left end point by leaving α in *both* sides, which made the corresponding confidence level 90%. We can still see the correspondence. Because the 90% (two-sided) confidence interval for $\hat{p}$ doesn't contain 0.50, we reject the null hypothesis. Using the two-sided interval also tells us that the home team winning percentage is unlikely to be greater than 56.5%, an added benefit to understanding. You can see the relationship between the two confidence intervals in Figure 7.

There's another good reason for finding a confidence interval along with a hypothesis test. Although the test can tell us whether the observed statistic differs from the hypothesized value, it doesn't say by how much. Often, business decisions depend not only on whether there is a statistically significant difference, but also on whether the difference is meaningful. For the home field advantage, the corresponding confidence interval shows that over a full season, home field advantage adds an average of about two to six extra victories for a team. That could make a meaningful difference in both the team's standing and in the size of the crowd.

The story is similar for means. Previously, we found a 95% confidence interval for the mean profit on a sales representative's policies to be ($942.48, $1935.32). Intervals are naturally two-sided and this 95% confidence interval leaves 0.025 on each side of the mean not covered. In the current chapter, we tested the hypothesis that the mean value was $1500. But unlike the confidence interval, our test is one-sided because our alternative is $\mu < 1500$. So checking to see if $1500 is too high to be in the interval is equivalent to performing the hypothesis test at an α of 0.025—one side of the confidence interval. (Or, you could use a 90% confidence interval to test the hypothesis at $\alpha = 0.05$.) In this example, $1500 is clearly within the interval, so we fail to reject the null hypothesis. There is no evidence to suggest that the true mean is less than $1500.

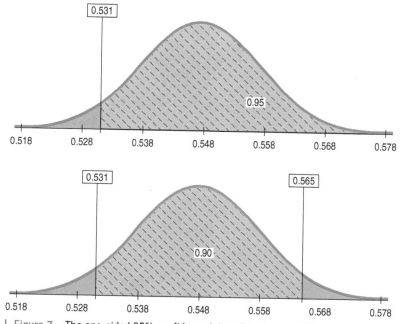

Figure 7 The one-sided 95% confidence interval (top) leaves 5% on one side (in this case the left), but leaves the other side unbounded. The 90% confidence interval is symmetric and matches the one-sided interval on the side of interest. Both intervals indicate that a one-sided test of $p = 0.50$ would be rejected at $\alpha = 0.05$ for any value of $\hat{p}$ greater than 0.531.

Just Checking

4 A bank is testing a new method for getting delinquent customers to pay their past-due credit card bills. The standard way was to send a letter (costing about $0.60 each) asking the customer to pay. That worked 30% of the time. The bank wants to test a new method that involves sending a DVD to the customer encouraging them to contact the bank and set up a payment plan. Developing and sending the DVD costs about $10.00 per customer. What is the parameter of interest? What are the null and alternative hypotheses?

5 The bank sets up an experiment to test the effectiveness of the DVD. The DVD is mailed to several randomly selected delinquent customers, and employees keep track of how many customers then contact the bank to arrange payments. The bank just got back the results on their test of the DVD strategy. A 90% confidence interval for the

success rate is (0.29, 0.45). Their old send-a-letter method had worked 30% of the time. Can you reject the null hypothesis and conclude that the method increases the proportion at $\alpha = 0.05$? Explain.

6 Given the confidence interval the bank found in the trial of the DVD mailing, what would you recommend be done? Should the bank scrap the DVD strategy?

7 The mileage rewards program at a major airline company has just completed a test market of a new arrangement with a hotel partner to try to increase engagement of valued customers with the program. The cost to the rewards program of the hotel offer is $35.00 per customer. From the test market, a 95% confidence interval for the revenue generated is ($37.95, $55.05). What does that say about the viability of the new arrangement?

Guided Example   Credit Card Promotion

Shutterstock

A credit card company plans to offer a special incentive program to customers who charge at least $500 next month. The marketing department has pulled a sample of 500 customers from the same month last year and noted that the mean amount charged was $478.19 and the median amount was $216.48. The finance department says that the only relevant quantity is the proportion of customers who spend more than $500. If that proportion is not more than 25%, the program will lose money.

Among the 500 customers, 148 or 29.6% of them charged $500 or more. Can we use a confidence interval to test whether the goal of 25% for all customers was met?

PLAN

Setup State the problem and discuss the variables and the context.

We want to know whether 25% or more of the customers will spend $500 or more in the next month and qualify for the special program. We will use the data from the same month a year ago to estimate the proportion and see whether the proportion was at least 25%.

Hypotheses The null hypothesis is that the proportion qualifying is 25%. The alternative is that it is higher. It's clearly a one-sided test, so if we use a confidence interval, we'll have to be careful about what level we use.

The statistic is $\hat{p} = 0.296$, the proportion of customers who charged $500 or more.

$$H_O: p = 0.25$$
$$H_A: p > 0.25$$

Model Check the conditions. (Because this is a confidence interval, we use the observed successes and failures to check the Success/Failure condition.)

✓ **Independence Assumption.** Customers are not likely to influence one another when it comes to spending on their credit cards.

✓ **Randomization Condition.** This is a random sample from the company's database.

✓ **10% Condition.** The sample is less than 10% of all customers.

✓ **Success/Failure Condition.** There were 148 successes and 352 failures, both at least 10. The sample is large enough.

State your method. Here we are using a confidence interval to test a hypothesis.

Under these conditions, the sampling model is Normal. We'll create a one-proportion z-interval.

DO

Mechanics Write down the given information and determine the sample proportion.

$n = 500$, so

To use a confidence interval, we need a confidence level that corresponds to the alpha level of the test. If we use $\alpha = 0.05$, we should construct a 90% confidence interval because this is a one-sided test. That will leave 5% on *each* side of the observed proportion. Determine the standard error of the sample proportion and the margin of error. The critical value is $z^* = 1.645$.

$$\hat{p} = \frac{148}{500} = 0.296 \text{ and}$$

$$SE(\hat{p}) = \sqrt{\frac{\hat{p}\hat{q}}{n}} = \sqrt{\frac{(0.296)(0.704)}{500}} = 0.020$$

$$ME = z^* \times SE(\hat{p})$$
$$= 1.645(0.020) = 0.033$$

The confidence interval is estimate ± margin of error.

The 90% confidence interval is 0.296 ± 0.033 or $(0.263, 0.329)$.

REPORT

Conclusion Link the confidence interval to your decision about the null hypothesis, then state your conclusion in context.

MEMO

Re: Credit card promotion

Our study of a sample of customer records indicates that between 26.3% and 32.9% of customers charge $500 or more. We are 90% confident that this interval includes the true value. Because the minimum suitable value of 25% is below this interval, we conclude that it is not a plausible value, and so we reject the null hypothesis that only 25% of the customers charge more than $500 a month. The goal appears to have been met assuming that the month we studied is typical.

For Example — Confidence intervals and hypothesis tests

Question: Construct appropriate confidence intervals for testing the two hypotheses and show how we could have reached the same conclusions from these intervals.

Answer: The test of proportion was two-sided, so we construct a 95% confidence interval for the true proportion:

$$\hat{p} \pm 1.96 SE(\hat{p}) = 0.29 \pm 1.96 \times \sqrt{\frac{(0.29)(0.71)}{200}} = (0.227, 0.353).$$ Since 0.20 is not a plausible value, we reject the null hypothesis.

The test of means is one-sided so we construct a one-sided 95% confidence interval, using the t critical value of 1.672:

$$(\bar{y} - t^* SE(\bar{y}), \infty) = \left(26.05 - 1.672 \times \frac{10.2}{\sqrt{58}}, \infty\right) = (23.81, \infty)$$

We can see that the hypothesized value of $24.85 is in this interval, so we fail to reject the null hypothesis.

10 Two Types of Errors

Nobody's perfect. Even with lots of evidence, we can still make the wrong decision. In fact, when we perform a hypothesis test, we can make mistakes in *two* ways:

I. The null hypothesis is true, but we mistakenly reject it.
II. The null hypothesis is false, but we fail to reject it.

These two types of errors are known as **Type I** and **Type II errors**, respectively. One way to keep the names straight is to remember that we start by assuming the null hypothesis is true, so a Type I error is the first kind of error we could make.

In medical disease testing, the null hypothesis is usually the assumption that a person is healthy. The alternative is that he or she has the disease we're testing for. So a Type I error is a *false positive*—a healthy person is diagnosed with the disease. A Type II error, in which an infected person is diagnosed as disease free, is a *false negative*. These errors have other names, depending on the particular discipline and context.

Which type of error is more serious depends on the situation. In a jury trial, a Type I error occurs if the jury convicts an innocent person. A Type II error occurs if the jury fails to convict a guilty person. Which seems more serious? In medical diagnosis, a false negative could mean that a sick patient goes untreated. A false positive might mean that the person receives unnecessary treatments or even surgery.

In business planning, a false positive result could mean that money will be invested in a project that turns out not to be profitable. A false negative result might mean that money won't be invested in a project that would have been profitable. Which error is worse, the lost investment or the lost opportunity? The answer always depends on the situation, the cost, and your point of view.

Here's an illustration of the situations:

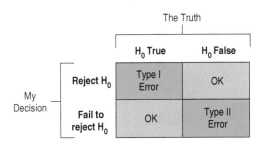

Figure 8 The two types of errors occur on the diagonal where the truth and decision don't match. Remember that we *start* by assuming H_0 to be true, so an error made (rejecting it) when H_0 is true is called a Type I error. A Type II error is made when H_0 is false (and we fail to reject it).

How often will a Type I error occur? It happens when the null hypothesis is true but we've had the bad luck to draw an unusual sample. To reject H_0, the P-value must fall below α. When H_0 is true, that happens *exactly* with probability α. So when you choose level α, you're setting the probability of a Type I error to α.

What if H_0 is not true? Then we can't possibly make a Type I error. You can't get a false positive from a sick person. A Type I error can happen only when H_0 is true.

When H_0 is false and we reject it, we have done the right thing. A test's ability to detect a false hypothesis is called the **power** of the test. In a jury trial, power is a measure of the ability of the criminal justice system to convict people who are guilty. We'll have a lot more to say about power soon.

When H_0 is false but we fail to reject it, we have made a Type II error. We assign the letter β to the probability of this mistake. What's the value of β? That's harder to assess than α because we don't know what the value of the parameter really is. When H_0 is true, it specifies a single parameter value. But when H_0 is false, we don't have a specific one; we have many possible values. We can compute the probability β for any parameter value in H_A, but the choice of which one to pick is not always clear.

One way to focus our attention is by thinking about the *effect size*. That is, ask: "How big a difference would matter?" Suppose a charity wants to test whether placing personalized address labels in the envelope along with a request for a donation increases the response rate above the baseline of 5%. If the minimum response that would pay for the address labels is 6%, they would calculate β for the alternative $p = 0.06$.

Of course, we could reduce β for *all* alternative parameter values by increasing α. By making it easier to reject the null, we'd be more likely to reject it whether it's true or not. The only way to reduce *both* types of error is to collect more evidence or, in statistical terms, to collect more data. Otherwise, we just wind up trading off one kind of error against the other. Whenever you design a survey or experiment, it's a good idea to calculate β (for a reasonable α level). Use a parameter value in the alternative that corresponds to an effect size that you want to be able to detect. Too often, studies fail because their sample sizes are too small to detect the change they are looking for.

Notation Alert!

In Statistics, α is the probability of a Type I error and β is the probability of a Type II error.

The *Probabilities* of a Type II Error

The null hypothesis specifies a single value for the parameter. So it's easy to calculate the probability of a Type I error. But the alternative gives a whole range of possible values, and we may want to find a β for several of them.

Sample Size and Power

We have seen ways to find a sample size by specifying the margin of error. Choosing the sample size to achieve a specified β (for a particular alternative value) is sometimes more appropriate, but the calculation is more complex and lies beyond the scope of this text.

Just Checking

8 Remember our bank that's sending out DVDs to try to get customers to make payments on delinquent loans? It is looking for evidence that the costlier DVD strategy produces a higher success rate than the letters it has been sending. Explain what a Type I error is in this context and what the consequences would be to the bank.

9 What's a Type II error in the bank experiment context and what would the consequences be?

10 If the DVD strategy *really* works well—actually getting 60% of the people to pay off their balances—would the power of the test be higher or lower compared to a 32% payoff rate? Explain briefly.

11 Recall the mileage program test market of Question 7. Suppose after completing the hotel partnership, the mean revenue per customer is $40.26. Has a Type I or Type II error been made? Explain.

For Example   Type I and Type II errors

Question: Suppose that a year later, a full accounting of all the transactions finds that 26.5% of visits resulted in sales with an average purchase amount of $26.25. Have any errors been made?

Answer: We rejected the null hypothesis that $p = 0.20$ and in fact $p = 0.265$, so we did not make a Type I error (the only error we could have made when rejecting the null hypothesis). For the mean amount, we failed to reject that the mean had increased from $24.85 but actually the mean had increased to $26.25 so we made a Type II error—we failed to reject the null hypothesis when it was false.

---

11   Power

Power and Effect Size

When planning a study, it's wise to think about the size of the effect we're looking for. We've called the effect size the difference between the null hypothesis and the observed statistic. In planning, it's the difference between the null hypothesis and a particular alternative we're interested in. It's easier to see a larger effect size, so the power of the study will increase with the effect size.

Once the study has been completed we'll base our business decision on the observed effect size, the difference between the null hypothesis and the observed value.

Remember, we can never prove a null hypothesis true. We can only fail to reject it. But when we fail to reject a null hypothesis, it's natural to wonder whether we looked hard enough. Might the null hypothesis actually be false and our test too weak to tell?

When the null hypothesis actually *is* false, we hope our test is strong enough to reject it. We'd like to know how likely we are to succeed. The power of the test gives us a way to think about that. The power of a test is the probability that it correctly rejects a false null hypothesis. When the power is high, we can be confident that we've looked hard enough. We know that β is the probability that a test *fails* to reject a false null hypothesis, so the power of the test is the complement, $1 - \beta$. We might have just written $1 - \beta$, but power is such an important concept that it gets its own name.

Whenever a study fails to reject its null hypothesis, the test's power comes into question. Was the sample size big enough to detect an effect had there been one? Might we have missed an effect large enough to be interesting just because we failed to gather sufficient data or because there was too much variability in the data we could gather? Might the problem be that the experiment simply lacked adequate power to detect their ability?

When we calculate power, we base our calculation on the smallest effect that might influence our business decision. The value of the power depends on how large this effect is. For proportions, that effect size is $p - p_0$; for means it's $\mu - \mu_0$. The power depends directly on the effect size. It's easier to see larger effects, so the further p_0 is from p (or μ is from μ_0), the greater the power.

How can we decide what power we need? Choice of power is more a financial or scientific decision than a statistical one because to calculate the power, we need to specify the alternative parameter value we're interested in. In other words, power is calculated for a particular effect size, and it changes depending on the size of the effect we want to detect.

Graph It!

It makes intuitive sense that the larger the effect size, the easier it should be to see it. Obtaining a larger sample size decreases the probability of a Type II error, so it increases the power. It also makes sense that the more we're willing to accept a Type I error, the less likely we will be to make a Type II error.

Figure 9 may help you visualize the relationships among these concepts. Although we'll use proportions to show the ideas, a similar picture and similar statements also hold true for means. Suppose we are testing $H_0: p = p_0$ against the alternative $H_A: p > p_0$. We'll reject the null if the observed proportion, $\hat{p}$, is big enough. By *big enough*, we mean $\hat{p} > p^*$ for some critical value p^* (shown as the red region in the right tail of the upper curve). The upper model shows a picture of the sampling distribution model for the proportion when the null hypothesis is true. If the null were true, then this would be a picture of that truth. We'd make a Type I error whenever the sample gave us $\hat{p} > p^*$ because we would reject the (true) null hypothesis. Unusual samples like that would happen only with probability α.

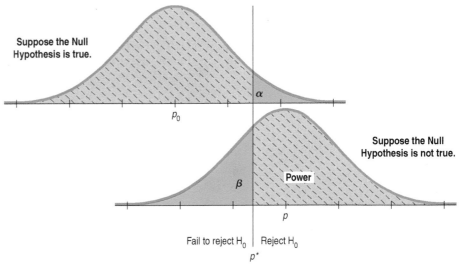

Figure 9 The power of a test is the probability that it rejects a false null hypothesis. The upper figure shows the null hypothesis model. We'd reject the null in a one-sided test if we observed a value in the red region to the right of the critical value, p^*. The lower figure shows the model if we assume that the true value is p. If the true value of p is greater than p_0, then we're more likely to observe a value that exceeds the critical value and make the correct decision to reject the null hypothesis. The power of the test is the green region on the right of the lower figure. Of course, even drawing samples whose observed proportions are distributed around p, we'll sometimes get a value in the red region on the left and make a Type II error of failing to reject the null.

In reality, though, the null hypothesis is rarely *exactly* true. The lower probability model supposes that H_0 is not true. In particular, it supposes that the true value is p, not p_0. It shows a distribution of possible observed $\hat{p}$ values around this true value. Because of sampling variability, sometimes $\hat{p} < p^*$ and we fail to reject the (false) null hypothesis. Then we'd make a Type II error. The area under the curve to the left of p^* in the bottom model represents how often this happens. The probability is β. In this picture, β is less than half, so most of the time we *do* make the right decision. The *power* of the test—the probability that we make the right decision—is shown as the region to the right of p^*. It's $1 - \beta$.

We calculate p^* based on the upper model because p^* depends only on the null model and the alpha level. No matter what the true proportion, p^* doesn't change. After all, we don't *know* the truth, so we can't use it to determine the critical value. But we always reject H_0 when $\hat{p} > p^*$.

How often we reject H_0 when it's *false* depends on the effect size. We can see from the picture that if the true proportion were further from the hypothesized value, the bottom curve would shift to the right, making the power greater.

We can see several important relationships from this figure:

- Power $= 1 - \beta$.
- Moving the critical value (p^* in the case of proportions) to the right, reduces α, the probability of a Type I error, but increases β, the probability of a Type II error. It correspondingly reduces the power.
- The larger the true effect size, the real difference between the hypothesized value and the true population value, the smaller the chance of making a Type II error and the greater the power of the test.

If the two proportions (or means) are very far apart, the two models will barely overlap, and we would not be likely to make any Type II errors at all—but then, we are unlikely to really need a formal hypothesis testing procedure to see such an obvious difference.

Reducing Both Type I and Type II Errors

Figure 9 seems to show that if we reduce Type I errors, we automatically must increase Type II errors. But there is a way to reduce both. Can you think of it?

If we can make both curves narrower, as shown in Figure 10, then the probability of both Type I errors and Type II errors will decrease, and the power of the test will increase.

How can we do that? The only way is to reduce the standard deviations by increasing the sample size. (Remember, these are pictures of sampling distribution models, not of data.) Increasing the sample size works regardless of the true population parameters. But recall the curse of diminishing returns. The standard deviation of the sampling distribution model decreases only as the *square root* of the sample size, so to halve the standard deviations, we must *quadruple* the sample size.

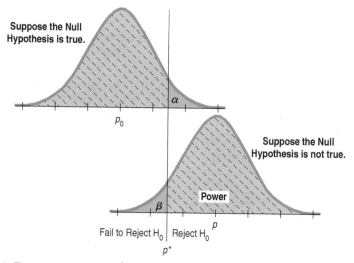

Figure 10 Making the standard deviations smaller increases the power without changing the alpha level or the corresponding *z*-critical value. The proportions are just as far apart as in Figure 9, but the error rates are reduced. A similar picture could be drawn for testing means.

What Can Go Wrong?

- **Don't confuse proportions and means.** When you treat your data as categorical, counting successes and summarizing with a sample proportion, make inferences using the Normal model methods. When you treat your data as quantitative, summarizing with a sample mean, make your inferences using Student's *t* methods.

- **Don't base your null hypotheses on what you see in the data.** You are not allowed to look at the data first and then adjust your null hypothesis so that it will be rejected. If the mean spending of 10 customers turns out to be $\bar{y} = \$24.94$ with a standard error of $5, don't form a null hypothesis just big enough so you'll be able to reject it like $H_0: \mu = \$26.97$. The null hypothesis should not be based on the data you collect. It should describe the "nothing interesting" or "nothing has changed" situation.

- **Don't base your alternative hypothesis on the data either.** You should always think about the situation you are investigating and base your alternative hypothesis on that. Are you interested only in knowing whether something has *increased*? Then write a one-tail (upper tail) alternative. Or would you be equally interested in a change in either direction? Then you want a two-tailed alternative. You should decide whether to do a one- or two-tailed test based on what results would be of interest to you, not on what you might see in the data.

- **Don't make your null hypothesis what you want to show to be true.** Remember, the null hypothesis is the status quo, the nothing-is-strange-here position a skeptic would take. You wonder whether the data cast doubt on that. You can reject the null hypothesis, but you can never "accept" or "prove" the null.

- **Don't forget to check the conditions.** The reasoning of inference depends on randomization. No amount of care in calculating a test result can save you from a biased sample. The probabilities you compute depend on the independence assumption. And your sample must be large enough to justify your use of a Normal model.

- **Don't believe too strongly in arbitrary alpha levels.** There's not really much difference between a P-value of 0.051 and a P-value of 0.049, but sometimes it's regarded as the difference between night (having to retain H_0) and day (being able to shout to the world that your results are "statistically significant"). It may just be better to report the P-value and a confidence interval and let the world (perhaps your manager or client) decide along with you.

- **Don't confuse practical and statistical significance.** A large sample size can make it easy to discern even a trivial change from the null hypothesis value. On the other hand, you could miss an important difference if your test lacks sufficient power.

- **Don't forget that in spite of all your care, you might make a wrong decision.** No one can ever reduce the probability of a Type I error (α) or of a Type II error (β) to zero (but increasing the sample size helps).

Ethics in Action

Many retailers have recognized the importance of staying connected to their in-store customers via the Internet. Retailers not only use the Internet to inform their customers about specials and promotions, but also to send them e-coupons redeemable for discounts. Shellie Cooper, longtime owner of a small organic food store, specializes in locally produced organic foods and products. Over the years Shellie's customer base has been quite stable, consisting mainly of health-conscious individuals who tend not to be very price sensitive, opting to pay higher prices for better-quality local, organic products. However, faced with increasing competition from grocery chains offering more organic choices, Shellie is now thinking of offering coupons. She needs to decide between the newspaper and the Internet. She recently read that the percentage of consumers who use printable Internet coupons is on the rise but, at 15%, is much less than the 40% who clip and redeem newspaper coupons. Nonetheless, she's interested in learning more about the Internet and sets up a meeting with Jack Kasor, a Web consultant. She discovers that for an initial investment and continuing monthly fee, Jack would design Shellie's website, host it on his server, and broadcast e-coupons to her customers at regular intervals. While she was concerned about the difference in redemption rates for e-coupons vs. newspaper coupons, Jack assured her that e-coupon redemptions are continuing to rise and that she should expect between 15% and 40% of her customers to redeem them. Shellie agreed to give it a try. After the first six months, Jack informed Shellie that the proportion of her customers who redeemed e-coupons was significantly greater than 15%. He determined this by selecting several broadcasts at random and found the number redeemed (483) out of the total number sent (3000). Shellie thought that this was positive and made up her mind to continue the use of e-coupons.

ETHICAL ISSUE *Statistical vs. practical significance. While it is true that the percentage of Shellie's customers redeeming e-coupons is significantly greater than 15% statistically, in fact, the percentage is just over 16%. This difference amounts to about 33 customers more than 15%, which may not be of practical significance to Shellie· (related to Item A, ASA Ethical Guidelines). Mentioning a range of 15% to 40% may mislead Shellie into expecting a value somewhere in the middle.*

ETHICAL SOLUTION *Jack should report the difference between the observed value and the hypothesized value to Shellie, especially since there are costs associated with continuing e-coupons. Perhaps he should recommend that she reconsider using the newspaper.*

What Have We Learned?

Learning Objectives

■ Know how to formulate a null and alternative hypothesis for a question of interest.

- The null hypothesis specifies a parameter and a (null) value for that parameter.
- The alternative hypothesis specifies a range of plausible values should we fail to reject the null.

■ Be able to perform a hypothesis test for a proportion.

- The null hypothesis has the form $H_0: p = p_0$.
- We estimate the standard deviation of the sampling distribution of the sample proportion by assuming that the null hypothesis is true:

$$SD(\hat{p}) = \sqrt{\frac{p_0 q_0}{n}}$$

- We refer the statistic $z = \dfrac{\hat{p} - p_0}{SD(\hat{p})}$ to the standard Normal model.

(continued)

- ■ Be able to perform a hypothesis test for a mean.
  - The null hypothesis has the form $H_0: \mu = \mu_0$.
  - We estimate the standard error of the sampling distribution as
    $$SE(\bar{y}) = \frac{s}{\sqrt{n}}.$$
  - We refer the test statistic $t = \dfrac{\bar{y} - \mu_0}{SE(\bar{y})}$ to the Student's t distribution with $n - 1$ degrees of freedom.

- ■ Understand P-values.
  - A P-value is the estimated probability of observing a statistic value at least as far from the (null) hypothesized value as the one we have actually observed.
  - A small P-value indicates that the statistic we have observed would be unlikely were the null hypothesis true. That leads us to doubt the null.
  - A large P-value just tells us that we have insufficient evidence to doubt the null hypothesis. In particular, it does not prove the null to be true.

- ■ Know the reasoning of hypothesis testing.
  - State the **hypotheses**.
  - Determine (and check assumptions for) the sampling distribution **model**.
  - Calculate the test statistic—the **mechanics**.
  - State your **conclusions and decisions**.

- ■ Be able to decide on a two-sided or one-sided alternative hypothesis, and justify your decision.

- ■ Compare P-values to a pre-determined α-level to decide whether to reject the null hypothesis.

- ■ Know the value of estimating and reporting the effect size.
  - A test may be statistically significant, but practically meaningless if the estimated effect is of trivial importance.

- ■ Be aware of the risks of making errors when testing hypotheses.
  - A Type I error can occur when rejecting a null hypothesis if that hypothesis is, in fact, true.
  - A Type II error can occur when failing to reject a null hypothesis if that hypothesis is, in fact, false.

- ■ Understand the concept of the power of a test.
  - We are particularly concerned with power when we fail to reject a null hypothesis.
  - The power of a test reports, for a specified effect size, the probability that the test would reject a false null hypothesis.
  - Remember that increasing the sample size will generally improve the power of any test.

Terms

Alpha level

The threshold P-value that determines when we reject a null hypothesis. Using an alpha level of α, if we observe a statistic whose P-value based on the null hypothesis is less than α, we reject that null hypothesis.

Alternative hypothesis

The hypothesis that proposes what we should conclude if we find the null hypothesis to be unlikely.

Critical value	The value in the sampling distribution model of the statistic whose P-value is equal to the alpha level. Any statistic value further from the null hypothesis value than the critical value will have a smaller P-value than α and will lead to rejecting the null hypothesis. The critical value is often denoted with an asterisk, as z^* or t^*, for example.
Effect size	The difference between the null hypothesis and an observed (or proposed) value.
Null hypothesis	The claim being assessed in a hypothesis test. Usually, the null hypothesis is a statement of "no change from the traditional value," "no effect," "no difference," or "no relationship." For a claim to be a testable null hypothesis, it must specify a value for some population parameter that can form the basis for assuming a sampling distribution for a test statistic.
One-sample *t*-test for the mean	The one-sample-*t*-test for the mean tests the hypothesis $H_0: \mu = \mu_0$ using the statistic $t_{n-1} = \dfrac{\bar{y} - \mu_0}{SE(\bar{y})}$, where $SE(\bar{y}) = \dfrac{s}{\sqrt{n}}$.
One-proportion *z*-test	A test of the null hypothesis that the proportion of a single sample equals a specified value ($H_0: p = p_0$) by comparing the statistic $z = \dfrac{\hat{p} - p_0}{SD(\hat{p})}$ to a standard Normal model.
One-sided alternative	An alternative hypothesis is one-sided (e.g., $H_A: p > p_0$ or $H_A: p < p_0$) when we are interested in deviations in *only one* direction away from the hypothesized parameter value.
P-value	The probability of observing a value for a test statistic at least as far from the hypothesized value as the statistic value actually observed if the null hypothesis is true. A small P-value indicates that the observation obtained is improbable given the null hypothesis and thus provides evidence against the null hypothesis.
Power	The probability that a hypothesis test will correctly reject a false null hypothesis. To find the power of a test, we must specify a particular alternative parameter value as the "true" value. For any specific value in the alternative, the power is $1 - \beta$.
Significance level	Another term for the alpha level, used most often in a phrase such as "at the 5% significance level."
Two-sided alternative	An alternative hypothesis is two-sided (e.g. $H_A: \mu \neq \mu_0$) when we are interested in deviations in *either* direction away from the hypothesized parameter value.
Type I error	The error of rejecting a null hypothesis when in fact it is true (also called a "false positive"). The probability of a Type I error is α.
Type II error	The error of failing to reject a null hypothesis when in fact it is false (also called a "false negative"). The probability of a Type II error is commonly denoted β and depends on the effect size.

Technology Help: Hypothesis Tests

Although most statistics packages offer ways to test hypotheses for means, many do not offer special commands for proportions. You can always report the "success" and "failure" status for each case as 1 or 0, but packages are likely to then treat the proportion as a mean (which, of course, it is for such data) and base inferences on Student's *t*. Some programs will allow you to specify the standard deviation and some will accept summary proportions.

In some programs you can reconstruct the original values from the summary proportions. Because of the different approaches, if you use a computer package, you may notice slight discrepancies between your answers and the answers in the back of the text, but they're not important.

Reports about hypothesis tests generated by technologies don't follow a standard form. Most will name the test and provide the test statistic value, its standard deviation, and the P-value. But these elements may not be labeled clearly. For example, the expressions "Prob > |z|" or "Prob > |t|" denote a two-sided alternative by use of the absolute value symbol. They give the probability of being as far or farther on either side from the null hypothesis than the observed data. That is a fancy (and not very clear) way of saying P-value. In some packages, you can specify that the test be one-sided. Others might report three P-values, covering the ground for both one-sided tests and the two-sided test.

Sometimes a confidence interval and hypothesis test are automatically given together. The confidence interval ought to be for the corresponding confidence level: $1 - \alpha$.

Often, the standard deviation of the statistic is called the "standard error," and usually that's appropriate because we've had to estimate its value from the data. That's not the case for

(continued)

proportions, however: We get the standard deviation for a proportion from the null hypothesis value. Nevertheless, you may see the standard deviation called a "standard error" even for tests with proportions.

It's common for statistics packages and calculators to report more digits of "precision" than could possibly have been found from the data. You can safely ignore them. Round values such as the standard deviation to one digit more than the number of digits reported in your data.

Here are the kind of results you might see in typical computer output.

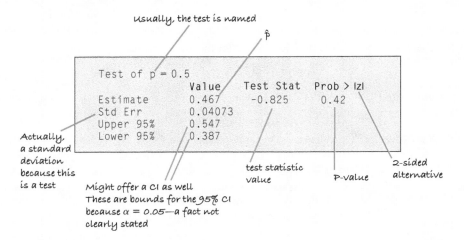

Usually, the test is named

$\hat{p}$

Test of p = 0.5

	Value	Test Stat	Prob > |z|
Estimate	0.467	-0.825	0.42
Std Err	0.04073		
Upper 95%	0.547		
Lower 95%	0.387		

Actually, a standard deviation because this is a test

Might offer a CI as well
These are bounds for the 95% CI because α = 0.05—a fact not clearly stated

test statistic value

P-value

2-sided alternative

Statistics packages offer convenient ways to make histograms of the data. That means you have no excuse for skipping the check that the data are nearly Normal.

Here's what the package output might look like for a hypothesis test of a mean (although no package we know gives the results in exactly this form):

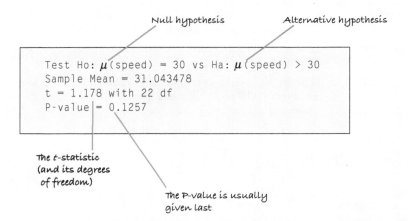

Null hypothesis

Alternative hypothesis

Test Ho: μ(speed) = 30 vs Ha: μ(speed) > 30
Sample Mean = 31.043478
t = 1.178 with 22 df
P-value = 0.1257

The *t*-statistic (and its degrees of freedom)

The P-value is usually given last

The package computes the sample mean and sample standard deviation of the variable and finds the P-value from the *t*-distribution based on the appropriate number of degrees of freedom. All modern statistics packages report P-values. The package may also provide additional information such as the sample mean, sample standard deviation, *t*-statistic value, and degrees of freedom. These are useful for interpreting the resulting P-value and telling the difference between a meaningful result and one that is merely statistically significant. Statistics packages that report the estimated standard deviation of the sampling distribution usually label it "standard error" or "SE."

Inference results are also sometimes reported in a table. You may have to read carefully to find the values you need. Often, test results and the corresponding confidence interval bounds are given together. And often you must read carefully to find the alternative hypotheses. On the next page is an example of that kind of output.

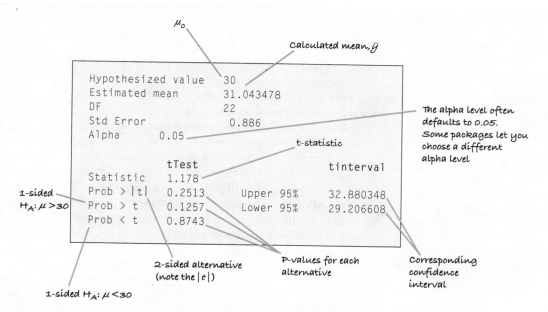

The commands to do inference for means on common statistics programs and calculators are not always obvious. (By contrast, the resulting output is usually clearly labeled and easy to read.) The guides for each program can help you start navigating.

EXCEL   XLSTAT

Inference methods in Excel can be handled by simply typing in the appropriate formulas. For example, suppose your data consist of 100 observations in cells A1:A100 and you want to do a two sided test of the null hypothesis that the mean is equal to 0.5.

- In cell B2, enter "=AVERAGE(A1:A100)" to compute the sample mean.
- In cell B3, enter "=STDEV(A1:A100)/SQRT(100)" to compute the standard error of the mean.
- In cell B4, enter "=(B2 − 0.5)/B3" to compute the test statistic.
- In cell B5, enter "=TDIST(B4,99,2)" to compute the p-value.

JMP

For a **categorical** variable that holds category labels, the **Distribution** platform includes tests and intervals of proportions.

- For summarized data, put the category names in one variable and the frequencies in an adjacent variable.
- Designate the frequency column to have the role of frequency.
- Then use the Distribution platform test.

For a hypothesis test,

- Click the red triangle next to the variable's name and choose **Test Mean** from the menu. Then fill in the resulting dialog.

Comments

JMP uses slightly different methods for proportion inferences than those discussed in this text. Your answers are likely to be slightly different. "Moment" is a fancy statistical term for means, standard deviations, and other related statistics.

MINITAB

For proportions, choose **Basic Statistics** from the **Stat** menu.

- Choose **1 Proportion** from the Basic Statistics submenu.
- If the data are category names in a variable, assign the variable from the variable list box to the **Samples in columns** box.
- If you have summarized data, click the **Summarized Data** button and fill in the number of trials and the number of successes.
- Click the **Options** button and specify the remaining details.
- If you have a large sample, check **Use test and interval based on Normal distribution.**
- Click the **OK** button.

For means,

- From the **Stat** menu, choose the **Basic Statistics** submenu.
- From that menu, choose **1-sample t**. . . . Then fill in the dialog.

Comments

When working from a variable that names categories, MINITAB treats the last category as the "success" category. You can specify how the categories should be ordered.

SPSS

SPSS does not find hypothesis tests for proportions. For means,

- From the **Analyze** menu, choose the **Compare Means** submenu.
- From that, choose **One-Sample t-test** command.

Comments

The commands suggest neither a single mean nor an interval. But the results provide both a test and an interval.

Brief CASE

Metal Production

Ingots are huge pieces of metal, often weighing in excess of 20,000 pounds, made in a giant mold. They must be cast in one large piece for use in fabricating large structural parts for cars and planes. If they crack while being made, the crack may propagate into the zone required for the part, compromising its integrity. Airplane manufacturers insist that metal for their planes be defect-free, so the ingot must be made over if any cracking is detected.

Even though the metal from the cracked ingot is recycled, the scrap cost runs into the tens of thousands of dollars. Metal manufacturers would like to avoid cracking if at all possible, but only about 75% of the ingots have been free of cracks. The data from 5000 ingots produced after some changes were made to the process are found in the file **Ingots**. The variable *Crack* indicates whether a crack was found (1) or not (0). The variable *Impurities* shows the amount (in ppm) of impurities found in a sample from each ingot. Select a random sample of 100 ingots and test the claim that the cracking rate has decreased from 25%. Also test whether the mean impurity level for the cracked ingots is greater than 500 ppm. Find confidence intervals for the cracking rate and for the mean impurity of the cracked ingots. Now select a random sample of 1000 ingots and test the claims and find the confidence intervals again. Prepare a short report about your findings including any differences you see between the conclusions from two samples.

iStockphoto

Mark Evans/iStockphoto

Loyalty Program

A marketing manager has sent out 10,000 mail pieces to a random sample of customers to test a new web-based loyalty program and see its impact on customer spending. The customers either received nothing (No Offer), a free companion airline ticket (Free Flight), or free flight insurance on their next flight (Free Insurance). The analyst who designed the test used a stratified random sample to ensure that all the market segments are represented, but the manager has several concerns. First, she worries that the *Travel* segment (which comprises 25% of all customers) is underrepresented (variable *Segment*). In addition, she worries that fewer than 1/3 of the customers in that segment were held out as controls and received no offer. Finally, she wants to know the mean amount of customers in the *Travel* segment for each of the three possible *Offers*. Using the data found in **Loyalty_Program** at www.pearsonhighered.com/Sharpe, write a short report to the manager testing the appropriate hypotheses and summarizing your findings. Include in your report 95% confidence intervals for the proportion of customers who responded to the offer by signing up for the loyalty program in the various segments. (The variable *Response* indicates a 1 for responders and 0 for nonresponders.)

Exercises

SECTION 1

1. For each of the following situations, define the parameter (proportion or mean) and write the null and alternative hypotheses in terms of parameter values. Example: We want to know if the proportion of up days in the stock market is 50%. Answer: Let p = the proportion of up days. H_0: $p = 0.5$ vs. H_A: $p \neq 0.5$.

a) A casino wants to know if their slot machine really delivers the 1 in 100 win rate that it claims.

b) Last year customers spent an average of $35.32 per visit to the company's website. Based on a random sample of purchases this year, the company wants to know if the mean this year has changed.

c) A pharmaceutical company wonders if their new drug has a cure rate different from the 30% reported by the placebo.

d) A bank wants to know if the percentage of customers using their website has changed from the 40% that used it before their system crashed last week.

2. As in Exercise 1, for each of the following situations, define the parameter and write the null and alternative hypotheses in terms of parameter values.

a) Seat-belt compliance in Massachusetts was 65% in 2008. The state wants to know if it has changed.

b) Last year, a survey found that 45% of the employees were willing to pay for on-site day care. The company wants to know if that has changed.

c) Regular card customers have a default rate of 6.7%. A credit card bank wants to know if that rate is different for their Gold card customers.

d) Regular card customers have been with the company for an average of 17.3 months. The credit card bank wants to know if their Gold card customers have been with the company on average the same amount of time.

SECTION 3

3. Which of the following are true? If false, explain briefly.

a) A very high P-value is strong evidence that the null hypothesis is false.

b) A very low P-value proves that the null hypothesis is false.

c) A high P-value shows that the null hypothesis is true.

d) A P-value below 0.05 is always considered sufficient evidence to reject a null hypothesis.

4. Which of the following are true? If false, explain briefly.

a) A very low P-value provides evidence against the null hypothesis.

b) A high P-value is strong evidence in favor of the null hypothesis.

c) A P-value above 0.10 shows that the null hypothesis is true.

d) If the null hypothesis is true, you can't get a P-value below 0.01.

SECTION 4

5. A consulting firm had predicted that 35% of the employees at a large firm would take advantage of a new company Credit Union, but management is skeptical. They doubt the rate is that high. A survey of 300 employees shows that 138 of them are currently taking advantage of the Credit Union. From the sample proportion

a) Find the standard deviation of the sample proportion based on the null hypothesis.

b) Find the z-statistic.

c) Does the z-statistic seem like a particularly large or small value?

6. A survey of 100 CEOs finds that 60 think the economy will improve next year. Is there evidence that the rate is higher among all CEOs than the 55% reported by the public at large?

a) Find the standard deviation of the sample proportion based on the null hypothesis.

b) Find the z-statistic.

c) Does the z-statistic seem like a particularly large or small value?

SECTION 5

7. For each of the following, write out the null and alternative hypothesis, being sure to state whether it is one-sided or two-sided.

a) A company reports that last year 40% of their reports in accounting were on time. From a random sample this year, they want to know if that proportion has changed.

b) A company wants to know if average click-through rates (in minutes) are shorter than the 5.4 minutes that customers spent on their old website before making a purchase.

c) Last year, 42% of the employees enrolled in at least one wellness class at the company's site. Using a survey, they want to know if a greater percentage is planning to take a wellness class this year.

d) A political candidate wants to know from recent polls if she's going to garner a majority of votes in next week's election.

8. For each of the following, write out the alternative hypothesis, being sure to indicate whether it is one-sided or two-sided.

a) *Consumer Reports* discovered that 20% of a certain computer model had warranty problems over the first three months. From a random sample, the manufacturer wants to know if a new model has improved that rate.

b) The last time a philanthropic agency requested donations, 4.75% of people responded. From a recent pilot mailing, they wonder if that rate has increased.

c) The average age of a customer of a clothing store is 35.2 years. The company wants to know if customers who use their website are younger on average.

d) A student wants to know if other students on her campus prefer Coke or Pepsi.

SECTION 6

9. An owner of a store wants to know if the mean age of all customers is 25 years old.

a) What is the null hypothesis?

b) Is the alternative one- or two-sided?

c) What is the value of the test statistic?

d) What is the P-value of the test statistic?

e) What do you conclude at $\alpha = 0.05$?

f) Given a 95% confidence interval, what might you have concluded? Explain.

20	32	34	29	30
30	30	14	29	11
38	22	44	48	26
25	22	32	35	32
35	42	44	44	48

10. An analyst wants to know if the mean purchase amount of all transactions is at least $40.

a) What is the null hypothesis?
b) Is the alternative one- or two-sided?
c) What is the value of the test statistic?
d) What is the P-value of the test statistic?
e) What do you conclude at $\alpha = 0.05$?
f) Given a 90% confidence interval, what might you have concluded? Explain.

39.05	2.73	32.92	47.51
37.91	34.35	64.48	51.96
56.95	81.58	47.80	11.72
21.57	40.83	38.24	32.98
75.16	74.30	47.54	65.62

SECTION 7

11. Which of the following statements are true? If false, explain briefly.

a) Using an alpha level of 0.05, a P-value of 0.04 results in rejecting the null hypothesis.
b) The alpha level depends on the sample size.
c) With an alpha level of 0.01, a P-value of 0.10 results in rejecting the null hypothesis.
d) Using an alpha level of 0.05, a P-value of 0.06 means the null hypothesis is true.

12. Which of the following statements are true? If false, explain briefly.

a) It is better to use an alpha level of 0.05 than an alpha level of 0.01.
b) If we use an alpha level of 0.01, then a P-value of 0.001 is statistically significant.
c) If we use an alpha level of 0.01, then we reject the null hypothesis if the P-value is 0.001.
d) If the P-value is 0.01, we reject the null hypothesis for any alpha level greater than 0.01.

SECTION 8

13. For each of the following situations, find the critical value(s) for z or t.

a) $H_0: p = 0.5$ vs. $H_A: p \neq 0.5$ at $\alpha = 0.05$.
b) $H_0: p = 0.4$ vs. $H_A: p > 0.4$ at $\alpha = 0.05$.
c) $H_0: \mu = 10$ vs. $H_A: \mu \neq 10$ at $\alpha = 0.05$; $n = 36$.
d) $H_0: p = 0.5$ vs. $H_A: p > 0.5$ at $\alpha = 0.01$; $n = 345$.
e) $H_0: \mu = 20$ vs. $H_A: \mu < 20$ at $\alpha = 0.01$; $n = 1000$.

14. For each of the following situations, find the critical value for z or t.

a) $H_0: \mu = 105$ vs. $H_A: \mu \neq 105$ at $\alpha = 0.05$; $n = 61$.
b) $H_0: p = 0.05$ vs. $H_A: p > 0.05$ at $\alpha = 0.05$.
c) $H_0: p = 0.6$ vs. $H_A: p \neq 0.6$ at $\alpha = 0.01$.
d) $H_0: p = 0.5$ vs. $H_A: p < 0.5$ at $\alpha = 0.01$; $n = 500$.
e) $H_0: p = 0.2$ vs. $H_A: p < 0.2$ at $\alpha = 0.01$.

SECTION 9

15. Suppose that you are testing the hypotheses $H_0: p = 0.20$ vs. $H_A: p \neq 0.20$. A sample of size 250 results in a sample proportion of 0.25.

a) Construct a 95% confidence interval for p.
b) Based on the confidence interval, at $\alpha = .05$ can you reject H_0? Explain.
c) What is the difference between the standard error and standard deviation of the sample proportion?
d) Which is used in computing the confidence interval?

16. Suppose that you are testing the hypotheses $H_0: p = 0.40$ vs. $H_A: p > 0.40$. A sample of size 200 results in a sample proportion of 0.55.

a) Construct a 90% confidence interval for p.
b) Based on the confidence interval, at $\alpha = .05$ can you reject H_0? Explain.
c) What is the difference between the standard error and standard deviation of the sample proportion?
d) Which is used in computing the confidence interval?

17. Suppose that you are testing the hypotheses $H_0: \mu = 16$ vs. $H_A: \mu < 16$. A sample of size 25 results in a sample mean of 16.5 and a standard deviation of 2.0.

a) What is the standard error of the mean?
b) What is the critical value of t^* for a 90% confidence interval?
c) Construct a 90% confidence interval for μ.
d) Based on the confidence interval, at $\alpha = 0.05$ can you reject H_0? Explain.

18. Suppose that you are testing the hypotheses $H_0: \mu = 80$ vs. $H_A: \mu \neq 80$. A sample of size 61 results in a sample mean of 75 and a standard deviation of 1.5.

a) What is the standard error of the mean?
b) What is the critical value of t^* for a 95% confidence interval?
c) Construct a 95% confidence interval for μ.
d) Based on the confidence interval, at $\alpha = 0.05$ can you reject H_0? Explain.

SECTION 10

19. For each of the following situations, state whether a Type I, a Type II, or neither error has been made. Explain briefly.

a) A bank wants to know if the enrollment on their website is above 30% based on a small sample of customers. They test $H_0: p = 0.3$ vs. $H_A: p > 0.3$ and reject the null hypothesis. Later they find out that actually 28% of all customers enrolled.

b) A student tests 100 students to determine whether other students on her campus prefer Coke or Pepsi and finds no evidence that preference for Coke is not 0.5. Later, a marketing company tests all students on campus and finds no difference.

c) A human resource analyst wants to know if the applicants this year score, on average, higher on their placement exam than the 52.5 points the candidates averaged last year. She samples 50 recent tests and finds the average to be 54.1 points. She fails to reject the null hypothesis that the mean is 52.5 points. At the end of the year, they find that the candidates this year had a mean of 55.3 points.

d) A pharmaceutical company tests whether a drug lifts the headache relief rate from the 25% achieved by the placebo. They fail to reject the null hypothesis because the P-value is 0.465. Further testing shows that the drug actually relieves headaches in 38% of people.

20. For each of the following situations, state whether a Type I, a Type II, or neither error has been made.

a) A test of $H_0: \mu = 25$ vs. $H_A: \mu > 25$ rejects the null hypothesis. Later it is discovered that $\mu = 24.9$.

b) A test of $H_0: p = 0.8$ vs. $H_A: p < 0.8$ fails to reject the null hypothesis. Later it is discovered that $p = 0.9$.

c) A test of $H_0: p = 0.5$ vs. $H_A: p \neq 0.5$ rejects the null hypothesis. Later is it discovered that $p = 0.65$.

d) A test of $H_0: p = 0.7$ vs. $H_A: p < 0.7$ fails to reject the null hypothesis. Later is it discovered that $p = 0.6$.

CHAPTER EXERCISES

21. Hypotheses. Write the null and alternative hypotheses to test each of the following situations.

a) An online clothing company is concerned about the timeliness of their deliveries. The VP of Operations and Marketing recently stated that she wanted the percentage of products delivered on time to be greater than 90%, and she wants to know if the company has succeeded.

b) A realty company recently announced that the proportion of houses taking more than three months to sell is now greater than 50%.

c) A financial firm's accounting reports that after improvements in their system, they now have an error rate below 2%.

22. More hypotheses. Write the null and alternative hypotheses to test each of the following situations.

a) A business magazine article reports that, in 1990, 35% of CEOs had an MBA degree. Has the percentage changed?

b) Recently, 20% of cars of a certain model have needed costly transmission work after being driven between 50,000 and 100,000 miles. The car manufacturer hopes that the redesign of a transmission component has solved this problem.

c) A market researcher for a cola company decides to field test a new flavor soft drink, planning to market it only if he is sure that over 60% of the people like the flavor.

23. Deliveries. The clothing company in Exercise 21a looks at a sample of delivery reports. They test the hypothesis that 90% of the deliveries are on time against the alternative that greater than 90% are on time and find a P-value of 0.22. Which of these conclusions is appropriate?

a) There's a 22% chance that 90% of the deliveries are on time.

b) There's a 78% chance that 90% of the deliveries are on time.

c) There's a 22% chance that the sample they drew shows the correct percentage of on-time deliveries

d) There's a 22% chance that natural sampling variation could produce a sample with an observed proportion of on-time deliveries such as the one they obtained if, in fact, 90% of deliveries are on time.

24. House sales. The realty company in Exercise 21b looks at a recent sample of houses that have sold. On testing the null hypothesis that 50% of the houses take more than three months to sell against the hypothesis that more than 50% of the houses take more than three months to sell, they find a P-value of 0.034. Which of these conclusions is appropriate?

a) There's a 3.4% chance that 50% of the houses take more than three months to sell.

b) If 50% of the houses take more than three months to sell, there's a 3.4% chance that a random sample would produce a sample proportion as high as the one they obtained.

c) There's a 3.4% chance that the null hypothesis is correct.

d) There's a 96.6% chance that 50% of the houses take more than three months to sell.

25. P-value. Have harsher penalties and ad campaigns increased seat-belt use among drivers and passengers? Observations of commuter traffic have failed to find evidence of a significant change compared with three years ago. Explain what the study's P-value of 0.17 means in this context.

26. Another P-value. A company developing scanners to search for hidden weapons at airports has concluded that a new device is significantly better than the current scanner. The company made this decision based on a P-value of 0.03. Explain the meaning of the P-value in this context.

27. Ad campaign. An information technology analyst believes that they are losing customers on their website who find the checkout and purchase system too complicated. She adds a one-click feature to the website, to make it easier but finds that only about 10% of the customers are using it. She decides to launch an ad awareness campaign to tell customers about the new feature in the hope of increasing the percentage. She doesn't see much of a difference, so she hires a consultant to help her. The consultant selects a random sample of recent purchases, tests the hypothesis that the ads produced no change against the alternative that the percent who use the one-click feature is now greater than 10%, and finds a P-value of 0.22. Which conclusion is appropriate? Explain.

a) There's a 22% chance that the ads worked.

b) There's a 78% chance that the ads worked.

c) There's a 22% chance that the null hypothesis is true.

d) There's a 22% chance that natural sampling variation could produce poll results like these if the use of the one-click feature has increased.

e) There's a 22% chance that natural sampling variation could produce poll results like these if there's really no change in website use.

28. Mutual funds. A mutual fund manager claims that at least 70% of the stocks she selects will increase in price over the next year. We examined a sample of 200 of her selections over the past three years. Our P-value turns out to be 0.03. Test an appropriate hypothesis. Which conclusion is appropriate? Explain.

a) There's a 3% chance that the fund manager is correct.

b) There's a 97% chance that the fund manager is correct.

c) There's a 3% chance that a random sample could produce the results we observed, so it's reasonable to conclude that the fund manager is correct.

d) There's a 3% chance that a random sample could produce the results we observed if $p = .7$, so it's reasonable to conclude that the fund manager is not correct.

e) There's a 3% chance that the null hypothesis is correct.

29. Product effectiveness. A pharmaceutical company's old antacid formula provided relief for 70% of the people who used it. The company tests a new formula to see if it is better and gets a P-value of 0.27. Is it reasonable to conclude that the new formula and the old one are equally effective? Explain.

30. Car sales. A German automobile company is counting on selling more cars to the younger market segment—drivers under the age of 20. The company's market researchers survey to investigate whether or not the proportion of today's high school seniors who own their own cars is higher than it was a decade ago. They find a P-value of 0.017. Is it reasonable to conclude that more high school seniors have cars? Explain.

31. False claims? A candy company claims that in a large bag of holiday M&M's® half the candies are red and half the candies are green. You pick candies at random from a bag and discover that of the first 20 you eat, 12 are red.

a) If it were true that half are red and half are green, what is the probability you would have found that at least 12 out of 20 were red?

b) Do you think that half of the M&M's® candies in the bag are really red? Explain.

32. Scratch off. A retail company offers a "scratch off" promotion. Upon entering the store, you are given a card. When you pay, you may scratch off the coating. The company advertises that half the cards are winners and have immediate cash-back savings of $5 (the others offer $1 off any future purchase of coffee in the cafe). You aren't sure the percentage is really 50% winners.

a) The first time you shop there, you get the coffee coupon. You try again and again get the coffee coupon. Do two failures in a row convince you that the true fraction of winners isn't 50%? Explain.

b) You try a third time. You get coffee again! What's the probability of not getting a cash savings three times in a row if half the cards really do offer cash savings?

c) Would three losses in a row convince you that the store is cheating?

d) How many times in a row would you have to get the coffee coupon instead of cash savings to be pretty sure that the company isn't living up to its advertised percentage of winners? Justify your answer by calculating a probability and explaining what it means.

33. E-commerce. A market researcher at a major clothing company that has traditionally relied on catalog mail-order sales decides to investigate whether the amount of online sales has changed. She compares the mean monthly online sales of the past several months with a historical figure for mean monthly sales for online purchases. She gets a P-value of 0.01. Explain in this context what the 1% represents.

34. Performance standards. The United States Golf Association (USGA) sets performance standards for golf balls. For example, the initial velocity of the ball may not exceed 250 feet per second when measured by an apparatus approved by the USGA. Suppose a manufacturer introduces a new kind of ball and provides a randomly selected sample of balls for testing. Based on the mean speed in the sample, the USGA comes up with a P-value of 0.34. Explain in this context what the 34% represents.

35. Social Security payments. The average monthly Social Security benefit for widows and widowers in 2005 was $967 (*Statistical Abstract of the United States*, U.S. Census Bureau). Payments vary from region to region. In Texas, the 2005 average monthly benefit equaled $940. A social welfare advocate from a rural Texas county believed the 2005 average Social Security benefit for widows and widowers differed significantly from the overall Texas average. To test this assumption, the advocate randomly sampled 100 widow/widower monthly benefit payments and found the sample mean = $915 with a standard deviation of $90.

a) Find and interpret a 95% confidence interval estimate for the sample mean 2005 Social Security widow/widower benefit in the rural Texas county.

b) In a hypothesis test performed to determine whether the county's average payment was different, the test was rejected with a P-value = .007 (using the same sample results shown above and a level of significance = .05). Explain how the confidence interval constructed in part a is consistent with the hypothesis test results. Your discussion should include level of confidence, the interval bounds, the P-value, and the hypothesis test decision.

36. Social Security payments, part 2. In a neighboring county, a newspaper wrote that widow/widower Social Security benefits were significantly lower in the county than in all the other counties of Texas. The newspaper reported that the average 2005 monthly benefit for widows and widowers was $900, based on a random sample of 100 with standard deviation of $90.

a) Find and interpret a 95% confidence interval estimate for the sample mean Social Security widow/widower benefit in this county.

b) Is this county's average widow/widower benefit different from the Texas average of $940?

37. Spike poll. In August 2004, *Time* magazine reported the results of a random telephone poll commissioned by the Spike network. Of the 1302 men who responded, only 39 said that their most important measure of success was their work.

a) Estimate the percentage of all American males who measure success primarily from their work. Use a 98% confidence interval. Don't forget to check the conditions first.

b) Some believe that few contemporary men judge their success primarily by their work. Suppose we wished to conduct a hypothesis test to see if the fraction has fallen below the 5% mark. What does your confidence interval indicate? Explain.

c) What is the significance level of this test? Explain.

38. Stocks. A young investor in the stock market is concerned that investing in the stock market is actually gambling, since the chance of the stock market going up on any given day is 50%. She decides to track her favorite stock for 250 days and finds that on 140 days the stock was "up."

a) Find a 95% confidence interval for the proportion of days the stock is "up." Don't forget to check the conditions first.

b) Does your confidence interval provide any evidence that the market is not random? Explain.

c) What is the significance level of this test? Explain.

39. Economy. In 2008, a Gallup Poll asked 2336 U.S. adults, aged 18 or over, how they rated economic conditions. In a poll conducted from January 27 through February 1, 2008, 24% rated the economy as Excellent/Good. A recent media outlet claimed that the percentage of Americans who felt the economy was in Excellent/Good shape was, in fact, 28%. Does the Gallup Poll support this claim?

a) Test the appropriate hypothesis. Find a 95% confidence interval for the sample proportion of U.S. adults who rated the economy as Excellent/Good. Check conditions.

b) Does your confidence interval provide evidence to support the claim?

c) What is the significance level of the test in b? Explain.

40. Economy, part 2. The same Gallup Poll data from Exercise 39 also reported that 33% of those surveyed rated the economy as Poor. The same media outlet claimed the

true proportion to be 30%. Does the Gallup Poll support this claim?

a) Test the appropriate hypothesis. Find a 95% confidence interval for the sample proportion of U.S. adults who rated the economy as Poor. Check conditions.

b) Does your confidence interval provide evidence to support the claim.

c) What is the significance level of the test in b? Explain.

41. Convenient alpha. An enthusiastic junior executive has run a test of his new marketing program. He reports that it resulted in a "significant" increase in sales. A footnote on his report explains that he used an alpha level of 7.2% for his test. Presumably, he performed a hypothesis test against the null hypothesis of no change in sales.

a) If instead he had used an alpha level of 5%, is it more or less likely that he would have rejected his null hypothesis? Explain.

b) If he chose the alpha level 7.2% so that he could claim statistical significance, explain why this is not an ethical use of statistics.

42. Safety. The manufacturer of a new sleeping pill suspects that it may increase the risk of sleepwalking, which could be dangerous. A test of the drug fails to reject the null hypothesis of increased sleepwalking when tested at alpha = .01.

a) If the test had been performed at alpha = .05, would the test have been more or less likely to reject the null hypothesis of no increase in sleepwalking?

b) Which alpha level do you think the company should use? Why?

43. Product testing. Since many people have trouble programming their VCRs, an electronics company has developed what it hopes will be easier instructions. The goal is to have at least 96% of customers succeed at being able to program their VCRs. The company tests the new system on 200 people, 188 of whom were successful. Is this strong evidence that the new system fails to meet the company's goal? A student's test of this hypothesis is shown here. How many mistakes can you find?

$$H_0: \hat{p} = 0.96$$
$$H_A: \hat{p} \neq 0.96$$
$$\text{SRS, } 0.96(200) > 10$$
$$\frac{188}{200} = 0.94; \ SD(\hat{p}) = \sqrt{\frac{(0.94)(0.06)}{200}} = 0.017$$
$$z = \frac{0.96 - 0.94}{0.017} = 1.18$$
$$P = P(z > 1.18) = 0.12$$

There is strong evidence that the new system does not work.

44. Marketing. In November 2001, the *Ag Globe Trotter* newsletter reported that 90% of adults drink milk. A regional farmers organization planning a new marketing campaign across its multicounty area polls a random sample of 750 adults living there. In this sample, 657 people said that they drink milk. Do these responses provide strong evidence that the 90% figure is not accurate for this region? Correct the mistakes you find in the following student's attempt to test an appropriate hypothesis.

$H_0: \hat{p} = 0.9$

$H_A: \hat{p} < 0.9$

SRS, $750 > 10$

$\dfrac{657}{750} = 0.876; SD(\hat{p}) = \sqrt{\dfrac{(0.88)(0.12)}{750}} = 0.012$

$z = \dfrac{0.876 - 0.94}{0.012} = -2$

$P = P(z > -2) = 0.977$

There is more than a 97% chance that the stated percentage is correct for this region.

45. E-commerce, part 2. The average age of online consumers a few years ago was 23.3 years. As older individuals gain confidence with the Internet, it is believed that the average age has increased. We would like to test this belief.

a) Write appropriate hypotheses.

b) We plan to test the null hypothesis by selecting a random sample of 40 individuals who have made an online purchase during 2007. Do you think the necessary assumptions for inference are satisfied? Explain.

c) The online shoppers in our sample had an average age of 24.2 years, with a standard deviation of 5.3 years. What's the P-value for this result?

d) Explain (in context) what this P-value means.

e) What's your conclusion?

46. Fuel economy. A company with a large fleet of cars hopes to keep gasoline costs down and sets a goal of attaining a fleet average of at least 26 miles per gallon. To see if the goal is being met, they check the gasoline usage for 50 company trips chosen at random, finding a mean of 25.02 mpg and a standard deviation of 4.83 mpg. Is this strong evidence that they have failed to attain their fuel economy goal?

a) Write appropriate hypotheses.

b) Are the necessary assumptions to perform inference satisfied?

c) Test the hypothesis and find the P-value.

d) Explain what the P-value means in this context.

e) State an appropriate conclusion.

47. Pricing for competitiveness. SLIX wax is developing a new high performance fluorocarbon wax for cross country ski racing designed to be used under a wide variety of conditions. In order to justify the price marketing wants, the wax needs to be very fast. Specifically, the mean time to finish their standard test course should be less than 55 seconds for the former Olympic champion who is now their consultant. To test it, the consultant will ski the course 8 times.

a) The champion's times are 56.3, 65.9, 50.5, 52.4, 46.5, 57.8, 52.2, and 43.2 seconds to complete the test course. Should they market the wax? Explain.

b) Suppose they decide not to market the wax after the test, but it turns out that the wax really does lower the champion's average time to less than 55 seconds. What kind of error have they made? Explain the impact to the company of such an error.

48. Popcorn. Pop's Popcorn, Inc. needs to determine the optimum power and time settings for their new licorice-flavored microwave popcorn. They want to find a combination of power and time that delivers high-quality popcorn with less than 10% of the kernels left unpopped, on average—a value that their market research says is demanded by their customers. Their research department experiments with several settings and determines that power 9 at 4 minutes is optimum. Their tests confirm that this setting meets the less than 10% requirement. They change the instructions on the box and promote a new money back guarantee of less than 10% unpopped kernels.

a) If, in fact, the setting results in more than 10% kernels unpopped, what kind of error have they made? What will the consequence be for the company?

b) To reduce the risk of making an error, the president (Pop himself) tells them to test 8 more bags of popcorn (selected at random) at the specified setting. They find the following percentage of unpopped kernels: 7, 13.2, 10, 6, 7.8, 2.8, 2.2, 5.2. Does this provide evidence that the setting meets their goal of less than than 10% unpopped? Explain.

49. Environment. In the 1980s, it was generally believed that congenital abnormalities affected about 5% of the nation's children. Some people believe that the increase in the number of chemicals in the environment has led to an increase in the incidence of abnormalities. A recent study examined 384 children and found that 46 of them showed signs of an abnormality. Is this strong evidence that the risk has increased? (We consider a P-value of around 5% to represent reasonable evidence.)

a) Write appropriate hypotheses.

b) Check the necessary assumptions.

c) Perform the mechanics of the test. What is the P-value?

d) Explain carefully what the P-value means in this context.

e) What's your conclusion?

f) Do environmental chemicals cause congenital abnormalities?

50. Billing company. A billing company that collects bills for doctors' offices in the area is concerned that the percentage of bills being paid by Medicare has risen. Historically, that percentage has been 31%. An examination of 8368 recent bills reveals that 32% of these bills are being paid by Medicare. Is this evidence of a change in the percent of bills being paid by Medicare?

a) Write appropriate hypotheses.

b) Check the assumptions and conditions.

c) Perform the test and find the P-value.

d) State your conclusion.

e) Do you think this difference is meaningful? Explain.

51. Education. The National Center for Education Statistics monitors many aspects of elementary and secondary education nationwide. Their 1996 numbers are often used as a baseline to assess changes. In 1996, 34% of students had not been absent from school even once during the previous month. In the 2000 survey, responses from 8302 students showed that this figure had slipped to 33%. Officials would be concerned if student attendance were declining. Do these figures give evidence of a decrease in student attendance?

a) Write appropriate hypotheses.
b) Check the assumptions and conditions.
c) Perform the test and find the P-value.
d) State your conclusion.
e) Do you think this difference is meaningful? Explain.

52. Consumer confidence. At various times in 2007, when asked if economic conditions were getting better or worse, consistently more than 20% of U.S. adults said better. On January 19–20, 2008, when Gallup polled 2590 U.S. adults, only 13% said that conditions were getting better. Do these responses give evidence that consumer confidence has decreased from the 2007 level?

a) Write appropriate hypotheses.
b) Check the assumptions and conditions.
c) Perform the test and find the P-value.
d) State your conclusion.
e) Do you think this difference is meaningful? Explain.

53. Retirement. A survey of 1000 workers indicated that approximately 520 have invested in an individual retirement account. National data suggests that 44% of workers invest in individual retirement accounts.

a) Create a 95% confidence interval for the proportion of workers who have invested in individual retirement accounts based on the survey.
b) Does this provide evidence of a change in behavior among workers? Using your confidence interval, test an appropriate hypothesis and state your conclusion.

54. Customer satisfaction. A company hopes to improve customer satisfaction, setting as a goal no more than 5% negative comments. A random survey of 350 customers found only 10 with complaints.

a) Create a 95% confidence interval for the true level of dissatisfaction among customers.
b) Does this provide evidence that the company has reached its goal? Using your confidence interval, test an appropriate hypothesis and state your conclusion.

55. Maintenance costs. A limousine company is concerned with increasing costs of maintaining their fleet of 150 cars. After testing, the company found that the emissions systems of 7 out of the 22 cars they tested failed to meet pollution control guidelines. They had forecasted costs assuming that a total of 30 cars would need updating to meet the latest guidelines. Is this strong evidence that more than 20% of the fleet might be out of compliance? Test an appropriate hypothesis and state your conclusion. Be sure the appropriate assumptions and conditions are satisfied before you proceed.

56. Damaged goods. An appliance manufacturer stockpiles washers and dryers in a large warehouse for shipment to retail stores. Sometimes in handling them the appliances get damaged. Even though the damage may be minor, the company must sell those machines at drastically reduced prices. The company goal is to keep the proportion of damaged machines below 2%. One day an inspector randomly checks 60 washers and finds that 5 of them have scratches or dents. Is this strong evidence that the warehouse is failing to meet the company goal? Test an appropriate hypothesis and state your conclusion. Be sure the appropriate assumptions and conditions are satisfied before you proceed.

57. WebZine. A magazine called *WebZine* is considering the launch of an online edition. The magazine plans to go ahead only if it's convinced that more than 25% of current readers would subscribe. The magazine contacts a simple random sample of 500 current subscribers, and 137 of those surveyed expressed interest. What should the magazine do? Test an appropriate hypothesis and state your conclusion. Be sure the appropriate assumptions and conditions are satisfied before you proceed.

58. Truth in advertising. A garden center wants to store leftover packets of vegetable seeds for sale the following spring, but the center is concerned that the seeds may not germinate at the same rate a year later. The manager finds a packet of last year's green bean seeds and plants them as a test. Although the packet claims a germination rate of 92%, only 171 of 200 test seeds sprout. Is this evidence that the seeds have lost viability during a year in storage? Test an appropriate hypothesis and state your conclusion. Be sure the appropriate assumptions and conditions are satisfied before you proceed.

59. Women executives. A company is criticized because only 13 of 43 people in executive-level positions are women. The company explains that although this proportion is lower than it might wish, it's not surprising given that only 40% of their employees are women. What do you think? Test an appropriate hypothesis and state your conclusion. Be sure the appropriate assumptions and conditions are satisfied before you proceed.

60. Jury. Census data for a certain county shows that 19% of the adult residents are Hispanic. Suppose 72 people are called for jury duty, and only 9 of them are Hispanic. Does this apparent underrepresentation of Hispanics call into question the fairness of the jury selection system? Explain.

61. Nonprofit. A nonprofit company concerned with the school dropout rates in the United States has designed a tutoring program aimed at students between 16 to 18 years old. The National Center for Education Statistics reported that the high school dropout rate in the United States for the year 2000 was 10.9%. One school district, who adopted the use of the nonprofit's tutoring program and whose dropout rate has always been very close to the national average, reported in 2004 that 175 of their 1782 students dropped out. Is their experience evidence that the tutoring program has been effective? Explain.

62. Real estate. A national real estate magazine advertised that 15% of first-time home buyers had a family income below $40,000. A national real estate firm believes this percentage is too low and samples 100 of its records. The firm finds that 25 of its first-time home buyers did have a family income below $40,000. Does the sample suggest that the proportion of first-time home buyers with an income less than $40,000 is more than 15%? Comment and write up your own conclusions based on an appropriate confidence interval as well as a hypothesis test. Include any assumptions you made about the data.

63. Public relations. According to the U.S. Department of Transportation (DOT), passengers filed more complaints about airline service in 2007 than in 2006. One airline's public relations department says that their airline rarely loses luggage. Furthermore, it claims that when it does, 90% of the time the bags are recovered and delivered within 24 hours. A consumer group surveys a large number of air travelers and finds that 103 of 122 people who lost luggage were reunited with their missing items within 24 hours. Does this cast doubt on the airline's claim? Explain.

64. TV ads. A start-up company is about to market a new computer printer. It decides to gamble by running commercials during the Super Bowl. The company hopes that name recognition will be worth the high cost of the ads. The goal of the company is that over 40% of the public recognize its brand name and associate it with computer equipment. The day after the game, a pollster contacts 420 randomly chosen adults and finds that 181 of them know that this company manufactures printers. Would you recommend that the company continue to advertise during the Super Bowl? Explain.

65. Business ethics. One study reports that 30% of newly hired MBAs are confronted with unethical business practices during their first year of employment. One business school dean wondered if her MBA graduates had similar experiences. She surveyed recent graduates from her school's MBA program to find that 27% of the 120 graduates from the previous year claim to have encountered unethical business practices in the workplace. Can she conclude that her graduates' experiences are different?

66. Stocks, part 2. A young investor believes that he can beat the market by picking stocks that will increase in value. Assume that on average 50% of the stocks selected by a portfolio manager will increase over 12 months. Of the 25 stocks that the young investor bought over the last 12 months, 14 have increased. Can he claim that he is better at predicting increases than the typical portfolio manager?

67. U.S. politics. The national elections in 2008 apparently drew more interest and debate among voters than prior U.S. elections. A national sample of 2020 U.S. adults, aged 18 and older, surveyed over the telephone (using both landlines and cell phones) between January 30 and February 2 in 2008 by Gallup revealed that 71% reported that they had given "quite a lot" of thought to the upcoming election for president. Is there any evidence that the percentage has changed from the historically reported benchmark of 58% during the same timeframe in 2004?

a) Find the z-score of the observed proportion.
b) Compare the z-score to the critical value for a 0.1% significance level using a two-sided alternative.
c) Explain your conclusion.

68. iPod reliability. MacInTouch reported that several versions of the iPod reported failure rates of 20% or more. From a customer survey, the color iPod, first released in 2004, showed 64 failures out of 517. Is there any evidence that the failure rate for this model may be lower than the 20% rate of previous models?

a) Find the z-score of the observed proportion.
b) Compare the z-score to the critical value for a 0.1% significance level using a one-sided alternative.
c) Explain your conclusion.

69. Testing cars. A clean air standard requires that vehicle exhaust emissions not exceed specified limits for various pollutants. Many states require that cars be tested annually to be sure they meet these standards. Suppose state regulators double-check a random sample of cars that a suspect repair shop has certified as okay. They will revoke the shop's license if they find significant evidence that the shop is certifying vehicles that do not meet standards.

a) In this context, what is a Type I error?
b) In this context, what is a Type II error?
c) Which type of error would the shop's owner consider more serious?
d) Which type of error might environmentalists consider more serious?

70. Quality control. Production managers on an assembly line must monitor the output to be sure that the level of defective products remains small. They periodically inspect a random sample of the items produced. If they find a significant increase in the proportion of items that must be rejected, they will halt the assembly process until the problem can be identified and repaired.

a) Write null and alternative hypotheses for this problem.
b) What is the Type I and Type II error in this context?
c) Which type of error would the factory owner consider more serious?
d) Which type of error might customers consider more serious?

71. Testing cars, again. As in Exercise 69, state regulators are checking up on repair shops to see if they are certifying vehicles that do not meet pollution standards.

a) In this context, what is meant by the power of the test the regulators are conducting?
b) Will the power be greater if they test 20 or 40 cars? Why?
c) Will the power be greater if they use a 5% or a 10% level of significance? Why?
d) Will the power be greater if the repair shop's inspectors are only a little out of compliance or a lot? Why?

72. Quality control, part 2. Consider again the task of the quality control inspectors in Exercise 70.

a) In this context, what is meant by the power of the test the inspectors conduct?
b) They are currently testing 5 items each hour. Someone has proposed they test 10 items each hour instead. What are the advantages and disadvantages of such a change?
c) Their test currently uses a 5% level of significance. What are the advantages and disadvantages of changing to a significance level of 1%?
d) Suppose that as a day passes one of the machines on the assembly line produces more and more items that are defective. How will this affect the power of the test?

73. Statistics software. A Statistics professor has observed that for several years about 13% of the students who initially enroll in his Introductory Statistics course withdraw before the end of the semester. A salesperson suggests that he try a statistics software package that gets students more involved with computers, predicting that it will cut the dropout rate. The software is expensive, and the salesperson offers to let the professor use it for a semester to see if the dropout rate goes down significantly. The professor will have to pay for the software only if he chooses to continue using it.

a) Is this a one-tailed or two-tailed test? Explain.
b) Write the null and alternative hypotheses.
c) In this context, explain what would happen if the professor makes a Type I error.
d) In this context, explain what would happen if the professor makes a Type II error.
e) What is meant by the power of this test?

74. Radio ads. A company is willing to renew its advertising contract with a local radio station only if the station can prove that more than 20% of the residents of the city have heard the ad and recognize the company's product. The radio station conducts a random phone survey of 400 people.

a) What are the hypotheses?
b) The station plans to conduct this test using a 10% level of significance, but the company wants the significance level lowered to 5%. Why?
c) What is meant by the power of this test?
d) For which level of significance will the power of this test be higher? Why?
e) They finally agree to use $\alpha = 0.05$, but the company proposes that the station call 600 people instead of the 400 initially proposed. Will that make the risk of Type II error higher or lower? Explain.

75. Statistics software, part 2. Initially, 203 students signed up for the Statistics course in Exercise 73. They used the software suggested by the salesperson, and only 11 dropped out of the course.

a) Should the professor spend the money for this software? Support your recommendation with an appropriate test.
b) Explain what your P-value means in this context.

76. Radio ads, part 2. The company in Exercise 74 contacts 600 people selected at random, and 133 can remember the ad.

a) Should the company renew the contract? Support your recommendation with an appropriate test.
b) Explain carefully what your P-value means in this context.

77. Investment. Investment style plays a role in constructing a mutual fund. Many individual stocks can be grouped into two distinct groups: Growth and Value. A Growth stock is one with high earning potential and often pays little or no dividends to shareholders. Conversely, Value stocks are commonly viewed as steady or more conservative stocks with a lower earning potential. A family is trying to decide what type of funds to invest in. An independent advisor claims that Value Mutual Funds provided an annualized return of greater than 8% over a recent 5-year period. Below are the summary statistics for the 5-year return for a random sample of such Value funds.

Variable	N	Mean	SE Mean	StDev
5 yr Return	35	8.418	0.493	2.916

	Minimum	Q1	Median	Q3	Maximum
	2.190	6.040	7.980	10.840	14.320

Test the hypothesis that the mean 5-year return for value funds is greater than 8%, assuming a significance level of 5%. What does this evidence say about the portfolio managers' claim that the annualized 5-year return was greater than 8%? State your conclusion.

78. Manufacturing. A tire manufacturer is considering a newly designed tread pattern for its all-weather tires. Tests have indicated that these tires will provide better gas mileage and longer tread life. The last remaining test is for braking effectiveness. The company hopes the tire will allow a car traveling at 60 mph to come to a complete stop within an average of 125 feet after the brakes are applied. They will adopt the new tread pattern unless there is strong evidence that the tires do not meet this objective. The distances (in feet) for 10 stops on a test track were 129, 128, 130, 132, 135, 123, 102, 125, 128, and 130. Should the company adopt the new tread pattern? Test an appropriate hypothesis and state your conclusion. Explain how you dealt with the outlier and why you made the recommendation you did.

79. Collections. Credit card companies lose money on cardholders who fail to pay their minimum payments. They use a variety of methods to encourage their delinquent cardholders to pay their credit card balances, such as letters, phone calls and eventually the hiring of a collection agency. To justify the cost of using the collection agency, the agency must collect an average of at least $200 per customer. After a trial period during which the agency attempted to collect from a random sample of 100 delinquent cardholders, the 90% confidence interval on the mean collected amount was reported as ($190.25, $250.75). Given this, what recommendation(s) would you make to the credit card company about using the collection agency?

80. Free gift. A philanthropic organization sends out "free gifts" to people on their mailing list in the hope that the receiver will respond by sending back a donation. Typical gifts are mailing labels, greeting cards, or post cards. They want to test out a new gift that costs $0.50 per item to produce and mail. They mail it to a "small" sample of 2000 customers and find a 90% confidence interval of the mean donation to be ($0.489, $0.879). As a consultant, what recommendation(s) would you make to the organization about using this gift?

81. Collections, part 2. The owner of the collection agency in Exercise 79 is quite certain that they can collect more than $200 per customer on average. He urges that the credit card company run a larger trial. Do you think a larger trial might help the company make a better decision? Explain.

82. Free gift, part 2. The philanthropic organization of Exercise 80 decided to go ahead with the new gift. In mailings to 98,000 prospects, the new mailing yielded an average of $0.78. If they had decided based on their initial trial *not* to use this gift, what kind of error would they have made? What aspects of their initial trial might have suggested to you (as their consultant) that a larger trial would be worthwhile?

Just Checking Answers

1 You can't conclude that the null hypothesis is true. You can conclude only that the experiment was unable to reject the null hypothesis. They were unable, on the basis of 12 patients, to show that aspirin was effective.

2 The null hypothesis is H_0: $p = 0.75$.

3 With a P-value of 0.0001, this is very strong evidence against the null hypothesis. We can reject H_0 and conclude that the improved version of the drug gives relief to a higher proportion of patients.

4 The parameter of interest is the proportion, p, of all delinquent customers who will pay their bills. H_0: $p = 0.30$ and H_A: $p > 0.30$.

5 At $\alpha = 0.05$, you can't reject the null hypothesis because 0.30 is contained in the 90% confidence interval—it's plausible that sending the DVDs is no more effective than sending letters.

6 The confidence interval is from 29% to 45%. The DVD strategy is more expensive and may not be worth it. We can't distinguish the success rate from 30% given the results of this experiment, but 45% would represent a large improvement. The bank should consider another trial, increasing the sample size to get a narrower confidence interval.

7 The confidence interval suggests that at 95% confidence, even in the worst case, the arrangement will generate a mean profit of at least $37.95 − $35.00 = $2.95 per customer. On the other hand, it may generate a profit as high as $55.05 − $35.00 = $20.05 per customer.

8 A Type I error would mean deciding that the DVD success rate is higher than 30%, when it isn't. The bank would adopt a more expensive method for collecting payments that's no better than its original, less expensive strategy.

9 A Type II error would mean deciding that there's not enough evidence to say the DVD strategy works when in fact it does. The bank would fail to discover an effective method for increasing revenue from delinquent accounts.

10 Higher; the larger the effect size, the greater the power. It's easier to detect an improvement to a 60% success rate than to a 32% rate.

11 No error has been made. The confidence interval from the test market suggested that the mean revenue was above the $35 cost per customer, and in fact that's what happened.

Answers

SECTION EXERCISE ANSWERS

1. a) Let p = probability of winning on the slot machine. $H_0: p = 0.01$ vs. $H_A: p \neq 0.01$

b) Let μ = mean spending per customer this year. $H_0: \mu = \$35.32$ vs. $H_A: \mu \neq \$35.32$

c) Let p = proportion of patients cured by the new drug. $H_0: p = 0.3$ vs. $H_A: p \neq 0.3$

d) Let p = proportion of clients now using the website. $H_0: p = 0.4$ vs. $H_A: p \neq 0.4$

3. a) False. A high P-value shows that the data are consistent with the null hypothesis, but provides no evidence for rejecting the null hypothesis.

b) False. It results in rejecting the null hypothesis, but does not prove that it is false.

c) False. A high P-value shows that the data are consistent with the null hypothesis but does not prove that the null hypothesis is true.

d) False. Whether a P-value provides enough evidence to reject the null hypothesis depends on the risk of a type I error that one is willing to assume (the α level).

5. a) $SE(\hat{p}) = \sqrt{\dfrac{p_0 q_0}{n}} = \sqrt{\dfrac{(0.35)(0.65)}{300}} = 0.028$

b) $z = \dfrac{\hat{p} - p_0}{SD(\hat{p})} = \dfrac{0.46 - 0.35}{0.028} = 3.93$

c) Yes, that's an unusually large z-value.

7. a) $H_0: p = 0.40$ vs. $H_A: p \neq 0.40$. Two-sided.

b) $H_0: \mu = 5.4$ vs. $H_A: \mu < 5.4$. One-sided.

c) $H_0: p = 0.42$ vs. $H_A: p > 0.42$. One-sided.

d) $H_0: p = 0.50$ vs. $H_A: p > 0.50$. One-sided.

9. a) $H_0: \mu = 25$

b) Two-sided: $\mu \neq 25$

c) 3.476

d) 0.0020

e) Reject H_0. There is strong evidence that the mean age is not 25.

f) Because the 95% confidence interval does not contain 25, we can reject H_0 at $\alpha = 0.05$.

11. a) True.

b) False. The alpha level is set independently and does not depend on the sample size.

c) False. The P-value would have to be less than 0.01 to reject the null hypothesis.

d) False. It simply means we do not have enough evidence at that alpha level to reject the null hypothesis.

13. a) $z = \pm 1.96$

b) $z = 1.645$

c) $t = \pm 2.03$

d) $z = 2.33$; n is not relevant for critical values for z.

e) $z = -2.33$

15. a) $(0.196, 0.304)$

b) No, because 0.20 is a plausible value.

c) The SE is based on $\hat{p}$: $SE(\hat{p}) = \sqrt{\dfrac{\hat{p}\hat{q}}{n}} = \sqrt{\dfrac{(0.25)(0.75)}{250}} = 0.0274$. The SD is based on the hypothesized value 0.20, so $SD(\hat{p}) = \sqrt{\dfrac{p_0 q_0}{n}} \sqrt{\dfrac{(0.20)(0.80)}{250}} = 0.0253$.

d) The SE since it is sample based.

17. a) $SE = \dfrac{s}{\sqrt{n}} = \dfrac{2.0}{\sqrt{25}} = 0.4$

b) t^* with 24 df for a 90% confidence interval is 1.711.

c) $(15.82, 17.18)$

d) No, we fail to reject H_0 (one-sided) at $\alpha = 0.05$ because 16.0 is in the corresponding two-sided 90% confidence interval.

19. a) Type I error. The actual value is not greater than 0.3 but they rejected the null hypothesis.

b) No error. The actual value is 0.50, which was not rejected.

c) Type II error. The actual value was 55.3 points, which is greater than 52.5.

d) Type II error. The null hypothesis was not rejected, but it was false. The true relief rate was greater than 0.25.

CHAPTER EXERCISE ANSWER

21. a) Let p be the percentage of products delivered on time. $H_0: p = 0.90$ vs. $H_A: p > 0.90$

b) Let p be the proportion of houses taking more than 3 months to sell. $H_0: p = 0.50$ vs. $H_A: p > 0.50$

c) Let p be the error rate. $H_0: p = 0.02$ vs. $H_A: p < 0.02$

23. Statement d is correct.

25. If the rate of seat-belt usage after the campaign is the same as the rate of seat-belt usage before the campaign, there is a 17% chance of observing a rate of seat-belt usage after the campaign this large or larger in a sample of the same size by natural sampling variation alone.

27. Statement e is correct.

29. No, we can say only that there is a 27% chance of seeing the observed effectiveness just from natural sampling if $p = 0.7$. There is no *evidence* that the new formula is more effective, but we can't conclude that they are equally effective.

31. a) 0.186 (using the normal model) 0.252 using exact probabilities.

b) It seems reasonable to think there really may have been half of each. We would expect to get 12 or more reds out of 20 more than 15% of the time, so there's no real evidence that the company's claim is not true. The two sided P-value is greater than 0.30.

33. If in fact the mean monthly sales due to online purchases has not changed, then only 1 out of every 100 samples would be expected to have mean sales as different from the historical figure as the mean sales observed in the sample.

35. a) $897.14 to $932.86
We are 95% confident the interval $897.14 to $932.86 contains the true mean Social Security benefit for widows and widowers in the Texas county.

b) With a P-value of .007, the hypothesis test results are significant and we reject the null hypothesis. We conclude the mean benefit payment for the Texas county is different from the $940 for the state. The 95% confidence interval estimate is $897.14 to $932.86. Since the interval does not contain the hypothesized mean of $940, we have evidence that the mean is unlikely to be $940.

37. a) Conditions are satisfied: random sample; less than 10% of population; more than 10 successes and failures; (1.9%, 4.1%).

b) Since 5% is not in the interval, there is strong evidence that fewer than 5% of all men use work as their primary measure of success.

c) $\alpha = 0.01$; it's a lower-tail test based on a 98% confidence interval.

39. a) Conditions are satisfied: random sample; less than 10% of population; more than 10 successes and failures; (0.223, 0.257); we are 95% confident that the true proportion of U.S. adults who rate the economy as Excellent/Good is between 0.223 and 0.257.

b) No. Since 0.28 is not within the interval, there is evidence that the proportion is not 28%.

c) $\alpha = 0.05$; it's a two-tail test based on a 95% confidence interval.

41. a) Less likely

b) Alpha levels must be chosen *before* examining the data. Otherwise the alpha level could always be selected to reject the null hypothesis.

43. 1. Use p, not $\hat{p}$, in hypotheses.

2. The question is about *failing* to meet the goal. H_A should be $p < 0.96$.

3. Did not check $nq = (200)(0.04) = 8$. Since $nq < 10$, the Success/Failure condition is violated. Didn't check the 10% condition.

4. $\hat{p} = \dfrac{188}{200} = 0.94$; $SD(\hat{p}) = \sqrt{\dfrac{pq}{n}} = \sqrt{\dfrac{(0.96)(0.04)}{200}} \approx 0.014$

The student used $\hat{p}$ and $\hat{q}$.

5. z is incorrect; should be $z = \dfrac{0.94 - 0.96}{0.014} \approx -1.43$.

6. $P = P(z < -1.43) = 0.076$

7. There is only weak evidence that the new system has failed to meet the goal.

45. a) $H_0: \mu = 23.3$; $H_A: \mu > 23.3$

b) **Randomization condition:** The 40 online shoppers were selected randomly. **Nearly Normal condition:** We should examine the distribution of the sample to check for serious skewness and outliers, but with a large sample of 40 shoppers, it should be safe to proceed.

c) 0.145

d) If the mean age of shoppers is still 23.3 years, there is a 14.5% chance of getting a sample mean of 24.2 years or older simply from natural sampling variation.

e) There is no evidence to suggest that the mean age of online shoppers has increased from the mean of 23.3 years.

47. a) $H_0: \mu = 55$; $H_A: \mu < 55$; **Independence assumption:** Since the times are not randomly selected, we will assume that the times are independent and representative of all the champion's times. **Nearly Normal condition:** The histogram of the times is unimodal and roughly symmetric; P-value = 0.235; fail to reject H_0. There is insufficient evidence to conclude the mean time is less than 55 seconds. They should not market the new ski wax.

b) Type II error. They won't market a competitive wax and thus lose the potential profit from having done so.

49. a) Let p = the percentage of children with genetic abnormalities. $H_0: p = 0.05$ vs. $H_A: p > 0.05$

b) SRS (not clear from information provided); $384 < 10\%$ of all children; $np = (384)(0.05) = 19.2 > 10$ and $nq = (384)(0.95) = 364.8 > 10$.

c) $z = 6.28$, $P < 0.0001$

d) If 5% of children have genetic abnormalities, the chance of observing 46 children with genetic abnormalities in a random sample of 384 children is essentially 0.

e) Reject H_0. There is strong evidence that more than 5% of children have genetic abnormalities.

f) We don't know that environmental chemicals cause genetic abnormalities, only that the rate is higher now than in the past.

51. a) Let p = the percentage of students in 2000 with perfect attendance the previous month. $H_0: p = 0.34$ vs. $H_A: p < 0.34$

b) Although not specifically stated, assume that the National Center for Education Statistics used random sampling; $8302 < 10\%$ of all students; $np = (8302)(0.34) = 2822.68 > 10$ and $nq = (8302)(0.66) = 5479.32 > 10$.

c) $z = -1.92$, $P = 0.027$

d) Reject H_0 at $\alpha = 0.05$. There is evidence to suggest that the percentage of students with perfect attendance in the previous month has decreased in 2000.

e) This result is statistically significant at $\alpha = 0.05$, but it's not clear that it has any practical significance since the percentage dropped only from 34% to 33%.

53. a) SRS (not clear from information provided); $1000 < 10\%$ of all workers; $n\hat{p} = 520 > 10$ and $n\hat{q} = 480 > 10$; (0.489, 0.551); we are 95% confident that between 48.9% and 55.1% of workers have invested in individual retirement accounts.

b) Let p = the percentage of workers who have invested. $H_0: p = 0.44$ vs. $H_A: p \neq 0.44$; since 44% is not in the 95% confidence interval, we reject H_0 at $\alpha = 0.05$. There is strong evidence that the percentage of workers who have invested in individual retirement accounts was not 44%. In fact, our sample indicates an increase in the percentage of adults who invest in individual retirement accounts.

55. Let p = the percentage of cars with faulty emissions. $H_0: p = 0.20$ vs. $H_A: p > 0.20$; two conditions are not satisfied: $22 > 10\%$ of the population of 150 cars and $np = (22)(0.20) = 4.4 < 10$. It's not a good idea to proceed with a hypothesis test.

57. Let p = the percentage of readers interested in an online edition. $H_0: p = 0.25$ vs. $H_A: p > 0.25$; SRS; $500 < 10\%$ of all potential subscribers; $np = (500)(0.25) = 125 > 10$ and $nq = (500)(0.75) = 375 > 10$; $z = 1.24$, P = 0.1076. Since the P-value is high, we fail to reject H_0. There is insufficient evidence to suggest that the proportion of interested readers is greater than 25%. The magazine should not publish the online edition.

59. Let p = the proportion of female executives. $H_0: p = 0.40$ vs. $H_A: p < 0.40$; data are for all executives in this company and may not be able to be generalized to all companies; $np = (43)(0.40) = 17.2 > 10$ and $nq = (43)(0.60) = 25.8 > 10$; $z = -1.31$, P = 0.0955. Since the P-value is high, we fail to reject H_0. There is insufficient evidence to suggest proportion of female executives is any different from the overall proportion of 40% female employees at the company.

61. Let p = the proportion of dropouts at this high school. $H_0: p = 0.109$ vs. $H_A: p < 0.109$; assume that the students at this high school are representative of all students nationally; $1792 < 10\%$ of all students nationally; $np = (1782)(0.109) = 194.238 > 10$ and $nq = (1782)(0.891) = 1587.762 > 10$; $z = -1.46$, P = 0.072. Since the P-value = $0.072 > 0.05$, we fail to reject H_0. There is insufficient evidence of a decrease in dropout rate from 10.9%.

63. Let p = the proportion of lost luggage returned the next day. $H_0: p = 0.90$ vs. $H_A: p < 0.90$; it is reasonable to think that the people surveyed were independent with regard to their luggage woes; although not stated, we will hope that the survey was conducted randomly, or at least that these air travelers are representative of all air travelers for that airline; $122 < 10\%$ of all air travelers on the airline; $np = (122)(0.90) = 109.8 > 10$ and $nq = (122)(0.10) = 12.2 > 10$; $z = -2.05$, P = 0.0201. Since the P-value is low, we reject H_0. There is evidence that the proportion of lost luggage returned the next day is lower than the 90% claimed by the airline.

65. H_0: These MBA students are exposed to unethical practices at a similar rate to others in the program ($p = 0.30$).

H_A: These students are exposed to unethical practices at a different rate than other students ($p \neq 0.30$).

There is no reason to believe that students' rates would influence others; the professor considers this class typical of other classes; $120 < 10\%$ of all students in the MBA program; 27% of $120 = 32.4$—use 32 graduates; $np = 36 > 10$ and $nq = 84 > 10$; $z = -0.717$, $P = 0.4733$. Since the P-value is > 0.05, we fail to reject the null hypothesis. There is little evidence that the rate at which these students are exposed to unethical business practices is different from that reported in the study.

67. a) $z = 11.8$

b) $11.8 > 3.29$, if we assume a two-sided 0.1% significance level.

c) We conclude that the percent of U.S. adults giving "quite a lot" of thought to the upcoming election is significantly different in 2008 than it was in 2004.

69. a) The regulators decide that the shop is not meeting standards when it actually is.

b) The regulators certify the shop when it is not meeting the standards.

c) Type I

d) Type II

71. a) The probability of detecting that the shop is not meeting standards when they are not.

b) 40 cars produces higher power because n is larger

c) 10%; more chance to reject H_0.

d) A lot; larger problems are easier to detect.

73. a) One-tailed; we are testing to see if a decrease in the dropout rate is associated with the software.

b) H_0: The dropout rate does not change following the use of the software ($p = 0.13$).

H_A: The dropout rate decreases following the use of the software ($p < 0.13$).

c) The professor buys the software but the dropout rate has not actually decreased.

d) The professor doesn't buy the software and the dropout rate has actually decreased.

e) The probability of buying the software when the dropout rate has actually decreased.

75. a) H_0: The dropout rate does not change following the use of the software ($p = 0.13$).

H_A: The dropout rate decreases following the use of the software ($p < 0.13$).

One student's decision about dropping out should not influence another's decision; this year's class of 203 students is probably representative of all statistics students; $203 < 10\%$ of all students; $np = (203)(0.13) = 26.39 > 10$ and $nq = (203)(0.87) = 176.61 > 10$; $z = -3.21$, $P = 0.0007$. Since the P-value is very low, we reject H_0. There is strong evidence that the dropout rate has dropped since use of the software program was implemented. As long as the professor feels confident that this class of statistics students is representative of all potential students, then he should buy the program.

b) The chance of observing 11 or fewer dropouts in a class of 203 is only 0.07% if the dropout rate is really 13%.

77. **Independence assumption:** We assume that these mutual funds were selected at random and that 35 funds are less than 10% of all value funds. **Nearly Normal condition:** A histogram shows a nearly normal distribution.

H_0: $\mu = 8$; H_A: $\mu > 8$; P-value $= 0.201$; fail to reject H_0. There is insufficient evidence that the mean 5-year return is greater than 8% for value funds.

79. Given this confidence interval, we cannot reject the null hypothesis of a mean $200 collection using $\alpha = 0.05$. However, the confidence interval suggests that there may be a large upside potential. The collection agency may be collecting as much as $250 per customer on average, or as little as $190 on average. If the possibility of collecting $250 on average is of interest to them, they may want to collect more data.

81. Yes, there is a large ($50) upside potential. The larger trial will likely narrow the confidence interval and make the decision clearer.

Tables and Selected Formulas

Table D

Critical Values d_L and d_U of the Durbin-Watson Statistic (Critical Values are One-Sided)[a]

$\alpha = 0.05$

n	$k=1$ d_L	d_U	$k=2$ d_L	d_U	$k=3$ d_L	d_U	$k=4$ d_L	d_U	$k=5$ d_L	d_U
15	1.08	1.36	.95	1.54	.82	1.75	.69	1.97	.56	2.21
16	1.10	1.37	.98	1.54	.86	1.73	.74	1.93	.62	2.15
17	1.13	1.38	1.02	1.54	.90	1.71	.78	1.90	.67	2.10
18	1.16	1.39	1.05	1.53	.93	1.69	.82	1.87	.71	2.06
19	1.18	1.40	1.08	1.53	.97	1.68	.86	1.85	.75	2.02
20	1.20	1.41	1.10	1.54	1.00	1.68	.90	1.83	.79	1.99
21	1.22	1.42	1.13	1.54	1.03	1.67	.93	1.81	.83	1.96
22	1.24	1.43	1.15	1.54	1.05	1.66	.96	1.80	.86	1.94
23	1.26	1.44	1.17	1.54	1.08	1.66	.99	1.79	.90	1.92
24	1.27	1.45	1.19	1.55	1.10	1.66	1.01	1.78	.93	1.90
25	1.29	1.45	1.21	1.55	1.12	1.66	1.04	1.77	.95	1.89
26	1.30	1.46	1.22	1.55	1.14	1.65	1.06	1.76	.98	1.88
27	1.32	1.47	1.24	1.56	1.16	1.65	1.08	1.76	1.01	1.86
28	1.33	1.48	1.26	1.56	1.18	1.65	1.10	1.75	1.03	1.85
29	1.34	1.48	1.27	1.56	1.20	1.65	1.12	1.74	1.05	1.84
30	1.35	1.49	1.28	1.57	1.21	1.65	1.14	1.74	1.07	1.83
31	1.36	1.50	1.30	1.57	1.23	1.65	1.16	1.74	1.09	1.83
32	1.37	1.50	1.31	1.57	1.24	1.65	1.18	1.73	1.11	1.82
33	1.38	1.51	1.32	1.58	1.26	1.65	1.19	1.73	1.13	1.81
34	1.39	1.51	1.33	1.58	1.27	1.65	1.21	1.73	1.15	1.81
35	1.40	1.52	1.34	1.58	1.28	1.65	1.22	1.73	1.16	1.80
36	1.41	1.52	1.35	1.59	1.29	1.65	1.24	1.73	1.18	1.80
37	1.42	1.53	1.36	1.59	1.31	1.66	1.25	1.72	1.19	1.80
38	1.43	1.54	1.37	1.59	1.32	1.66	1.26	1.72	1.21	1.79
39	1.43	1.54	1.38	1.60	1.33	1.66	1.27	1.72	1.22	1.79
40	1.44	1.54	1.39	1.60	1.34	1.66	1.29	1.72	1.23	1.79
45	1.48	1.57	1.43	1.62	1.38	1.67	1.34	1.72	1.29	1.78
50	1.50	1.59	1.46	1.63	1.42	1.67	1.38	1.72	1.34	1.77
55	1.53	1.60	1.49	1.64	1.45	1.68	1.41	1.72	1.38	1.77
60	1.55	1.62	1.51	1.65	1.48	1.69	1.44	1.73	1.41	1.77
65	1.57	1.63	1.54	1.66	1.50	1.70	1.47	1.73	1.44	1.77
70	1.58	1.64	1.55	1.67	1.52	1.70	1.49	1.74	1.46	1.77
75	1.60	1.65	1.57	1.68	1.54	1.71	1.51	1.74	1.49	1.77
80	1.61	1.66	1.59	1.69	1.56	1.72	1.53	1.74	1.51	1.77
85	1.62	1.67	1.60	1.70	1.57	1.72	1.55	1.75	1.52	1.77
90	1.63	1.68	1.61	1.70	1.59	1.73	1.57	1.75	1.54	1.78
95	1.64	1.69	1.62	1.71	1.60	1.73	1.58	1.75	1.56	1.78
100	1.65	1.69	1.63	1.72	1.61	1.74	1.59	1.76	1.57	1.78

$\alpha = 0.01$

n	$k=1$ d_L	d_U	$k=2$ d_L	d_U	$k=3$ d_L	d_U	$k=4$ d_L	d_U	$k=5$ d_L	d_U
15	.81	1.07	.70	1.25	.59	1.46	.49	1.70	.39	1.96
16	.84	1.09	.74	1.25	.63	1.44	.53	1.66	.44	1.90
17	.87	1.10	.77	1.25	.67	1.43	.57	1.63	.48	1.85
18	.90	1.12	.80	1.26	.71	1.42	.61	1.60	.52	1.80
19	.93	1.13	.83	1.26	.74	1.41	.65	1.58	.56	1.77
20	.95	1.15	.86	1.27	.77	1.41	.68	1.57	.60	1.74
21	.97	1.16	.89	1.27	.80	1.41	.72	1.55	.63	1.71
22	1.00	1.17	.91	1.28	.83	1.40	.75	1.54	.66	1.69
23	1.02	1.19	.94	1.29	.86	1.40	.77	1.53	.70	1.67
24	1.04	1.20	.96	1.30	.88	1.41	.80	1.53	.72	1.66
25	1.05	1.21	.98	1.30	.90	1.41	.83	1.52	.75	1.65
26	1.07	1.22	1.00	1.31	.93	1.41	.85	1.52	.78	1.64
27	1.09	1.23	1.02	1.32	.95	1.41	.88	1.51	.81	1.63
28	1.10	1.24	1.04	1.32	.97	1.41	.90	1.51	.83	1.62
29	1.12	1.25	1.05	1.33	.99	1.42	.92	1.51	.85	1.61
30	1.13	1.26	1.07	1.34	1.01	1.42	.94	1.51	.88	1.61
31	1.15	1.27	1.08	1.34	1.02	1.42	.96	1.51	.90	1.60
32	1.16	1.28	1.10	1.35	1.04	1.43	.98	1.51	.92	1.60
33	1.17	1.29	1.11	1.36	1.05	1.43	1.00	1.51	.94	1.59
34	1.18	1.30	1.13	1.36	1.07	1.43	1.01	1.51	.95	1.59
35	1.19	1.31	1.14	1.37	1.08	1.44	1.03	1.51	.97	1.59
36	1.21	1.32	1.15	1.38	1.10	1.44	1.04	1.51	.99	1.59
37	1.22	1.32	1.16	1.38	1.11	1.45	1.06	1.51	1.00	1.59
38	1.23	1.33	1.18	1.39	1.12	1.45	1.07	1.52	1.02	1.58
39	1.24	1.34	1.19	1.39	1.14	1.45	1.09	1.52	1.03	1.58
40	1.25	1.34	1.20	1.40	1.15	1.46	1.10	1.52	1.05	1.58
45	1.29	1.38	1.24	1.42	1.20	1.48	1.16	1.53	1.11	1.58
50	1.32	1.40	1.28	1.45	1.24	1.49	1.20	1.54	1.16	1.59
55	1.36	1.43	1.32	1.47	1.28	1.51	1.25	1.55	1.21	1.59
60	1.38	1.45	1.35	1.48	1.32	1.52	1.28	1.56	1.25	1.60
65	1.41	1.47	1.38	1.50	1.35	1.53	1.31	1.57	1.28	1.61
70	1.43	1.49	1.40	1.52	1.37	1.55	1.34	1.58	1.31	1.61
75	1.45	1.50	1.42	1.53	1.39	1.56	1.37	1.59	1.34	1.62
80	1.47	1.52	1.44	1.54	1.42	1.57	1.39	1.60	1.36	1.62
85	1.48	1.53	1.46	1.55	1.43	1.58	1.41	1.60	1.39	1.63
90	1.50	1.54	1.47	1.56	1.45	1.59	1.43	1.61	1.41	1.64
95	1.51	1.55	1.49	1.57	1.47	1.60	1.45	1.62	1.42	1.64
100	1.52	1.56	1.50	1.58	1.48	1.60	1.46	1.63	1.44	1.65

[a] n = number of observations; k = number of independent variables.

Source: This table is reproduced from *Biometrika*, 41 (1951): 173 and 175, with the permission of the *Biometrika* Trustees.

From Appendix D of *Business Statistics*, Second Edition, Norean R. Sharpe, Richard D. De Veaux, Paul F. Velleman.

Table F

Numerator df

α = .01	1	2	3	4	5	6	7	8	9	10	11	12	13	14	15	16	17	18	19	20	21	22
1	4052.2	4999.3	5403.5	5624.3	5764.0	5859.0	5928.3	5981.0	6022.4	6055.9	6083.4	6106.7	6125.8	6143.0	6157.0	6170.0	6181.2	6191.4	6200.7	6208.7	6216.1	6223.1
2	98.50	99.00	99.16	99.25	99.30	99.33	99.36	99.38	99.39	99.40	99.41	99.42	99.42	99.43	99.43	99.44	99.44	99.44	99.45	99.45	99.45	99.46
3	34.12	30.82	29.46	28.71	28.24	27.91	27.67	27.49	27.34	27.23	27.13	27.05	26.98	26.92	26.87	26.83	26.79	26.75	26.72	26.69	26.66	26.64
4	21.20	18.00	16.69	15.98	15.52	15.21	14.98	14.80	14.66	14.55	14.45	14.37	14.31	14.25	14.20	14.15	14.11	14.08	14.05	14.02	13.99	13.97
5	16.26	13.27	12.06	11.39	10.97	10.67	10.46	10.29	10.16	10.05	9.96	9.89	9.82	9.77	9.72	9.68	9.64	9.61	9.58	9.55	9.53	9.51
6	13.75	10.92	9.78	9.15	8.75	8.47	8.26	8.10	7.98	7.87	7.79	7.72	7.66	7.60	7.56	7.52	7.48	7.45	7.42	7.40	7.37	7.35
7	12.25	9.55	8.45	7.85	7.46	7.19	6.99	6.84	6.72	6.62	6.54	6.47	6.41	6.36	6.31	6.28	6.24	6.21	6.18	6.16	6.13	6.11
8	11.26	8.65	7.59	7.01	6.63	6.37	6.18	6.03	5.91	5.81	5.73	5.67	5.61	5.56	5.52	5.48	5.44	5.41	5.38	5.36	5.34	5.32
9	10.56	8.02	6.99	6.42	6.06	5.80	5.61	5.47	5.35	5.26	5.18	5.11	5.05	5.01	4.96	4.92	4.89	4.86	4.83	4.81	4.79	4.77
10	10.04	7.56	6.55	5.99	5.64	5.39	5.20	5.06	4.94	4.85	4.77	4.71	4.65	4.60	4.56	4.52	4.49	4.46	4.43	4.41	4.38	4.36
11	9.65	7.21	6.22	5.67	5.32	5.07	4.89	4.74	4.63	4.54	4.46	4.40	4.34	4.29	4.25	4.21	4.18	4.15	4.12	4.10	4.08	4.06
12	9.33	6.93	5.95	5.41	5.06	4.82	4.64	4.50	4.39	4.30	4.22	4.16	4.10	4.05	4.01	3.97	3.94	3.91	3.88	3.86	3.84	3.82
13	9.07	6.70	5.74	5.21	4.86	4.62	4.44	4.30	4.19	4.10	4.02	3.96	3.91	3.86	3.82	3.78	3.75	3.72	3.69	3.66	3.64	3.62
14	8.86	6.51	5.56	5.04	4.69	4.46	4.28	4.14	4.03	3.94	3.86	3.80	3.75	3.70	3.66	3.62	3.59	3.56	3.53	3.51	3.48	3.46
15	8.68	6.36	5.42	4.89	4.56	4.32	4.14	4.00	3.89	3.80	3.73	3.67	3.61	3.56	3.52	3.49	3.45	3.42	3.40	3.37	3.35	3.33
16	8.53	6.23	5.29	4.77	4.44	4.20	4.03	3.89	3.78	3.69	3.62	3.55	3.50	3.45	3.41	3.37	3.34	3.31	3.28	3.26	3.24	3.22
17	8.40	6.11	5.19	4.67	4.34	4.10	3.93	3.79	3.68	3.59	3.52	3.46	3.40	3.35	3.31	3.27	3.24	3.21	3.19	3.16	3.14	3.12
18	8.29	6.01	5.09	4.58	4.25	4.01	3.84	3.71	3.60	3.51	3.43	3.37	3.32	3.27	3.23	3.19	3.16	3.13	3.10	3.08	3.05	3.03
19	8.18	5.93	5.01	4.50	4.17	3.94	3.77	3.63	3.52	3.43	3.36	3.30	3.24	3.19	3.15	3.12	3.08	3.05	3.03	3.00	2.98	2.96
20	8.10	5.85	4.94	4.43	4.10	3.87	3.70	3.56	3.46	3.37	3.29	3.23	3.18	3.13	3.09	3.05	3.02	2.99	2.96	2.94	2.92	2.90
21	8.02	5.78	4.87	4.37	4.04	3.81	3.64	3.51	3.40	3.31	3.24	3.17	3.12	3.07	3.03	2.99	2.96	2.93	2.90	2.88	2.86	2.84
22	7.95	5.72	4.82	4.31	3.99	3.76	3.59	3.45	3.35	3.26	3.18	3.12	3.07	3.02	2.98	2.94	2.91	2.88	2.85	2.83	2.81	2.78
23	7.88	5.66	4.76	4.26	3.94	3.71	3.54	3.41	3.30	3.21	3.14	3.07	3.02	2.97	2.93	2.89	2.86	2.83	2.80	2.78	2.76	2.74
24	7.82	5.61	4.72	4.22	3.90	3.67	3.50	3.36	3.26	3.17	3.09	3.03	2.98	2.93	2.89	2.85	2.82	2.79	2.76	2.74	2.72	2.70
25	7.77	5.57	4.68	4.18	3.85	3.63	3.46	3.32	3.22	3.13	3.06	2.99	2.94	2.89	2.85	2.81	2.78	2.75	2.72	2.70	2.68	2.66
26	7.72	5.53	4.64	4.14	3.82	3.59	3.42	3.29	3.18	3.09	3.02	2.96	2.90	2.86	2.81	2.78	2.75	2.72	2.69	2.66	2.64	2.62
27	7.68	5.49	4.60	4.11	3.78	3.56	3.39	3.26	3.15	3.06	2.99	2.93	2.87	2.82	2.78	2.75	2.71	2.68	2.66	2.63	2.61	2.59
28	7.64	5.45	4.57	4.07	3.75	3.53	3.36	3.23	3.12	3.03	2.96	2.90	2.84	2.79	2.75	2.72	2.68	2.65	2.63	2.60	2.58	2.56
29	7.60	5.42	4.54	4.04	3.73	3.50	3.33	3.20	3.09	3.00	2.93	2.87	2.81	2.77	2.73	2.69	2.66	2.63	2.60	2.57	2.55	2.53
30	7.56	5.39	4.51	4.02	3.70	3.47	3.30	3.17	3.07	2.98	2.91	2.84	2.79	2.74	2.70	2.66	2.63	2.60	2.57	2.55	2.53	2.51
32	7.50	5.34	4.46	3.97	3.65	3.43	3.26	3.13	3.02	2.93	2.86	2.80	2.74	2.70	2.65	2.62	2.58	2.55	2.53	2.50	2.48	2.46
35	7.42	5.27	4.40	3.91	3.59	3.37	3.20	3.07	2.96	2.88	2.80	2.74	2.69	2.64	2.60	2.56	2.53	2.50	2.47	2.44	2.42	2.40
40	7.31	5.18	4.31	3.83	3.51	3.29	3.12	2.99	2.89	2.80	2.73	2.66	2.61	2.56	2.52	2.48	2.45	2.42	2.39	2.37	2.35	2.33
45	7.23	5.11	4.25	3.77	3.45	3.23	3.07	2.94	2.83	2.74	2.67	2.61	2.55	2.51	2.46	2.43	2.39	2.36	2.34	2.31	2.29	2.27
50	7.17	5.06	4.20	3.72	3.41	3.19	3.02	2.89	2.78	2.70	2.63	2.56	2.51	2.46	2.42	2.38	2.35	2.32	2.29	2.27	2.24	2.22
60	7.08	4.98	4.13	3.65	3.34	3.12	2.95	2.82	2.72	2.63	2.56	2.50	2.44	2.39	2.35	2.31	2.28	2.25	2.22	2.20	2.17	2.15
75	6.99	4.90	4.05	3.58	3.27	3.05	2.89	2.76	2.65	2.57	2.49	2.43	2.38	2.33	2.29	2.25	2.22	2.18	2.16	2.13	2.11	2.09
100	6.90	4.82	3.98	3.51	3.21	2.99	2.82	2.69	2.59	2.50	2.43	2.37	2.31	2.27	2.22	2.19	2.15	2.12	2.09	2.07	2.04	2.02
120	6.85	4.79	3.95	3.48	3.17	2.96	2.79	2.66	2.56	2.47	2.40	2.34	2.28	2.23	2.19	2.15	2.12	2.09	2.06	2.03	2.01	1.99
140	6.82	4.76	3.92	3.46	3.15	2.93	2.77	2.64	2.54	2.45	2.38	2.31	2.26	2.21	2.17	2.13	2.10	2.07	2.04	2.01	1.99	1.97
180	6.78	4.73	3.89	3.43	3.12	2.90	2.74	2.61	2.51	2.42	2.35	2.28	2.23	2.18	2.14	2.10	2.07	2.04	2.01	1.98	1.96	1.94
250	6.74	4.69	3.86	3.40	3.09	2.87	2.71	2.58	2.48	2.39	2.32	2.26	2.20	2.15	2.11	2.07	2.04	2.01	1.98	1.95	1.93	1.91
400	6.70	4.66	3.83	3.37	3.06	2.85	2.68	2.56	2.45	2.37	2.29	2.23	2.17	2.13	2.08	2.05	2.01	1.98	1.95	1.92	1.90	1.88
1000	6.66	4.63	3.80	3.34	3.04	2.82	2.66	2.53	2.43	2.34	2.27	2.20	2.15	2.10	2.06	2.02	1.98	1.95	1.92	1.90	1.87	1.85

Denominator df

Table F (cont.)

Numerator df

$\alpha = .01$	23	24	25	26	27	28	29	30	32	35	40	45	50	60	75	100	120	140	180	250	400	1000
1	6228.7	6234.3	6239.9	6244.5	6249.2	6252.9	6257.1	6260.4	6266.9	6275.3	6286.4	6295.7	6302.3	6313.0	6323.7	6333.9	6339.5	6343.2	6347.9	6353.5	6358.1	6362.8
2	99.46	99.46	99.46	99.46	99.46	99.46	99.46	99.47	99.47	99.47	99.48	99.48	99.48	99.48	99.48	99.49	99.49	99.49	99.49	99.50	99.50	99.50
3	26.62	26.60	26.58	26.56	26.55	26.53	26.52	26.50	26.48	26.45	26.41	26.38	26.35	26.32	26.28	26.24	26.22	26.21	26.19	26.17	26.15	26.14
4	13.95	13.93	13.91	13.89	13.88	13.86	13.85	13.84	13.81	13.79	13.75	13.71	13.69	13.65	13.61	13.58	13.56	13.54	13.53	13.51	13.49	13.47
5	9.49	9.47	9.45	9.43	9.42	9.40	9.39	9.38	9.36	9.33	9.29	9.26	9.24	9.20	9.17	9.13	9.11	9.10	9.08	9.06	9.05	9.03
6	7.33	7.31	7.30	7.28	7.27	7.25	7.24	7.23	7.21	7.18	7.14	7.11	7.09	7.06	7.02	6.99	6.97	6.96	6.94	6.92	6.91	6.89
7	6.09	6.07	6.06	6.04	6.03	6.02	6.00	5.99	5.97	5.94	5.91	5.88	5.86	5.82	5.79	5.75	5.74	5.72	5.71	5.69	5.68	5.66
8	5.30	5.28	5.26	5.25	5.23	5.22	5.21	5.20	5.18	5.15	5.12	5.09	5.07	5.03	5.00	4.96	4.95	4.93	4.92	4.90	4.89	4.87
9	4.75	4.73	4.71	4.70	4.68	4.67	4.66	4.65	4.63	4.60	4.57	4.54	4.52	4.48	4.45	4.41	4.40	4.39	4.37	4.35	4.34	4.32
10	4.34	4.33	4.31	4.30	4.28	4.27	4.26	4.25	4.23	4.20	4.17	4.14	4.12	4.08	4.05	4.01	4.00	3.98	3.97	3.95	3.94	3.92
11	4.04	4.02	4.01	3.99	3.98	3.96	3.95	3.94	3.92	3.89	3.86	3.83	3.81	3.78	3.74	3.71	3.69	3.68	3.66	3.64	3.63	3.61
12	3.80	3.78	3.76	3.75	3.74	3.72	3.71	3.70	3.68	3.65	3.62	3.59	3.57	3.54	3.50	3.47	3.45	3.44	3.42	3.40	3.39	3.37
13	3.60	3.59	3.57	3.56	3.54	3.53	3.52	3.51	3.49	3.46	3.43	3.40	3.38	3.34	3.31	3.27	3.25	3.24	3.23	3.21	3.19	3.18
14	3.44	3.43	3.41	3.40	3.38	3.37	3.36	3.35	3.33	3.30	3.27	3.24	3.22	3.18	3.15	3.11	3.09	3.08	3.06	3.05	3.03	3.02
15	3.31	3.29	3.28	3.26	3.25	3.24	3.23	3.21	3.19	3.17	3.13	3.10	3.08	3.05	3.01	2.98	2.96	2.95	2.93	2.91	2.90	2.88
16	3.20	3.18	3.16	3.15	3.14	3.12	3.11	3.10	3.08	3.05	3.02	2.99	2.97	2.93	2.90	2.86	2.84	2.83	2.81	2.80	2.78	2.76
17	3.10	3.08	3.07	3.05	3.04	3.03	3.01	3.00	2.98	2.96	2.92	2.89	2.87	2.83	2.80	2.76	2.75	2.73	2.72	2.70	2.68	2.66
18	3.02	3.00	2.98	2.97	2.95	2.94	2.93	2.92	2.90	2.87	2.84	2.81	2.78	2.75	2.71	2.68	2.66	2.65	2.63	2.61	2.59	2.58
19	2.94	2.92	2.91	2.89	2.88	2.87	2.86	2.84	2.82	2.80	2.76	2.73	2.71	2.67	2.64	2.60	2.58	2.57	2.55	2.54	2.52	2.50
20	2.88	2.86	2.84	2.83	2.81	2.80	2.79	2.78	2.76	2.73	2.69	2.67	2.64	2.61	2.57	2.54	2.52	2.50	2.49	2.47	2.45	2.43
21	2.82	2.80	2.79	2.77	2.76	2.74	2.73	2.72	2.70	2.67	2.64	2.61	2.58	2.55	2.51	2.48	2.46	2.44	2.43	2.41	2.39	2.37
22	2.77	2.75	2.73	2.72	2.70	2.69	2.68	2.67	2.65	2.62	2.58	2.55	2.53	2.50	2.46	2.42	2.40	2.39	2.37	2.35	2.34	2.32
23	2.72	2.70	2.69	2.67	2.66	2.64	2.63	2.62	2.60	2.57	2.54	2.51	2.48	2.45	2.41	2.37	2.35	2.34	2.32	2.30	2.29	2.27
24	2.68	2.66	2.64	2.63	2.61	2.60	2.59	2.58	2.56	2.53	2.49	2.46	2.44	2.40	2.37	2.33	2.31	2.30	2.28	2.26	2.24	2.22
25	2.64	2.62	2.60	2.59	2.58	2.56	2.55	2.54	2.52	2.49	2.45	2.42	2.40	2.36	2.33	2.29	2.27	2.26	2.24	2.22	2.20	2.18
26	2.60	2.58	2.57	2.55	2.54	2.53	2.51	2.50	2.48	2.45	2.42	2.39	2.36	2.33	2.29	2.25	2.23	2.22	2.20	2.18	2.16	2.14
27	2.57	2.55	2.54	2.52	2.51	2.49	2.48	2.47	2.45	2.42	2.38	2.35	2.33	2.29	2.26	2.22	2.20	2.18	2.17	2.15	2.13	2.11
28	2.54	2.52	2.51	2.49	2.48	2.46	2.45	2.44	2.42	2.39	2.35	2.32	2.30	2.26	2.23	2.19	2.17	2.15	2.13	2.11	2.10	2.08
29	2.51	2.49	2.48	2.46	2.45	2.44	2.42	2.41	2.39	2.36	2.33	2.30	2.27	2.23	2.20	2.16	2.14	2.12	2.11	2.08	2.07	2.05
30	2.49	2.47	2.45	2.44	2.42	2.41	2.40	2.39	2.36	2.34	2.30	2.27	2.25	2.21	2.17	2.13	2.11	2.10	2.08	2.06	2.04	2.02
32	2.44	2.42	2.41	2.39	2.38	2.36	2.35	2.34	2.32	2.29	2.25	2.22	2.20	2.16	2.12	2.08	2.06	2.05	2.03	2.01	1.99	1.97
35	2.38	2.36	2.35	2.33	2.32	2.30	2.29	2.28	2.26	2.23	2.19	2.16	2.14	2.10	2.06	2.02	2.00	1.98	1.96	1.94	1.92	1.90
40	2.31	2.29	2.27	2.26	2.24	2.23	2.22	2.20	2.18	2.15	2.11	2.08	2.06	2.02	1.98	1.94	1.92	1.90	1.88	1.86	1.84	1.82
45	2.25	2.23	2.21	2.20	2.18	2.17	2.16	2.14	2.12	2.09	2.05	2.02	2.00	1.96	1.92	1.88	1.85	1.84	1.82	1.79	1.77	1.75
50	2.20	2.18	2.17	2.15	2.14	2.12	2.11	2.10	2.08	2.05	2.01	1.97	1.95	1.91	1.87	1.82	1.80	1.79	1.76	1.74	1.72	1.70
60	2.13	2.12	2.10	2.08	2.07	2.05	2.04	2.03	2.01	1.98	1.94	1.90	1.88	1.84	1.79	1.75	1.73	1.71	1.69	1.66	1.64	1.62
75	2.07	2.05	2.03	2.02	2.00	1.99	1.97	1.96	1.94	1.91	1.87	1.83	1.81	1.76	1.72	1.67	1.65	1.63	1.61	1.58	1.56	1.53
100	2.00	1.98	1.97	1.95	1.93	1.92	1.91	1.89	1.87	1.84	1.80	1.76	1.74	1.69	1.65	1.60	1.57	1.55	1.53	1.50	1.47	1.45
120	1.97	1.95	1.93	1.92	1.90	1.89	1.87	1.86	1.84	1.81	1.76	1.73	1.70	1.66	1.61	1.56	1.53	1.51	1.49	1.46	1.43	1.40
140	1.95	1.93	1.91	1.89	1.88	1.86	1.85	1.84	1.81	1.78	1.74	1.70	1.67	1.63	1.58	1.53	1.50	1.48	1.46	1.43	1.40	1.37
180	1.92	1.90	1.88	1.86	1.85	1.83	1.82	1.81	1.78	1.75	1.71	1.67	1.64	1.60	1.55	1.49	1.47	1.45	1.42	1.39	1.35	1.32
250	1.89	1.87	1.85	1.83	1.82	1.80	1.79	1.77	1.75	1.72	1.67	1.64	1.61	1.56	1.51	1.46	1.43	1.41	1.38	1.34	1.31	1.27
400	1.86	1.84	1.82	1.80	1.79	1.77	1.76	1.75	1.72	1.69	1.64	1.61	1.58	1.53	1.48	1.42	1.39	1.37	1.33	1.30	1.26	1.22
1000	1.83	1.81	1.79	1.77	1.76	1.74	1.73	1.72	1.69	1.66	1.61	1.58	1.54	1.50	1.44	1.38	1.35	1.33	1.29	1.25	1.21	1.16

Denominator df

Table F (cont.)

Numerator df

$\alpha = .05$	1	2	3	4	5	6	7	8	9	10	11	12	13	14	15	16	17	18	19	20	21	22
1	161.4	199.5	215.7	224.6	230.2	234.0	236.8	238.9	240.5	241.9	243.0	243.9	244.7	245.4	245.9	246.5	246.9	247.3	247.7	248.0	248.3	248.6
2	18.51	19.00	19.16	19.25	19.30	19.33	19.35	19.37	19.38	19.40	19.40	19.41	19.42	19.42	19.43	19.43	19.44	19.44	19.44	19.45	19.45	19.45
3	10.13	9.55	9.28	9.12	9.01	8.94	8.89	8.85	8.81	8.79	8.76	8.74	8.73	8.71	8.70	8.69	8.68	8.67	8.67	8.66	8.65	8.65
4	7.71	6.94	6.59	6.39	6.26	6.16	6.09	6.04	6.00	5.96	5.94	5.91	5.89	5.87	5.86	5.84	5.83	5.82	5.81	5.80	5.79	5.79
5	6.61	5.79	5.41	5.19	5.05	4.95	4.88	4.82	4.77	4.74	4.70	4.68	4.66	4.64	4.62	4.60	4.59	4.58	4.57	4.56	4.55	4.54
6	5.99	5.14	4.76	4.53	4.39	4.28	4.21	4.15	4.10	4.06	4.03	4.00	3.98	3.96	3.94	3.92	3.91	3.90	3.88	3.87	3.86	3.86
7	5.59	4.74	4.35	4.12	3.97	3.87	3.79	3.73	3.68	3.64	3.60	3.57	3.55	3.53	3.51	3.49	3.48	3.47	3.46	3.44	3.43	3.43
8	5.32	4.46	4.07	3.84	3.69	3.58	3.50	3.44	3.39	3.35	3.31	3.28	3.26	3.24	3.22	3.20	3.19	3.17	3.16	3.15	3.14	3.13
9	5.12	4.26	3.86	3.63	3.48	3.37	3.29	3.23	3.18	3.14	3.10	3.07	3.05	3.03	3.01	2.99	2.97	2.96	2.95	2.94	2.93	2.92
10	4.96	4.10	3.71	3.48	3.33	3.22	3.14	3.07	3.02	2.98	2.94	2.91	2.89	2.86	2.85	2.83	2.81	2.80	2.79	2.77	2.76	2.75
11	4.84	3.98	3.59	3.36	3.20	3.09	3.01	2.95	2.90	2.85	2.82	2.79	2.76	2.74	2.72	2.70	2.69	2.67	2.66	2.65	2.64	2.63
12	4.75	3.89	3.49	3.26	3.11	3.00	2.91	2.85	2.80	2.75	2.72	2.69	2.66	2.64	2.62	2.60	2.58	2.57	2.56	2.54	2.53	2.52
13	4.67	3.81	3.41	3.18	3.03	2.92	2.83	2.77	2.71	2.67	2.63	2.60	2.58	2.55	2.53	2.51	2.50	2.48	2.47	2.46	2.45	2.44
14	4.60	3.74	3.34	3.11	2.96	2.85	2.76	2.70	2.65	2.60	2.57	2.53	2.51	2.48	2.46	2.44	2.43	2.41	2.40	2.39	2.38	2.37
15	4.54	3.68	3.29	3.06	2.90	2.79	2.71	2.64	2.59	2.54	2.51	2.48	2.45	2.42	2.40	2.38	2.37	2.35	2.34	2.33	2.32	2.31
16	4.49	3.63	3.24	3.01	2.85	2.74	2.66	2.59	2.54	2.49	2.46	2.42	2.40	2.37	2.35	2.33	2.32	2.30	2.29	2.28	2.26	2.25
17	4.45	3.59	3.20	2.96	2.81	2.70	2.61	2.55	2.49	2.45	2.41	2.38	2.35	2.33	2.31	2.29	2.27	2.26	2.24	2.23	2.22	2.21
18	4.41	3.55	3.16	2.93	2.77	2.66	2.58	2.51	2.46	2.41	2.37	2.34	2.31	2.29	2.27	2.25	2.23	2.22	2.20	2.19	2.18	2.17
19	4.38	3.52	3.13	2.90	2.74	2.63	2.54	2.48	2.42	2.38	2.34	2.31	2.28	2.26	2.23	2.21	2.20	2.18	2.17	2.16	2.14	2.13
20	4.35	3.49	3.10	2.87	2.71	2.60	2.51	2.45	2.39	2.35	2.31	2.28	2.25	2.22	2.20	2.18	2.17	2.15	2.14	2.12	2.11	2.10
21	4.32	3.47	3.07	2.84	2.68	2.57	2.49	2.42	2.37	2.32	2.28	2.25	2.22	2.20	2.18	2.16	2.14	2.12	2.11	2.10	2.08	2.07
22	4.30	3.44	3.05	2.82	2.66	2.55	2.46	2.40	2.34	2.30	2.26	2.23	2.20	2.17	2.15	2.13	2.11	2.10	2.08	2.07	2.06	2.05
23	4.28	3.42	3.03	2.80	2.64	2.53	2.44	2.37	2.32	2.27	2.24	2.20	2.18	2.15	2.13	2.11	2.09	2.08	2.06	2.05	2.04	2.02
24	4.26	3.40	3.01	2.78	2.62	2.51	2.42	2.36	2.30	2.25	2.22	2.18	2.15	2.13	2.11	2.09	2.07	2.05	2.04	2.03	2.01	2.00
25	4.24	3.39	2.99	2.76	2.60	2.49	2.40	2.34	2.28	2.24	2.20	2.16	2.14	2.11	2.09	2.07	2.05	2.04	2.02	2.01	2.00	1.98
26	4.23	3.37	2.98	2.74	2.59	2.47	2.39	2.32	2.27	2.22	2.18	2.15	2.12	2.09	2.07	2.05	2.03	2.02	2.00	1.99	1.98	1.97
27	4.21	3.35	2.96	2.73	2.57	2.46	2.37	2.31	2.25	2.20	2.17	2.13	2.10	2.08	2.06	2.04	2.02	2.00	1.99	1.97	1.96	1.95
28	4.20	3.34	2.95	2.71	2.56	2.45	2.36	2.29	2.24	2.19	2.15	2.12	2.09	2.06	2.04	2.02	2.00	1.99	1.97	1.96	1.95	1.93
29	4.18	3.33	2.93	2.70	2.55	2.43	2.35	2.28	2.22	2.18	2.14	2.10	2.08	2.05	2.03	2.01	1.99	1.97	1.96	1.94	1.93	1.92
30	4.17	3.32	2.92	2.69	2.53	2.42	2.33	2.27	2.21	2.16	2.13	2.09	2.06	2.04	2.01	1.99	1.98	1.96	1.95	1.93	1.92	1.91
32	4.15	3.29	2.90	2.67	2.51	2.40	2.31	2.24	2.19	2.14	2.10	2.07	2.04	2.01	1.99	1.97	1.95	1.94	1.92	1.91	1.90	1.88
35	4.12	3.27	2.87	2.64	2.49	2.37	2.29	2.22	2.16	2.11	2.07	2.04	2.01	1.99	1.96	1.94	1.92	1.91	1.89	1.88	1.87	1.85
40	4.08	3.23	2.84	2.61	2.45	2.34	2.25	2.18	2.12	2.08	2.04	2.00	1.97	1.95	1.92	1.90	1.89	1.87	1.85	1.84	1.83	1.81
45	4.06	3.20	2.81	2.58	2.42	2.31	2.22	2.15	2.10	2.05	2.01	1.97	1.94	1.92	1.89	1.87	1.86	1.84	1.82	1.81	1.80	1.78
50	4.03	3.18	2.79	2.56	2.40	2.29	2.20	2.13	2.07	2.03	1.99	1.95	1.92	1.89	1.87	1.85	1.83	1.81	1.80	1.78	1.77	1.76
60	4.00	3.15	2.76	2.53	2.37	2.25	2.17	2.10	2.04	1.99	1.95	1.92	1.89	1.86	1.84	1.82	1.80	1.78	1.76	1.75	1.73	1.72
75	3.97	3.12	2.73	2.49	2.34	2.22	2.13	2.06	2.01	1.96	1.92	1.88	1.85	1.83	1.80	1.78	1.76	1.74	1.73	1.71	1.70	1.69
100	3.94	3.09	2.70	2.46	2.31	2.19	2.10	2.03	1.97	1.93	1.89	1.85	1.82	1.79	1.77	1.75	1.73	1.71	1.69	1.68	1.66	1.65
120	3.92	3.07	2.68	2.45	2.29	2.18	2.09	2.02	1.96	1.91	1.87	1.83	1.80	1.78	1.75	1.73	1.71	1.69	1.67	1.66	1.64	1.63
140	3.91	3.06	2.67	2.44	2.28	2.16	2.08	2.01	1.95	1.90	1.86	1.82	1.79	1.76	1.74	1.72	1.70	1.68	1.66	1.65	1.63	1.62
180	3.89	3.05	2.65	2.42	2.26	2.15	2.06	1.99	1.93	1.88	1.84	1.81	1.77	1.75	1.72	1.70	1.68	1.66	1.64	1.63	1.61	1.60
250	3.88	3.03	2.64	2.41	2.25	2.13	2.05	1.98	1.92	1.87	1.83	1.79	1.76	1.73	1.71	1.68	1.66	1.65	1.63	1.61	1.60	1.58
400	3.86	3.02	2.63	2.39	2.24	2.12	2.03	1.96	1.90	1.85	1.81	1.78	1.74	1.72	1.69	1.67	1.65	1.63	1.61	1.60	1.58	1.57
1000	3.85	3.00	2.61	2.38	2.22	2.11	2.02	1.95	1.89	1.84	1.80	1.76	1.73	1.70	1.68	1.65	1.63	1.61	1.60	1.58	1.57	1.55

Denominator df

Table F (cont.)

Numerator df

α = .05	23	24	25	26	27	28	29	30	32	35	40	45	50	60	75	100	120	140	180	250	400	1000
1	248.8	249.1	249.3	249.5	249.6	249.8	250.0	250.1	250.4	250.7	251.1	251.5	251.8	252.2	252.6	253.0	253.3	253.4	253.6	253.8	254.0	254.2
2	19.45	19.45	19.46	19.46	19.46	19.46	19.46	19.46	19.46	19.47	19.47	19.47	19.48	19.48	19.48	19.49	19.49	19.49	19.49	19.49	19.49	19.49
3	8.64	8.64	8.63	8.63	8.63	8.62	8.62	8.62	8.61	8.60	8.59	8.59	8.58	8.57	8.56	8.55	8.55	8.55	8.54	8.54	8.53	8.53
4	5.78	5.77	5.77	5.76	5.76	5.75	5.75	5.75	5.74	5.73	5.72	5.71	5.70	5.69	5.68	5.66	5.66	5.65	5.65	5.64	5.64	5.63
5	4.53	4.53	4.52	4.52	4.51	4.50	4.50	4.50	4.49	4.48	4.46	4.45	4.44	4.43	4.42	4.41	4.40	4.39	4.39	4.38	4.38	4.37
6	3.85	3.84	3.83	3.83	3.82	3.82	3.81	3.81	3.80	3.79	3.77	3.76	3.75	3.74	3.73	3.71	3.70	3.70	3.69	3.69	3.68	3.67
7	3.42	3.41	3.40	3.40	3.39	3.39	3.38	3.38	3.37	3.36	3.34	3.33	3.32	3.30	3.29	3.27	3.27	3.26	3.25	3.25	3.24	3.23
8	3.12	3.12	3.11	3.10	3.10	3.09	3.08	3.08	3.07	3.06	3.04	3.03	3.02	3.01	2.99	2.97	2.97	2.96	2.95	2.95	2.94	2.93
9	2.91	2.90	2.89	2.89	2.88	2.87	2.87	2.86	2.85	2.84	2.83	2.81	2.80	2.79	2.77	2.76	2.75	2.74	2.73	2.73	2.72	2.71
10	2.75	2.74	2.73	2.72	2.72	2.71	2.70	2.70	2.69	2.68	2.66	2.65	2.64	2.62	2.60	2.59	2.58	2.57	2.57	2.56	2.55	2.54
11	2.62	2.61	2.60	2.59	2.59	2.58	2.58	2.57	2.56	2.55	2.53	2.52	2.51	2.49	2.47	2.46	2.45	2.44	2.43	2.43	2.42	2.41
12	2.51	2.51	2.50	2.49	2.48	2.48	2.47	2.47	2.46	2.44	2.43	2.41	2.40	2.38	2.37	2.35	2.34	2.33	2.33	2.32	2.31	2.30
13	2.43	2.42	2.41	2.41	2.40	2.39	2.39	2.38	2.37	2.36	2.34	2.33	2.31	2.30	2.28	2.26	2.25	2.25	2.24	2.23	2.22	2.21
14	2.36	2.35	2.34	2.33	2.33	2.32	2.31	2.31	2.30	2.28	2.27	2.25	2.24	2.22	2.21	2.19	2.18	2.17	2.16	2.15	2.15	2.14
15	2.30	2.29	2.28	2.27	2.27	2.26	2.25	2.25	2.24	2.22	2.20	2.19	2.18	2.16	2.14	2.12	2.11	2.11	2.10	2.09	2.08	2.07
16	2.24	2.24	2.23	2.22	2.21	2.21	2.20	2.19	2.18	2.17	2.15	2.14	2.12	2.11	2.09	2.07	2.06	2.05	2.04	2.03	2.02	2.02
17	2.20	2.19	2.18	2.17	2.17	2.16	2.15	2.15	2.14	2.12	2.10	2.09	2.08	2.06	2.04	2.02	2.01	2.00	1.99	1.98	1.98	1.97
18	2.16	2.15	2.14	2.13	2.13	2.12	2.11	2.11	2.10	2.08	2.06	2.05	2.04	2.02	2.00	1.98	1.97	1.96	1.95	1.94	1.93	1.92
19	2.12	2.11	2.11	2.10	2.09	2.08	2.08	2.07	2.06	2.05	2.03	2.01	2.00	1.98	1.96	1.94	1.93	1.92	1.91	1.90	1.89	1.88
20	2.09	2.08	2.07	2.07	2.06	2.05	2.05	2.04	2.03	2.01	1.99	1.98	1.97	1.95	1.93	1.91	1.90	1.89	1.88	1.87	1.86	1.85
21	2.06	2.05	2.05	2.04	2.03	2.02	2.02	2.01	2.00	1.98	1.96	1.95	1.94	1.92	1.90	1.88	1.87	1.86	1.85	1.84	1.83	1.82
22	2.04	2.03	2.02	2.01	2.00	2.00	1.99	1.98	1.97	1.96	1.94	1.92	1.91	1.89	1.87	1.85	1.84	1.83	1.82	1.81	1.80	1.79
23	2.01	2.01	2.00	1.99	1.98	1.97	1.97	1.96	1.95	1.93	1.91	1.90	1.88	1.86	1.84	1.82	1.81	1.81	1.79	1.78	1.77	1.76
24	1.99	1.98	1.97	1.97	1.96	1.95	1.95	1.94	1.93	1.91	1.89	1.88	1.86	1.84	1.82	1.80	1.79	1.78	1.77	1.76	1.75	1.74
25	1.97	1.96	1.96	1.95	1.94	1.93	1.93	1.92	1.91	1.89	1.87	1.86	1.84	1.82	1.80	1.78	1.77	1.76	1.75	1.74	1.73	1.72
26	1.96	1.95	1.94	1.93	1.92	1.91	1.91	1.90	1.89	1.87	1.85	1.84	1.82	1.80	1.78	1.76	1.75	1.74	1.73	1.72	1.71	1.70
27	1.94	1.93	1.92	1.91	1.90	1.90	1.89	1.88	1.87	1.86	1.84	1.82	1.81	1.79	1.76	1.74	1.73	1.72	1.71	1.70	1.69	1.68
28	1.92	1.91	1.91	1.90	1.89	1.88	1.88	1.87	1.86	1.84	1.82	1.80	1.79	1.77	1.75	1.73	1.71	1.71	1.69	1.68	1.67	1.66
29	1.91	1.90	1.89	1.88	1.88	1.87	1.86	1.85	1.84	1.83	1.81	1.79	1.77	1.75	1.73	1.71	1.70	1.69	1.68	1.67	1.66	1.65
30	1.90	1.89	1.88	1.87	1.86	1.85	1.85	1.84	1.83	1.81	1.79	1.77	1.76	1.74	1.72	1.70	1.68	1.68	1.66	1.65	1.64	1.63
32	1.87	1.86	1.85	1.85	1.84	1.83	1.82	1.82	1.80	1.79	1.77	1.75	1.74	1.71	1.69	1.67	1.66	1.65	1.64	1.63	1.61	1.60
35	1.84	1.83	1.82	1.82	1.81	1.80	1.79	1.79	1.77	1.76	1.74	1.72	1.70	1.68	1.66	1.63	1.62	1.61	1.60	1.59	1.58	1.57
40	1.80	1.79	1.78	1.77	1.77	1.76	1.75	1.74	1.73	1.72	1.69	1.67	1.66	1.64	1.61	1.59	1.58	1.57	1.55	1.54	1.53	1.52
45	1.77	1.76	1.75	1.74	1.73	1.73	1.72	1.71	1.70	1.68	1.66	1.64	1.63	1.60	1.58	1.55	1.54	1.53	1.52	1.51	1.49	1.48
50	1.75	1.74	1.73	1.72	1.71	1.70	1.69	1.69	1.67	1.66	1.63	1.61	1.60	1.58	1.55	1.52	1.51	1.50	1.49	1.47	1.46	1.45
60	1.71	1.70	1.69	1.68	1.67	1.66	1.66	1.65	1.64	1.62	1.59	1.57	1.56	1.53	1.51	1.48	1.47	1.46	1.44	1.43	1.41	1.40
75	1.67	1.66	1.65	1.64	1.63	1.63	1.62	1.61	1.60	1.58	1.55	1.53	1.52	1.49	1.47	1.44	1.42	1.41	1.40	1.38	1.37	1.35
100	1.64	1.63	1.62	1.61	1.60	1.59	1.58	1.57	1.56	1.54	1.52	1.49	1.48	1.45	1.42	1.39	1.38	1.36	1.35	1.33	1.31	1.30
120	1.62	1.61	1.60	1.59	1.58	1.57	1.56	1.55	1.54	1.52	1.50	1.47	1.46	1.43	1.40	1.37	1.35	1.34	1.32	1.30	1.29	1.27
140	1.61	1.60	1.59	1.57	1.57	1.56	1.55	1.54	1.53	1.51	1.48	1.46	1.44	1.41	1.38	1.35	1.33	1.32	1.30	1.29	1.27	1.25
180	1.59	1.58	1.57	1.56	1.55	1.54	1.53	1.52	1.51	1.49	1.46	1.44	1.42	1.39	1.36	1.33	1.31	1.30	1.28	1.26	1.24	1.22
250	1.57	1.56	1.55	1.54	1.53	1.52	1.51	1.50	1.49	1.47	1.44	1.42	1.40	1.37	1.34	1.31	1.29	1.27	1.25	1.23	1.21	1.18
400	1.56	1.54	1.53	1.52	1.51	1.50	1.50	1.49	1.47	1.45	1.42	1.40	1.38	1.35	1.32	1.28	1.26	1.25	1.23	1.20	1.18	1.15
1000	1.54	1.53	1.52	1.51	1.50	1.49	1.48	1.47	1.46	1.43	1.41	1.38	1.36	1.33	1.30	1.26	1.24	1.22	1.20	1.17	1.14	1.11

Denominator df

Table F (cont.)

Numerator df

$\alpha = .1$	1	2	3	4	5	6	7	8	9	10	11	12	13	14	15	16	17	18	19	20	21	22
1	39.9	49.5	53.6	55.8	57.2	58.2	58.9	59.4	59.9	60.2	60.5	60.7	60.9	61.1	61.2	61.3	61.5	61.6	61.7	61.7	61.8	61.9
2	8.53	9.00	9.16	9.24	9.29	9.33	9.35	9.37	9.38	9.39	9.40	9.41	9.41	9.42	9.42	9.43	9.43	9.44	9.44	9.44	9.44	9.45
3	5.54	5.46	5.39	5.34	5.31	5.28	5.27	5.25	5.24	5.23	5.22	5.22	5.21	5.20	5.20	5.20	5.19	5.19	5.19	5.18	5.18	5.18
4	4.54	4.32	4.19	4.11	4.05	4.01	3.98	3.95	3.94	3.92	3.91	3.90	3.89	3.88	3.87	3.86	3.86	3.85	3.85	3.84	3.84	3.84
5	4.06	3.78	3.62	3.52	3.45	3.40	3.37	3.34	3.32	3.30	3.28	3.27	3.26	3.25	3.24	3.23	3.22	3.22	3.21	3.21	3.20	3.20
6	3.78	3.46	3.29	3.18	3.11	3.05	3.01	2.98	2.96	2.94	2.92	2.90	2.89	2.88	2.87	2.86	2.85	2.85	2.84	2.84	2.83	2.83
7	3.59	3.26	3.07	2.96	2.88	2.83	2.78	2.75	2.72	2.70	2.68	2.67	2.65	2.64	2.63	2.62	2.61	2.61	2.60	2.59	2.59	2.58
8	3.46	3.11	2.92	2.81	2.73	2.67	2.62	2.59	2.56	2.54	2.52	2.50	2.49	2.48	2.46	2.45	2.45	2.44	2.43	2.42	2.42	2.41
9	3.36	3.01	2.81	2.69	2.61	2.55	2.51	2.47	2.44	2.42	2.40	2.38	2.36	2.35	2.34	2.33	2.32	2.31	2.30	2.30	2.29	2.29
10	3.29	2.92	2.73	2.61	2.52	2.46	2.41	2.38	2.35	2.32	2.30	2.28	2.27	2.26	2.24	2.23	2.22	2.22	2.21	2.20	2.19	2.19
11	3.23	2.86	2.66	2.54	2.45	2.39	2.34	2.30	2.27	2.25	2.23	2.21	2.19	2.18	2.17	2.16	2.15	2.14	2.13	2.12	2.12	2.11
12	3.18	2.81	2.61	2.48	2.39	2.33	2.28	2.24	2.21	2.19	2.17	2.15	2.13	2.12	2.10	2.09	2.08	2.08	2.07	2.06	2.05	2.05
13	3.14	2.76	2.56	2.43	2.35	2.28	2.23	2.20	2.16	2.14	2.12	2.10	2.08	2.07	2.05	2.04	2.03	2.02	2.01	2.01	2.00	1.99
14	3.10	2.73	2.52	2.39	2.31	2.24	2.19	2.15	2.12	2.10	2.07	2.05	2.04	2.02	2.01	2.00	1.99	1.98	1.97	1.96	1.96	1.95
15	3.07	2.70	2.49	2.36	2.27	2.21	2.16	2.12	2.09	2.06	2.04	2.02	2.00	1.99	1.97	1.96	1.95	1.94	1.93	1.92	1.92	1.91
16	3.05	2.67	2.46	2.33	2.24	2.18	2.13	2.09	2.06	2.03	2.01	1.99	1.97	1.95	1.94	1.93	1.92	1.91	1.90	1.89	1.88	1.88
17	3.03	2.64	2.44	2.31	2.22	2.15	2.10	2.06	2.03	2.00	1.98	1.96	1.94	1.93	1.91	1.90	1.89	1.88	1.87	1.86	1.86	1.85
18	3.01	2.62	2.42	2.29	2.20	2.13	2.08	2.04	2.00	1.98	1.95	1.93	1.92	1.90	1.89	1.87	1.86	1.85	1.84	1.84	1.83	1.82
19	2.99	2.61	2.40	2.27	2.18	2.11	2.06	2.02	1.98	1.96	1.93	1.91	1.89	1.88	1.86	1.85	1.84	1.83	1.82	1.81	1.81	1.80
20	2.97	2.59	2.38	2.25	2.16	2.09	2.04	2.00	1.96	1.94	1.91	1.89	1.87	1.86	1.84	1.83	1.82	1.81	1.80	1.79	1.79	1.78
21	2.96	2.57	2.36	2.23	2.14	2.08	2.02	1.98	1.95	1.92	1.90	1.87	1.86	1.84	1.83	1.81	1.80	1.79	1.78	1.78	1.77	1.76
22	2.95	2.56	2.35	2.22	2.13	2.06	2.01	1.97	1.93	1.90	1.88	1.86	1.84	1.83	1.81	1.80	1.79	1.78	1.77	1.76	1.75	1.74
23	2.94	2.55	2.34	2.21	2.11	2.05	1.99	1.95	1.92	1.89	1.87	1.84	1.83	1.81	1.80	1.78	1.77	1.76	1.75	1.74	1.74	1.73
24	2.93	2.54	2.33	2.19	2.10	2.04	1.98	1.94	1.91	1.88	1.85	1.83	1.81	1.80	1.78	1.77	1.76	1.75	1.74	1.73	1.72	1.71
25	2.92	2.53	2.32	2.18	2.09	2.02	1.97	1.93	1.89	1.87	1.84	1.82	1.80	1.79	1.77	1.76	1.75	1.74	1.73	1.72	1.71	1.70
26	2.91	2.52	2.31	2.17	2.08	2.01	1.96	1.92	1.88	1.86	1.83	1.81	1.79	1.77	1.76	1.75	1.73	1.72	1.71	1.71	1.70	1.69
27	2.90	2.51	2.30	2.17	2.07	2.00	1.95	1.91	1.87	1.85	1.82	1.80	1.78	1.76	1.75	1.74	1.72	1.71	1.70	1.70	1.69	1.68
28	2.89	2.50	2.29	2.16	2.06	2.00	1.94	1.90	1.87	1.84	1.81	1.79	1.77	1.75	1.74	1.73	1.71	1.70	1.69	1.69	1.68	1.67
29	2.89	2.50	2.28	2.15	2.06	1.99	1.93	1.89	1.86	1.83	1.80	1.78	1.76	1.75	1.73	1.72	1.71	1.69	1.68	1.68	1.67	1.66
30	2.88	2.49	2.28	2.14	2.05	1.98	1.93	1.88	1.85	1.82	1.79	1.77	1.75	1.74	1.72	1.71	1.70	1.69	1.68	1.67	1.66	1.65
32	2.87	2.48	2.26	2.13	2.04	1.97	1.92	1.88	1.83	1.81	1.78	1.76	1.74	1.72	1.71	1.69	1.68	1.67	1.66	1.65	1.64	1.64
35	2.85	2.46	2.25	2.11	2.02	1.95	1.90	1.85	1.82	1.79	1.76	1.74	1.72	1.70	1.69	1.67	1.66	1.65	1.64	1.63	1.62	1.62
40	2.84	2.44	2.23	2.09	2.00	1.93	1.87	1.83	1.79	1.76	1.74	1.71	1.70	1.68	1.66	1.65	1.64	1.62	1.61	1.61	1.60	1.59
45	2.82	2.42	2.21	2.07	1.98	1.91	1.85	1.81	1.77	1.74	1.72	1.70	1.68	1.66	1.64	1.63	1.62	1.60	1.59	1.58	1.58	1.57
50	2.81	2.41	2.20	2.06	1.97	1.90	1.84	1.80	1.76	1.73	1.70	1.68	1.66	1.64	1.63	1.61	1.60	1.59	1.58	1.57	1.56	1.55
60	2.79	2.39	2.18	2.04	1.95	1.87	1.82	1.77	1.74	1.71	1.68	1.66	1.64	1.62	1.60	1.59	1.58	1.56	1.55	1.54	1.53	1.53
75	2.77	2.37	2.16	2.02	1.93	1.85	1.80	1.75	1.72	1.69	1.66	1.63	1.61	1.60	1.58	1.57	1.55	1.54	1.53	1.52	1.51	1.50
100	2.76	2.36	2.14	2.00	1.91	1.83	1.78	1.73	1.69	1.66	1.64	1.61	1.59	1.57	1.56	1.54	1.53	1.52	1.50	1.49	1.48	1.48
120	2.75	2.35	2.13	1.99	1.90	1.82	1.77	1.72	1.68	1.65	1.63	1.60	1.58	1.56	1.55	1.53	1.52	1.50	1.49	1.48	1.47	1.46
140	2.74	2.34	2.12	1.99	1.89	1.82	1.76	1.71	1.68	1.64	1.62	1.59	1.57	1.55	1.54	1.52	1.51	1.50	1.48	1.47	1.46	1.45
180	2.73	2.33	2.11	1.98	1.88	1.81	1.75	1.70	1.67	1.63	1.61	1.58	1.56	1.54	1.53	1.51	1.50	1.48	1.47	1.46	1.45	1.44
250	2.73	2.32	2.11	1.97	1.87	1.80	1.74	1.69	1.66	1.62	1.60	1.57	1.55	1.53	1.51	1.50	1.49	1.47	1.46	1.45	1.44	1.43
400	2.72	2.32	2.10	1.96	1.86	1.79	1.73	1.69	1.65	1.61	1.59	1.56	1.54	1.52	1.50	1.49	1.47	1.46	1.45	1.44	1.43	1.42
1000	2.71	2.31	2.09	1.95	1.85	1.78	1.72	1.68	1.64	1.61	1.58	1.55	1.53	1.51	1.49	1.48	1.46.	1.45	1.44	1.43	1.42	1.41

Denominator df

Table F (cont.)

Numerator df

Denominator df

α = .1	23	24	25	26	27	28	29	30	32	35	40	45	50	60	75	100	120	140	180	250	400	1000
1	61.9	62.0	62.1	62.1	62.1	62.2	62.2	62.3	62.3	62.4	62.5	62.6	62.7	62.8	62.9	63.0	63.1	63.1	63.1	63.2	63.2	63.3
2	9.45	9.45	9.45	9.45	9.45	9.46	9.46	9.46	9.46	9.46	9.47	9.47	9.47	9.47	9.48	9.48	9.48	9.48	9.49	9.49	9.49	9.49
3	5.18	5.18	5.17	5.17	5.17	5.17	5.17	5.17	5.17	5.16	5.16	5.16	5.15	5.15	5.15	5.14	5.14	5.14	5.14	5.14	5.14	5.1
4	3.83	3.83	3.83	3.83	3.82	3.82	3.82	3.82	3.81	3.81	3.80	3.80	3.80	3.79	3.78	3.78	3.78	3.77	3.77	3.77	3.77	3.76
5	3.19	3.19	3.19	3.18	3.18	3.18	3.18	3.17	3.17	3.16	3.16	3.15	3.15	3.14	3.13	3.13	3.12	3.12	3.12	3.11	3.11	3.11
6	2.82	2.82	2.81	2.81	2.81	2.81	2.80	2.80	2.80	2.79	2.78	2.77	2.77	2.76	2.75	2.75	2.74	2.74	2.74	2.73	2.73	2.72
7	2.58	2.58	2.57	2.57	2.56	2.56	2.56	2.56	2.55	2.54	2.54	2.53	2.52	2.51	2.51	2.50	2.49	2.49	2.49	2.48	2.48	2.47
8	2.41	2.40	2.40	2.40	2.39	2.39	2.39	2.38	2.38	2.37	2.36	2.35	2.35	2.34	2.33	2.32	2.32	2.31	2.31	2.30	2.30	2.30
9	2.28	2.28	2.27	2.27	2.26	2.26	2.26	2.25	2.25	2.24	2.23	2.22	2.22	2.21	2.20	2.19	2.18	2.18	2.18	2.17	2.17	2.16
10	2.18	2.18	2.17	2.17	2.17	2.16	2.16	2.16	2.15	2.14	2.13	2.12	2.12	2.11	2.10	2.09	2.08	2.08	2.07	2.07	2.06	2.06
11	2.11	2.10	2.10	2.09	2.09	2.08	2.08	2.08	2.07	2.06	2.05	2.04	2.04	2.03	2.02	2.01	2.00	2.00	1.99	1.99	1.98	1.98
12	2.04	2.04	2.03	2.03	2.02	2.02	2.01	2.01	2.01	2.00	1.99	1.98	1.97	1.96	1.95	1.94	1.93	1.93	1.92	1.92	1.91	1.91
13	1.99	1.98	1.98	1.97	1.97	1.96	1.96	1.96	1.95	1.94	1.93	1.92	1.92	1.90	1.89	1.88	1.88	1.87	1.87	1.86	1.86	1.85
14	1.94	1.94	1.93	1.93	1.92	1.92	1.92	1.91	1.91	1.90	1.89	1.88	1.87	1.86	1.85	1.83	1.83	1.82	1.82	1.81	1.81	1.80
15	1.90	1.90	1.89	1.89	1.88	1.88	1.88	1.87	1.87	1.86	1.85	1.84	1.83	1.82	1.80	1.79	1.79	1.78	1.78	1.77	1.76	1.76
16	1.87	1.87	1.86	1.86	1.85	1.85	1.84	1.84	1.83	1.82	1.81	1.80	1.79	1.78	1.77	1.76	1.75	1.75	1.74	1.73	1.73	1.72
17	1.84	1.84	1.83	1.83	1.82	1.82	1.81	1.81	1.80	1.79	1.78	1.77	1.76	1.75	1.74	1.73	1.72	1.71	1.71	1.70	1.70	1.69
18	1.82	1.81	1.80	1.80	1.80	1.79	1.79	1.78	1.78	1.77	1.75	1.74	1.74	1.72	1.71	1.70	1.69	1.69	1.68	1.67	1.67	1.66
19	1.79	1.79	1.78	1.78	1.77	1.77	1.76	1.76	1.75	1.74	1.73	1.72	1.71	1.70	1.69	1.67	1.67	1.66	1.65	1.65	1.64	1.64
20	1.77	1.77	1.76	1.76	1.75	1.75	1.74	1.74	1.73	1.72	1.71	1.70	1.69	1.68	1.66	1.65	1.64	1.64	1.63	1.62	1.62	1.61
21	1.75	1.75	1.74	1.74	1.73	1.73	1.72	1.72	1.71	1.70	1.69	1.68	1.67	1.66	1.64	1.63	1.62	1.62	1.61	1.60	1.60	1.59
22	1.74	1.73	1.73	1.72	1.72	1.71	1.71	1.70	1.69	1.68	1.67	1.66	1.65	1.64	1.63	1.61	1.60	1.60	1.59	1.59	1.58	1.57
23	1.72	1.72	1.71	1.70	1.70	1.69	1.69	1.69	1.68	1.67	1.66	1.64	1.64	1.62	1.61	1.59	1.59	1.58	1.57	1.57	1.56	1.55
24	1.71	1.70	1.70	1.69	1.69	1.68	1.68	1.67	1.66	1.65	1.64	1.63	1.62	1.61	1.59	1.58	1.57	1.57	1.56	1.55	1.54	1.54
25	1.70	1.69	1.68	1.68	1.67	1.67	1.66	1.66	1.65	1.64	1.63	1.62	1.61	1.59	1.58	1.56	1.56	1.55	1.54	1.54	1.53	1.52
26	1.68	1.68	1.67	1.67	1.66	1.66	1.65	1.65	1.64	1.63	1.61	1.60	1.59	1.58	1.57	1.55	1.54	1.54	1.53	1.52	1.52	1.51
27	1.67	1.67	1.66	1.65	1.65	1.64	1.64	1.64	1.63	1.62	1.60	1.59	1.58	1.57	1.55	1.54	1.53	1.53	1.52	1.51	1.50	1.50
28	1.66	1.66	1.65	1.64	1.64	1.63	1.63	1.63	1.62	1.61	1.59	1.58	1.57	1.56	1.54	1.53	1.52	1.51	1.51	1.50	1.49	1.48
29	1.65	1.65	1.64	1.64	1.63	1.62	1.62	1.62	1.61	1.60	1.58	1.57	1.56	1.55	1.53	1.52	1.51	1.50	1.50	1.49	1.48	1.47
30	1.64	1.64	1.63	1.63	1.62	1.62	1.61	1.61	1.60	1.59	1.57	1.56	1.55	1.54	1.52	1.51	1.50	1.49	1.49	1.48	1.47	1.46
32	1.63	1.62	1.62	1.61	1.60	1.60	1.59	1.59	1.58	1.57	1.56	1.54	1.53	1.52	1.50	1.49	1.48	1.47	1.46	1.46	1.45	1.44
35	1.61	1.60	1.60	1.59	1.58	1.58	1.57	1.57	1.56	1.55	1.53	1.52	1.51	1.50	1.48	1.47	1.46	1.45	1.44	1.43	1.43	1.42
40	1.58	1.57	1.57	1.56	1.56	1.55	1.55	1.54	1.53	1.52	1.51	1.49	1.48	1.47	1.45	1.43	1.42	1.42	1.41	1.40	1.39	1.38
45	1.56	1.55	1.55	1.54	1.53	1.53	1.52	1.52	1.51	1.50	1.48	1.47	1.46	1.44	1.43	1.41	1.40	1.39	1.38	1.37	1.37	1.36
50	1.54	1.54	1.53	1.52	1.52	1.51	1.51	1.50	1.49	1.48	1.46	1.45	1.44	1.42	1.41	1.39	1.38	1.37	1.36	1.35	1.34	1.33
60	1.52	1.51	1.50	1.50	1.49	1.49	1.48	1.48	1.47	1.45	1.44	1.42	1.41	1.40	1.38	1.36	1.35	1.34	1.33	1.32	1.31	1.30
75	1.49	1.49	1.48	1.47	1.47	1.46	1.45	1.45	1.44	1.43	1.41	1.40	1.38	1.37	1.35	1.33	1.32	1.31	1.30	1.29	1.27	1.26
100	1.47	1.46	1.45	1.45	1.44	1.43	1.43	1.42	1.41	1.40	1.38	1.37	1.35	1.34	1.32	1.29	1.28	1.27	1.26	1.25	1.24	1.22
120	1.46	1.45	1.44	1.43	1.43	1.42	1.41	1.41	1.40	1.39	1.37	1.35	1.34	1.32	1.30	1.28	1.26	1.26	1.24	1.23	1.22	1.20
140	1.45	1.44	1.43	1.42	1.42	1.41	1.41	1.40	1.39	1.38	1.36	1.34	1.33	1.31	1.29	1.26	1.25	1.24	1.23	1.22	1.20	1.19
180	1.43	1.43	1.42	1.41	1.40	1.40	1.39	1.39	1.38	1.36	1.34	1.33	1.32	1.29	1.27	1.25	1.23	1.22	1.21	1.20	1.18	1.16
250	1.42	1.41	1.41	1.40	1.39	1.39	1.38	1.37	1.36	1.35	1.33	1.31	1.30	1.28	1.26	1.23	1.22	1.21	1.19	1.18	1.16	1.14
400	1.41	1.40	1.39	1.39	1.38	1.37	1.37	1.36	1.35	1.34	1.32	1.30	1.29	1.26	1.24	1.21	1.20	1.19	1.17	1.16	1.14	1.12
1000	1.40	1.39	1.38	1.38	1.37	1.36	1.36	1.35	1.34	1.32	1.30	1.29	1.27	1.25	1.23	1.20	1.18	1.17	1.15	1.13	1.11	1.08

Table R

n	d_2	d_3	D_3	D_4
2	1.128	0.852	0	3.267
3	1.693	0.888	0	2.574
4	2.059	0.880	0	2.282
5	2.326	0.864	0	2.114
6	2.534	0.848	0	2.004
7	2.704	0.833	0.076	1.924
8	2.847	0.820	0.136	1.864
9	2.970	0.808	0.184	1.816
10	3.078	0.797	0.223	1.777
11	3.173	0.787	0.256	1.744
12	3.258	0.779	0.283	1.717
13	3.336	0.771	0.307	1.693
14	3.407	0.763	0.328	1.672
15	3.472	0.756	0.347	1.653
16	3.532	0.750	0.363	1.637
17	3.588	0.744	0.378	1.622
18	3.640	0.738	0.391	1.608
19	3.689	0.734	0.403	1.597
20	3.735	0.728	0.415	1.585
21	3.778	0.724	0.425	1.575
22	3.819	0.721	0.434	1.566
23	3.858	0.716	0.443	1.557
24	3.895	0.711	0.451	1.548
25	3.931	0.709	0.459	1.541

Two-tail probability	0.20	0.10	0.05	0.02	0.01	
One-tail probability	0.10	0.05	0.025	0.01	0.005	

	df						df
Table T							
Values of t_α	1	3.078	6.314	12.706	31.821	63.657	1
	2	1.886	2.920	4.303	6.965	9.925	2
	3	1.638	2.353	3.182	4.541	5.841	3
	4	1.533	2.132	2.776	3.747	4.604	4
	5	1.476	2.015	2.571	3.365	4.032	5
	6	1.440	1.943	2.447	3.143	3.707	6
	7	1.415	1.895	2.365	2.998	3.499	7
	8	1.397	1.860	2.306	2.896	3.355	8
	9	1.383	1.833	2.262	2.821	3.250	9
	10	1.372	1.812	2.228	2.764	3.169	10
	11	1.363	1.796	2.201	2.718	3.106	11
	12	1.356	1.782	2.179	2.681	3.055	12
	13	1.350	1.771	2.160	2.650	3.012	13
	14	1.345	1.761	2.145	2.624	2.977	14
	15	1.341	1.753	2.131	2.602	2.947	15
	16	1.337	1.746	2.120	2.583	2.921	16
	17	1.333	1.740	2.110	2.567	2.898	17
	18	1.330	1.734	2.101	2.552	2.878	18
	19	1.328	1.729	2.093	2.539	2.861	19
	20	1.325	1.725	2.086	2.528	2.845	20
	21	1.323	1.721	2.080	2.518	2.831	21
	22	1.321	1.717	2.074	2.508	2.819	22
	23	1.319	1.714	2.069	2.500	2.807	23
	24	1.318	1.711	2.064	2.492	2.797	24
	25	1.316	1.708	2.060	2.485	2.787	25
	26	1.315	1.706	2.056	2.479	2.779	26
	27	1.314	1.703	2.052	2.473	2.771	27
	28	1.313	1.701	2.048	2.467	2.763	28
	29	1.311	1.699	2.045	2.462	2.756	29
	30	1.310	1.697	2.042	2.457	2.750	30
	32	1.309	1.694	2.037	2.449	2.738	32
	35	1.306	1.690	2.030	2.438	2.725	35
	40	1.303	1.684	2.021	2.423	2.704	40
	45	1.301	1.679	2.014	2.412	2.690	45
	50	1.299	1.676	2.009	2.403	2.678	50
	60	1.296	1.671	2.000	2.390	2.660	60
	75	1.293	1.665	1.992	2.377	2.643	75
	100	1.290	1.660	1.984	2.364	2.626	100
	120	1.289	1.658	1.980	2.358	2.617	120
	140	1.288	1.656	1.977	2.353	2.611	140
	180	1.286	1.653	1.973	2.347	2.603	180
	250	1.285	1.651	1.969	2.341	2.596	250
	400	1.284	1.649	1.966	2.336	2.588	400
	1000	1.282	1.646	1.962	2.330	2.581	1000
	∞	1.282	1.645	1.960	2.326	2.576	∞
Confidence levels		80%	90%	95%	98%	99%	

Two tails

$-t_{\alpha/2}$　0　$t_{\alpha/2}$

One tail

0　t_α

Table W1
Critical Values of T_L and T_U for the Wilcoxon Rank Sum Test: Independent Samples

Test statistic is the rank sum associated with the smaller sample (if equal sample sizes, either rank sum can be used). Reject the null hypothesis at the indicated α level if the test statistic falls below the lower bound, T_L, or above the upper bound, T_U. For groups larger than 10, use the Normal approximation given in the text.

a. $\alpha = .025$ one-tailed; $\alpha = .05$ two-tailed

n_2 \ n_1	3		4		5		6		7		8		9		10	
	T_L	T_U	T_L	T_U	T_L	T_U	T_L	T_U	T_L	T_U	T_L	T_U	T_L	T_U	T_L	T_U
3	5	16	6	18	6	21	7	23	7	26	8	28	8	31	9	33
4	6	18	11	25	12	28	12	32	13	35	14	38	15	41	16	44
5	6	21	12	28	18	37	19	41	20	45	21	49	22	53	24	56
6	7	23	12	32	19	41	26	52	28	56	29	61	31	65	32	70
7	7	26	13	35	20	45	28	56	37	68	39	73	41	78	43	83
8	8	28	14	38	21	49	29	61	39	73	49	87	51	93	54	98
9	8	31	15	41	22	53	31	65	41	78	51	93	63	108	66	114
10	9	33	16	44	24	56	32	70	43	83	54	98	66	114	79	131

a. $\alpha = .05$ one-tailed; $\alpha = .10$ two-tailed

n_2 \ n_1	3		4		5		6		7		8		9		10	
	T_L	T_U	T_L	T_U	T_L	T_U	T_L	T_U	T_L	T_U	T_L	T_U	T_L	T_U	T_L	T_U
3	6	15	7	17	7	20	8	22	9	24	9	27	10	29	11	31
4	7	17	12	24	13	27	14	30	15	33	16	36	17	39	18	42
5	7	20	13	27	19	36	20	40	22	43	24	46	25	50	26	54
6	8	22	14	30	20	40	28	50	30	54	32	58	33	63	35	67
7	9	24	15	33	22	43	30	54	39	66	41	71	43	76	46	80
8	9	27	16	36	24	46	32	58	41	71	52	84	54	90	57	95
9	10	29	17	39	25	50	33	63	43	76	54	90	66	105	69	111
10	11	31	18	42	26	54	35	67	46	80	57	95	69	111	83	127

Table W2

Critical Values of T_0 in the Wilcoxon Paired Difference Signed-Rank Test. Reject the null hypothesis at the indicated α levels if the test statistic is larger than the corresponding critical value.

One-Tailed	Two-Tailed	$n = 5$	$n = 6$	$n = 7$	$n = 8$	$n = 9$	$n = 10$
$\alpha = .05$	$\alpha = .10$	1	2	4	6	8	11
$\alpha = .025$	$\alpha = .05$		1	2	4	6	8
$\alpha = .01$	$\alpha = .02$			0	2	3	5
$\alpha = .005$	$\alpha = .01$				0	2	3
		$n = 11$	$n = 12$	$n = 13$	$n = 14$	$n = 15$	$n = 16$
$\alpha = .05$	$\alpha = .10$	14	17	21	26	30	36
$\alpha = .025$	$\alpha = .05$	11	14	17	21	25	30
$\alpha = .01$	$\alpha = .02$	7	10	13	16	20	24
$\alpha = .005$	$\alpha = .01$	5	7	10	13	16	19
		$n = 17$	$n = 18$	$n = 19$	$n = 20$	$n = 21$	$n = 22$
$\alpha = .05$	$\alpha = .10$	41	47	54	60	68	75
$\alpha = .025$	$\alpha = .05$	35	40	46	52	59	66
$\alpha = .01$	$\alpha = .02$	28	33	38	43	49	56
$\alpha = .005$	$\alpha = .01$	23	28	32	37	43	49
		$n = 23$	$n = 24$	$n = 25$	$n = 26$	$n = 27$	$n = 28$
$\alpha = .05$	$\alpha = .10$	83	92	101	110	120	130
$\alpha = .025$	$\alpha = .05$	73	81	90	98	107	117
$\alpha = .01$	$\alpha = .02$	62	69	77	85	93	102
$\alpha = .005$	$\alpha = .01$	55	61	68	76	84	92
		$n = 29$	$n = 30$	$n = 31$	$n = 32$	$n = 33$	$n = 34$
$\alpha = .05$	$\alpha = .10$	141	152	163	175	188	201
$\alpha = .025$	$\alpha = .05$	127	137	148	159	171	183
$\alpha = .01$	$\alpha = .02$	111	120	130	141	151	162
$\alpha = .005$	$\alpha = .01$	100	109	118	128	138	149
		$n = 35$	$n = 36$	$n = 37$	$n = 38$	$n = 39$	
$\alpha = .05$	$\alpha = .10$	214	228	242	256	271	
$\alpha = .025$	$\alpha = .05$	195	208	222	235	250	
$\alpha = .01$	$\alpha = .02$	174	186	198	211	224	
$\alpha = .005$	$\alpha = .01$	160	171	183	195	208	
		$n = 40$	$n = 41$	$n = 42$	$n = 43$	$n = 44$	$n = 45$
$\alpha = .05$	$\alpha = .10$	287	303	319	336	353	371
$\alpha = .025$	$\alpha = .05$	264	279	295	311	327	344
$\alpha = .01$	$\alpha = .02$	238	252	267	281	297	313
$\alpha = .005$	$\alpha = .01$	221	234	248	262	277	292
		$n = 46$	$n = 47$	$n = 48$	$n = 49$	$n = 50$	
$\alpha = .05$	$\alpha = .10$	389	408	427	446	466	
$\alpha = .025$	$\alpha = .05$	361	379	397	415	434	
$\alpha = .01$	$\alpha = .02$	329	345	362	380	398	
$\alpha = .005$	$\alpha = .01$	307	323	339	356	373	

Source: From F. Wilcoxon and R. A. Wilcox, "Some Rapid Approximate Statistical Procedures," 1964. Copyright © 1964 by BASF Corporation.

Right-tail probability		0.10	0.05	0.025	0.01	0.005
Table X	df					
Values of χ^2_α	1	2.706	3.841	5.024	6.635	7.879
	2	4.605	5.991	7.378	9.210	10.597
	3	6.251	7.815	9.348	11.345	12.838
	4	7.779	9.488	11.143	13.277	14.860
	5	9.236	11.070	12.833	15.086	16.750
	6	10.645	12.592	14.449	16.812	18.548
	7	12.017	14.067	16.013	18.475	20.278
	8	13.362	15.507	17.535	20.090	21.955
	9	14.684	16.919	19.023	21.666	23.589
	10	15.987	18.307	20.483	23.209	25.188
	11	17.275	19.675	21.920	24.725	26.757
	12	18.549	21.026	23.337	26.217	28.300
	13	19.812	22.362	24.736	27.688	29.819
	14	21.064	23.685	26.119	29.141	31.319
	15	22.307	24.996	27.488	30.578	32.801
	16	23.542	26.296	28.845	32.000	34.267
	17	24.769	27.587	30.191	33.409	35.718
	18	25.989	28.869	31.526	34.805	37.156
	19	27.204	30.143	32.852	36.191	38.582
	20	28.412	31.410	34.170	37.566	39.997
	21	29.615	32.671	35.479	38.932	41.401
	22	30.813	33.924	36.781	40.290	42.796
	23	32.007	35.172	38.076	41.638	44.181
	24	33.196	36.415	39.364	42.980	45.559
	25	34.382	37.653	40.647	44.314	46.928
	26	35.563	38.885	41.923	45.642	48.290
	27	36.741	40.113	43.195	46.963	49.645
	28	37.916	41.337	44.461	48.278	50.994
	29	39.087	42.557	45.722	59.588	52.336
	30	40.256	43.773	46.979	50.892	53.672
	40	51.805	55.759	59.342	63.691	66.767
	50	63.167	67.505	71.420	76.154	79.490
	60	74.397	79.082	83.298	88.381	91.955
	70	85.527	90.531	95.023	100.424	104.213
	80	96.578	101.879	106.628	112.328	116.320
	90	107.565	113.145	118.135	124.115	128.296
	100	118.499	124.343	129.563	135.811	140.177

Table Z					SECOND DECIMAL PLACE IN Z						
Areas under the standard Normal curve	*0.09*	*0.08*	*0.07*	*0.06*	*0.05*	*0.04*	*0.03*	*0.02*	*0.01*	*0.00*	*z*
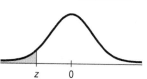										0.0000†	−3.9
	0.0001	0.0001	0.0001	0.0001	0.0001	0.0001	0.0001	0.0001	0.0001	0.0001	−3.8
	0.0001	0.0001	0.0001	0.0001	0.0001	0.0001	0.0001	0.0001	0.0001	0.0001	−3.7
	0.0001	0.0001	0.0001	0.0001	0.0001	0.0001	0.0001	0.0001	0.0002	0.0002	−3.6
	0.0002	0.0002	0.0002	0.0002	0.0002	0.0002	0.0002	0.0002	0.0002	0.0002	−3.5
	0.0002	0.0003	0.0003	0.0003	0.0003	0.0003	0.0003	0.0003	0.0003	0.0003	−3.4
	0.0003	0.0004	0.0004	0.0004	0.0004	0.0004	0.0004	0.0005	0.0005	0.0005	−3.3
	0.0005	0.0005	0.0005	0.0006	0.0006	0.0006	0.0006	0.0006	0.0007	0.0007	−3.2
	0.0007	0.0007	0.0008	0.0008	0.0008	0.0008	0.0009	0.0009	0.0009	0.0010	−3.1
	0.0010	0.0010	0.0011	0.0011	0.0011	0.0012	0.0012	0.0013	0.0013	0.0013	−3.0
	0.0014	0.0014	0.0015	0.0015	0.0016	0.0016	0.0017	0.0018	0.0018	0.0019	−2.9
	0.0019	0.0020	0.0021	0.0021	0.0022	0.0023	0.0023	0.0024	0.0025	0.0026	−2.8
	0.0026	0.0027	0.0028	0.0029	0.0030	0.0031	0.0032	0.0033	0.0034	0.0035	−2.7
	0.0036	0.0037	0.0038	0.0039	0.0040	0.0041	0.0043	0.0044	0.0045	0.0047	−2.6
	0.0048	0.0049	0.0051	0.0052	0.0054	0.0055	0.0057	0.0059	0.0060	0.0062	−2.5
	0.0064	0.0066	0.0068	0.0069	0.0071	0.0073	0.0075	0.0078	0.0080	0.0082	−2.4
	0.0084	0.0087	0.0089	0.0091	0.0094	0.0096	0.0099	0.0102	0.0104	0.0107	−2.3
	0.0110	0.0113	0.0116	0.0119	0.0122	0.0125	0.0129	0.0132	0.0136	0.0139	−2.2
	0.0143	0.0146	0.0150	0.0154	0.0158	0.0162	0.0166	0.0170	0.0174	0.0179	−2.1
	0.0183	0.0188	0.0192	0.0197	0.0202	0.0207	0.0212	0.0217	0.0222	0.0228	−2.0
	0.0233	0.0239	0.0244	0.0250	0.0256	0.0262	0.0268	0.0274	0.0281	0.0287	−1.9
	0.0294	0.0301	0.0307	0.0314	0.0322	0.0329	0.0336	0.0344	0.0351	0.0359	−1.8
	0.0367	0.0375	0.0384	0.0392	0.0401	0.0409	0.0418	0.0427	0.0436	0.0446	−1.7
	0.0455	0.0465	0.0475	0.0485	0.0495	0.0505	0.0516	0.0526	0.0537	0.0548	−1.6
	0.0559	0.0571	0.0582	0.0594	0.0606	0.0618	0.0630	0.0643	0.0655	0.0668	−1.5
	0.0681	0.0694	0.0708	0.0721	0.0735	0.0749	0.0764	0.0778	0.0793	0.0808	−1.4
	0.0823	0.0838	0.0853	0.0869	0.0885	0.0901	0.0918	0.0934	0.0951	0.0968	−1.3
	0.0985	0.1003	0.1020	0.1038	0.1056	0.1075	0.1093	0.1112	0.1131	0.1151	−1.2
	0.1170	0.1190	0.1210	0.1230	0.1251	0.1271	0.1292	0.1314	0.1335	0.1357	−1.1
	0.1379	0.1401	0.1423	0.1446	0.1469	0.1492	0.1515	0.1539	0.1562	0.1587	−1.0
	0.1611	0.1635	0.1660	0.1685	0.1711	0.1736	0.1762	0.1788	0.1814	0.1841	−0.9
	0.1867	0.1894	0.1922	0.1949	0.1977	0.2005	0.2033	0.2061	0.2090	0.2119	−0.8
	0.2148	0.2177	0.2206	0.2236	0.2266	0.2296	0.2327	0.2358	0.2389	0.2420	−0.7
	0.2451	0.2483	0.2514	0.2546	0.2578	0.2611	0.2643	0.2676	0.2709	0.2743	−0.6
	0.2776	0.2810	0.2843	0.2877	0.2912	0.2946	0.2981	0.3015	0.3050	0.3085	−0.5
	0.3121	0.3156	0.3192	0.3228	0.3264	0.3300	0.3336	0.3372	0.3409	0.3446	−0.4
	0.3483	0.3520	0.3557	0.3594	0.3632	0.3669	0.3707	0.3745	0.3783	0.3821	−0.3
	0.3859	0.3897	0.3936	0.3974	0.4013	0.4052	0.4090	0.4129	0.4168	0.4207	−0.2
	0.4247	0.4286	0.4325	0.4364	0.4404	0.4443	0.4483	0.4522	0.4562	0.4602	−0.1
	0.4641	0.4681	0.4721	0.4761	0.4801	0.4840	0.4880	0.4920	0.4960	0.5000	−0.0

† For $z \leq -3.90$ the areas are 0.0000 to four decimal places.

Table Z (cont.)

Areas under the standard Normal curve

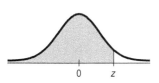

SECOND DECIMAL PLACE IN Z

z	0.00	0.01	0.02	0.03	0.04	0.05	0.06	0.07	0.08	0.09
0.0	0.5000	0.5040	0.5080	0.5120	0.5160	0.5199	0.5239	0.5279	0.5319	0.5359
0.1	0.5398	0.5438	0.5478	0.5517	0.5557	0.5596	0.5636	0.5675	0.5714	0.5753
0.2	0.5793	0.5832	0.5871	0.5910	0.5948	0.5987	0.6026	0.6064	0.6103	0.6141
0.3	0.6179	0.6217	0.6255	0.6293	0.6331	0.6368	0.6406	0.6443	0.6480	0.6517
0.4	0.6554	0.6591	0.6628	0.6664	0.6700	0.6736	0.6772	0.6808	0.6844	0.6879
0.5	0.6915	0.6950	0.6985	0.7019	0.7054	0.7088	0.7123	0.7157	0.7190	0.7224
0.6	0.7257	0.7291	0.7324	0.7357	0.7389	0.7422	0.7454	0.7486	0.7517	0.7549
0.7	0.7580	0.7611	0.7642	0.7673	0.7704	0.7734	0.7764	0.7794	0.7823	0.7852
0.8	0.7881	0.7910	0.7939	0.7967	0.7995	0.8023	0.8051	0.8078	0.8106	0.8133
0.9	0.8159	0.8186	0.8212	0.8238	0.8264	0.8289	0.8315	0.8340	0.8365	0.8389
1.0	0.8413	0.8438	0.8461	0.8485	0.8508	0.8531	0.8554	0.8577	0.8599	0.8621
1.1	0.8643	0.8665	0.8686	0.8708	0.8729	0.8749	0.8770	0.8790	0.8810	0.8830
1.2	0.8849	0.8869	0.8888	0.8907	0.8925	0.8944	0.8962	0.8980	0.8997	0.9015
1.3	0.9032	0.9049	0.9066	0.9082	0.9099	0.9115	0.9131	0.9147	0.9162	0.9177
1.4	0.9192	0.9207	0.9222	0.9236	0.9251	0.9265	0.9279	0.9292	0.9306	0.9319
1.5	0.9332	0.9345	0.9357	0.9370	0.9382	0.9394	0.9406	0.9418	0.9429	0.9441
1.6	0.9452	0.9463	0.9474	0.9484	0.9495	0.9505	0.9515	0.9525	0.9535	0.9545
1.7	0.9554	0.9564	0.9573	0.9582	0.9591	0.9599	0.9608	0.9616	0.9625	0.9633
1.8	0.9641	0.9649	0.9656	0.9664	0.9671	0.9678	0.9686	0.9693	0.9699	0.9706
1.9	0.9713	0.9719	0.9726	0.9732	0.9738	0.9744	0.9750	0.9756	0.9761	0.9767
2.0	0.9772	0.9778	0.9783	0.9788	0.9793	0.9798	0.9803	0.9808	0.9812	0.9817
2.1	0.9821	0.9826	0.9830	0.9834	0.9838	0.9842	0.9846	0.9850	0.9854	0.9857
2.2	0.9861	0.9864	0.9868	0.9871	0.9875	0.9878	0.9881	0.9884	0.9887	0.9890
2.3	0.9893	0.9896	0.9898	0.9901	0.9904	0.9906	0.9909	0.9911	0.9913	0.9916
2.4	0.9918	0.9920	0.9922	0.9925	0.9927	0.9929	0.9931	0.9932	0.9934	0.9936
2.5	0.9938	0.9940	0.9941	0.9943	0.9945	0.9946	0.9948	0.9949	0.9951	0.9952
2.6	0.9953	0.9955	0.9956	0.9957	0.9959	0.9960	0.9961	0.9962	0.9963	0.9964
2.7	0.9965	0.9966	0.9967	0.9968	0.9969	0.9970	0.9971	0.9972	0.9973	0.9974
2.8	0.9974	0.9975	0.9976	0.9977	0.9977	0.9978	0.9979	0.9979	0.9980	0.9981
2.9	0.9981	0.9982	0.9982	0.9983	0.9984	0.9984	0.9985	0.9985	0.9986	0.9986
3.0	0.9987	0.9987	0.9987	0.9988	0.9988	0.9989	0.9989	0.9989	0.9990	0.9990
3.1	0.9990	0.9991	0.9991	0.9991	0.9992	0.9992	0.9992	0.9992	0.9993	0.9993
3.2	0.9993	0.9993	0.9994	0.9994	0.9994	0.9994	0.9994	0.9995	0.9995	0.9995
3.3	0.9995	0.9995	0.9995	0.9996	0.9996	0.9996	0.9996	0.9996	0.9996	0.9997
3.4	0.9997	0.9997	0.9997	0.9997	0.9997	0.9997	0.9997	0.9997	0.9997	0.9998
3.5	0.9998	0.9998	0.9998	0.9998	0.9998	0.9998	0.9998	0.9998	0.9998	0.9998
3.6	0.9998	0.9998	0.9999	0.9999	0.9999	0.9999	0.9999	0.9999	0.9999	0.9999
3.7	0.9999	0.9999	0.9999	0.9999	0.9999	0.9999	0.9999	0.9999	0.9999	0.9999
3.8	0.9999	0.9999	0.9999	0.9999	0.9999	0.9999	0.9999	0.9999	0.9999	0.9999
3.9	1.0000†									

† For $z \geq 3.90$, the areas are 1.0000 to four decimal places.

TABLE OF RANDOM DIGITS

ROW										
1	96299	07196	98642	20639	23185	56282	69929	14125	38872	94168
2	71622	35940	81807	59225	18192	08710	80777	84395	69563	86280
3	03272	41230	81739	74797	70406	18564	69273	72532	78340	36699
4	46376	58596	14365	63685	56555	42974	72944	96463	63533	24152
5	47352	42853	42903	97504	56655	70355	88606	61406	38757	70657
6	20064	04266	74017	79319	70170	96572	08523	56025	89077	57678
7	73184	95907	05179	51002	83374	52297	07769	99792	78365	93487
8	72753	36216	07230	35793	71907	65571	66784	25548	91861	15725
9	03939	30763	06138	80062	02537	23561	93136	61260	77935	93159
10	75998	37203	07959	38264	78120	77525	86481	54986	33042	70648
11	94435	97441	90998	25104	49761	14967	70724	67030	53887	81293
12	04362	40989	69167	38894	00172	02999	97377	33305	60782	29810
13	89059	43528	10547	40115	82234	86902	04121	83889	76208	31076
14	87736	04666	75145	49175	76754	07884	92564	80793	22573	67902
15	76488	88899	15860	07370	13431	84041	69202	18912	83173	11983
16	36460	53772	66634	25045	79007	78518	73580	14191	50353	32064
17	13205	69237	21820	20952	16635	58867	97650	82983	64865	93298
18	51242	12215	90739	36812	00436	31609	80333	96606	30430	31803
19	67819	00354	91439	91073	49258	15992	41277	75111	67496	68430
20	09875	08990	27656	15871	23637	00952	97818	64234	50199	05715
21	18192	95308	72975	01191	29958	09275	89141	19558	50524	32041
22	02763	33701	66188	50226	35813	72951	11638	01876	93664	37001
23	13349	46328	01856	29935	80563	03742	49470	67749	08578	21956
24	69238	92878	80067	80807	45096	22936	64325	19265	37755	69794
25	92207	63527	59398	29818	24789	94309	88380	57000	50171	17891
26	66679	99100	37072	30593	29665	84286	44458	60180	81451	58273
27	31087	42430	60322	34765	15757	53300	97392	98035	05228	68970
28	84432	04916	52949	78533	31666	62350	20584	56367	19701	60584
29	72042	12287	21081	48426	44321	58765	41760	43304	13399	02043
30	94534	73559	82135	70260	87936	85162	11937	18263	54138	69564
31	63971	97198	40974	45301	60177	35604	21580	68107	25184	42810
32	11227	58474	17272	37619	69517	62964	67962	34510	12607	52255
33	28541	02029	08068	96656	17795	21484	57722	76511	27849	61738
34	11282	43632	49531	78981	81980	08530	08629	32279	29478	50228
35	42907	15137	21918	13248	39129	49559	94540	24070	88151	36782
36	47119	76651	21732	32364	58545	50277	57558	30390	18771	72703
37	11232	99884	05087	76839	65142	19994	91397	29350	83852	04905
38	64725	06719	86262	53356	57999	50193	79936	97230	52073	94467
39	77007	26962	55466	12521	48125	12280	54985	26239	76044	54398
40	18375	19310	59796	89832	59417	18553	17238	05474	33259	50595

Selected Formulas

$Range = Max - Min$
$IQR = Q3 - Q1$
Outlier Rule-of-Thumb: $y < Q1 - 1.5 \times IQR$ or $y > Q3 + 1.5 \times IQR$

$$\bar{y} = \frac{\sum y}{n}$$

$$s = \sqrt{\frac{\sum(y - \bar{y})^2}{n - 1}}$$

$$z = \frac{y - \mu}{\sigma} \text{ (model based)} \qquad z = \frac{y - \bar{y}}{s} \text{ (data based)}$$

$$r = \frac{\sum z_x \tilde{z}_y}{n - 1}$$

$$\hat{y} = b_0 + b_1 x \qquad \text{where } b_1 = r\frac{s_y}{s_x} \text{ and } b_0 = \bar{y} - b_1\bar{x}$$

$$P(\mathbf{A}) = 1 - P(\mathbf{A}^C)$$

$$P(\mathbf{A} \text{ or } \mathbf{B}) = P(\mathbf{A}) + P(\mathbf{B}) - P(\mathbf{A} \text{ and } \mathbf{B})$$

$$P(\mathbf{A} \text{ and } \mathbf{B}) = P(\mathbf{A}) \times P(\mathbf{B}|\mathbf{A})$$

$$P(\mathbf{B}|\mathbf{A}) = \frac{P(\mathbf{A} \text{ and } \mathbf{B})}{P(\mathbf{A})}$$

If $\mathbf{A}$ and $\mathbf{B}$ are independent, $P(\mathbf{B}|\mathbf{A}) = P(\mathbf{B})$

$$E(X) = \mu = \sum x \cdot P(x) \qquad Var(X) = \sigma^2 = \sum(x - \mu)^2 P(x)$$

$$E(X \pm c) = E(X) \pm c \qquad Var(X \pm c) = Var(X)$$

$$E(aX) = aE(X) \qquad Var(aX) = a^2 Var(X)$$

$$E(X \pm Y) = E(X) \pm E(Y) \qquad Var(X \pm Y) = Var(X) + Var(Y)$$

$$\text{if } X \text{ and } Y \text{ are independent}$$

Geometric: $\qquad P(x) = q^{x-1}p \qquad \mu = \frac{1}{p} \qquad \sigma = \sqrt{\frac{q}{p^2}}$

Binomial: $\qquad P(x) = {}_nC_x p^x q^{n-x} \qquad \mu = np \qquad \sigma = \sqrt{npq}$

$$\hat{p} = \frac{x}{n} \qquad \mu(\hat{p}) = p \qquad SD(\hat{p}) = \sqrt{\frac{pq}{n}}$$

Poisson probability model for successes: Poisson (λ)
λ = mean number of successes.
X = number of successes.

$$P(X = x) = \frac{e^{-\lambda}\lambda^x}{x!}$$

$$\text{Expected value:} \qquad E(X) = \lambda$$
$$\text{Standard deviation:} \qquad SD(X) = \sqrt{\lambda}$$

Sampling distribution of $\bar{y}$:
(CLT) As n grows, the sampling distribution approaches the Normal model with

$$\mu(\bar{y}) = \mu_y \qquad SD(\bar{y}) = \frac{\sigma}{\sqrt{n}}$$

Inference:

Confidence interval for parameter = **statistic ± critical value × SE(statistic)**

$$\text{Test statistic} = \frac{statistic - parameter}{SD(statistic)}$$

Parameter	Statistic	SD(statistic)	SE(statistic)
p	$\hat{p}$	$\sqrt{\dfrac{pq}{n}}$	$\sqrt{\dfrac{\hat{p}\hat{q}}{n}}$
μ	$\bar{y}$	$\dfrac{\sigma}{\sqrt{n}}$	$\dfrac{s}{\sqrt{n}}$
$\mu_1 - \mu_2$	$\bar{y}_1 - \bar{y}_2$	$\sqrt{\dfrac{\sigma_1^2}{n_1} + \dfrac{\sigma_2^2}{n_2}}$	$\sqrt{\dfrac{s_1^2}{n_1} + \dfrac{s_2^2}{n_2}}$
μ_d	$\bar{d}$	$\dfrac{\sigma_d}{\sqrt{n}}$	$\dfrac{s_d}{\sqrt{n}}$
σ_ε	$s_e = \sqrt{\dfrac{\sum(y-\hat{y})^2}{n-2}}$	(divide by $n - k - 1$ in multiple regression)	
β_1	b_1	(in simple regression)	$\dfrac{s_e}{s_x\sqrt{n-1}}$
μ_ν	$\hat{y}_\nu$	(in simple regression)	$\sqrt{SE^2(b_1)\cdot(x_\nu - \bar{x})^2 + \dfrac{s_e^2}{n}}$
y_ν	$\hat{y}_\nu$	(in simple regression)	$\sqrt{SE^2(b_1)\cdot(x_\nu - \bar{x})^2 + \dfrac{s_e^2}{n} + s_e^2}$

Pooling: For testing difference between proportions: $\hat{p}_{pooled} = \dfrac{y_1 + y_2}{n_1 + n_2}$

For testing difference between means: $s_p = \sqrt{\dfrac{(n_1 - 1)s_1^2 + (n_2 - 1)s_2^2}{n_1 + n_2 - 2}}$

Substitute these pooled estimates in the respective SE formulas for both groups when assumptions and conditions are met.

Chi-square: $\chi^2 = \sum \dfrac{(Obs - Exp)^2}{Exp}$

Assumptions for Inference	And the Conditions That Support or Override Them

Proportions (z)

- **One sample**
  1. Individuals are independent.
  2. Sample is sufficiently large.

  1. SRS and $n < 10\%$ of the population.
  2. Successes and failures each ≥ 10.

Means (t)

- **One Sample** (df $= n - 1$)
  1. Individuals are independent.
  2. Population has a Normal model.

  1. SRS and $n < 10\%$ of the population.
  2. Histogram is unimodal and symmetric.*

- **Matched pairs** (df $= n - 1$)
  1. Data are matched.
  2. Individuals are independent.
  3. Population of differences is Normal.

  1. (Think about the design.)
  2. SRS and $n < 10\%$ OR random allocation.
  3. Histogram of differences is unimodal and symmetric.*

- **Two independent samples** (df from technology)
  1. Groups are independent.
  2. Data in each group are independent.
  3. Both populations are Normal.

  1. (Think about the design.)
  2. SRSs and $n < 10\%$ OR random allocation.
  3. Both histograms are unimodal and symmetric.*

Distributions/Association (χ^2)

- **Goodness of fit** (df = # of cells $- 1$; one variable, one sample compared with population model)
  1. Data are counts.
  2. Data in sample are independent.
  3. Sample is sufficiently large.

  1. (Are they?)
  2. SRS and $n < 10\%$ of the population.
  3. All expected counts ≥ 5.

- **Homogeneity** [df $= (r - 1)(c - 1)$; many groups compared on one variable]
  1. Data are counts.
  2. Data in groups are independent.
  3. Groups are sufficiently large.

  1. (Are they?)
  2. SRSs and $n < 10\%$ OR random allocation.
  3. All expected counts ≥ 5.

- **Independence** [df $= (r - 1)(c - 1)$; sample from one population classified on two variables]
  1. Data are counts.
  2. Data are independent.
  3. Sample is sufficiently large.

  1. (Are they?)
  2. SRSs and $n < 10\%$ of the population.
  3. All expected counts ≥ 5.

Regression with k predictors (t, df $= n - k - 1$)

- **Association** of each quantitative predictor with the response variable
  1. Form of relationship is linear.

  2. Errors are independent.
  3. Variability of errors is constant.

  4. Errors follow a Normal model.

  1. Scatterplots of y against each x are straight enough. Scatterplot of residuals against predicted values shows no special structure.
  2. No apparent pattern in plot of residuals against predicted values.
  3. Plot of residuals against predicted values has constant spread, doesn't "thicken."
  4. Histogram of residuals is approximately unimodal and symmetric, or Normal probability plot is reasonably straight.*

Analysis of Variance (F, df dependent on number of factors and number of levels in each)

- **Equality** of the mean response across levels of categorical predictors
  1. Additive Model (if there are 2 factors with no interaction term).
  2. Independent errors.
  3. Equal variance across treatment levels.

  4. Errors follow a Normal model.

  1. Interaction plot shows parallel lines (otherwise include an interaction term if possible).
  2. Randomized experiment or other suitable randomization.
  3. Plot of residuals against predicted values has constant spread. Boxplots (partial boxplots for 2 factors) show similar spreads.
  4. Histogram of residuals is unimodal and symmetric, or Normal probability plot is reasonably straight.

*Less critical as n increases

Quick Guide to Inference

Plan				Do			Report
Inference about?	One group or two?	Procedure	Model	Parameter	Estimate	SE	Chapter
Proportions	One sample	1-Proportion z-Interval	z	p	$\hat{p}$	$\sqrt{\dfrac{\hat{p}\hat{q}}{n}}$	10
		1-Proportion z-Test				$\sqrt{\dfrac{p_0 q_0}{n}}$	11
Means	One sample	t-Interval t-Test	t df $= n-1$	μ	$\bar{y}$	$\dfrac{s}{\sqrt{n}}$	12
	Two independent groups	2-Sample t-Test 2-Sample t-Interval	t df from technology	$\mu_1 - \mu_2$	$\bar{y}_1 - \bar{y}_2$	$\sqrt{\dfrac{s_1^2}{n_1} + \dfrac{s_2^2}{n_2}}$	13
	Matched pairs	Paired t-Test Paired t-Interval	t df $= n-1$	μ_d	$\bar{d}$	$\dfrac{s_d}{\sqrt{n}}$	14
Distributions (one categorical variable)	One Sample	Goodness-of-Fit	χ^2 df $=$ *cells* $- 1$				15
	Many independent groups	Homogeneity χ^2 Test	χ^2 df $= (r-1)(c-1)$			$\sum \dfrac{(Obs - Exp)^2}{Exp}$	
Independence (two categorical variables)	One sample	Independence χ^2 Test					
Association (two quantitative variables)	One sample	Linear Regression t-Test or Confidence Interval for β	t df $= n-2$	β_1	b_1	$\dfrac{s_e}{s_x \sqrt{n-1}}$ (compute with technology)	16
		*Confidence Interval for μ_v		μ_v	$\hat{y}_v$	$\sqrt{SE^2(b_1) \cdot (x_v - \bar{x})^2 + \dfrac{s_e^2}{n}}$	
		*Prediction Interval for y_v		y_v	$\hat{y}_v$	$\sqrt{SE^2(b_1) \cdot (x_v - \bar{x})^2 + \dfrac{s_e^2}{n} + s_e^2}$	
Association (one quantitative variable fit modeled by k quantitative variables)	One sample	Multiple Regression t-test or Confidence interval for each β_j	t $df = n - (k+1)$	β_j	b_j	(from technology)	17, 18, 19
		F test for regression model	F $df = k$ and $n - (k+1)$			MST/MSE	18, 19
Association (one quantitative and two or more categorical variables)	Two or more	ANOVA	F $df = k - 1$ and $N - k$			MST/MSE	23

ndex